CW00820618

TOPICS IN
ABSTRACT ALGEBRA

FOURTH EDITION

TOPICS IN
ABSTRACT ALGEBRA
FOURTH EDITION

M K Sen
University of Calcutta

Shamik Ghosh
Jadavpur University

Parthasarathi Mukhopadhyay
R K Mission Residential College (Autonomous)
Narendrapur

Sunil Kumar Maity
University of Calcutta

Universities Press

All rights reserved. No part of the material may be reproduced or utilised in any form, or by any means, electronic or mechanical, including photocopying, recording, or by any information storage and retrieval system, without written permission from the publisher.

TOPICS IN ABSTRACT LAGEBRA, FOURTH EDITION

UNIVERSITIES PRESS (INDIA) PRIVATE LIMITED

Registered Office
3-6-747/1/A & 3-6-754/1, Himayatnagar, Hyderabad 500 029, Telangana, India
info@universitiespress.com, www.universitiespress.com

Distributed by
Orient Blackswan Private Limited

Registered Office
3-6-752 Himayatnagar, Hyderabad 500 029, Telangana, India

Other Offices
Bengaluru / Chennai / Guwahati / Hyderabad / Kolkata /
Mumbai / New Delhi / Noida / Patna / Visakhapatnam

© Universities Press (India) Private Limited 2004, 2006, 2019, 2022

First published 2004
Second Edition 2006
Reprinted 2009, 2011, 2012, 2013, 2015, 2017
Third Edition 2019
Revised and reprinted 2020
Fourth Edition 2022

501824

ISBN   978-93-93330-24-6

Cover and book design
© Universities Press (India) Private Limited 2004, 2006, 2019, 2022

Typeset in LaTex by the Authors

Printed in India by
Rajiv Book Binding House, Delhi

Published by
Universities Press (India) Private Limited
3-6-747/1/A & 3-6-754/1, Himayatnagar, Hyderabad 500 029, Telangana, India

To
Samadrita, Daivik, Rishaan
Prantar
Sanchari, Madhurima
Prakriti

About the Authors

Dr M K Sen is a noted algebraist and author of several books on Abstract Algebra and Discrete Mathematics published in India and abroad. He retired from the Department of Pure Mathematics, University of Calcutta, after a rich career of more than thirty years of teaching Abstract Algebra. Still actively engaged in research on various topics of Abstract Algebra, Dr Sen has visited many premier Universities and mathematical institutes in India and abroad.

Dr Shamik Ghosh, a student of Dr Sen, went to Marquette University, Milwaukee, USA, for post-doctoral research under the BOYSCAST fellowship. He started his teaching career at the Scottish Church College, Calcutta, in 1992. He was a visiting faculty at IIT Kharagpur and later moved to Kalyani University. Currently he is Professor and Head of the Department of Mathematics at Jadavpur University.

Dr Parthasarathi Mukhopadhyay, also a student of Dr Sen, is Associate Professor at the Mathematics Department of Ramakrishna Mission Residential College, Narendrapur, an autonomous college affiliated to the University of Calcutta. He has been teaching Abstract and Linear Algebra for the past twenty-five years. An author of several books on Mathematics, Dr Mukhopadhyay has published and lectured widely on topics in his areas of interest that include the Algebraic Theory of Semirings and History of Mathematics, at various academic fora within India and abroad.

Dr Sunil Kumar Maity, yet another student of Dr Sen, was a student of Dr Mukhopadhyay during his UG days. Dr Maity is currently Associate Professor and Head of the Department at the Department of Pure Mathematics, University of Calcutta. Earlier, he served as Assistant Professor of Mathematics at Raiganj (University) College before moving to Burdwan University in 2005. An active researcher in the area of Theory of Semirings, Dr Maity has been teaching Abstract and Linear Algebra in UG and PG courses for over a decade and a half.

Contents

Preface to the Fourth Edition

We are happy to note the enthusiastic appreciation of the third edition of this book from all the relevant quarters, in spite of the serious impediments that happened in academics all around due to Covid-19 pandemic. In the third edition, we have already revamped the book as per the requirements of the pan India syllabus of Choice Based Credit System (CBCS) introduced by the UGC. In the present edition, some well-thought suggestions of a few of our friends and colleagues have motivated us to include a new Appendix on *Automorphism of Groups* along with Worked-out Exercises and Exercises with due hints towards solution.

We have made necessary revision of the text and included numerous Examples, Worked-out Exercises and Exercises. In the Answers section, a large number of Exercises now have Hints towards their solutions. Particular importance has been given to the problems of the MCQ type, as these are extremely important in many a present-day competitive examination. We believe this will help the students to prepare themselves for various examinations with a greater confidence. Chapters on *Finite Abelian Groups* and the section on *Group Actions* remain at relevant places as per the need of the present syllabus. As before, Boolean Algebra will remain available in the website **www.universitiespress.com/mksen/topicsinabstractalgebra**, which has been carefully laid out as an online support to this book. Topics like *Euler's Phi Function* and *Chinese Remainder Theorem* have been amalgamated into the main body of the text at an appropriate position, along with a section on *Arithmetic Functions* in general.

We have tried our level best to eliminate the printing errors that we could detect, although in spite of our sincere effort there may still be some left; we regret and record our prior apology for such an eventuality. We would like to thank all at the Universities Press for their cooperation. We invite constructive suggestions from any reader of this book, which may kindly be forwarded to any of the following e-mail addresses: senmk9@gmail.com, ghoshshamik@yahoo.com, dugumita@gmail.com, or sskmaity@yahoo.com. We shall be elated and our efforts deemed worthwhile if this new edition proves to be beneficial to our beloved students, for whom it has been written.

Kolkata,
March, 2022

M. K. Sen
Shamik Ghosh
Parthasarathi Mukhopadhyay
Sunil Kumar Maity

Preface to the First Edition

I have often pondered over the roles of knowledge or experience, on the one hand, and imagination or intuition, on the other, in the process of discovery. I believe that there is a certain fundamental conflict between the two, and knowledge, by advocating caution, tends to inhibit the flight of imagination. Therefore a certain naiveté, unburdened by conventional wisdom, can sometimes be a positive asset.

—**Harish-Chandra**

It is not at all difficult to trace books on Abstract Algebra in both Indian and International markets. And many of them, we must say, are really good ones and can be classified as classics. Why, then, yet another one on the same subject? Perhaps we owe an explanation here. From our experience, we feel that most of these books, well-written as they are, do not solve many problems, which would have immensely helped the students, mainly the beginners. Moreover these are not written according to any specific syllabus. There is another set of books, which satisfies the purpose of examination reasonably well, but fails lamentably to motivate the students to dive deep into the subject. The present book is an industrious effort to combine these two ends. To satisfy the basic needs of a student with reference to the syllabus and examination, the book begins without any prerequisite. It then gradually unfolds the inner essence of the subject, its gradual genesis, with a hint of history here and there and tries to develop the flavor of abstraction from the proper perspective. It is designed in accordance with the new UGC syllabus for all Indian universities at the undergraduate advanced/honours level and also for the first year post-graduate students of many Indian Universities. Students appearing for their NET, GATE, SET, JAM or MCA examination will find this book useful too. Moreover, the course material of Abstract Algebra offered to a student of engineering/technical institutes is covered in this book.

We begin with the elementary concepts of set-theory and provide an elaborate and a comprehensive treatment on various aspects of it. The algebra of sets, binary relations, with special emphasis on the congruence relation on the set of integers and its recent application to ISBN, functions (or mappings) and binary operations, constitute the first chapter. Chapter two contains algebraic theories on integers, which include divisibility properties, mathematical induction methods, theory on prime numbers and solution methods of linear Diophantine equations. The next chapter begins a discussion of the concept of the algebraic structure: groups. The theory of groups has been developed gradually through a few subsequent chapters. The first one contains basic definitions, a lot of illustrative important examples with motivations and elementary properties. Next we consider permutation groups. A detailed study with many illustrations has been provided in this chapter in order to make a student comfortable with calculation. Then we develop theories on substructures of groups: subgroups, cosets of subgroups, Lagrange's theorem and its applications, normal subgroups and quotient groups. This chapter also includes the study of cyclic groups. Chapter six begins with the study of homomorphisms of groups and extends up to isomorphism theorems. Chapter seven contains the definitions and results on the direct product of groups. In chapter eight, we indicate the application of group-theory in the study of symmetry and show that various permutation groups and their subgroups arise from the symmetry of geometrical figures. The next chapter presents a study of finite groups through Cauchy's theorem, Sylow theorems along with the class equation, an essential tool to appreciate these theorems. The study of group-theory ends in chapter ten with an account of certain results on simple groups.

The final part of this book deals with the theory of rings. It consists of four chapters. In chapter eleven, we include elementary properties, some special classes of rings, especially Boolean rings, integral domains, division rings and fields and their substructures, viz., subrings and subfields. Chapter twelve deals with the ideals and homomorphisms of rings. Here we discuss prime and maximal ideals and embedding of rings. The next chapter contains factorization in an integral domain with a special emphasis on Euclidean domains, principal ideal domains and unique factorization domains. Finally, we conclude the book with a chapter on polynomial rings with a special study of irreducibility of polynomials.

For most of the students, going through dry theoretical concepts only, is a dreadful experience. So to keep the student interested and motivated to learn the theory, one must take recourse to examples, as is often done in classroom teaching. To this end, our book provides a rich collection of numerous examples, a large number of worked out exercises and visual illustrations wherever necessary. Each chapter is divided into some sections according to the need of the subject and we have given problems at the end of every section under two categories. We have solved some of the expository problems under the *Worked Out Exercise*, followed by a good number of well-planned problems in the *Exercise*, to be solved by the students, so as to develop his/her clarity of concepts and maturity in understanding the subject as well. We have also included some objective and multiple choice questions in the exercises, keeping in view the present-day need of certain examinations. Some particularly interesting but difficult problems are incorporated for an advanced reader and these are marked with ♦ in case of a Worked Out Exercise and with † in case of an Exercise. Answers to a large number of exercises with necessary hints are provided at the end of the book. Certain mathematically intriguing facts and explanations are given in the form of footnotes at relevant pages. Some mind-boggling relevant problems and recent developments are discussed in the form of Appendix at the end of the book. Quite a few references to relevant websites, for a more interested student, are provided towards finding the latest information on those topics.

We take this opportunity to record our sincere thanks to Prof. T.K. Mukherjee, Department of Mathematics, Jadavpur University, for his illuminating suggestions. We are happy to acknowledge the invaluable help of one of our most brilliant students, Mr. Sunil Kumar Maity, of the Department of Pure Mathematics, University of Calcutta. Grateful thanks are due to Mrs. Monisha Sen, Mrs. Nandita Ghosh and Mrs. Madhumita Mukhopadhyay for their constant encouragement and moral support. Finally we would like to thank Mr. Madhu Reddy, Mr. Tapan Das and Ms. Priyadarshini Bhattacharya of Orient Longman, for making this project a success.

In spite of our honest effort, there may still be some typographical mistakes, for which we apologize in advance. We welcome comments or suggestions concerning the text. These may please be forwarded to the following e-mail addresses: senmk_6@eth.net or, shamikghosh@vsnl.net or, dugumita@vsnl.net

Kolkata,   M.K. Sen
June,2003   Shamik Ghosh
                                                                              Parthasarathi Mukhopadhyay

Chapter 1

Preliminaries

"Mathematics as an expression of the human mind reflects the active will, the contemplative reason and the desire for aesthetic perfection. Its basic elements are logic and intuition, analysis and construction, generality and individuality. Though different traditions may emphasize different aspects, it is only the interplay of these antithetic forces and the struggle for their synthesis that constitute the life, usefulness and supreme value of mathematical science"— so conceived Courant and Robbins in their classic exposition entitled "What is Mathematics?" No wonder that this oldest branch of science has earned, in its own right, the appellation *"The Queen of Science"*. One of the most fascinating aspects of the last century mathematics has been its recognition of the power of the abstract approach that transcends the confines of immediate utility. This book aims to acquaint the beginners, with the elements of that part of modern mathematics, which is nowadays referred to as "Abstract Algebra"— the algebra that has emerged not only as an independent and vigorous branch of mathematics, but has also been instrumental in interlacing almost all other branches of mathematics — so much so, that one is often tempted to talk about the *"algebraization"* of mathematics.

Though one may object to this as an absurd oversimplification, it is often said that *mathematics is all about sets and functions*. There should be no doubt, however, in view of the pivotal role that these key concepts play, that this naive maxim does come very close to the fact.

1.1 Sets

This section sets the stage for all that follows and also serves as an appropriate place for codifying certain technical terminologies used throughout the text. The *mathematical theory of sets* grew out of the German mathematician George Cantor's (1845 - 1918) study of infinite sets of real numbers. The language of sets has since become an important tool for all branches of mathematics, as a basis for precise description of higher concepts and for mathematical reasoning.

What is a *set* after all? It is fascinating to know that the answer to this very obvious and apparently tame question had once put the very foundation of the theory of sets into jeopardy. We invite the interested reader to go through Appendix A for further information in this regard. However, in this text we adopt a naive and intuitive point of view and introduce the *definition* of a ***set*** in the light of Cantor. *A set is a well-defined collection of distinct objects* of our perception or of our thought, to be conceived as a whole. To develop a perfectly balanced working idea of sets, it is sufficient for a beginner to concentrate only on the first part (in italics) of this definition. Note that, here *well-defined* is an adjective to the *collection* and not to the distinct objects that are to be collected to form a set. By this, it is meant that there should be no ambiguity whatsoever regarding the membership of such a collection[1]. For example, one can talk about the set of all positive integers, though no one really knows all of them (!), but a collection of *some* positive integers is *not* a set, as it is not clear whether a particular positive integer, say 5, is a member of this collection or not.

We shall adopt the convention to denote a set by upper case letters of the English alphabet, viz., $A, B, C \ldots$ and to denote the objects in it (also referred to as ***elements***) by lower case letters, viz., $a, b, c, \ldots$. A set X is called a ***finite set*** if it contains only n number of elements, for some nonnegative integer n; otherwise it is said to be an ***infinite set***. If x is an element of a set A, we write $x \in A$. [The symbol $\in$ stands for *belongs to*, which like many other notations, was introduced in 1889 by Italian mathematician G. Peano (1858-1932) and which is believed to be a stylized form of the Greek *epsilon*]. On the other hand, $x \notin A$ stands for 'x does not belong to A', e.g., if we consider the set P of positive prime integers then $2 \in P$ but $4 \notin P$.

There are usually two methods of designating a particular set. The *roster method*, where one may denote a set by listing its elements within curly braces. For example,

---

[1]Interestingly, it may still not always be possible to actually determine whether an object is in a set or not. For example, consider the set S of all positive prime integers. Before 1992, if someone posed the question: "Is $2^{2^9} + 1$ *a member of the set S?*"—no one would have been able to answer, though certainly this number could only be prime or composite, as there was never a third choice. In 1992, this number was proved to be composite. So now we may give the answer in the negative. Numbers F_n of the form $2^{2^n} + 1$, for nonnegative integers n, are called **Fermat numbers** after Pierre de Fermat(1601-1665). Incidentally, there is no known $n > 4$, for which F_n is prime. One may refer to **http://www.prothsearch.net/fermat** for more details.

$\{a, e, i, o, u\}$ is the set consisting of vowels in the English language. This technique may sometimes be used for infinite sets also, if it is convenient. For example, the set of all nonnegative integers may be denoted by $\{0, 1, 2, 3, \ldots\}$. However if such a listing is not practicable, we may take recourse to the other method, which may aptly be called the *set-builder method*, where a set is designated by stating the builder of the set, which is nothing but the common well-defined characteristics enjoyed by every element of the set. In other words, the set A of elements x, for which some common statement $p(x)$ holds good is written as $A = \{x \mid p(x)\}$. For example, the set $\{x \mid x^4 = 1\}$ in set builder form is the same as the set $\{1, -1, i, -i\}$ in roster form where $i^2 = -1$.

In the sequel, we shall use the following standard notations throughout to denote some important sets:

$\mathbb{N}$	:	the set of all natural numbers (i.e., all positive integers)
$\mathbb{Z}$	:	the set of all integers
$\mathbb{N}_0$	:	the set of all nonnegative integers
$\mathbb{E}$	:	the set of all even integers
$\mathbb{Q}$	:	the set of all rational numbers
$\mathbb{Q}^*$	:	the set of all nonzero rational numbers
$\mathbb{Q}^+$	:	the set of all positive rational numbers
$\mathbb{R}$	:	the set of all real numbers
$\mathbb{R}^*$	:	the set of all nonzero real numbers
$\mathbb{R}^+$	:	the set of all positive real numbers
$\mathbb{C}$	:	the set of all complex numbers
$\mathbb{C}^*$	:	the set of all nonzero complex numbers

We further declare that for a set S, we will use the notation $|S|$ to denote the number[2] of elements of the set S.

Definition 1.1.1. A set X is said to be a ***subset*** of a set Y, written as $X \subseteq Y$, if every element of X is an element of Y and in this case, we say X is contained in Y. Note that it is equivalent to say that Y contains X (or, Y is a ***superset*** of X), written as $Y \supseteq X$.

Furthermore, X is said to be a ***proper subset*** of Y, if X is a subset of Y and if

---

[2] A word of caution here is imperative. Strictly speaking, the notation $|S|$ denotes the number of elements where S is a finite set. However, for an infinite set S, this notation stands for ***cardinal number*** of the set S— a concept, which is applicable to finite sets also and which is beyond the scope of discussion here. It may however be stated that the cardinal number of a *finite* set happens to coincide always with the number of elements of that set.

there exists at least one element in Y which is not in X. This is denoted by $X \subset Y$. It is easy to see that $X \subseteq X$ for any set X. Note that $\mathbb{N} \subset \mathbb{R} \subset \mathbb{C}$.

Definition 1.1.2. Two sets, X and Y are said to be **equal** if every element of X is an element of Y and vice versa, i.e., if $X \subseteq Y$ and $Y \subseteq X$. We denote it by $X = Y$.

Example 1.1.3. **(i)** The set of all even positive integers is a proper subset of the set of all integers. In notations, $\{2n \mid n \in \mathbb{N}\} \subset \mathbb{Z}$.

(ii) The set $\{x \in \mathbb{R} \mid 1 < x < 2\}$ is an infinite set. Note that such a set cannot be represented in roster form. This set is also denoted by $(1, 2)$ and one may write $(1,2) = \{x \in \mathbb{R} \mid 1 < x < 2\}$.

(iii) It is trivial to see that $\{1, 2, 3\} = \{3, 1, 2\}$.

(iv) The set $\{x \mid x$ is a positive even prime integer$\} = \{2\}$. Such sets having only one element in them are called a **singleton set**.

Definition 1.1.4. A set is said to be an **empty set** (or **null set**) if it has no element[3]. Such a set is denoted by $\emptyset$.

The set $\{n \in \mathbb{Z} \mid n$ is a root of $x^2 + 1 = 0\}$ is an example of empty set. We assume that the empty set is a subset of every set[4]. To avoid the logical difficulties that arise in the foundation of set theory, we further assume that, each discussion involving a number of sets takes place with respect to an *arbitrarily chosen but fixed* set. This set is called a **universal set**[5] for that discussion and is generally denoted by U. It has to be such a set that, all the sets under consideration in that problem are subsets of U.

For example, in a discussion involving the sets $X = \{1, 2, 3\}, Y = \{2, 4, 6, 8\}$, and $Z = \{1, 3, 5, 7\}$, one may choose $U = \{x \in \mathbb{N} \mid 1 \leq x \leq 8\}$ as a universal set. However, if one feels like, any superset of U is also good enough to be a universal set for this problem.

---

[3]Observe that, whenever the well-defined builder of a set is a self-contradictory statement, the corresponding set becomes an example of empty set. However, it must be understood that the conceptual *empty set* refers to a *unique* set and thus we may talk about *the empty set*.

[4]This assumption at first sight may seem somewhat paradoxical, but it is in agreement with the interpretation of the definition of a subset. Because the statement $\emptyset \subset X$, *for every set X*, could be false only if the empty set $\emptyset$ would contain an element which was not in X and since the empty set contains no element at all, this is impossible, independent of what the set X is! Thus the statement is *vacuously satisfied*.

[5]It may clearly be understood— though the name may appear to suggest otherwise— that by no means are we proposing a set which is *universal* for all the problems; rather it may vary from problem to problem, and even more— for a problem involving certain sets, the choice of a universal set need not be unique, but once chosen, subject to the conditions stated above, it must be kept fixed throughout the subsequent discussions of that problem.

Definition 1.1.5. For any set X, the ***power set*** of X is the set of all subsets of the given set X. We denote it by $\mathcal{P}(X) = \{A \,|\, A \text{ is a subset of } X\}$.

For example, let $X = \{a, b, c\}$. Then the power set of X is given by $\mathcal{P}(X) = \left\{\emptyset, \{a\}, \{b\}, \{c\}, \{a, b\}, \{a, c\}, \{b, c\}, X\right\}$.

It is worth mentioning that for a finite set X, if $|X| = k$, then $|\mathcal{P}(X)| = 2^k$ (cf. Worked-out Exercise 2.2.1), of which $2^k - 1$ are proper subsets of X. Also note that $\mathcal{P}(\emptyset) = \{\emptyset\}$.

A fact of fundamental importance is that, given any two sets, we can combine them by means of so called *algebraic operations on sets* to form new sets, as we shall now define.

Definition 1.1.6. The ***union*** of two sets X and Y, denoted by $X \cup Y$ is defined to be the set

$$X \cup Y = \{x \,|\, x \in X \text{ or}^6 \ x \in Y\}.$$

Definition 1.1.7. The ***intersection*** of two sets X and Y, denoted by $X \cap Y$ is defined to be the set

$$X \cap Y = \{x \,|\, x \in X \text{ and } x \in Y\}.$$

From the above definition, it is clear that the set $X \cap Y$ comprises of the common elements of the sets X and Y, i.e., every element of $X \cap Y$ must be an element of X as well as of Y. Hence we have, $X \cap Y \subseteq X$ and $X \cap Y \subseteq Y$. Again from the definition of the union of sets we see that every element of X must be an element of $X \cup Y$, so that $X \subseteq X \cup Y$; for a similar reason, $Y \subseteq X \cup Y$; consequently, we find that $X \cap Y \subseteq X$, $Y \subseteq X \cup Y$. Furthermore, in particular, if $X \subseteq Y$, then $X \cup Y = Y$ and $X \cap Y = X$.

Example 1.1.8. Let $X = \{a, b, c, d, e\}$, $Y = \{c, d, e, f, g, h\}$ and $Z = \{h, p, q, r\}$. Then $X \cup Y = \{a, b, c, d, e, f, g, h\}$, $X \cap Y = \{c, d, e\}$, $X \cap Z = \emptyset$, $Y \cap Z = \{h\}$ and $X \cup Z = \{a, b, c, d, e, h, p, q, r\}$.

Definition 1.1.9. Two sets X and Y are said to be ***disjoint*** if $X \cap Y = \emptyset$, i.e., there is no element common to both the sets X and Y.

---

[6]It is important to have a clear understanding of the conjunctive *or* used in this definition. The common usage of *or* in the English language carries an exclusive sense e.g., *either it is raining or it is not raining*— this *or* excludes the possibility of both happening simultaneously. But the mathematical *or* carries an inclusive sense— using it in the above definition, what we mean is this— the element 'x', to be in the union of X and Y, must either belong to X or Y or maybe, it belongs to both.

In Example 1.1.8, the set X and Z are disjoint sets.

The following theorem enlists some fundamental properties of the union and intersection of sets.

Theorem 1.1.10. *Let X, Y and Z be any three sets. Then,*

$$(i) \quad X \cup U = U, \qquad X \cap U = X$$
$$(ii) \quad X \cup \emptyset = X, \qquad X \cap \emptyset = \emptyset \qquad \text{(laws of identity)}$$
$$(iii) \quad X \cup X = X, \qquad X \cap X = X \qquad \text{(laws of idempotence)}$$
$$(iv) \quad X \cup Y = Y \cup X, \quad X \cap Y = Y \cap X \,\text{(laws of commutativity)}$$
$$(v) \quad (X \cup Y) \cup Z = X \cup (Y \cup Z),$$
$$\qquad (X \cap Y) \cap Z = X \cap (Y \cap Z) \qquad \text{(laws of associativity)}$$
$$(vi) \quad X \cup (Y \cap Z) = (X \cup Y) \cap (X \cup Z),$$
$$\qquad X \cap (Y \cup Z) = (X \cap Y) \cup (X \cap Z) \quad \text{(laws of distributivity)}$$
$$(vii) \quad X \cap (X \cup Y) = X, \quad X \cup (X \cap Y) = X \,\text{(laws of absorption)}$$

Proof. We leave it as a routine exercise. □

We now generalize the notions of union and intersection from two sets to an arbitrary collection of sets. To begin with, let us consider a finite collection of n sets, say $X_1, X_2, \ldots X_n$, $(n \geq 2)$. In this case, we write[7]

$$\bigcup_{i=1}^{n} X_i = X_1 \cup X_2 \cup \ldots \cup X_n = \{x \,|\, x \in X_i \text{ for some } i, 1 \leq i \leq n\}$$

and

$$\bigcap_{i=1}^{n} X_i = X_1 \cap X_2 \cap \ldots \cap X_n = \{x \,|\, x \in X_i \text{ for all } i, 1 \leq i \leq n\}.$$

To generalize it further for any arbitrary family of sets, finite or infinite, we introduce the notion of an index set. A set I is said to be an **index set** for a family $\mathcal{A}$ of sets, if for any $\alpha \in I$, there exists a set $A_\alpha \in \mathcal{A}$ and $\mathcal{A} = \{A_\alpha \,|\, \alpha \in I\}$. Note that I can be any nonempty set, finite or infinite. We now define the union and intersection of the sets

---

[7]It is to be carefully noted that part (v) of Theorem 1.1.10 plays a very important role in enabling us to extend the scope of the definition of union and intersection beyond three sets. Indeed, in both of these definitions, two sets were combined to yield a third set and it is the associativity of both these operations that allows us to dispense with the parentheses, as by virtue of associativity, we come to the conclusion that, the order in which the operations are made is of no significance.

A_α, $\alpha \in I$, as follows:

$$\bigcup_{\alpha \in I} A_\alpha = \{x \mid x \in A_\alpha \text{ for at least one } \alpha \in I\}$$

$$\bigcap_{\alpha \in I} A_\alpha = \{x \mid x \in A_\alpha \text{ for all } \alpha \in I\}[8].$$

Here the sets A_α are said to be ***mutually disjoint***, if for $\alpha, \beta \in I, \alpha \neq \beta$ implies that $A_\alpha \cap A_\beta = \emptyset$. For example, let us consider the family $\mathcal{F} = \{I_n \mid n \in \mathbb{N}\}$, where

$$I_n = \{x \in \mathbb{R} \mid -(1+\frac{1}{n}) < x < (1+\frac{1}{n})\}.$$

Observe that, here $\mathbb{N}$ is the index set and $I_1 \supset I_2 \supset I_3 \supset \ldots\ldots$. A little reflection will enable you to see that

$$\bigcup_{n \in \mathbb{N}} I_n = \{x \in \mathbb{R} \mid -2 < x < 2\} \quad \text{and} \quad \bigcap_{n \in \mathbb{N}} I_n = \{x \in \mathbb{R} \mid -1 \leq x \leq 1\}.$$

Definition 1.1.11. Given two sets X and Y, the ***difference*** of them denoted by $X \backslash Y$ (also known as the ***relative complement*** of Y in X) is the set

$$X \backslash Y = \{x \mid x \in X \text{ but } x \notin Y\}.$$

For example, let $X = \{1,2,3,4\}$ and $Y = \{3,4,5,6\}$. Then $X \backslash Y = \{1,2\}$ and $Y \backslash X = \{5,6\}$, which immediately shows that the difference of sets is noncommutative. We further point out that for any set X and Y, $X \backslash X = \emptyset, X \backslash \emptyset = X, \emptyset \backslash X = \emptyset$ and $X \cup Y = (X \backslash Y) \cup (Y \backslash X) \cup (X \cap Y)$.

Definition 1.1.12. The ***complement*** of a set X with respect to a universal set U is denoted by X' and defined to be

$$X' = \{x \in U \mid x \notin X\}.$$

From this definition, it is clear that $X' = U \backslash X$.

In the next theorem, we enlist some important properties of the complement of a set.

---

[8]While the index set I needs to be nonempty, such a restriction is not required for the family $\mathcal{A}$. In fact, if $\mathcal{A}$ is an empty family (i.e., there is no member of this family), then the above definitions of union and intersection give (keeping in mind that, all the sets under discussion are subsets of a universal set U) $\cup_{\alpha \in I} A_\alpha = \emptyset$ and $\cap_{\alpha \in I} A_\alpha = U$. While the first equality is quite obvious, the second one may seem to be puzzling. Observe that, to be in $\cap_{\alpha \in I} A_\alpha$, an element is required to belong to each member A_α of the family $\mathcal{A}$ and if there does not exist any such A_α in $\mathcal{A}$ (as $\mathcal{A}$ is empty), then every element in U satisfies this requirement *vacuously*.

Theorem 1.1.13. *Let X and Y be any two sets and U be a universal set under consideration. Then,*

(i) $X \cup X' = U$ *and* $X \cap X' = \emptyset$

(ii) $(X')' = X$

(iii) $X \setminus Y = X \cap Y'$

(iv) $(X \cup Y)' = X' \cap Y'$ *and* $(X \cap Y)' = X' \cup Y'$(**De Morgan's laws**).

Proof. It is quite routine and left as an exercise. $\square$

Definition 1.1.14. The ***symmetric difference*** of two sets X and Y, denoted by $X \Delta Y$, is defined to be $X \Delta Y = (X \setminus Y) \cup (Y \setminus X)$. Hence $X \Delta Y$ is the set of those elements which is either only in X or only in Y, but not in both. From the definition it is clear that the symmetric difference of two sets is commutative, i.e., $X \Delta Y = Y \Delta X$. It is also associative, the proof of which is quite routine, though somewhat lengthy. [cf. Problem 7(g) of Exercises 1.1].

It is meaningless to ask, *how does a set look like*? Nevertheless, the English logician John Venn (1834-1923) came forward in 1880 with a kind of pictorial representation for sets and their fundamental operations.

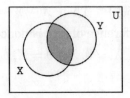

Fig.1a: $X \cap Y$

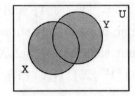

Fig.1b: $X \cup Y$

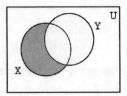

Fig.1c: $X \setminus Y$

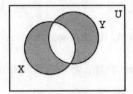

Fig.1d: $X \Delta Y$

Though admittedly loose and imprecise, and therefore somewhat contrary to the very spirit of logical rigorousness lying at the heart of set theory, a beginner may still find this diagrammatic approach very convenient for developing the so called *abstract visualization*, which is essential to *see* the mental image of these abstract happenings.

These are called **Venn diagrams**, where the universal set U is represented by a rectangle and all its subsets, under consideration, by circles drawn within the rectangle. Further, the shaded portion in each diagram (Figs. 1a, b, c and d) represents the corresponding set. The adjoining figures illustrate the intersection, union, difference and symmetric difference of sets, by Venn diagram.

Note that it is not possible to give diagrammatic presentation of the null set by shading; however, disjoint sets are represented in the following way (Fig. 1e):

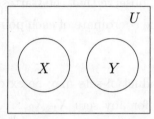

Fig.1e: $X \cap Y = \emptyset$

Let us now define a concept which is of fundamental importance in developing the subject.

Definition 1.1.15. Let X and Y be two nonempty sets and $x \in X, y \in Y$. The **ordered pair** of elements x and y, denoted by (x, y), is the set $\big\{\{x\}, \{x, y\}\big\}$. Clearly, $(x, y) = \big\{\{x\}, \{x, y\}\big\} \neq \big\{\{y\}, \{x, y\}\big\} = (y, x)$ whenever $x \neq y$.

Theorem 1.1.16. *The ordered pairs* $(x, y) = (z, w)$ *if and only if* $x = z$ *and* $y = w$, *for* $x, z \in X$; $y, w \in Y$.

Proof. If $x = z$ and $y = w$ for $x, z \in X$ and $y, w \in Y$, it follows immediately that $\{x\} = \{z\}$ and $\{x, y\} = \{z, w\}$, whence $\big\{\{x\}, \{x, y\}\big\} = \big\{\{z\}, \{z, w\}\big\}$ and so $(x, y) = (z, w)$.

Conversely, suppose that $(x, y) = (z, w)$. This implies that

$$\big\{\{x\}, \{x, y\}\big\} = \big\{\{z\}, \{z, w\}\big\}.$$

Clearly, $\{x\} \in \big\{\{x\}, \{x, y\}\big\}$ whence $\{x\} \in \big\{\{z\}, \{z, w\}\big\}$. This implies that either $\{x\} = \{z\}$ or, $\{x\} = \{z, w\}$. Now, if $\{x\} = \{z\}$, we must have $\{x, y\} = \{z, w\}$ whence, it follows that $x = z$ and $y = w$. However, if $\{x\} = \{z, w\}$, then we must have $\{x, y\} = \{z\}$. But this implies that $x = z = w$ and $x = y = z$ which in turn gives $x = y = z = w$. Hence the theorem. $\qquad\square$

Definition 1.1.17. The **Cartesian product** of two nonempty sets X and Y, denoted by $X \times Y$, is the set $\{(x, y) \mid x \in X, y \in Y\}$. We assume, $X \times \emptyset = \emptyset = \emptyset \times X$ for any set X.

Observe that if $|X| = m$ and $|Y| = n$, then $|X \times Y| = mn$. One can consider the Cartesian product $X \times X$ of a set X with itself[9].

The set of the elements (x, x) in $X \times X$ is called the **diagonal** of X and is sometimes denoted by Δ_X.

For example, let $X = \{1, 2\}$ and $Y = \{3, 4\}$, then $X \times Y = \{(1, 3), (1, 4),$ $(2, 3), (2, 4)\}$ and $Y \times X = \{(3, 1), (3, 2), (4, 1), (4, 2)\}$. Clearly, if $X \neq Y$ then $X \times Y \neq Y \times X$.

For the set $\mathbb{R}$ of real numbers, observe that the Cartesian product $\mathbb{R} \times \mathbb{R}$ is nothing but the Cartesian plane, where the coordinate of each point is given by an ordered pair of real numbers and vice versa.

The idea of the Cartesian product of sets may be extended to any finite[10] number of nonempty sets. For example, for any sets $X_1, X_2, \ldots, X_n$, the Cartesian product, denoted by $X_1 \times X_2 \times \ldots \times X_n$ or, equivalently by $\prod_{i=1}^{n} X_i$, is the set of all *ordered n-tuples* $(x_1, x_2, \ldots, x_n)$, where each $x_i \in X_i$ for $i = 1, 2, \ldots n$.

For convenience, we may write X^n to represent $X \times X \times \ldots \times X$ which is the *n-fold Cartesian product* of X with itself. Clearly, $\mathbb{R}^3$ denotes the usual three-dimensional space.

Worked-out Exercises

$\Diamond$ **Exercise 1.1.1.** Let A, B and C denote the subsets of a set S, and C' denote the complement of C in S. If $A \cap C = B \cap C$ and $A \cap C' = B \cap C'$, then prove that $A = B$.

Solution. Here S is the given universal set.

$$
\begin{aligned}
A &= A \cap S \\
  &= A \cap (C \cup C') \\
  &= (A \cap C) \cup (A \cap C') \quad \text{[by \textit{distributivity}]} \\
  &= (B \cap C) \cup (B \cap C') \quad \text{[by given conditions]} \\
  &= B \cap (C \cup C') \quad \text{[by \textit{distributivity}]} \\
  &= B \cap S \\
  &= B.
\end{aligned}
$$

---

[9]The ordered pair $(x, x) \in X \times X$ turns out to be the set $\big\{\{x\}\big\}$ according to Definition 1.1.15.

[10]The corresponding idea for any infinite family of nonempty sets is out of scope here.

◊ **Exercise 1.1.2.** Let A, B and C be three sets such that $A \cap B = A \cap C$ and $A \cup B = A \cup C$, then prove that $B = C$.

Solution. Indeed,

$$
\begin{aligned}
B &= B \cup (A \cap B) &&\text{[by } absorptivity\text{]}\\
&= B \cup (A \cap C) &&\text{[by given condition]}\\
&= (B \cup A) \cap (B \cup C) &&\text{[by } distributivity\text{]}\\
&= (A \cup B) \cap (B \cup C) &&\text{[by } commutativity\text{]}\\
&= (A \cup C) \cap (B \cup C) &&\text{[by given condition]}\\
&= (A \cap B) \cup C &&\text{[by } distributivity\text{]}\\
&= (A \cap C) \cup C &&\text{[by given condition]}\\
&= C. &&\text{[by } absorptivity\text{]}
\end{aligned}
$$

◊ **Exercise 1.1.3.** For three subsets A, B and C of a set S, if $(A \cap C) \cup (B \cap C') = \emptyset$, prove that $A \cap B = \emptyset$ where C' is the complement of C in S.

Solution. Here, $(A \cap C) \cup (B \cap C') = \emptyset$ which implies that $(A \cap C) = \emptyset$ and $(B \cap C') = \emptyset$. Now, $B \cap C' = \emptyset$ implies $B \setminus C = \emptyset$, i.e., either $B = C$ or $B \subset C$ or else, $B = \emptyset$. If $B = C$, then from $A \cap C = \emptyset$, it follows that $A \cap B = \emptyset$. Again if $B \subseteq C$, then $A \cap B \subseteq A \cap C = \emptyset$ gives $A \cap B = \emptyset$. Finally if $B = \emptyset$, then it trivially follows that $A \cap B = \emptyset$.

◊ **Exercise 1.1.4.** Prove that an equivalent definition of symmetric difference of two sets A and B is

$$A \Delta B = (A \cup B) \setminus (A \cap B).$$

Solution. We know $A \Delta B = (A \setminus B) \cup (B \setminus A)$. Hence we are to show that $(A \setminus B) \cup (B \setminus A) = (A \cup B) \setminus (A \cap B)$. (Let us solve it by using Theorem 1.1.13). Indeed,

$$
\begin{aligned}
&(A \cup B) \setminus (A \cap B)\\
&= (A \cup B) \cap (A \cap B)' &&\text{[as } X \setminus Y = X \cap Y'\text{]}\\
&= (A \cup B) \cap (A' \cup B') &&\text{[by } De\ Morgan's\ law\text{]}\\
&= \big((A \cup B) \cap A'\big) \cup \big((A \cup B) \cap B'\big) &&\text{[by } distributivity\text{]}\\
&= (A \cap A') \cup (B \cap A') \cup (A \cap B') \cup (B \cap B') &&\text{[-do-]}\\
&= \emptyset \cup (B \setminus A) \cup (A \setminus B) \cup \emptyset &&\text{[as } X \cap X' = \emptyset\text{]}\\
&= (B \setminus A) \cup (A \setminus B) &&\text{[as } X \cup \emptyset = X\text{]}\\
&= (A \setminus B) \cup (B \setminus A). &&\text{[by } commutativity\text{]}
\end{aligned}
$$

◊ **Exercise 1.1.5.** Prove that, for any three nonempty sets A, B and C

$$A \times (B \setminus C) = (A \times B) \setminus (A \times C).$$

Solution. Let $(x, y) \in A \times (B \setminus C)$. This gives

$$x \in A; \quad y \in B \setminus C$$
$$\Rightarrow \quad x \in A; \quad y \in B \text{ but } y \notin C$$
$$\Rightarrow \quad (x, y) \in A \times B \text{ ; but } (x, y) \notin A \times C \text{ (as } y \notin C)$$
$$\Rightarrow \quad (x, y) \in (A \times B) \setminus (A \times C).$$

So, $A \times (B \setminus C) \subseteq (A \times B) \setminus (A \times C).$ $\qquad \ldots (i)$

Turning the matter around, let $(x, y) \in (A \times B) \setminus (A \times C)$. This gives

$$(x, y) \in A \times B \text{ ; but } (x, y) \notin A \times C$$
$$\Rightarrow \quad x \in A, y \in B \text{ but } (x, y) \notin A \times C$$
$$\Rightarrow \quad x \in A, y \in B \text{ but } y \notin C \quad \text{(as } x \in A)$$
$$\Rightarrow \quad x \in A; \quad y \in B \setminus C$$
$$\Rightarrow \quad (x, y) \in A \times (B \setminus C).$$

Hence, $(A \times B) \setminus (A \times C) \subseteq A \times (B \setminus C).$ $\qquad \ldots (ii)$

Combining (i) and (ii) we conclude that $A \times (B \setminus C) = (A \times B) \setminus (A \times C).$

$\Diamond$ **Exercise 1.1.6.** Justify the following set-theoretic statements or else give counter examples to disprove. Let A, B and C be subsets of a set U.

(a) $A \triangle C = B \triangle C \Rightarrow A = B.$

(b) $(A \setminus C) \setminus (B \setminus C) = (A \setminus B) \setminus C.$

(c) $(A \setminus B)' = (B \setminus A)'.$

Solution. (a) **True.**

Let $x \in A$. We shall consider two cases separately.

<u>CASE I.</u> $x \notin C.$

Then, $x \in A \setminus C \subseteq (A \setminus C) \cup (C \setminus A) = A \triangle C = B \triangle C$ (given). So, $x \in (B \setminus C) \cup (C \setminus B)$. But since $x \notin C$, $x \notin C \setminus B$, whence it follows that $x \in B \setminus C \subseteq B.$

<u>CASE II.</u> $x \in C.$

Here $x \in A \cap C$ so that $x \notin (A \cup C) \setminus (A \cap C) = A \triangle C$ (cf. Worked-out Exercise 1.1.4). Now, if possible, let $x \notin B$. Then, $x \in C \setminus B \subseteq (C \setminus B) \cup (B \setminus C) = B \triangle C = A \triangle C$ (given)— a contradiction. Hence, $x \in B$ and consequently, we have $A \subseteq B.$

In an essentially similar manner it can be proved that $B \subseteq A$. Consequently, $A = B.$

(b)   **True.**

Indeed,

$$(A \setminus C) \setminus (B \setminus C)$$
$$= (A \cap C') \setminus (B \cap C') \qquad \text{[since } X \setminus Y = X \cap Y']$$
$$= (A \cap C') \cap (B \cap C')'$$
$$= (A \cap C') \cap \left(B' \cup (C')'\right) \qquad \text{[by \textit{De Morgan's law}]}$$
$$= (A \cap C') \cap (B' \cup C) \qquad \text{[since } (X')' = X]$$
$$= \left((A \cap C') \cap B'\right) \cup \left((A \cap C') \cap C\right) \qquad \text{[by \textit{distributivity}]}$$
$$= \left(A \cap (C' \cap B')\right) \cup \left(A \cap (C' \cap C)\right) \qquad \text{[by \textit{associativity}]}$$
$$= \left(A \cap (B' \cap C')\right) \cup (A \cap \emptyset) \qquad \text{[by \textit{commutativity}]}$$
$$= \left((A \cap B') \cap C'\right) \cup \emptyset \qquad \text{[by \textit{associativity}]}$$
$$= (A \setminus B) \cap C' \qquad \text{[since } X \cup \emptyset = X]$$
$$= (A \setminus B) \setminus C.$$

(c) **False.**

Let $U = \{a, b, c, d, e, f, g\}$, $A = \{a, b, e, f\}$ and $B = \{b, f, g\}$.

Then, $(A \setminus B) = \{a, e\}, (B \setminus A) = \{g\}$. Now, $(A \setminus B)' = U \setminus (A \setminus B) = \{b, c, d, f, g\}$ and $(B \setminus A)' = U \setminus (B \setminus A) = \{a, b, c, d, e, f\}$. Clearly, $(A \setminus B)' \neq (B \setminus A)'$.

Exercises

1. Let $P = \{x \in \mathbb{N} \mid 2 < x \leq 8\}, Q = \{x \in \mathbb{N} \mid 0 \leq x < 5\}$ and $R = \{x \in \mathbb{N} \mid 1 \leq x \leq 10\}$. Take as universal set, $U = \{x \in \mathbb{Z} \mid -2 \leq x < 12\}$.

   a) Find (i) $P \cup R$ (ii) $Q \cap R$ (iii) $P \Delta R$ (iv) Q'

   b) Verify that (i) $(P \cup Q)' = P' \cap Q'$ (ii) $P \cap (P \cup R) = P$ (iii) $P \cup (Q \cap R) = (P \cup Q) \cap (P \cup R)$.

2. Let $A = \{x \in \mathbb{R} \mid 1 < x \leq 5\}$ and $B = \{x \in \mathbb{R} \mid 3 \leq x \leq 8\}$. Find $A \cup B, A \cap B, A \setminus B, B \setminus A$.

3. Does every set admit a subset? Give an example of a set that has only one proper subset.

4. A set X has 5 elements. Find $n\left(\mathcal{P}(X)\right)$ and $\mathcal{P}\left(\mathcal{P}(\mathcal{P}(\emptyset))\right)$.

5. Let I_n denote the first n natural numbers. Describe the set $I_n \setminus I_m$ if (i) $n > m$ (ii) $n = m$ (iii) $n < m$.

6. Suppose P and Q are two sets. R is such a set that contains elements belonging to P or Q but not both. T is such a set that contains elements belonging to Q or complement of P but not both. Show that R is the complement of T.

7. Let A, B and C be three sets. Prove the following:

   a) $\left((A \setminus B) \cup (A \cap B)\right) \cap \left((B \setminus A) \cup (A \cup B)'\right) = \emptyset$.

   b) $A \setminus (B \cap C) = (A \setminus B) \cup (A \setminus C)$.

   c) $A \setminus (B \cup C) = (A \setminus B) \cap (A \setminus C)$.

   d) $A \setminus (A \setminus B) = A \cap B$.

   e) $A \cap (B \setminus C) = (A \cap B) \setminus (A \cap C)$.

   f) $A \cap (B \Delta C) = (A \cap B) \Delta (A \cap C)$.

   g) $A \Delta (B \Delta C) = (A \Delta B) \Delta C$.

   h) $A \times B = \bigcup \{ A \times \{b\} \mid b \in B \}$.

   i) $A \times (B \cap C) = (A \times B) \cap (A \times C)$.

   j) $A \times (B \cup C) = (A \times B) \cup (A \times C)$.

   k) $(A \times C) \cap (B \times D) = (A \cap B) \times (C \cap D)$.

   l) $(A \times C) \setminus (B \times D) = \{(A \setminus B) \times (C \setminus D)\} \cup \{(A \cap B) \times (C \setminus D)\} \cup \{(A \setminus B) \times (C \cap D)\}$.

8. Let A, B and C be finite subsets of a set U. Show that

   a) $|A \setminus B| = |A| - |A \cap B|$.

   b) $|A \cup B| \le |A| + |B|$, equality holds only when $A \cap B = \emptyset$.

   c) $|A \cup B| = |A| + |B| - |A \cap B|$.

   d) $|A \cup B \cup C| = |A| + |B| + |C| - |A \cap B| - |B \cap C| - |C \cap A| + |A \cap B \cap C|$.

9. In an examination, 70% of the candidates passed in Mathematics, 73% passed in Physics and 64% passed in both the subjects. If 63 candidates failed in both the subjects, then using the Venn diagram find the total number of candidates who appeared for the examination.

10. Prove the following set-theoretic statements if you find them correct or else give counter examples. The sets A, B and C are subsets of a set U.

   a) $A \cup (B \setminus C) = (A \cup B) \setminus (A \cup C)$.

   b) $(A \setminus B) \setminus C = A \setminus (B \cup C)$.

   c) $(A \cup B) \setminus A = A \setminus B$.

   d) $A \setminus C = B \setminus C$ if and only if $A \cup C = B \cup C$.

1.2 Relations

In this section, we shall study the decomposition of a nonempty set X into nonempty subsets that have no element in common with each other and altogether exhaust the set X. Towards this, we introduce the concept of relation, where we shall see that the central role behind this is that of the ordered pairs.

Definition 1.2.1. A ***binary relation***[11] or simply a ***relation*** $\Re$ from a set A into a set B is a subset of $A \times B$.

---

[11]Since this relation is derived out of ordered pairs of elements, it is called binary relation. Instead, if one defines a relation of the ordered triplets, one may talk about a *ternary relation*. Indeed, n-ary relations (for any positive integral value of n) on a set is perfectly definable, but since we shall have no occasion to deal with them, we drop any adjective to *relation* and henceforth simply mention of a relation in the sense of a binary relation.

In other words, any subset $\Re$ of the Cartesian product $A \times B$ is a relation from A into B; i.e., $\Re$ is a set comprising of some ordered pairs like (a, b), where $a \in A$ and $b \in B$. If $(a, b) \in \Re$, we say that a is $\Re$-related to b and denote it by $a\,\Re\,b$ (or, $\Re(a) = b$). If however $(a, b) \notin \Re$, i.e., if a is not $\Re$-related to b, we denote it by $a\,\bcancel{\Re}\,b$. Observe that for each pair $a \in A$ and $b \in B$, exactly one of the possibilities $a\,\Re\,b$ or $a\,\bcancel{\Re}\,b$ holds.

Sometimes $\Re$ may be a relation from a set A to itself, i.e., $\Re \subseteq A \times A$ and then we speak of a *relation on A*.

Many examples of relation, mathematical or not, may be given.

Example 1.2.2. (a)   Let A denote the set of names of all the districts in West Bengal and $B = Z^*$. With each district x in A, let us associate the number of colleges, say n, in that district, as in the year 2018. Then $\Re = \{(x, n) \,|\, x \in A$ and n is the number of colleges in x, as in the year 2018 $\} \subseteq A \times Z^*$ and hence $\Re$ defines a relation from A into Z^*.

(b)   Let $A = \{1, 2, 3\}$, $B = \{p, q, r\}$ and $\Re = \{(1, q), (2, r), (3, q), (1, p)\}$. Clearly, $\Re$ is a subset of $A \times B$ and hence is a relation from A into B. Observe that, here $2\,\Re\,r$ but $3\,\bcancel{\Re}\,p$.

(c)   Let $P = \{1, 2, 3, 4, 5, 6\}$ and let $\Re$ be defined as, *for $a, b \in P$, $a\,\Re\,b$ if and only if a, b are mutually prime*, i.e., $g.c.d(a, b) = 1$. Then $\Re \subseteq P \times P$, as can be easily verified. Observe that $2\,\Re\,3$ but $2\,\bcancel{\Re}\,4$. Here $\Re$ is a relation on P.

(d)   Let there be a collection of some subsets of a given set U. Note that, for any two of these subsets, say A and B, either $A \subseteq B$ or $A \nsubseteq B$. It is plain to see that '$\subseteq$' (*of being subset*) defines a relation on $\mathcal{P}(U)$.

(e)   Let us consider the set $\mathbb{R}$ of real numbers. Any relation on $\mathbb{R}$ is a subset of $\mathbb{R}^2 (= \mathbb{R} \times \mathbb{R})$. Since $\mathbb{R}^2$ can be visualized as the Cartesian plane, we may try to represent pictorially, some convenient relation on $\mathbb{R}$. Indeed, the relation say $\Re$, defined on $\mathbb{R}$, consisting of all those ordered pairs of real numbers (x, y) that satisfy $x^2 + y^2 = 9$ can be easily *seen* to be a circle with its centre at the origin (0,0) and radius 3 units.

It is worth mentioning that for a set A, since any subset of $A \times A$ is defined to be a relation on A, we must admit $A \times A$ itself and the null set $\emptyset$ to be relations on A. They are called the **universal relation** and the **empty relation** respectively. Note that, for any relation $\Re$ on a set A, we have $\emptyset \subseteq \Re \subseteq A \times A$.

Definition 1.2.3. Let $\Re$ be a relation from a set A into a set B. Then the **domain** of $\Re$, denoted by $\mathcal{D}(\Re)$, is the set

$$\{a \,|\, a \in A \text{ and there exists } b \in B \text{ such that } (a, b) \in \Re\}.$$

The **range** or **image** of $\Re$, denoted by $\mathcal{I}(\Re)$, is the set

$$\{b \,|\, b \in B \text{ and there exists } a \in A \text{ such that } (a,b) \in \Re\}.$$

For example, let $A = \{4, 5, 6, 9\}$ and $B = \{20, 22, 24, 28, 30\}$. Let us define a relation $\Re$ from A into B by stipulating, '$a\,\Re\,b$ *if and only if a divides b, where $a \in A$ and $b \in B$.*' Then it is clear that

$$\Re = \{(4, 20), (4, 24), (4, 28), (5, 20), (5, 30), (6, 24), (6, 30)\}.$$

Here $\mathcal{D}(\Re) = \{4, 5, 6\}$ and $\mathcal{I}(\Re) = \{20, 24, 28, 30\}$.

Definition 1.2.4. Let $\Re$ be a relation from a set A into a set B. The **inverse** of $\Re$, denoted by $\Re^{-1}$, is the relation from B into A, which consists of those ordered pairs which, when reversed, belong to $\Re$, i.e., $\Re^{-1} = \{(b, a) \,|\, (a, b) \in \Re\}$.

For example, let us refer to Example 1.2.2(b). Here, $\Re^{-1} = \{(q, 1), (r, 2), (q, 3), (p, 1)\}$. It is trivial to see that the domain of $\Re^{-1}$ is the range of $\Re$ and vice versa. Furthermore, $(\Re^{-1})^{-1} = \Re$.

Definition 1.2.5. Let $\Re$ be a relation from a set A into a set B and $\mathcal{L}$ be a relation from B into a set C. The **composition** of $\Re$ and $\mathcal{L}$, denoted by[12] $\mathcal{L} \circ \Re$ is the relation from A into C, defined by $a\,(\mathcal{L} \circ \Re)\,c$, if there exists some $b \in B$ such that $a\,\Re\,b$ and $b\,\mathcal{L}\,c$ for all $a \in A, c \in C$.

Let $\Re$ be a relation on a set A. We give the following recursive definition of $\Re^n, n \in \mathbb{N}$ as :

$$\begin{aligned} \Re^1 &= \Re \\ \Re^n &= \Re \circ \Re^{n-1}, \text{ if } n > 1. \end{aligned}$$

Remark 1.2.6. Supposing the sets A, B and C of Definition 1.2.5 are finite and with a considerably small number of elements, there is an interesting way of tabular representation of a relation, which in a way is quite convenient in finding the outcome of the composition of relations, (whenever it is definable). To illustrate this, let us consider $A = \{a, b, c, d\}, B = \{x, y, z\}$ and $C = \{p, q, r, s\}$. Further, let $\Re$ be a relation from A into B and $\mathcal{L}$ be a relation from B and C, given by $\Re = \{(a, y), (b, x), (c, z), (d, x)\}$ and $\mathcal{L} = \{(x, q), (x, r), (y, s), (z, p)\}$.

---

[12]The reason behind the apparent reversal of order in the notation will be better appreciated after the introduction of composition of functions in a later section.

We now make the tabular representations for $\Re$ and $\mathcal{L}$ as follows:

$$M_{\Re} = \begin{array}{c|ccc} A\backslash B & x & y & z \\ \hline a & 0 & 1 & 0 \\ b & 1 & 0 & 0 \\ c & 0 & 0 & 1 \\ d & 1 & 0 & 0 \end{array} \qquad M_{\mathcal{L}} = \begin{array}{c|cccc} B\backslash C & p & q & r & s \\ \hline x & 0 & 1 & 1 & 0 \\ y & 0 & 0 & 0 & 1 \\ z & 1 & 0 & 0 & 0 \end{array}$$

The rule for making these rectangular arrays is quite simple, viz., put 1 or 0 in each position of the array according as the corresponding elements of respective sets are related or not. For example, as $(a, y) \in \Re$, put 1 at the intersection of the *row of a* and *column of y* in the array and so on. This array is called the *matrix of the relation*. To find the composition relation $\mathcal{L} \circ \Re$, we first *multiply the matrices*[13] $M_{\Re}$ and $M_{\mathcal{L}}$ and obtain the matrix M (say), given by

$$M = \begin{array}{c|cccc} A\backslash C & p & q & r & s \\ \hline a & 0 & 0 & 0 & 1 \\ b & 0 & 1 & 1 & 0 \\ c & 1 & 0 & 0 & 0 \\ d & 0 & 1 & 1 & 0 \end{array}$$

Now the *nonzero entries* in this matrix will tell us which elements are related under $\mathcal{L} \circ \Re$. Indeed, $\mathcal{L} \circ \Re = \{(a, s), (b, q), (b, r), (c, p), (d, q), (d, r)\}$.

Definition 1.2.7. Let A be a set and $\Re$ be a relation on A. Then $\Re$ is called

(i)   **reflexive**, if for all $a \in A$, $a \Re a$;

(ii)   **symmetric**, if for all $a, b \in A$, whenever $a \Re b$ holds, $b \Re a$ must also hold;

(iii)   **transitive**, if for all $a, b, c \in A$, whenever $a \Re b$ and $b \Re c$ hold, $a \Re c$ must also hold.

Observe that the relation $\Re$ is

not reflexive, if there exists $a \in A$ such that $(a, a) \notin \Re$;

not symmetric, if there exist $a, b \in A$ such that $(a, b) \subset \Re$ but $(b, a) \notin \Re$;

not transitive, if there exist $a, b, c \in A$ such that $(a, b) \in \Re$, $(b, c) \in \Re$ but $(a, c) \notin \Re$.

The next concept is of paramount importance in the entire subject.

Definition 1.2.8. A relation $\Re$ on a set A is called an **equivalence relation** if $\Re$ is reflexive, symmetric and transitive.

---

[13]It is assumed that the reader is accustomed with the matrix multiplication rules. If however that is not the case, the reader may skip this remark and proceed without any difficulty.

For example, let $A = \{a, b, c, d\}$ and $\rho = \{(a, a), (b, b), (c, c), (d, d),\ (a, c), (c, a)\}$. It can be easily seen that ρ is an equivalence relation on A. The most natural example of an equivalence relation is perhaps the *equality relation* among the real numbers, given by '$(a, b) \in \rho$ *if and only if* $a = b$, *for all* $a, b \in \mathbb{R}$'.

It must be clearly understood that reflexiveness, symmetry and transitivity of a relation are independent[14] of each other, in the sense that no two of them imply the other. Following examples given in a tabular format will give a more comprehensive idea. We leave the verifications to the reader as a routine exercise.

Example 1.2.9. Let $\Re$ be a binary relation on $\mathbb{R}$.

	reflexive	symmetric	transitive	$x \Re y$ iff
1.	✗	✗	✗	$y = 2x$
2.	✗	✗	✓	$x < y$
3.	✗	✓	✗	$x \neq y$
4.	✗	✓	✓	$xy > 0$
5.	✓	✗	✗	$y \neq x + 2$
6.	✓	✗	✓	$x \leq y$
7.	✓	✓	✗	$xy \geq 0$
8.	✓	✓	✓	$x = y$

We now discuss some examples in details to highlight the aforesaid independence.

Example 1.2.10. (a) Let $\Re_1$ be a relation on $\mathbb{Z}$ defined as: '*for all* $a, b \in \mathbb{Z}, a \Re_1 b$ *if and only if* $ab \geq 0$'. Here, since for all $a \in \mathbb{Z}, a^2 \geq 0$ so $a \Re_1 a$ for all $a \in \mathbb{Z}$ holds, whence $\Re_1$ is reflexive. If $a \Re_1 b$ for some $a, b \in \mathbb{Z}$, then $ab \geq 0$ implies that $ba \geq 0$ and hence $b \Re_1 a$, whence $\Re_1$ is symmetric. Now $\Re_1$ is *not transitive*. Indeed, $-5 \Re_1 0$ and $0 \Re_1 7$ but $-5 \not\Re_1 7$. Hence this relation is *reflexive* and *symmetric* but *not transitive*.

(b) Let $\Re_2$ be a relation on $\mathbb{N}$ such that, '$a \Re_2 b$ *if and only if* $a \mid b$ (*i.e.*, a *divides* b) *in* $\mathbb{N}$.' Here $2 \mid 4$ whereas $4 \nmid 2$ so that $4 \not\Re_2 2$ showing that $\Re_2$ is *not symmetric*. A moment's reflection will show that $\Re_2$ is both *reflexive* and *transitive*.

(c) Let $A = \{1, 2, 3, 4\}$ and let us consider the following relations on A.

i) $\rho_1 = \{(1, 2), (2, 1), (2, 2), (1, 1), (1, 3), (2, 3)\}$;

ii) $\rho_2 = \{(2, 3), (3, 2)\}$;

iii) $\rho_3 = \{(1, 1), (2, 2), (3, 3), (4, 4), (1, 2), (2, 3)\}$.

---

[14]That symmetry and transitivity together do not imply reflexiveness, was first justified by Peano in *Notations de Logique Mathématique*, Turin, 1894, p. 45. A critical logical analysis may also be found in *The Principles of Mathematics* by Bertrand Russell.

We leave it to the reader to verify that ρ_1 is neither reflexive nor symmetric though transitive; ρ_2 is neither reflexive nor transitive though symmetric; ρ_3 is reflexive but neither symmetric nor transitive.

A given relation $\Re$ on a finite set S may have a nice pictorial representation. Before we proceed with the subject further, we would like to discuss it in brief. Consider a black dot for each of the elements of S and label it accordingly. Now join the dot labeled a_i with the dot labeled a_j by an arrowed arc *if and only if* $a_i \Re a_j$. In case $a_i \Re a_i$ for some a_i, the arrowed arc from a_i should come back to itself, forming thereby a *loop*. The resulting diagram of $\Re$ is called a ***directed graph*** representation of the relation $\Re$, where each of the dots is called a ***vertex*** and an arrow from one of the dots to the other is called a ***directed edge*** or an ***arc*** of the directed graph.

Thus we define the ordered pair $(S, \Re)$ as the directed graph (*digraph*, as we shall prefer to call it) of the relation $\Re$. Note that two vertices $a_i, a_j \in S$ are said to be ***adjacent*** whenever $(a_i, a_j) \in \Re$. Let us consider an example to describe the situation. Let $S = \{a, b, c, d\}$ and $\Re = \{(a, a), (b, b), (a, b), (b, a), (b, d), (c, d)\}$ be a relation on S.

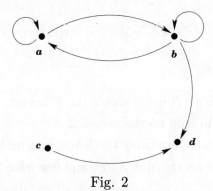

Fig. 2

Then the directed graph $(S, \Re)$ is given by the above diagram (Fig 2). It is worth mentioning that the way the figure is drawn is not important, rather its main aim is to show the relationship among the vertices.

Interestingly, one can very easily, almost like a child's play, create examples of various relations on finite sets, by means of digraphs.

Indeed, take a finite number of dots on a sheet of paper, label them and join any of these dots to any other dot according to your will (only *don't repeat* the joining of the same pair of points by similar arcs!), and observe that you have created an example of a relation, on the finite set of points considered. Now observe further that different properties of the relation can be visually analyzed easily from the digraph.

The following list may help you:

i)   The relation is *reflexive* if and only if there is a loop on each vertex of the digraph.

(ii)   The relation is *symmetric* if and only if, whenever there is an arc from a vertex a (say) to another vertex b (say), there must be an arc from b to a also.

(iii)   The relation is *transitive* if and only if, whenever there is an arc from a vertex a (say) to a vertex b (say), and an arc from b to a vertex c(say), there must be an arc from a to c also.

We now give another example of a digraph representation of a relation and try to apply these criteria to adjudge its nature.

Let $S = \{1, 2, 3, 4, 5\}$ and $\Re = \{(1, 1), (4, 4), (3, 5), (5, 3), (4, 1), (2, 1), (1, 4), (1, 2), (4, 5)\}$ be a relation on S.

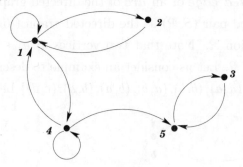

Fig. 3

The corresponding digraph drawn above (Fig. 3) shows the following:

(i) $\Re$ *is not reflexive* : there is no loop on the vertex 2.

(ii) $\Re$ *is not symmetric* : there is an arc from 4 to 5 but none from 5 to 4.

(iii) $\Re$ *is not transitive* : there is an arc from 3 to 5 and one from 5 to 3, but none from 3 to 3.

The following theorem gives a necessary and sufficient condition for a binary relation to be an equivalence relation.

Theorem 1.2.11. *Let ρ be a relation on a set A. Then ρ is an equivalence relation on A if and only if*

(i) $\Delta_A \subseteq \rho$ where $\Delta_A = \{(a, a) \mid a \in A\}$,

(ii) $\rho = \rho^{-1}$ and

(iii) $\rho \circ \rho \subseteq \rho$.

Proof. Suppose ρ is an equivalence relation. Since ρ must be reflexive, for all $a \in A$, $(a, a) \in \rho$ whence $\Delta_A \subseteq \rho$. Now, let $(a, b) \in \rho$; since ρ is symmetric, $(b, a) \in \rho$, i.e., $(a, b) \in \rho^{-1}$ [vide Definition 1.2.4] whence $\rho \subseteq \rho^{-1}$. The reverse inclusion follows in an essentially similar manner and hence $\rho = \rho^{-1}$. Now, let $(a, b) \in \rho \circ \rho$; then there exists some $c \in A$ such that $(a, c) \in \rho$ and $(c, b) \in \rho$. Since ρ is transitive, this gives $(a, b) \in \rho$, whence $\rho \circ \rho \subseteq \rho$.

Conversely, suppose that the conditions hold good. Now, by virtue of (i), the relation ρ is reflexive. Let $(a, b) \in \rho$; then by (ii), $(a, b) \in \rho^{-1}$, i.e., $(b, a) \in \rho$ and hence ρ is symmetric. Finally, let $(a, b), (b, c) \in \rho$. This gives us that $(a, c) \in \rho \circ \rho \subseteq \rho$ [by (iii)] and hence ρ is transitive. Consequently, ρ is an equivalence relation. □

Remark 1.2.12. In view of the proof of the last theorem, it can be easily seen that, given any relation $\Re$ on a set A, the relation $\Re \cup \Delta_A$ is reflexive and $\Re \cup \Re^{-1}$ is symmetric. This is why these relations are referred to as the *reflexive closure* and *symmetric closure* of the relation $\Re$. The *transitive closure* of $\Re$ is denoted by $\Re^{\infty}$ and is understood as

$$\Re \cup \Re^2 \cup \Re^3 \cup \ldots \text{ or, using a more compact notation, as } \bigcup_{n=1}^{\infty} \Re^n.$$

We now prove in brief that $\Re^{\infty}$, as defined above, is the smallest transitive relation on A containing $\Re$. We begin by showing that $\Re^{\infty}$ is transitive; for if $(a, b), (b, c) \in \Re^{\infty}$, then there exist positive integers m, n (say), such that $(a, b) \in \Re^m$, $(b, c) \in \Re^n$. A little reflection with the definition on composition of relations [vide Definition 1.2.5] enables one to appreciate that $(a, c) \in \Re^n \circ \Re^m = \Re^{m+n} \subseteq \Re^{\infty}$, whence $\Re^{\infty}$ is clearly transitive. Further, it is plain to observe that $\Re = \Re^1 \subseteq \Re^{\infty}$. Now, let $\mathfrak{G}$ be a transitive relation on A containing $\Re$. Then $\Re^2 = \Re \circ \Re \subseteq \mathfrak{G} \circ \mathfrak{G} \subseteq \mathfrak{G}$, [by Theorem 1.2.11(iii)] which, by the repeated application of the same argument, gives that $\Re^n \subseteq \mathfrak{G}$ for $n = 1, 2, 3 \ldots$ Thus we have $\Re^{\infty} \subseteq \mathfrak{G}$, proving our claim.

We further point out that the smallest equivalence relation on A containing $\Re$ is $\left(\Re \cup \Re^{-1} \cup \Delta_A\right)^{\infty}$. [Prove it !]

Example 1.2.13. Let us consider a relation $\Re$ on a set $A = \{a, b, c\}$, given by $\Re = \{(a, a), (a, b), (b, c)\}$. Then the reflexive closure of $\Re$ is $\Re \cup \Delta_A = \Re \cup \{(a, a), (b, b), (c, c)\}$ $= \{(a, a), (a, b), (b, c), (b, b), (c, c)\}$. The symmetric closure of $\Re$ is $\Re \cup \Re^{-1} = \Re \cup \{(a, a), (b, a), (c, b)\} = \{(a, a), (a, b), (b, c), (b, a), (c, b)\}$. The transitive closure[15] of $\Re$ is $\bigcup_{n=1}^{3} \Re^n = \Re \cup \Re^2 \cup \Re^3 = \Re \cup \{(a, a), (a, b), (a, c)\} \cup \{(a, a), (a, b), (a, c)\} = \{(a, a), (a, b), (b, c), (a, c)\}$.

Finally, the smallest equivalence relation on A containing $\Re$ is given by $\Re^*$ (say), where $\Re^* = \left(\Re \cup \Re^{-1} \cup \Delta_A\right)^3 = \left(\{(a, a), (a, b), (b, c), (b, a), (c, b), (b, b), (c, c)\}\right)^3$, which can be easily calculated to see that, in this case $\Re^* = A \times A$.

---

[15]The transitive closure of a relation $\Re$ on a *finite set* with n elements can be shown to be $\Re \cup \Re^2 \cup \ldots \cup \Re^n$.

Definition 1.2.14. Let ρ be an equivalence relation on a set X. For all $x \in X$, let $[x]$ denote the set $[x] = \{y \in X \mid y \, \rho \, x\}$. The set $[x]$ is called the ***equivalence class*** determined by x with respect to ρ.

An interesting example may be observed in the set of fractions. By a *fraction* we mean a symbol of the form $\frac{a}{b}$, where a and b are integers and b is not zero. Two fractions $\frac{a}{b}$ and $\frac{c}{d}$ are defined to be *related if and only if* $ad = bc$. Verify that this relation is an equivalence among fractions. Observe that, here an equivalence class of fractions is what one usually calls a rational number. In fact, the rational number[16] $\frac{1}{2}$ can be seen as the equivalence class $\left\{ \ldots \frac{-2}{-4}, \frac{-1}{-2}, \frac{1}{2}, \frac{2}{4}, \frac{3}{6} \ldots \right\}$.

The next theorem furnishes some fundamental properties of equivalence classes.

Theorem 1.2.15. *Let ρ be an equivalence relation on the set A. Then,*

(i)   *for all* $a, \in A$, $[a] \neq \emptyset$,

(ii)   *if* $b \in [a]$ *then* $[a] = [b]$*, where* $a, b \in A$,

(iii)   *for all* $a, b \in A$*, either* $[a] = [b]$ *or* $[a] \cap [b] = \emptyset$ *and*

(iv)   *A is the union of all equivalence classes with respect to ρ, i.e., $A = \displaystyle\bigcup_{a \in A} [a]$.*

Proof. (i)   Let $a \in A$. Since ρ is reflexive, $a \, \rho \, a$. Hence, $a \in [a]$ and so $[a] \neq \emptyset$.

(ii)   Let $b \in [a]$; then $b \, \rho \, a$ and since ρ is symmetric, we have $a \, \rho \, b$. Now, let $x \in [a]$; then $x \, \rho \, a$ follows. So we have $x \, \rho \, a$ and $a \, \rho \, b$, which, by transitivity gives, $x \, \rho \, b$, i.e., $x \in [b]$ so that $[a] \subseteq [b]$. In a similar manner we can show that $[b] \subseteq [a]$, whence in view of Definition 1.1.2 we conclude that $[a] = [b]$.

(iii)   Let $a, b \in A$ and suppose $[a] \cap [b] \neq \emptyset$. Then there exists $x \in [a] \cap [b]$. So, $x \in [a]$ and $x \in [b]$, whence $x \, \rho \, a$ and $x \, \rho \, b$. Now, ρ is symmetric; hence $x \, \rho \, a$ implies $a \, \rho \, x$, whence $a \, \rho \, x$ and $x \, \rho \, b$ together with the transitivity of ρ give $a \, \rho \, b$, so that $a \in [b]$. This indicates by (ii), that $[a] = [b]$.

(iv)   Let $a \in A$. Then $a \in [a] \subseteq \displaystyle\bigcup_{a \in A} [a]$. Hence $A \subseteq \displaystyle\bigcup_{a \in A} [a]$. Observe that the reverse inclusion is obvious. Consequently, $A = \displaystyle\bigcup_{a \in A} [a]$. $\square$

We now introduce the idea of subdividing a nonempty set A into its nonintersecting nonempty subsets, in such a way that each element of A belongs to one and only one

---

[16]Though in our everyday usage, we often speak of *rational numbers* and *fractions* interchangeably, one must clearly understand that it is the rational numbers and not the fractions that constitute a part of the real number system.

of the given subsets. Such a subdivision is called a partition of a set and it is formally defined as follows:

Definition 1.2.16. Let A be a nonempty set and $\mathcal{P}$ be a collection of nonempty subsets of A. Then $\mathcal{P}$ is called a ***partition*** of A, if the following properties are satisfied:

(i) for all $A_i, A_j \in \mathcal{P}$, either $A_i = A_j$ or, $A_i \cap A_j = \emptyset$.

(ii) $A = \bigcup_{A_i \in \mathcal{P}} A_i$.

The Venn diagram of a partition of a set X into five nonempty subsets, say A, B, C, D and E is as follows (Fig. 4):

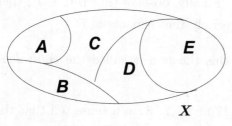

Fig. 4

An example of a partition of the set of all the alphabets in the English language can be made of the set of all vowels and the set of all consonants.

The next theorem, which is often referred to as the *fundamental theorem on equivalence relation*, is an automatic consequence of Theorem 1.2.15.

Theorem 1.2.17. *Let ρ be an equivalence relation on a set A. Then $\mathcal{P} = \{[a] \mid a \in A\}$ is a partition of A.*

In the above theorem, we have seen that a given equivalence relation on a set forces a partition of that set. Turning the matter around, we now prove that, corresponding to any given partition of a set, one can associate an equivalence relation.

Theorem 1.2.18. *Let $\mathcal{P}$ be a partition of a given set A. Define a relation ρ on A as follows: 'for all $a, b \in A$, $a\,\rho\,b$ if there exists $B \in \mathcal{P}$ such that $a, b \in B$'. Then ρ is an equivalence relation on A and the corresponding equivalence classes are precisely the elements of $\mathcal{P}$.*

Proof. Since $\mathcal{P}$ is a partition of A, we have $A = \bigcup_{B \in \mathcal{P}} B$. Now, let $a \in A$. So, $a \in B$ for some $B \in \mathcal{P}$. Since $a, a \in B$ and any two elements of B must be ρ-related, we have $a\,\rho\,a$, for all $a \in A$, as a was chosen arbitrarily. Hence ρ is reflexive. Now, let $a\,\rho\,b$; then $a, b \in B$ for some $B \in \mathcal{P}$, so that $b, a \in B$ also, whence $b\,\rho\,a$, showing that ρ is symmetric. Finally, let $a, b, c \in A$ such that $a \rho b$ and $b \rho c$. Then there exist $B, C \in \mathcal{P}$ such that $a, b \in B$ and $b, c \in C$. This indicates $b \in B \cap C$ so that $B \cap C \neq \emptyset$. But then naturally $B = C$ as $B, C \in \mathcal{P}$, which is a partition of A. So we have $a, c \in B$ whence, $a \rho c$ holds. This shows that ρ is transitive and consequently ρ is an equivalence relation.

Now, it is to be shown that the ρ-classes are precisely the elements of $\mathcal{P}$. Let $a \in A$; we consider the equivalence class $[a]$. Since $A = \bigcup_{B \in \mathcal{P}} B$, there exists $B \in \mathcal{P}$ such that $u \in B$. We assert $[a] = B$. Let $x \in [a]$. Then $x \rho a$, so that $x \in B$ as $a \in B$. Hence $[a] \subseteq B$. Again, since $a \in B$, we have $b \rho a$ for all $b \in B$ and so, $b \in [a]$ for all $b \in B$. Hence $B \subseteq [a]$, so that $[a] = B$. Finally, observe that if $C \in \mathcal{P}$, then $C = [u]$ for all $u \in C$. Thus the ρ-classes are precisely the elements of $\mathcal{P}$. $\square$

The relation ρ described in this theorem is called the *equivalence relation* on A *induced by the partition* $\mathcal{P}$.

Note that the Theorems 1.2.17 and 1.2.18, in a sense tell that there is practically no difference between the outcome of an equivalence relation on a set and a partition of it. If we begin with an equivalence relation, it eventually gives us a partition of the set into equivalence classes, while if we begin with a partition of a set, that in turn may give rise to an equivalence relation, considering those elements to be related, that belong to the same partition set.

At this point, let us describe a partition of a finite set induced by an equivalence relation on it, by means of a digraph. Let $S = \{1, 2, 3, 4, 5, 6\}$ and ρ be an equivalence relation defined on S, given by $\rho = \{(1,1), (2,2), (3,3), (4,4), (5,5), (6,6), (1,4), (4,1), (1,3), (3,1), (4,3), (3,4), (2,5), (5,2)\}$. Let us now draw the digraph of (S, ρ).

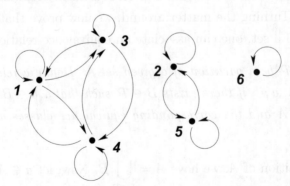

Fig. 5

Observe that the above digraph (Fig. 5) clearly shows a partition of the set S induced by ρ. Indeed, not all the vertices of the digraph are adjacent, i.e., not all of them are joined by arcs with each other. Rather, only those vertices that belong to the same partition set are joined. So one can easily find that the required partition of S, induced by ρ, is given by $\{1, 3, 4\}, \{2, 5\}, \{6\}$.

The next definition leads to a new direction.

Definition 1.2.19. A relation $\Re$ on a set A is said to be *antisymmetric* if for all $a, b \in A$, whenever both $a \Re b$ and $b \Re a$, then $a = b$.

Observe that the relation $\Re$ is not antisymmetric if there exist $a, b \in A$ such that $a \Re b$ and $b \Re a$, but $a \neq b$.

For example, let $A = \{1, 2, 3, 4\}$ and let $\Re$ be a relation on A given by

$$\Re = \{(1, 1), (1, 2), (2, 3), (3, 4), (4, 4), \}.$$

Clearly $\Re$ is antisymmetric.

However, it must clearly be understood that, for a relation, symmetry and anti-symmetry are in no way negatives of each other. Indeed, on a set, say $A = \{1, 2, 3, 4\}$, there can be relations like $\Re_1 = \{(2, 3), (3, 2), (2, 4), (1, 3)\}$ which is neither symmet-ric nor antisymmetric and $\Re_2 = \{(3, 3), (1, 1), (4, 4)\}$ which is both symmetric and antisymmetric (verify!).

Definition 1.2.20. A relation $\Re$ on a set A is said to be a *partial order* on A if $\Re$ is reflexive, antisymmetric and transitive. A partial order relation on a set A is usually denoted by $\leq$. The set A along with the partial order defined on it is called a *partially ordered set* or a *poset*.

We now give some examples of posets.

Example 1.2.21. (a)   Let A be any nonempty set and $\mathcal{P}(A)$ be the power set of A. Recall the relation discussed in Example 1.2.2(d). From the definition of a subset it follows that $X \subseteq X$ for all $X \in \mathcal{P}(A)$, whence '$\subseteq$' is reflexive. Again, if $X \subseteq Y$ and $Y \subseteq X$ for some $X, Y \in \mathcal{P}(A)$, we get $X = Y$ by the definition of equality of sets, whence '$\subseteq$' is antisymmetric. Finally, for $X, Y, Z \in \mathcal{P}(A)$ if $X \subseteq Y$ and $Y \subseteq Z$, then $X \subseteq Z$ and hence '$\subseteq$' is transitive. Consequently, the relation '$\subseteq$' is a partial order on $\mathcal{P}(A)$ and so $\left(\mathcal{P}(A), \subseteq\right)$ is a poset.

(b)   Let us consider the set $\mathbb{R}$ and define a relation on $\mathbb{R}$ by $\rho = \{(a, b) \in \mathbb{R} \times \mathbb{R} \mid a - b \leq 0\}$. We leave it to the reader as a routine exercise to verify that ρ is a partial order on $\mathbb{R}$ and hence $(\mathbb{R}, \rho)$ is a poset.

(c)   Let us consider the set $\mathbb{N}$ and define a relation $\Re$ on it as follows: '$\Re = \{(a, b) \in \mathbb{N} \times \mathbb{N} \mid a$ divides b in $\mathbb{N}\}$'. We prove that $\Re$ is antisymmetric and leave it to the reader to see that $\Re$ is reflexive and transitive as well. Now, towards antisymmetry of $\Re$, let $a \Re b$ and $b \Re a$, for some $a, b \in \Re$, i.e., $b = an = bmn$, whence we have $mn = 1$; but as $m, n \in \mathbb{N}$, $mn = 1$ means $m = n = 1$ so that we get $a = b$. Thus $\Re$ is antisymmetric.

It is noteworthy that if one defines this relation on $\mathbb{Z}$ instead of $\mathbb{N}$, then this relation fails to be antisymmetric. Indeed, $(2, -2) \in \Re$ and $(-2, 2) \in \Re$ in this case, but $2 \neq -2$, spoiling the antisymmetry of $\Re$.

Definition 1.2.22. A poset (A, ρ) is called a **linearly ordered set** or a **chain**, if for all $a, b \in A$, either $a \rho b$ or $b \rho a$ must hold.

It can be easily verified that the poset cited in Example 1.2.21(b) is actually a chain, whereas the poset in Example 1.2.21(a) is not. In fact, in 1.2.21(a) we may have $\{a\}, \{b\} \in \mathcal{P}(A)$ for some $a, b \in A$ such that $\{a\} \not\subseteq \{b\}$ and $\{b\} \not\subseteq \{a\}$.

We wish to put an end to this discussion on relations by merely mentioning that the idea of a poset paves the path towards a very important branch of abstract algebra, known as the *lattice theory*, an account of which is out of scope of this text.

Worked-out Exercises

$\diamond$ **Exercise 1.2.1.** For each of the following relations on $A = \{1, 2, 3, 4\}$, decide whether it is reflexive, symmetric, antisymmetric or transitive.

   (i) $\rho = \{(1, 3), (3, 1)\}$
   (ii) $\rho = \{(2, 2)\}$
   (iii) $\rho = \{(1, 2), (1, 4)\}$
   (iv) $\rho = \{(1, 1), (2, 2), (3, 3), (4, 4), (2, 3), (3, 2)\}$

Solution. (i)   Since $(1, 1) \notin \rho$, ρ is not reflexive. Further, we see that in ρ, whenever $(a, b) \in \rho$, we also have $(b, a) \in \rho$, whence ρ is symmetric. However, we observe that $(3, 1) \in \rho$, $(1, 3) \in \rho$ but $(3, 3) \notin \rho$ and so ρ is not transitive. Finally, here $(1, 3) \in \rho$ and $(3, 1) \in \rho$ but $1 \neq 3$. Hence ρ is not antisymmetric.

(ii)   Here ρ is not reflexive as $(1, 1) \notin \rho$. Now here $(a, b) \in \rho$ automatically implies that $(b, a) \in \rho$, because $a = 2 = b$. Hence ρ is symmetric. In an essentially similar manner it can be verified that ρ is transitive and antisymmetric.

(iii)   Since $(1, 1) \notin \rho$, it is not reflexive. Again, here $(1, 2) \in \rho$ but $(2, 1) \notin \rho$ and hence ρ is not symmetric either. But, ρ is transitive as there do not exist any two pairs of the form $(a, b), (b, c)$ in ρ. A similar argument establishes that ρ is antisymmetric (vacuously).

(iv) It is routine to check that ρ is reflexive, symmetric and transitive. However, we see that $2 \neq 3$, though $(2, 3)$ and $(3, 2)$ both belong to ρ, whence ρ is not antisymmetric.

◊ **Exercise 1.2.2.** Which of the relations described in the above Worked-out Exercise 1.2.1 are equivalence relations? In case there is any, describe the partitions of the set $A = \{1, 2, 3, 4\}$ induced by that equivalence relation.

Solution. We know that a relation is said to be an equivalence relation if it is reflexive, symmetric and transitive. Hence the relation described in the Worked-out Exercise 1.2.1 (iv) is the only equivalence relation out of the four.

It is easy to see that the partition of the set A induced by this equivalence relation is given by $\{1\}, \{2, 3\}, \{4\}$.

◊ **Exercise 1.2.3.** The following relations are defined on the set $\mathbb{R}$ of real numbers. Find whether these relations are reflexive, symmetric or transitive.

(i) $a \mathcal{R} b$ iff $|a - b| > 0$; (ii) $a \mathcal{R} b$ iff $1 + ab > 0$; (iii) $a \mathcal{R} b$ iff $|a| \leq b$.

Solution. (i) $\mathcal{R}$ is not reflexive, since for any $a \in \mathbb{R}$, $a - a = 0$ and hence $|a - a| \not> 0$, i.e., $a \mathcal{R} a$. Again, as $|a - b| = |b - a|$ so we have that, if $|a - b| > 0$ then $|b - a| > 0$, whence $a \mathcal{R} b$ implies $b \mathcal{R} a$ for all $a, b \in \mathbb{R}$. So $\mathcal{R}$ is symmetric. Here $\mathcal{R}$ is not transitive. Indeed, consider $1, 0 \in \mathbb{R}$. Then $|1 - 0| = |0 - 1| = 1 > 0$ shows that $1 \mathcal{R} 0$ and $0 \mathcal{R} 1$ but here $1 \mathcal{R} 1$ as $|1 - 1| = 0 \not> 0$.

(ii) Since $\forall a \in \mathbb{R}, a^2 \geq 0$, we have $1 + a^2 > 0$ and hence $a \mathcal{R} a \, \forall a \in \mathbb{R}$, whence $\mathcal{R}$ is reflexive. Again $\forall a, b \in \mathbb{R}$, if $1 + ab > 0$, then $1 + ba > 0$ as $ab = ba$, whence we have that whenever $a \mathcal{R} b$ holds, $b \mathcal{R} a$ also holds. So $\mathcal{R}$ is symmetric. However, $\mathcal{R}$ is not transitive. In fact, let us consider $3, -\frac{1}{9}, -6 \in \mathbb{R}$. Then, $1 + 3\left(-\frac{1}{9}\right) = 1 - \frac{1}{3} = \frac{2}{3} > 0$ shows $3 \mathcal{R} \left(-\frac{1}{9}\right)$ and $1 + \left(-\frac{1}{9}\right)(-6) = 1 + \frac{2}{3} = \frac{5}{3} > 0$ shows $\left(-\frac{1}{9}\right) \mathcal{R} (-6)$. But, as $1 + 3(-6) = 1 - 18 = -17 \not> 0$, we conclude that $3 \mathcal{R} (6)$, whence $\mathcal{R}$ is not a transitive relation.

(iii) Let us consider $-2 \in \mathbb{R}$, then $|-2| = 2 \not\leq -2$, whence $(-2) \mathcal{R} (-2)$ showing thereby that $\mathcal{R}$ is not reflexive. $\mathcal{R}$ is not symmetric either. Indeed, $|-2| = 2 \leq 5$ and so $-2 \mathcal{R} 5$; but $|5| = 5 \not\leq -2$, whence $5 \mathcal{R} - 2$ and consequently $\mathcal{R}$ is not symmetric. Now, let $p, q, r \in \mathbb{R}$ such that $p \mathcal{R} q$ and $q \mathcal{R} r$, i.e., $|p| \leq q$ and $|q| \leq r$. Now, since $q \geq |p| \geq 0$, we have $|q| = q$, whence $|p| \leq q \leq r$ gives $p \mathcal{R} r$ and so $\mathcal{R}$ is transitive.

◊ **Exercise 1.2.4.** In each of the following cases, examine whether the relation ρ is an equivalence relation on the set of all integers.

(i) $\rho = \{(a,b) \in \mathbb{Z} \times \mathbb{Z} : |a-b| \leq 3\}$

(ii) $\rho = \{(a,b) \in \mathbb{Z} \times \mathbb{Z} : a-b \text{ is a multiple of } 6\}$.

Solution. (i)   In this case, the relation ρ is not transitive. Indeed, we see that $2\,\rho\,5$ and $5\,\rho\,7$ hold, which can be easily checked from the given definition of ρ, but $2\,\not\rho\,7$ as $|2-7| = 5 \nleq 3$. Consequently, ρ is not a transitive relation and hence not an equivalence relation.

(ii)   Let us consider any integer $a \in \mathbb{Z}$. Then $a - a = 0 = 0 \cdot 6$ indicates that $a\,\rho\,a$ for all $a \in \mathbb{Z}$. Hence ρ is reflexive. Now, let $a\,\rho\,b$ for some $a, b \in \mathbb{Z}$. This means $a - b = 6n$ for some $n \in \mathbb{Z}$. But then, $b - a = 6(-n)$ where $-n \in \mathbb{Z}$ and this shows that $b\,\rho\,a$, whence ρ is symmetric. Finally, let $a, b, c \in \mathbb{Z}$ such that $a\,\rho\,b$ and $b\,\rho\,c$. Then $a - b = 6n_1$ and $b - c = 6n_2$ for some $n_1, n_2 \in \mathbb{Z}$. Then $a - b + b - c = 6(n_1 + n_2)$, i.e., $a - c = 6(n_1 + n_2)$, where $n_1 + n_2 \in \mathbb{Z}$. This shows that $a\,\rho\,c$, whence ρ is transitive. Consequently, ρ is an equivalence relation on $\mathbb{Z}$.

♦ **Exercise 1.2.5.** Let S be a finite set with n elements. Prove that the number of reflexive relations that can be defined on S is $2^{(n^2-n)}$; the number of symmetric relations is $2^{\frac{n(n+1)}{2}}$ and the number of relations that are both reflexive and symmetric is $2^{\frac{n(n-1)}{2}}$.

Solution. Here $|S| = n$ and so $|S \times S| = n^2$. We know that any subset of $S \times S$ is a relation on S. Now to be a reflexive relation, it must contain the diagonal Δ_S comprising of elements like $(a_1, a_1), (a_2, a_2), \ldots, (a_n, a_n)$, where $a_1, a_2, \ldots, a_n \in S$. Note that there are n such pairs. Now, with the remaining $n^2 - n$ elements of $S \times S$, one can think of $2^{(n^2-n)}$ subsets of $S \times S$, each of which, when made union with Δ_S that was set aside, will give us a reflexive relation. Hence, the number of reflexive relations on S is $2^{(n^2-n)}$.

Recall that a relation ρ on S is called symmetric, if whenever $(a, b) \in \rho$ for some $a, b \in S$, we have $(b, a) \in \rho$ also. In other words, whenever an ordered pair (a, b) belongs to a symmetric relation, it automatically invites the pair (b, a) to be a member of that relation, to preserve the symmetry. Now, if we put together each of the pairs like (a, b) and (b, a) and refer to them as a "twin" (for convenience of reference) then, setting aside the elements of the main diagonal, number of such "twins" in $S \times S$ is $\frac{n^2-n}{2}$. Now any symmetric relation on S can also include any number of elements from the main diagonal Δ_S, as the elements of the diagonal automatically conform to the requirement of symmetry. So the total number of elements available from $S \times S$ for making symmetric relations is $\frac{n^2-n}{2} + n$ (i.e., the sum of the number of "twins" and the number of elements in Δ_S) $= \frac{n^2+n}{2} = \frac{n(n+1)}{2}$. A moment's reflection now tells that any subset that can be made out of these $\frac{n(n+1)}{2}$ elements is a symmetric relation on S and consequently, the number of symmetric relations on S is $2^{\frac{n(n+1)}{2}}$.

Finally, for a relation to be both reflexive and symmetric, we have to vary our choices of elements from within the "twins" only, as here with each such choice, the entire diagonal Δ_S is to be made union for the relation to be reflexive. Hence, the number of subsets that can be made out of $\frac{n^2-n}{2}$ "twins" is the required number of relations on S that are both reflexive and symmetric. Hence, the number of such relations on S that are both reflexive and symmetric is $2^{\frac{n(n-1)}{2}}$.

◊ **Exercise 1.2.6.** Find all the equivalence relations on the set $A = \{1, 2, 3\}$.

Solution. If ρ is an equivalence relation on the set A, then we know that the equivalence classes with respect to ρ will give a partition of A. Again, given any partition $\mathcal{P}$ of the set A, there exists an equivalence relation on A, of which the equivalence classes are precisely the members of $\mathcal{P}$. Consequently, the number of equivalence relations on a finite set is equal to the number of different partitions of it. Since the number of elements of A is quite small here, we may easily work out the partitions of A to be $\{\{1\}, \{2\}, \{3\}\}, \{\{1\}, \{2,3\}\}, \{\{2\}, \{1,3\}\}, \{\{3\}, \{1,2\}\}$ and $\{\{1,2,3\}\}$. Now, it follows that the five equivalence relations on A are

$\rho_1 = \{(1,1), (2,2), (3,3)\}$; $\rho_2 = \{(1,1), (2,2), (3,3), (2,3), (3,2)\}$

$\rho_3 = \{(1,1), (2,2), (3,3), (1,3), (3,1)\}$;

$\rho_4 = \{(1,1), (2,2), (3,3), (1,2), (2,1)\}$

and $\rho_5 = A \times A$.

♦ **Exercise 1.2.7.** Suppose A be a set with n elements. Let us denote by $\phi(n, k)$, the number of partitions of the set A into k subsets ($1 \leq k \leq n$). Prove that

(a) $\phi(n, k) = 1$ when $k = 1$ or, n

$= \phi(n-1, k-1) + k\,\phi(n-1, k)$ when $1 < k < n$.

(b) Hence find how many different partitions can be made of a set, when $n = 4$.

Solution. (a) Since there is only one way to partition A with n elements into one subset, we have $\phi(n, 1) = 1$. Also, if we partition A into n subsets, i.e., when every subset will be a singleton, again there is exactly one way of doing so and hence $\phi(n, n) = 1$. Now, consider the case $1 < k < n$. Let us fix an element x in A arbitrarily. Now, if we consider $\{x\}$ as a member of the required partition of A into k subsets, then the remaining $n - 1$ elements of $A \setminus \{x\}$ has to be partitioned into $(k - 1)$ subsets and that can be done in $\phi(n-1, k-1)$ ways. On the other hand, to achieve the required partition of A, one can also partition $A \setminus \{x\}$ into k subsets and put the element x in any of these subsets. Observe that $(n-1)$ elements of $A \setminus \{x\}$ can be partitioned into k subsets in $\phi(n-1,k)$ ways and the element x can be admitted into a subset in k ways. Consequently, we have

$$\phi(n,k) = \phi(n-1,k-1) + k\,\phi(n-1,k), \qquad 1 < k < n.$$

(b)   Let $|A| = 4$, i.e., $n = 4$. We apply the recursive relation found in (a) and proceed as follows:

$\phi(1,1) = 1$

$\phi(2,1) = 1, \ \phi(2,2) = 1$

$\phi(3,1) = 1, \ \phi(3,2) = \phi(2,1) + 2\,\phi(2,2) = 1 + 2 = 3, \ \phi(3,3) = 1$

$\phi(4,1) = 1, \ \phi(4,2) = \phi(3,1) + 2\,\phi(3,2) = 1 + 2.3 = 7, \ \phi(4,3) = \phi(3,2) + 3\,\phi(3,3) = 3 + 3.1 = 6, \ \phi(4,4) = 1.$

It is now easily seen that the required total number of different partitions is

$$\sum_{k=1}^{4} \phi(4,k) = 1 + 7 + 6 + 1 = 15.$$

[**Remark.**   We would like to point out that in Worked-out Exercise 1.2.6, the number of partitions on $A = \{1,2,3\}$ is $\displaystyle\sum_{k=1}^{3} \phi(3,k)$, which can be calculated to be $1+3+1 = 5$. Hence we had only five equivalence relations that could have been defined on $A = \{1,2,3\}$.]

$\Diamond$ **Exercise 1.2.8.** Justify the following statements or else give counter examples to disprove.

  (i)   The intersection of two equivalence relations is again an equivalence relation.

  (ii)   The union of two equivalence relations is again an equivalence relation.

  (iii)   If $\mathcal{R}_1$ and $\mathcal{R}_2$ are two symmetric relations on a set, then so is $\mathcal{R}_1 \circ \mathcal{R}_2$.

  (iv)   If $\mathcal{R}_1$ is a reflexive and transitive relation then $\mathcal{R}_1 \circ \mathcal{R}_1$ is transitive.

Solution. (i) **True.** Let $\mathcal{R}$ and $\mathcal{L}$ be two equivalence relations on some set A. Now, since both $\mathcal{R}$ and $\mathcal{L}$ are reflexive, we have $\forall a \in A, (a,a) \in \mathcal{R}$ and $(a,a) \in \mathcal{L}$, whence $(a,a) \in \mathcal{R} \cap \mathcal{L}$ and consequently, $\mathcal{R} \cap \mathcal{L}$ is reflexive.

Now, let $a,b \in A$ such that $(a,b) \in \mathcal{R} \cap \mathcal{L}$ then, $(a,b) \in \mathcal{R}$ and $(a,b) \in \mathcal{L}$ so that $(b,a) \in \mathcal{R}$ and $(b,a) \in \mathcal{L}$ (as both $\mathcal{R}$ and $\mathcal{L}$ are symmetric), whence $(b,a) \in \mathcal{R} \cap \mathcal{L}$ proving that $\mathcal{R} \cap \mathcal{L}$ is symmetric.

Again, let for $a,b,c \in A, (a,b) \in \mathcal{R} \cap \mathcal{L}$ and $(b,c) \in \mathcal{R} \cap \mathcal{L}$. Then, $(a,b),(b,c) \in \mathcal{R}$ and $(a,b),(b,c) \in \mathcal{L}$ also. By transitivity of $\mathcal{R}$ and $\mathcal{L}$, we have $(a,c) \in \mathcal{R}$ as well as

$(a, c) \in \mathcal{L}$, whence $(a, c) \in \mathcal{R} \cap \mathcal{L}$ proving that $\mathcal{R} \cap \mathcal{L}$ is transitive. Consequently, $\mathcal{R} \cap \mathcal{L}$ is an equivalence relation on A.

(ii) **False.** Let $A = \{1, 2, 3\}$. We consider two equivalence relations on A given by

$$\mathcal{R} = \{(1,1), (2,2), (3,3), (2,3), (3,2)\}; \mathcal{L} = \{(1,1), (2,2), (3,3), (3,1), (1,3)\}.$$

Here $\mathcal{R} \cup \mathcal{L} = \{(1,1), (2,2), (3,3), (2,3), (3,2), (3,1), (1,3)\}$, which is not an equivalence relation as it lacks transitivity. Indeed, $(2,3), (3,1) \in \mathcal{R} \cup \mathcal{L}$ but $(2,1) \notin \mathcal{R} \cup \mathcal{L}$.

(iii) **False.** Let $A = \{1, 2, 3\}$, $\mathcal{R}_1 = \{(2,3), (3,2)\}$ and $\mathcal{R}_2 = \{(1,2), (2,1)\}$. Then clearly $\mathcal{R}_1$ and $\mathcal{R}_2$ are two symmetric relations on A. Now, $\mathcal{R}_1 \circ \mathcal{R}_2 = \{(1,3)\}$ which is not symmetric.

(iv) **True.** Let $\mathcal{R}_1$ be a reflexive and transitive relation on A. Let for some $a, b, c \in A$, $(a,b), (b,c) \in \mathcal{R}_1 \circ \mathcal{R}_1$. Then $(a,x), (x,b), (b,y), (y,c) \in \mathcal{R}_1$ for some $x, y \in A$. Now by transitivity of $\mathcal{R}_1$, $(a,b) \in \mathcal{R}_1$ and $(b,c) \in \mathcal{R}_1$, whence further $(a,c) \in \mathcal{R}_1$ also. Again as $\mathcal{R}_1$ is reflexive, $(a,a) \in \mathcal{R}_1$. Now, $(a,a), (a,c) \in \mathcal{R}_1$ together implies that $(a,c) \in \mathcal{R}_1 \circ \mathcal{R}_1$ and so $\mathcal{R}_1 \circ \mathcal{R}_1$ is transitive.

Exercises

1. For each of the following relations on $A = \{1, 2, 3, 4\}$, decide whether it is reflexive, symmetric, antisymmetric or transitive.

   (a) $\rho = \{(2, 4)\}$.

   (b) $\rho = \{(3, 4), (4, 3)\}$.

   (c) $\rho = \{(1, 1), (2, 2), (3, 3), (3, 4), (4, 3)\}$.

   (d) $\rho = \{(3, 3), (4, 4)\}$.

   (e) $\rho = \{(1, 1), (2, 2), (3, 3), (4, 4)\}$.

   (f) $\rho = \{(1, 2), (2, 3), (3, 4)\}$.

   (g) $\rho = \{(1, 1), (2, 2), (3, 3), (4, 4), (2, 3), (3, 2), (3, 4), (4, 3)\}$.

2. Which of the relations of Exercise 1 above are equivalence relations? If there is any, find the corresponding partition of the set A induced by the equivalence relation.

3. Find the number of reflexive relations on a set of three elements.

4. Find the number of symmetric relations on a set of three elements.

5. For the partition $\mathcal{P} = \left\{ \{a\}, \{b, c\}, \{d, e\} \right\}$, write the corresponding equivalence relation on the set $A = \{a, b, c, d, e\}$.

6. Let $A = \{n \in \mathbb{N} : 1 \leq n \leq 20\}$. For all $a, b \in A$, define a relation $\mathcal{R}$ on A by $a \mathcal{R} b$ if and only if $a - b = 5t$ for some $t \in \mathbb{Z}$. Show that $\mathcal{R}$ is an equivalence relation on A. Find all the equivalence classes.

7. Find out which of the following relations ρ are equivalence relations on the set of integers?

    i) $a\,\rho\,b$ if and only if $a^2 - b^2$ is a multiple of 7.

    ii) $a\,\rho\,b$ if and only if $a^2 = b^2$.

    iii) $a\,\rho\,b$ if and only if $a \leq |b|$.

    iv) $a\,\rho\,b$ if and only if $a - b$ is an even integer.

    v) $a\,\rho\,b$ if and only if $a \geq b$.

    vi) $a\,\rho\,b$ if and only if $|a| = |b|$.

    vii) $a\,\rho\,b$ if and only if $b = a^r$ for some positive integer r.

8. Examine whether the relation ρ defined on the set S is an equivalence relation.

    (a) $S = \mathbb{Z} \times \mathbb{Z}$ and ρ is defined by $(a, b)\,\rho\,(c, d)$ if and only if $a + d = b + c$.

    (b) $S = \mathbb{Z} \times \mathbb{Z} \setminus \{(0,0)\}$ and ρ is defined by $(a, b)\,\rho\,(c, d)$ if and only if $ad = bc$.

9. Consider the following relations:

    (i)   the relation '$\perp$' (perpendicular) on the set L of lines in a plane;

    (ii)   the relation '$\|$' (being identical or parallel) on the set L of lines in a plane;

    (iii) relation $\rho_1 = \{(1,1), (2,2), (3,4), (4,3), (4,4)\}$ on $A = \{1, 2, 3, 4\}$;

    (iv)   relation '$|$' of divisibility among the set of natural numbers.

    Find which of these relations are (a) reflexive (b) symmetric (c) transitive (d) antisymmetric.

10. Given a relation $\rho = \{(1,2), (2,3)\}$ on the set $\{1, 2, 3\}$, add a minimum number of ordered pairs of natural numbers so that the enlarged relation is symmetric, transitive and reflexive.

11. Let ρ be a relation defined on the set $\mathbb{N}$ of natural numbers as $\rho = \{(x, y) \in \mathbb{N} \times \mathbb{N} : 2x + y = 41\}$. Find the domain and range of ρ. Show that this relation is neither reflexive nor symmetric let alone transitive.

12. Let X be a nonempty set. Prove that the following conditions are equivalent:

    (a) ρ is an equivalence relation on X.

    (b) ρ is a reflexive relation on X and for all $x, y, z \in X$, if $x\,\rho\,y$ and $y\,\rho\,z$, then $z\,\rho\,x$.

    (c) ρ is a reflexive relation on X and for all $x, y, z \in X$, if $x\,\rho\,y$ and $x\,\rho\,z$, then $y\,\rho\,z$.

13. Let ρ_1 and ρ_2 be two equivalence relations on a set A such that $\rho_1 \circ \rho_2 = \rho_2 \circ \rho_1$. Prove that $\rho_1 \circ \rho_2$ is also an equivalence relation.

14. A relation $\mathcal{R}$ on the set of complex numbers is defined by $z_1\,\mathcal{R}\,z_2$ if and only if $\frac{(z_1 - z_2)}{(z_1 + z_2)}$ is real. Show that $\mathcal{R}$ is not an equivalence relation.

15. Let A be the set of first ten natural numbers. Define a relation ρ on A by $x\,\rho\,y$ if and only if x is a divisor of y for all $x, y \in A$. Prove that (A, ρ) is a poset.

16. Let $\Re = \{(a, b) \in \mathbb{Z} \times \mathbb{Z} \mid 3a + 4b = 7n, \text{ for some } n \in \mathbb{Z}\}$. Show that $\Re$ is an equivalence relation.

17. Define a relation '$\geq$' among all the complex numbers, of the form $a + ib$ where $a, b \in \mathbb{R}$ and $i^2 = -1$ by stipulating $a + ib \geq c + id$ if and only if $a \geq c$ and $b \geq d$ for all $a, b, c, d \in \mathbb{R}$. Prove that $\geq$ is a partial order relation on the set of complex numbers $\mathbb{C}$. Is it a linear order on $\mathbb{C}$? Justify your answer.

18. Prove the following assertions if you can, or else give counter examples to disprove.

    (a) If ρ is a transitive relation on a set A, then so is ρ^{-1}.

    (b) If ρ_1 and ρ_2 are transitive relations on a set A, then so is $\rho_1 \circ \rho_2$.

    (c) The symmetry and transitivity of a relation automatically implies its reflexivity.

    (d) Every relation must either be symmetric or antisymmetric.

    (e) Let ρ be a reflexive and transitive relation on a set A. Then $\rho \cap \rho^{-1}$ is an equivalence relation.

1.3 Congruence Relation

In this section, we discuss a particular type of equivalence relation on the set $\mathbb{Z}$. It is not just one example of equivalence relation but it has a far-reaching consequence as will be revealed in due course. It is known as congruence relation. The notion of congruence was first introduced by Karl Fredrich Gauss[17](1777-1855) in the beginning of the nineteenth century.

Fix a positive integer n in $\mathbb{Z}$. Define a relation, say $\equiv_n$ on $\mathbb{Z}$ as follows: '*for all* $a, b \in \mathbb{Z}, a \equiv_n b$ *if and only if* $n|(a-b)$, *i.e.*, $a - b = nk$ *for some* $k \in \mathbb{Z}$'. Let us now show that $\equiv_n$ is an equivalence relation on $\mathbb{Z}$.

Indeed, for all $a \in \mathbb{Z}$, $a - a = 0 = n0$, so that $a \equiv_n a$ for all $a \in \mathbb{Z}$, whence $\equiv_n$ is reflexive.

Now, let $a, b \in \mathbb{Z}$ and suppose $a \equiv_n b$. Then there exists $k \in \mathbb{Z}$, such that $a - b = nk$. This implies that $b - a = (-k)n$ and so $n|(b - a)$, i.e., $b \equiv_n a$, when $\equiv_n$ is symmetric.

Finally, let $a, b, c \in \mathbb{Z}$ and suppose $a \equiv_n b$ and $b \equiv_n c$. Then there exist $p, q \in \mathbb{Z}$ such that $a - b = pn$ and $b - c = qn$. This gives, on addition, $a - c = (p + q)n$, whence $a \equiv_n c$. Hence $\equiv_n$ is transitive.

Consequently, $\equiv_n$ is an equivalence relation on $\mathbb{Z}$.

This equivalence relation is called ***congruence modulo*** n and $a \equiv_n b$ is also denoted by $a \equiv b \,(\mathrm{mod}\, n)$. However, if $a - b$ is not divisible by n, then we may write $a \not\equiv b \,(\mathrm{mod}\, n)$. Observe that, we can prove directly from the above definition that two integers a and b are congruent, modulo a positive integer n, if and only if a and b leave the same remainder, when divided by n.

Example 1.3.1. 5 divides $23 - 13$. Hence $23 \equiv 13 \,(\mathrm{mod}\, 5)$. But $20 - 4$ is not divisible by 5. Hence $20 \not\equiv 4 \,(\mathrm{mod}\, 5)$.

---

[17]Aptly known as the *Prince of Mathematics*, this extraordinary mathematician was the son of a day labourer. In the words of Leopold Kronecker (1823-1891): "almost everything which the mathematics of our century has brought forth in the way of original scientific ideas is connected with the name of Gauss."

Definition 1.3.2. Let n be a positive integer and a be any integer. Then the subset of $\mathbb{Z}$ given by $\{b \in \mathbb{Z} \mid b \equiv a \,(\mathrm{mod}\,n)\}$ is called the **congruence class modulo n** of the integer a. We denote it by $[a]$.

Example 1.3.3. Let $n = 6$ and $a = 4$. Then the congruence class of 4, modulo 6 is the subset

$$
\begin{aligned}
[4] \quad &= \quad \{b \in \mathbb{Z} \mid b \equiv 4 \,(\mathrm{mod}\,6)\} \\
&= \quad \{b \in \mathbb{Z} \mid 6 \text{ divides } b - 4\} \\
&= \quad \{b \in \mathbb{Z} \mid b - 4 = 6k \text{ for some integer } k\} \\
&= \quad \{b \in \mathbb{Z} \mid b = 4 + 6k \text{ for some integer } k\} \\
&= \quad \{\ldots - 14, -8, -2, 4, 10, 16, 22, \ldots\}.
\end{aligned}
$$

The next theorem reveals some of the basic properties of congruence classes modulo m.

Theorem 1.3.4. *Let m be a positive integer. The congruence classes modulo m satisfy the following:*

(i) $[a] \neq \emptyset$, *for all integers a.*

(ii) *If $b \in [a]$, then $[b] = [a]$ for all integers a, b.*

(iii) *For all integers a, b, either $[a] \cap [b] = \emptyset$ or $[a] = [b]$.*

Proof. Since we have already seen that the relation congruence modulo m is an equivalence relation, the theorem follows directly from Theorem 1.2.15.   □

Consider the positive integer 6 and consider the congruence classes modulo 6. Now $9 \equiv 3\,(\mathrm{mod}\,6)$. Hence $9 \in [3]$. This implies that $[9] = [3]$. Likewise $[2] = [8], [1] = [7], [4] = [10]$ etc.

For any positive integer m, let $\mathbb{Z}_m$ denote the set of all congruence class modulo m.

Theorem 1.3.5. *The number of elements of $\mathbb{Z}_m$ is finite and this number is m.*

Proof. If k is any integer, then by division algorithm there exist integers q and r such that $k = qm + r$ where $0 \leq r \leq m - 1$.

This implies that m divides $k - r$ and so $k \equiv r\,(\,\mathrm{mod}\,m)$, i.e., $[k] = [r]$. Thus we find that for any integer k, there exists an integer $0 \leq r \leq m - 1$ such that $[k] = [r]$. Hence the number of congruence classes $[k]$ modulo m is less than or equal to m.

Now, let $[r]$ and $[t]$ be two congruence classes modulo m such that $0 \leq r, t \leq m-1$. Then
$$-(m-1) \leq r - t \leq (m-1).$$
Hence $[r] = [t]$ if and only if $r \equiv t \pmod{m}$, i.e., if and only if m divides $r - t$, i.e., if and only if $r - t = 0$, i.e., if and only if $r = t$. It follows that $[0], [1], [2], \ldots, [m-1]$ are the m distinct congruence classes and any congruence class $[k]$ is equal to one of these. Hence the theorem. $\square$

The following example will help to see the equivalence classes of the equivalence relation 'congruence modulo m'. For simplicity of calculation, let us take $m = 7$.

Example 1.3.6. We claim that $\mathbb{Z}_7 = \Big\{[0], [1], \ldots, [6]\Big\}$ and $[n] = \{0+n, \pm 7+n, \pm 14+n, \ldots\} = \{7q + n \mid q \in \mathbb{Z}\}$ for all $n \in \mathbb{Z}$.

To establish the claim, let $0 \leq p < q < 7$. Suppose $[p] = [q]$. Then $p \in [q]$ and hence $p \equiv_7 q$ so that $7 \mid p - q$, which is a contradiction to the choice of p and q. Hence we see that the equivalence classes $[0], [1], [2], \ldots, [6]$ are all distinct. Indeed, these are the only equivalence classes as we now illustrate.

Let i be any integer. By *division algorithm*, $i = 7m + r$ for some integers m and r such that $0 \leq r < 7$. Thus, $i - r = 7m$ and hence $7 \mid (i - r)$ so that $i \equiv_7 r$, whence $[i] = [r]$. But $0 \leq r < 7$ and consequently, $[i] \in \Big\{[0], [1], \ldots [6]\Big\}$, i.e., $\mathbb{Z}_7 = \Big\{[0], [1], \ldots [6]\Big\}$.

Now, let $n \in \mathbb{Z}$. Then $x \in [n]$ if and only if $7 \mid x - n$, i.e., if and only if $7q = x - n$ for some $q \in \mathbb{Z}$, i.e., if and only if $x = 7q + n$ for some $q \in \mathbb{Z}$. Consequently, for all $n = 0, 1, 2, \ldots, 6$, $[n] = [7q + n]$ for all $q \in \mathbb{Z}$. So we have,

for $n = 0$, $[0] = [7] = [14] = \ldots = [-7] = [-14] = \ldots$

for $n = 1$, $[1] = [8] = [15] = \ldots = [-6] = [-13] = \ldots$

and so on upto $n = 6$.

The following theorem shows that we can add and multiply congruences in an essentially similar manner to what we do for equality.

Theorem 1.3.7. *Let a, b, c, d denote integers and m be a positive integer.*

(i) If $a \equiv b \pmod{m}$ and $c \equiv d \pmod{m}$, then $a + c \equiv b + d \pmod{m}$.

(ii) If $a \equiv b \pmod{m}$ and $c \equiv d \pmod{m}$, then $ac \equiv bd \pmod{m}$.

Proof. (i) Since $m \mid (a-b)$ and $m \mid (c-d)$, then $m \mid \Big((a-b)+(c-d)\Big)$. But $(a-b)+(c-d) = (a+c)-(b+d)$. Hence $m \mid \Big((a+c)-(b+d)\Big)$. So it follows that $(a+c) \equiv (b+d) \pmod{m}$.

(ii) Since $m \mid (a - b)$, $m \mid c(a - b)$. Hence $m \mid (ca - cb)$. Again, $m \mid (c - d)$. Then $m \mid b(c-d)$, i.e., $m \mid (bc - bd)$. This implies that $m \mid (ac - bc) + (bc - bd)$, i.e., $m \mid (ac - bd)$. Hence $ac \equiv bd \pmod{m}$. $\square$

Corollary 1.3.8. *(i) If $a \equiv b \,(mod\, m)$, then $a + c \equiv b + c \,(mod\, m)$ for any integer c.*

(ii) If $a \equiv b \,(mod\, m)$, then $ac \equiv bc \,(mod\, m)$ for any integer c.

From the Theorem 1.3.7, we find that addition, subtraction or multiplication to both sides of a congruence by an integer does not change the congruence. But this may not be true if we divide both sides of a congruence by an integer. Consider the congruence $24 \equiv 12 (mod\, 4)$, i.e., $6 \cdot 4 \equiv 6 \cdot 2 (\,mod\, 4)$. If we divide both sides of this congruence by 6, then we obtain $4 \equiv 2 (mod\, 4)$. But 4 does not divide $4 - 2$. Hence $4 \not\equiv 2 (mod\, 4)$. The next theorem will throw some light in this regard.

Theorem 1.3.9. *Let a, b, c be integers and m be a positive integer.*

(i) $ab \equiv ac (mod\, m)$ if and only if $b \equiv c \left(mod\, \frac{m}{gcd(a,m)} \right)$.

(ii) If $ab \equiv ac (mod\, m)$ and $gcd(a, m) = 1$, then $b \equiv c (mod\, m)$.

Proof. (i)   Let $d = gcd(a, m)$. Since $m > 0, d \neq 0$, there exist integers r and t such that $gcd(t, r) = 1$ and $a = dr$, $m = dt$. Now $ab \equiv ac (mod\, m)$ implies that m divides $ab - ac$, i.e., dt divides $drb - drc$, i.e., t divides $r(b - c)$.

Since t and r are relatively prime, it follows that t divides $b - c$. Hence $b \equiv c (mod\, t)$, i.e., $b \equiv c (mod\, \frac{m}{d})$.

Conversely, assume that $b \equiv c (mod\, \frac{m}{d})$. Then $b - c = k\frac{m}{d}$ for some integer k. Hence,

$$ab - ac = k\frac{m}{d}a = km\frac{a}{d} = kmr = mkr.$$

So we find that m divides $ab - ac$, i.e., $ab \equiv ac (mod\, m)$.

(ii)   The proof of this part follows from (i).   □

Quite often, mathematics, in particular the so-called pure mathematics has been blamed for its lack of *usefulness* by people in and out of the mathematical arena. Though the score has long been settled in favour of mathematics (useless mathematics, if you like!) by none other than the person who is known as the *purest of the pure* mathematicians G.H. Hardy, in his charming manifesto, *A Mathematician's Apology*— an "eloquent description of the pleasure and power of mathematical invention"— some of its most pure and abstract branches have found some astonishing applications in everyday human life in recent times. We now take the liberty to discuss one such application of the concept of *congruences* to detect errors in strings of digits that are used nowadays to identify books worldwide. Aptly known as the *International Standard Book Number* or the ISBN, one may usually find it on the back cover of a book appearing as a string of digits.

Standard Book Number(SBN), as was earlier used in some English speaking countries, was transformed into the ISBN in 1972 and in India this system was put into operation from January 1985 by Raja Rammohun Roy National Agency for ISBN under the Ministry of Higher Education, MHRD, Government of India. An ISBN is assigned to each edition and its variants (except reprint) of a book. It is a string of 13 digits (referred to as ISBN-13) if assigned after January 1, 2007, and of 10 digits (referred to as ISBN-10) if assigned before 2007. The digits of an ISBN are arranged in four blocks (for an ISBN-10) or five blocks (for an ISBN-13), which are sometimes (but not always) separated by hyphens. The distinction between them at present is that, an ISBN-13 is always prefixed by the digits 978 or 979, which is prescribed by GS1 protocol, a not-for-profit organisation that develops and maintains Global Standards for business communication, towards its compatibility with EAN-13 (European Article Number) protocol of barcode presentation of an ISBN string. For example, the Bengali book *Feluda Samagra* of Ananda Publishers has its ISBN-10 : 81-7756-480-3 and ISBN-13 : 978-81-7756-480-8. Scanning from left to right the ISBN-13 string, the significance of each block of digits is as follows:

Ist block(of 3 digits) - Denotes a specified "prefix element" (978 or 979);

IInd block (group identifier of 1 to 5 digits) - Identifies the particular country or the language from where it is published (81 stands for India)[18];

IIIrd block- Identifies the particular publisher (7756 refers to Ananda Publishers);

IVth block- Identifies the particular edition, format of a specific title;

Vth block (of 1 digit) - Check digit.

Observe that, if you set aside the left most block of ISBN-13, then the other four blocks have the same significances as in ISBN-10. However, their check digits may not be the same. Our interest in ISBN, centres on check digits as they help us in determining the validity of ISBN, and this is where an application of congruences creeps in. Incidentally, two different congruences are employed to calculate the check digit in ISBN-10 and ISBN-13. We now explain how congruences are used to assign a check digit to a particular book.

The check digit that actually makes the ISBN-10 an example of error-correcting code[19] maybe any integer from one to ten, but since we have to restrict its representation

---

[18]Within the 978 prefix element, some of the group identifiers are : 0 or 1 for English-speaking countries; 2 for French-speaking countries; 3 for German-speaking countries; 4 for Japan; 5 for Russian-speaking countries; and 7 for People's Republic of China. An example of 5-digit group identifier is 99936, for Bhutan. Within prefix element 979, we have 10 for France, 11 for the Republic of Korea, and 12 for Italy.

[19]This is a widely used jargon from Coding Theory, a detailed account of which is out of scope here.

by a single numeral, as a convention the Roman numeral symbol X is used to denote ten. When the first nine digits of the ISBN-10 are known, say, $x_1, x_2, x_3, \ldots, x_8, x_9$, then the check digit x_{10} is determined by the congruence

$$1x_1 + 2x_2 + 3x_3 + \ldots + 9x_9 + 10x_{10} \equiv 0 \,(mod\, 11),$$

i.e., $$1x_1 + 2x_2 + 3x_3 + \ldots + 9x_9 \equiv x_{10} \,(mod\, 11).$$

For example, if we consider the book *Algebra* by Michael Artin, published by Prentice-Hall of India, bearing the ISBN 81-203-0871-9, one may easily verify that

$$1 \cdot 8 + 2 \cdot 1 + 3 \cdot 2 + 4 \cdot 0 + 5 \cdot 3 + 6 \cdot 0 + 7 \cdot 8 + 8 \cdot 7 + 9 \cdot 1 = 152 \equiv 9 \,(mod 11).$$

However, unlike the previous case, while calculating the check digit of ISBN-13, a congruence modulo 10 is used, whence the check digit, which is the remainder of the modular calculation is restricted between one of the ten digits from 0 to 9. When the first nine digits of the ISBN-13 are known, say, $x_1, x_2, x_3, \ldots, x_{11}, x_{12}$, then the check digit x_{13} is determined by the congruence

$$1x_1 + 3x_2 + 1x_3 + 3x_4 + \ldots\ldots + 3x_{12} + 1x_{13} \equiv 0 \,(mod\, 10),$$

i.e., $$x_{13} \equiv -(1x_1 + 3x_2 + 1x_3 + 3x_4 + \ldots\ldots + 3x_{12}) \,(mod\, 10).$$

For example the ISBN-13 check digit x_{13} of 978-0-306-40615 is calculated as follows:
$$x_{13} \equiv -(1 \cdot 9 + 3 \cdot 7 + 1 \cdot 8 + 3 \cdot 0 + 1 \cdot 3 + 3 \cdot 0 + 1 \cdot 6 + 3 \cdot 4 + 1 \cdot 0 + 3 \cdot 6 + 1 \cdot 1 + 3 \cdot 5) \,(mod\, 10)$$
$$\equiv -93 \,(mod\, 10) \equiv 7 \,(mod\, 10).$$ Hence $x_{13} = 7.$

In the modern age of information, it is quite natural that many publishers would like to process their inventories and billing procedures through computers. As it turns out, it is much easier for a computer (or the person who runs it) to deal with a string of digits, formulated with some definite order and method, than with the conventional identification of the book by means of its title, author's name, name of the publisher, edition etc. However, practical experience shows that while being transcribed, such a string of numbers is prone to two kinds of most common errors, viz., single digit typing error and error made by the interchange of two adjacent digits. Such an erroneous entry may lead to a shipment of some wrong books which were not actually ordered. The check digit is a mathematical means of detection of such errors. Indeed, it can be proved that the ISBN-10 check digit ensures that it will always be possible to detect these two most common types of error, i.e. if either of these types of error has occurred, the result will never be a valid ISBN, i.e., the sum of the digits multiplied by their weights in the prescribed manner will never be a multiple of 11. However, the system for thirteen digit codes in general, give a different check digit from the corresponding 10 digit ISBN, and does not provide the same protection against possible transposition. This is because the thirteen digit code was required to be compatible with the EAN format, and hence could not contain an "X". For example, if the difference between two adjacent digits is 5, say 6 and 1, the check digit of ISBN-13 will not be able to catch their transposition. Indeed, appearing as 61 or 16, they will respectively contribute to the sum, either $3 \times 6 + 1 \times 1 = 19$ or $3 \times 1 + 1 \times 6 = 9$, or the other way round. However, 19 and 9 are congruent modulo 10, and so they will produce the same final result modulo 10. The ISBN-10 formula uses the prime modulus 11 which avoids this blind spot, but requires more than the digits 0 to 9 towards expressing the check digit. On the other hand, with the help of ISBN one can also overcome the language barriers. A Chinese buyer can place an order by fax with a German publisher without specifying the book's title. Therefore, ISBN system serves the need of all the parties in the book distribution system.

Worked-out Exercises

$\Diamond$ **Exercise 1.3.1.** What is the remainder when 11^{40} is divided by 8 ?

Solution. By division algorithm, there exist integers q and r such that $11^{40} = 8q + r$, where $0 \leq r < 8$. So, if r is the required remainder, then $11^{40} \equiv r \pmod 8$ and $0 \leq r < 8$. Now $11 \equiv 3 \pmod 8$. Hence $11^2 \equiv 3^2 \pmod 8$. But $3^2 \equiv 1 \pmod 8$. Hence $11^2 \equiv 1 \pmod 8$. This implies that $(11^2)^{20} \equiv 1^{20} \pmod 8$, i.e., $11^{40} \equiv 1 \pmod 8$. Hence the remainder is 1.

$\Diamond$ **Exercise 1.3.2.** Find the remainder when $9 \cdot 4^{24} + 2 \cdot 9^{35}$ is divided by 5.

Solution. Since $4^2 \equiv 1 \pmod 5$, $4^{24} = (4^2)^{12} \equiv 1^{12} \pmod 5$, i.e., $4^{24} \equiv 1 \pmod 5$. Then $9 \cdot 4^{24} \equiv 9 \pmod 5 \equiv 4 \pmod 5$. Again $9^2 \equiv 1 \pmod 5$. Hence $9^{34} \equiv 1 \pmod 5$. Then $9 \cdot 9^{34} \equiv 9 \pmod 5$, i.e., $9^{35} \equiv 9 \pmod 5 \equiv 4 \pmod 5$. Hence $2 \cdot 9^{35} \equiv 8 \pmod 5$. So, it follows that $9 \cdot 4^{24} + 2 \cdot 9^{35} \equiv (4 + 8) \pmod 5$, i.e., $9 \cdot 4^{24} + 2 \cdot 9^{35} \equiv 12 \pmod 5$. But $12 \equiv 2 \pmod 5$. Therefore the required remainder is 2.

$\Diamond$ **Exercise 1.3.3.** What is the remainder when $1! + 2! + 3! + \ldots + 99! + 100!$ is divided by 18?

Solution. The required remainder is an integer r such that $0 \leq r < 18$ and $1! + 2! + 3! + \ldots + 99! + 100! \equiv r \pmod{18}$. Now, $6! = 6.5.4.3.2.1 = 18.5.4.2.1$. Hence 18 divides $6!$ This shows that $6! \equiv 0 \pmod{18}$. Then $k \cdot 6! \equiv 0 \pmod{18}$. Since for any $n \geq 6$, $n!$ is a multiple of $6!$, $n! \equiv 0 \pmod{18}$ for any $n \geq 6$. Now,

$$1! \equiv 1 \pmod{18},$$
$$2! \equiv 2 \pmod{18},$$
$$3! \equiv 6 \pmod{18},$$
$$4! \equiv 6 \pmod{18},$$
$$5! \equiv 12 \pmod{18},$$
$$\text{and} \qquad n! \equiv 0 \pmod{18}, \text{ for } n \geq 6.$$

Hence $1! + 2! + 3! + \ldots + 99! + 100! \equiv 27 \pmod{18}$. But $27 \equiv 9 \pmod{18}$. Hence $1! + 2! + 3! + \ldots + 99! + 100! \equiv 9 \pmod{18}$. This implies that the remainder is 9.

$\Diamond$ **Exercise 1.3.4.** Consider the equivalence relation ρ on $\mathbb{Z}$ given by $a \rho b$ if and only if $a^2 - b^2$ is a multiple of 5. Hence find the corresponding partition of $\mathbb{Z}$.

Solution. If $a \in \mathbb{Z}$, then we have $a = 5k + r$ where $0 \leq r < 5$. Hence $a^2 = 25k^2 + 10kr + r^2$ implies that $a^2 \equiv r^2 \pmod 5$.

$$\text{For} \quad r = 0, \quad r^2 \equiv 0 \pmod 5.$$
$$r = 1, \quad r^2 \equiv 1 \pmod 5.$$
$$r = 2, \quad r^2 \equiv 4 \pmod 5.$$
$$r = 3, \quad r^2 \equiv 9 \equiv 4 \pmod 5.$$
$$r = 4, \quad r^2 \equiv 16 \equiv 1 \pmod 5.$$

Hence $a^2 \equiv 0^2$ or 1^2 or $2^2 \pmod 5$. Consequently, there are only three congruence classes $[0], [1]$ and $[2]$. Here,

$$[0] = \{b \in \mathbb{Z} \mid b^2 \equiv 0 \pmod 5\} = \{5k \mid k \in \mathbb{Z}\} = A_1$$
$$[1] = \{b \in \mathbb{Z} \mid b^2 \equiv 1 \pmod 5\} = \{5k + 1 \mid k \in \mathbb{Z}\} \cup \{5k + 4 \mid k \in \mathbb{Z}\} = A_2$$
$$[2] = \{b \in \mathbb{Z} \mid b^2 \equiv 4 \pmod 5\} = \{5k + 2 \mid k \in \mathbb{Z}\} \cup \{5k + 3 \mid k \in \mathbb{Z}\} = A_3.$$

Hence $\{A_1, A_2, A_3\}$ is the corresponding partition of $\mathbb{Z}$.

Exercises

1. Determine whether the statement is true or false in each of the following cases:
   (i) $60 \equiv -3 \pmod 7$ (ii) $50 \equiv 13 \pmod 8$
   (iii) $8^4 \equiv 2 \pmod{13}$ (iv) $3^4 \equiv 1 \pmod 5$
   (v) $6 + 5^2 \equiv 3 + 2 \pmod 2$

2. What is the remainder when $6 \cdot 7^{32} + 7 \cdot 9^{45}$ is divided by 4?

3. Find the remainder when 7^{30} is divided by 4.

4. What is the remainder when $1! + 2! + 3! + \ldots + 50!$ is divided by 16 ?

5. What is the remainder when 4^{119} is divided by 9?

1.4 Functions (Mappings)

As we have already pointed out, the concept of function is of paramount importance in mathematics. Among many other reasons, it helps us to study the relationship between various algebraic structures. To put it in a somewhat naive manner, a function is a rule of correspondence between the elements of two sets. From the literature of mathematics, one may find that the term *function* was first coined around 1694 by the famous German mathematician Leibnitz (1646-1716), in context with the slope of a curve. Later in 1749, Swiss mathematician Euler (1707-1783) defined a function simply as a law governing the interdependence of variable quantities and made extensive use of it. However the present day conception of function is attributed to Dirichlet (1805-1859), who in 1837 proposed the definition of a function as a *rule of correspondence that assigns a unique value of the dependent variable to every permitted value of an independent variable"*. We shall shortly see that this idea, in essence, lies at the core of the formal definition of a function.

Given two sets A and B, a *function* (or, *mapping*) f from A to B (written as $f : A \to B$) assigns to each $a \in A$ exactly one $b \in B$; here b is called the value of the function at a or the *image* of a under f, whereas a is called the *preimage* of b under f and we denote this state of affairs by the notation $f(a) = b$. More formally, a function from A to B may be defined as a particular type of relation as follows:

Definition 1.4.1. For two nonempty sets A and B, a relation f from A into B is called a ***function*** or ***mapping*** from A into B if

(i)   domain of $f = A$ and

(ii) f is *well-defined* (or, *single valued*) in the sense that for all $(a,b), (a',b') \in f$, $a = a'$ implies that $b = b'$, i.e.,

$$a = a' \implies f(a) = f(a').$$

If we examine this definition closely, we see that, in order to show that a relation f from A into B is a function, we must prove that the domain of f is A, which means that every element of A has some image in B and further we have to show that f is well-defined, i.e., a single element of A cannot have more than one image in B. Combining these two, we see that $f \subseteq A \times B$ such that for all $a \in A$, there exists a unique $b \in B$ such that $(a,b) \in f$.

Remark 1.4.2. Corresponding to every function $f : A \to B$, if we look at the relation from A into B, given by $G(f) = \{(a, f(a)) \mid a \in A\}$, called the *graph* of the function

f, it can be easily seen that *every element of A is the first component of one and only one ordered pair in $G(f)$*. In particular, if we take $f : \mathbb{R} \to \mathbb{R}$, then $G(f)$, being a subset of $\mathbb{R} \times \mathbb{R}$, i.e., the Euclidean plane, can be pictorially represented and in usual terminology this representation is called the 'graph of f'. Note that in such a figure, the geometric interpretation of the above character (in italics) of a function is precisely that *each vertical line must intersect the graph (i.e., the diagram) at exactly one point*.

Further, it is worth pointing out, though of pure logical interest, that Definition 1.4.1 enables us to define functions with an empty domain also. Indeed, if $A = \emptyset$ then $\emptyset \times B = \emptyset$, which is clearly a subset of $\emptyset \times B$ and the well-definedness of this function is vacuously satisfied. We however, in the sequel, shall continue to consider functions on nonempty domains only.

For a function $f : A \to B$, the set A is referred to as the **domain** of the function and it is denoted by $\mathcal{D}(f)$, whereas the set B is called the **codomain** of f. The set $f(A) = \{f(x) : x \in A\}$ is naturally a subset of the codomain B. Some authors prefer to call the set $f(A)$ as the **range** of the function f and denote it by $Im(f)$.

Let us now give examples of relations, some of which are functions and some others which are not.

Example 1.4.3. (i) Let A denote the set of names of all those countries that qualified to the finals of the FIFA World Cup Football, Russia 2018, and B denote the set of names of all the football players of those countries enrolled for this event. Let us define a relation f by associating with each country in A, the name of the captain of its football team from B. Then clearly, $f \subseteq A \times B$ and assuming every country in A has one (and only one) captain of its football team, we have $\mathcal{D}(f) = A$ and f is well-defined. Hence f is a function from A to B. Well, if captainship is rotated among more than one players, as is done nowadays by some coaches, then this relation will fail to be a function, as it will no more be well-defined.

(ii) Let f be the subset of $\mathbb{Z} \times \mathbb{Z}$ defined by $f = \{(n, 4n - 5) : n \in \mathbb{Z}\}$. Then $\mathcal{D}(f) = \{n : n \in \mathbb{Z}\} = \mathbb{Z}$. To show that f is well-defined, let $n = m$ for some $n, m \in \mathbb{Z}$. Then $4n - 5 = 4m - 5$, whence $f(n) = f(m)$ and hence f is well-defined. Consequently, f is a function from $\mathbb{Z}$ to $\mathbb{Z}$.

(iii) Let f be the subset of $\mathbb{Q} \times \mathbb{Z}$ given by $f = \left\{\left(\frac{p}{q}, p + q\right) : p, q \in \mathbb{Z}, q \neq 0\right\}$. Observe that $\mathcal{D}(f) = \left\{\frac{p}{q} : p, q \in \mathbb{Z}, q \neq 0\right\} = \mathbb{Q}$. However, f is not well-defined. Indeed, we have $\frac{3}{5} = \frac{9}{15} \in \mathbb{Q}$ and $(\frac{3}{5}, 8), (\frac{9}{15}, 24) \in f$. But, $f(\frac{3}{5}) = 8 \neq 24 = f(\frac{9}{15})$ justifies our claim. Hence f is not a function from $\mathbb{Q}$ to $\mathbb{Z}$.

(iv) Let $A = \{a, b, c, d\}$, $B = \{1, 2, 3\}$ and f be a relation from A into B, given by $f = \{(a, 1), (b, 3), (c, 2)\}$. Note that here $\mathcal{D}(f) = \{a, b, c\} \subset A$ and consequently f is not a function from A to B.

Definition 1.4.4. A function $f : A \to A$ is said to be the **identity function (identity mapping)** if $f(x) = x$ for all $x \in A$. This function is usually denoted by ι_A.

Definition 1.4.5. A function $f : A \to B$ is said to be a **constant function** if $f(A)$ is a singleton subset of B, i.e., under a constant function, every element of the domain set goes to some fixed element in B.

For example, $f : \mathbb{Z} \to \mathbb{Z}$, defined by $f(x) = 0$ for all $x \in \mathbb{Z}$ is a constant function, where $Im(f) = \{0\}$.

Let us now develop the concept of *equality of two functions*. Let $f : X \to Y$ and $g : X \to Y$ be two functions. Clearly, $f, g \subseteq X \times Y$. Suppose $f = g$. Let x be any element of X. Then, $(x, f(x)) \in f = g$ and $(x, g(x)) \in g$. Since g is a function, every element of X can appear once and only once in the first component of the ordered pairs in g, whence due to its well-definedness, we must have $f(x) = g(x)$. Conversely, assume that $f(x) = g(x)$ for all $x \in X$. Let $(x, y) \in f$. Then $y = f(x) = g(x)$ gives $(x, y) \in g$, whence $f \subseteq g$. In an essentially similar manner, one can show that $g \subseteq f$. Hence, it follows that $f = g$. Thus we conclude that two functions $f : X \to Y$ and $g : X \to Y$ are **equal** if and only if $f(x) = g(x)$ for all $x \in X$.

For example, let $f : \mathbb{R}^+ \to \mathbb{R}$ be given by $f(x) = 1 + \frac{x}{|x|}$ and $g : \mathbb{R}^+ \to \mathbb{R}$ be given by $g(x) = 2$; then $f = g$.

Definition 1.4.6. Let us consider a function $f : A \to B$. Then,

(a) f is called **injective** (or, **one-one**,)[20] when for all $a_1, a_2 \in A$ if

$$a_1 \neq a_2 \implies f(a_1) \neq f(a_2)$$

(i.e., distinct elements of the domain are mapped to distinct images).

(b) f is called **surjective**[21] (or, **onto**) if $Im(f) = B$,

(i.e., for every $b \in B$ there exists at least one $a \in A$ such that $f(a) = b$).

(c) f is called **bijective** if f is both surjective and injective.

In this case it is often said that there is a **one-to-one correspondence** between the elements of the sets A and B.

---

[20] Some authors prefer to call it **one-to-one**.
[21] The word "sur" in French means "on".

Remark 1.4.7. A logically equivalent[22] definition of an injective function is as follows: *A function $f : A \to B$ is said to be injective when $f(a_1) = f(a_2)$ in B implies that $a_1 = a_2$ in A, for all $a_1, a_2 \in A$.*

Now let us have a closer look at different types of functions in terms of various examples. Note that there can be functions which are neither injective nor surjective, as we shall show in the following list of examples:

Example 1.4.8. (i) Consider the relation f on $\mathbb{Z}$ defined by $f(n) = |n|$ for all $n \in \mathbb{Z}$. It is easy to see that $\mathcal{D}(f) = \mathbb{Z}$ and f is well-defined. So f is a function. Here $f(2) = |2| = 2 = |-2| = f(-2)$ but $2 \neq -2$. This implies that f is *not injective*. Since for all $n \in \mathbb{Z}$, $f(n)$ is a nonnegative integer, we see that the negative integers in $\mathbb{Z}$ have no preimage under f, whence f is *not surjective*. Note that, here $f(\mathbb{Z}) = \mathbb{N}_0$. Observe that if we consider $f_1 : \mathbb{Z} \to \mathbb{N}_0$ by stipulating $f_1(n) = |n|$ for all $n \in \mathbb{Z}$, then f_1 becomes a *surjective (onto)* function but *not injective*.

(ii) Refer to Example 1.4.3(ii). Here $f(n) = 4n - 5$ for all $n \in \mathbb{Z}$. Let $n_1, n_2 \in \mathbb{Z}$ and suppose that $f(n_1) = f(n_2)$. Then, $4n_1 - 5 = 4n_2 - 5$, i.e., $n_1 = n_2$. Hence f is an *injective (one-one)* function. But f is *not surjective (onto)*. Indeed, here $10 \in \mathbb{Z}$ has no preimage under f. For otherwise, if $f(n) = 10$ for some $n \in \mathbb{Z}$, it would lead to $4n - 5 = 10$, i.e., $n = \frac{15}{4} \in \mathbb{Z}$, which is impossible.

Observe that, if we consider $f_1 : \mathbb{R} \to \mathbb{R}$ by defining $f_1(x) = 4x - 5$ for all $x \in \mathbb{R}$, then f_1 becomes an example of a function which is both *surjective* and *injective*, and consequently a *bijective* function.

Remark 1.4.9. In particular, if we consider functions from $\mathbb{R} \to \mathbb{R}$, then surjectivity and injectivity of these functions have some interesting geometrical features with reference to their graph, which can be plotted in the Euclidean plane $\mathbb{R} \times \mathbb{R}$.

If $f : \mathbb{R} \to \mathbb{R}$ is an *injective* function, then each horizontal line in $\mathbb{R} \times \mathbb{R}$ can intersect the graph of f in *at most one point*; whereas if f is a *surjective* function, then each horizontal line in $\mathbb{R} \times \mathbb{R}$ must intersect the graph of f in *at least one point*. Finally, if f is *bijective* then each horizontal line must intersect the graph of f in *exactly one point*.

For example, let us consider the graphs of the following functions from $\mathbb{R}$ to $\mathbb{R}$ given by $f(x) = \sqrt[3]{x^2}, g(x) = 2^x, h(x) = x^3 + 3|x|$ and $k(x) = x^3$ (as in Figs. 6a, b, c, d).

---

[22]Note that a statement of the form "if 'p' holds then 'q' holds" is logically equivalent to "if 'q' does not hold then 'p' does not hold", and is **not** logically equivalent to "if 'p' does not hold then 'q' does not hold". Let us try to explain its significance in terms of a nonmathematical statement. Try to appreciate that your statement like *if it rains then I shall not attend the lecture*, will not be binding on you in case it does not rain, but in the event of your attending the lecture it may be logically concluded that it is not raining.

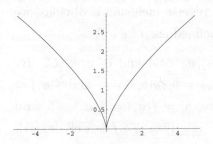

Fig.6a : $f(x) = \sqrt[3]{x^2}$

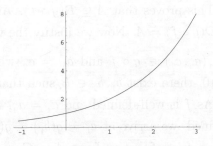

Fig.6b : $g(x) = 2^x$

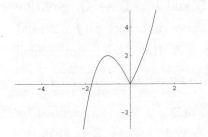

Fig.6c : $h(x) = x^3 + 3|x|$

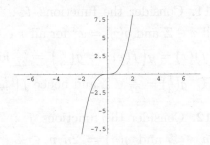

Fig.6d : $k(x) = x^3$

Applying the above mentioned characteristics, it can be verified that the function f is neither injective nor surjective; the function g is injective but not surjective; the function h is not injective though surjective; finally, the function k is both injective and surjective and hence bijective.

Definition 1.4.10. Let us consider functions $f : A \to B$ and $g : B \to C$. The **composition**, $\circ$ of f and g, written $g \circ f$ is the relation from A into C defined as $g \circ f = \Big\{(a,c) : a \in A, c \in C \text{ and } \exists\, b \in B \text{ such that } f(a) = b \text{ and } g(b) = c\Big\}(Fig.7)$. Note that $Im\,(f) \subseteq \mathcal{D}(g)$.

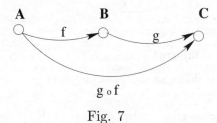

Fig. 7

Let $(g \circ f)(a) = c$. Now, since $c = g(b)$ and $b = f(a)$ for some $b \in B$, we combine them to get $c = g(b) = g\Big(f(a)\Big)$, whence we have $(g \circ f)(a) = g\Big(f(a)\Big)$. We assert that $g \circ f$ is a function from A to C. Towards proving this, first we have to show that $\mathcal{D}(g \circ f) = A$. Let $a \in A$. Now as f is a function from A to B, there exists $b \in B$ such that $f(a) = b$. Again, g is a function from B to C so that there exists $c \in C$ such that $g(b) = c$. Hence, $(g \circ f)(a) = g\Big(f(a)\Big) = g(b) = c$, i.e., $(a,c) \in g \circ f$, whence

$a \in \mathcal{D}(g \circ f)$. This proves that $A \subseteq \mathcal{D}(g \circ f)$. As the reverse inclusion is obvious, we conclude that $\mathcal{D}(g \circ f) = A$. Now we justify the well-definedness of $g \circ f$.

Let $(a_1, c_1), (a_2, c_2) \in g \circ f$ and $a_1 = a_2$ where $a_1, a_2 \in A$ and $c_1, c_2 \in C$. By Definition 1.4.10, there exist $b_1, b_2 \in B$ such that $f(a_1) = b_1, g(b_1) = c_1$ and $f(a_2) = b_2, g(b_2) = c_2$. As f is well-defined and $a_1 = a_2$, we have $b_1 = f(a_1) = f(a_2) = b_2$ and as g is well-defined, we arrive at $c_1 = g(b_1) = g(b_2) = c_2$. Thus $g \circ f$ is well-defined. Consequently, $g \circ f$ is a function from A to C.

Example 1.4.11. Consider the functions $f : \mathbb{Z} \to \mathbb{Q}$ and $g : \mathbb{Q} \to \mathbb{Q}$, given by $f(x) = \frac{1}{3}x$ for all $x \in \mathbb{Z}$ and $g(x) = x^3$ for all $x \in \mathbb{Q}$. Observe that, here $g \circ f : \mathbb{Z} \to \mathbb{Q}$ is given by $(g \circ f)(x) = g\left(f(x)\right) = g\left(\frac{x}{3}\right) = \frac{x^3}{27}$ for all $x \in \mathbb{Z}$. But $f \circ g$ is not defined here, as for $\frac{1}{3} \in \mathbb{Q}$, $g(\frac{1}{3}) = \frac{1}{27} \notin \mathbb{Z}$ and hence $f\left(\frac{1}{27}\right)$ makes no sense.

Example 1.4.12. Consider the functions $f : \mathbb{Z} \to \mathbb{Z}$ and $g : \mathbb{Z} \to \mathbb{Z}$, defined by $f(n) = (-1)^n, n \in \mathbb{Z}$ and $g(n) = 2n, n \in \mathbb{Z}$. Then, $g \circ f : \mathbb{Z} \to \mathbb{Z}$ is given by $(g \circ f)(n) = g\left(f(n)\right) = g\left((-1)^n\right) = 2(-1)^n, n \in \mathbb{Z}$, i.e., $(g \circ f)(n) = 2$ or -2, according as n is even or odd integer. Observe that, here one may define $f \circ g : \mathbb{Z} \to \mathbb{Z}$ by $(f \circ g)(n) = f\left(g(n)\right) = f(2n) = (-1)^{2n}, n \in \mathbb{Z}$, i.e., $(f \circ g)(n) = 1$ for all $n \in \mathbb{Z}$. This example shows that $g \circ f \neq f \circ g$, in general, even when both are defined; i.e., *composition of functions is noncommutative.*

Let us now discuss some important properties of the composition of functions. Observe the following diagrams (Figs. 8a and b) carefully:

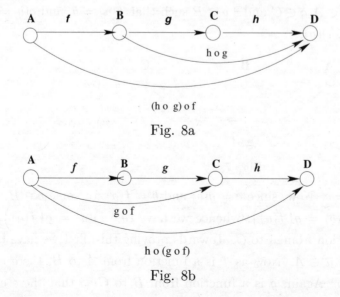

(h o g) o f

Fig. 8a

h o (g o f)

Fig. 8b

In fact, we have the following theorem:

Theorem 1.4.13. *Let $f : A \to B$, $g : B \to C$ and $h : C \to D$. Then we must have $h \circ (g \circ f) = (h \circ g) \circ f$, i.e., composition of functions is associative, provided the requisite compositions make sense.*

Proof. Observe that $h \circ (g \circ f) : A \to D$ and $(h \circ g) \circ f : A \to D$. Let $x \in A$. Then $\left[h \circ (g \circ f) \right](x) = h\left((g \circ f)(x)\right) = h\left(g(f(x))\right) = (h \circ g)\left(f(x)\right) = \left[(h \circ g) \circ f\right](x)$. Since x is any element of A, we conclude that $h \circ (g \circ f) = (h \circ g) \circ f$. $\qquad\square$

Theorem 1.4.14. *Suppose that $f : A \to B$ and $g : B \to C$. Then:*

(i) if f and g are both injective, then $g \circ f$ is also injective;

(ii) if $g \circ f$ is injective, then f is injective;

(iii) if f and g are both surjective, then $g \circ f$ is also so;

(iv) if $g \circ f$ is surjective, then g is surjective;

(v) if f and g are both bijective, then $g \circ f$ is also so;

(vi) if $g \circ f$ is bijective, then f is injective and g is surjective.

Proof. (i)   Let $a, a' \in A$. Suppose that $(g \circ f)(a) = (g \circ f)(a')$. Then, $g\left(f(a)\right) = g\left(f(a')\right)$ implies that $f(a) = f(a')$, since g is injective. Again, as f is injective, we conclude that $a = a'$. Hence $g \circ f$ is injective.

(ii)   If possible, let f be not injective. Then, there exist some $a_1, a_2 \in A$ such that $a_1 \neq a_2$ but $f(a_1) = f(a_2)$. This implies that $g\left(f(a_1)\right) = g\left(f(a_2)\right)$ as g is well-defined, i.e., $(g \circ f)(a_1) = (g \circ f)(a_2)$ — which contradicts the injectivity of $g \circ f$. Hence if $g \circ f$ is injective, so must be f.

(iii)   Let $c \in C$. Then there exists $b \in B$ such that $g(b) = c$ (as g is surjective). Again, as f is also surjective, there exists $a \in A$ such that $f(a) = b$. Thus, $(g \circ f)(a) = g\left(f(a)\right) = g(b) = c$. Hence $g \circ f$ is a surjective function.

(iv)   Let $c \in C$. Since $g \circ f : A \to C$ is surjective, there exists some $a \in A$ such that $(g \circ f)(a) = c$, i.e., $g\left(f(a)\right) = c$. This implies that for $c \in C$, there exists $f(a) \in B$ such that $f(a)$ is a preimage of c in B under g. Since c is an arbitrary element of C, we conclude that g is surjective.

(v)   This follows as an immediate consequence of parts (i) and (iii) put together.

(vi)   Follows from (ii) and (iv). $\qquad\square$

Recall the identity function as given in Definition 1.4.4. We leave it to the reader to verify that this function is bijective; furthermore, if $f : A \to B$ be any function and $\iota_A : A \to A$ and $\iota_B : B \to B$ be identity functions respectively on A and B then, $f \circ \iota_A = f = \iota_B \circ f$.

Now, for a function $f : A \to A$, let us give the following recursive definition:

$$
\begin{aligned}
f^0(a) &= a. \\
f^1(a) &= f(a). \\
f^{n+1}(a) &= (f \circ f^n)(a) \text{ for all } a \in A, n \in \mathbb{N}.
\end{aligned}
$$

It is interesting to observe that if A is a finite set and $f : A \to A$ is an injective function on A then, f is automatically surjective. Towards proving this assertion, let us first prove the following lemma:

Lemma 1.4.15. [23] *Let A be any set and $f : A \to A$ be an injective function. Then $f^n : A \to A$ is an injective function for all integers $n \geq 1$.*

Proof. If possible, let there be some integer, say $n > 1$ such that f^n is not injective. Assume further that k be the smallest such positive integer. So f^k is not injective, whence there must exist some $a, b \in A$ such that $a \neq b$ but yet $f^k(a) = f^k(b)$. But this implies that $f\left(f^{k-1}(a)\right) = f\left(f^{k-1}(b)\right)$ which in turn gives that $f^{k-1}(a) = f^{k-1}(b)$ since f is injective. By the choice of the integer k, we have that f^{k-1} is injective and hence we get $a = b$, which is a contradiction. So, our initial assumption was wrong and consequently, f^n is injective for all $n \geq 1$. $\qquad \square$

Theorem 1.4.16. *For any finite set A, if $f : A \to A$ is injective, then f is surjective also and hence is bijective.*

Proof. Let $a \in A$. Now as $f^n : A \to A$, we have that $f^n(a) \in A$ for all $n \geq 1$. This indicates that $a, f(a), f^2(a) \ldots \in A$. Since A is finite, there must exist positive integers r and s such that $r > s$ and $f^r(a) = f^s(a)$. But this means $f^s\left(f^{r-s}(a)\right) = f^s(a)$, which gives that $f^{r-s}(a) = a$, since by virtue of the Lemma 1.4.15 we have that f^s is injective. Call $a' = f^{r-s-1}(a) \in A$. Then $f(a') = f\left(f^{r-s-1}(a)\right) = f^{r-s}(a) = a$ shows that f is a surjective function and consequently a bijective function. $\qquad \square$

---

[23]Though a proof of this result follows from Theorem 1.4.14(i), we prefer to give an independent proof here.

Definition 1.4.17. Consider a function $f : A \to B$. Then f is called

(i) **left invertible** if there exists $g : B \to A$ such that, $g \circ f = \iota_A$ and then g is called a **left inverse** of f,

(ii) **right invertible** if there exists $h : B \to A$ such that, $f \circ h = \iota_B$ and then h is called a **right inverse** of f,

(iii) **invertible** if f is both left and right invertible.

Example 1.4.18. (i) Let $f : \mathbb{N} \to \mathbb{N}$ be defined by $f(n) = n+1$ for all $n \in \mathbb{N}$ and $g : \mathbb{N} \to \mathbb{N}$ be defined by $g(1) = 1$ and $g(n) = n-1$ for all $n(> 1) \in \mathbb{N}$. Hence $(g \circ f)(n) = g\big(f(n)\big) = g(n+1) = n+1-1 = n$ for all $n \in \mathbb{N}$, so that $g \circ f = \iota_{\mathbb{N}}$, whence g is a *left inverse* of f. Observe that here $(f \circ g)(1) = f\big(g(1)\big) = f(1) = 2$ and so $f \circ g \neq \iota_{\mathbb{N}}$ so that g *is not a right inverse* of f.

(ii) Let $f : \mathbb{Z} \to E_0^+$ be defined by $f(x) = |x| + x$ for all $x \in \mathbb{Z}$, where E_0^+ is the set of nonnegative even integers and let $g : E_0^+ \to \mathbb{Z}$ be defined by $g(x) = \frac{x}{2}$ for all $x \in E_0^+$. Then $(f \circ g)(x) = f\big(g(x)\big) = f\big(g(2n)\big)$ [as $x \in E_0^+, x = 2n$ for some nonnegative integer n] $= f(n) = |n| + n = 2n = x$. Hence g is a *right inverse* of f. Observe that, here $(g \circ f)(-1) = g\big(f(-1)\big) = g(0) = 0$ and hence $g \circ f \neq \iota_{\mathbb{Z}}$ so that g *is not a left inverse* of f.

(iii) Consider the function $f : \mathbb{R} \to \mathbb{R}$, defined by $f(x) = 3x + 4$ for all $x \in \mathbb{R}$ and the function $g : \mathbb{R} \to \mathbb{R}$, defined by $g(x) = \frac{x-4}{3}$ for all $x \in \mathbb{R}$. It is now a routine exercise to see that here both $g \circ f = f \circ g = \iota_{\mathbb{R}}$. Hence f is invertible and g is both a left as well as right inverse of f.

The above examples establish clearly that a function may or may not have a left (right) inverse. However, example (iii) shows that left and right inverses of the function f are the same. This is not a stray incident. In fact, whenever a function f is invertible, then its right and left inverses are the same. Indeed, let $f : A \to B$ be invertible and assume further that g be a left inverse and h be a right inverse of f. Then by definition we have $g \circ f = \iota_A$ and $f \circ h = \iota_B$. Now, $g = g \circ \iota_B = g \circ (f \circ h) = (g \circ f) \circ h = \iota_A \circ h = h$. This also justifies that inverse of a function, if exists, is unique and hence it is denoted by f^{-1}. Furthermore, observe that a function $f : A \to B$ is invertible if its inverse relation f^{-1} is a function from B to A.

Now since the existence of left (right) inverse of a function is not guaranteed, it would be useful to characterize those functions that admit left (right) inverse. This is presented in the following theorem.

Theorem 1.4.19. *Let us consider $f : A \to B$. Then,*

(i) f is left invertible if and only if f is injective,

(ii) f is right invertible if and only if f is surjective and

(iii) f is invertible if and only if f is bijective.

Proof. (i)   Suppose f is left invertible. Then there exists $g : B \to A$ such that $g \circ f = \iota_A$. Now to prove the injectivity of f, let us assume $f(a) = f(b)$ for some $a, b \in A$. Then we have, $g\big(f(a)\big) = g\big(f(b)\big)$ by well-definedness of the function g, whence $(g \circ f)(a) = (g \circ f)(b)$ and this implies that $\iota_A(a) = \iota_A(b)$, i.e., $a = b$. Thus f is injective.

Conversely, suppose f is injective. We have to show that f is left invertible. Towards this, we construct a function $g : B \to A$ which becomes the left inverse of f. Since $f : A \to B$ is injective, observe that, for any element $b \in B$, either there is no preimage in A or there exists a unique preimage, say $a_b \in A$, so that $f(a_b) = b$. Let us choose arbitrarily some element $a_0 \in A$ and fix it. We now define $g : B \to A$ by

$$
\begin{aligned}
g(b) \quad &= \quad a_0, \quad \text{if } b \text{ has no preimage under } f \\
&= \quad a_b, \quad \text{if } a_b \text{ is the unique preimage of } b \text{ under } f, \text{ i.e., } f(a_b) = b
\end{aligned}
$$

for all $b \in B$. Clearly, $\mathcal{D}(g) = B$. We leave it to the reader to verify that g is well-defined. (Observe that this requires injectivity of f). We now show that $g \circ f = \iota_A$. Let $a_1 \in A$ and $f(a_1) = b_1$ for some $b_1 \in B$. Then by definition of g, $g(b_1) = a_1$. So, $(g \circ f)(a_1) = g\big(f(a_1)\big) = g(b_1) = a_1 = \iota_A(a_1)$. Since a_1 is any element of A, we conclude that $g \circ f = \iota_A$.

(ii)   Suppose f is right invertible. Then there exists $h : B \to A$ such that $f \circ h = \iota_B$. Let $b \in B$. Then $h(b) \in A$. Suppose $h(b) = a \in A$. Then, $b = \iota_B(b) = (f \circ h)(b) = f\big(h(b)\big) = f(a)$. This shows that f is a surjective function.

Conversely, suppose f is surjective. Let $b \in B$. By surjectivity of f, there must exist some $a \in A$ such that $f(a) = b$. Let us consider the set of all preimages of b, say $A_b = \{a \in A : f(a) = b\}$. Then clearly $A_b \neq \emptyset$. Let us choose[24] $a_b \in A_b$ for each $b \in B$. [Note that such a choice is made arbitrarily, but once it is made, the elements chosen are fixed for the rest of the discussion.] Now, define $h_1 : B \to A$ such that $h_1(b) = a_b$ for all $b \in B$. It can be justified that h_1 is a function from B to A (though

---

[24]To an analytic mind, the permission of making such a 'choice' may surely pose a question. Indeed, this is done by virtue of the so called *Axiom of choice* which lies at the very foundation of the theory of sets. We introduce it in brief, in Appendix B.

the verification of well-definedness is highly nontrivial). We assert that h_1 is the right inverse of f. Indeed, let $b \in B$; then $(f \circ h_1)(b) = f(h_1(b)) = f(a_b) = b = \iota_B(b)$ and hence $f \circ h_1 = \iota_B$ proves our claim.

(iii)   It follows directly from (i) and (ii) above. $\square$

Two sets A and B are said to be **cardinally equivalent** (or, **equipotent**) written as $A \sim B$ if there exists a bijective function from A onto B. Note that the identity function on any set is bijective; also bijective functions are invertible and the inverse function is also bijective; furthermore, the composition of two bijective functions, when definable is bijective. In view of these facts, it follows that '$\sim$' is an equivalence relation among nonempty subsets of some universal set. If $A \sim B$, then A, B belong to the same equivalence class under '$\sim$' and we sometimes denote it by writing $|A| = |B|$. It can be easily seen that if both A and B are finite sets, then $|A| = |B|$ if and only if A and B have the same number of elements. If however A, B are infinite sets and $A \sim B$, then they are said to have the same **cardinal number**. We merely comment here that not all infinite sets have the same cardinal number[25] and take this opportunity to state (without proof) a classical theorem of this area, due to Schröder-Bernstein, which goes as follows:

Let A and B be two sets. If $A \sim Y$ for some subset Y of B and $B \sim X$ for some subset X of A, then $A \sim B$.

Now, let $f : A \to B$ and $A' \subseteq A$. Then the function f induces a function from A' to B in a natural way as the following definition shows:

Definition 1.4.20. Let $f : A \to B$ and $\emptyset \neq A' \subseteq A$. The **restriction** of f to A', written as $f\big|_{A'}$ is defined to be $f\big|_{A'} = \left\{ \left(a', f(a')\right) : a' \in A' \right\}$. Observe that $f\big|_{A'}$ has actually the same rule of correspondence as f except that its domain is a subset of that of f.

Definition 1.4.21. Let $f : A \to B$ and $A \subseteq A'$. A function $g : A' \to B$ is called an **extension** of f to A' if $g\big|_A = f$.

Note that a function may have more than one extension.

Example 1.4.22. (i)   Suppose $A = \{a \in \mathbb{R} : a > 0\}$. Let $f : A \to \mathbb{R}$ be given by $f(a) = \frac{|a|}{a}$; $a \in A$. Observe that, $g : \mathbb{R} \to \mathbb{R}$ defined by $g(a) = 1$, for all $a \in \mathbb{R}$, is an extension of f to $\mathbb{R}$, since $g\big|_A = f$.

---

[25]The cardinal number of $\mathbb{N}$ happens to be the same as that of $\mathbb{Q}$ but $\mathbb{R}$ has a different cardinal number.

(ii)   Let $f : \mathbb{R} \to \mathbb{R}_1$ where $\mathbb{R}_1 = \{x \in \mathbb{R} : -1 \le x \le 1\}$ be given by $f(x) = \sin x$ for all $x \in \mathbb{R}$. Suppose $A = \{x \in \mathbb{R} : -\frac{\pi}{2} \le x \le \frac{\pi}{2}\}$. Then the function $g : A \to \mathbb{R}_1$ given by $g(x) = \sin x$, for all $x \in A$ is a restriction of f to A.

A word of caution regarding another usage of the notation f^{-1}, which is usually used to denote the unique inverse of a bijective function f, is necessary.

Suppose $f : A \to B$ be a function. Let Q be a nonempty subset of B. Then the set $f^{-1}(Q) = \{a \in A : f(a) \in Q\}$ is called the **inverse image** of Q under f and $f^{-1}(Q) \subseteq A$. It must be clearly understood from the definition of inverse image, here $f^{-1} : B \to A$ may not exist, and so $f^{-1}(Q)$ is to be understood as the set of preimages of the elements of Q under f. If $P \subseteq A$, then the set $f(P) = \{f(a) : a \in P\} \subseteq B$ and $f(P)$ is called the **image** (or, **direct image**) of P under f. Let X, Y be two nonempty subsets of A. It is interesting to see that $f(X \cap Y) \ne f(X) \cap f(Y)$, in general.

Indeed, let $f : \mathbb{R} \to \mathbb{R}$ be given by $f(x) = x^2$ for all, $x \in \mathbb{R}$. Consider X to be the set of all nonnegative integers and Y to be the set of all nonpositive integers. Then, clearly $X, Y \subseteq \mathbb{R}$ and $X \cap Y = \{0\}$. Further, $f(X \cap Y) = f(\{0\}) = \{0\}$, whereas $f(X) = f(Y) = \{n^2 : n \in \mathbb{N} \cup \{0\}\}$, and hence $f(X) \cap f(Y) = f(X) \ne \{0\}$ proves our claim. However, such an equality holds good for all subsets X, Y of the domain of the function f if and only if f is injective. [See Worked-out Exercise 1.4.8(v)].

We have pointed out earlier, that a function may neither be surjective nor injective. However, before finishing this section, we would like to point out that any function from a set A into another set B is a composition of an injective function, a bijective function and a surjective function.

Suppose $f : A \longrightarrow B$ be a function. Define a binary relation ρ on the set A by

$$x \, \rho \, y \text{ if and only if } f(x) = f(y).$$

Then it is easy to verify that ρ is an equivalence relation on A. The set of all equivalence classes under this relation is given by $\{a\rho \mid a \in A\}$ and is called the **quotient set** of A by ρ. Let us denote it by A/ρ. Define the function $g : A \longrightarrow A/\rho$ by $g(a) = a\rho$ for all $a \in A$. Clearly g is a surjective.

Next consider the function $h : A/\rho \longrightarrow f(A)$ defined by $h(a\rho) = f(a)$. We first verify that h is well-defined. Indeed, for $a, b \in A$ with $a\rho = b\rho$, we have $a \, \rho \, b$ and so by definition of ρ we get $f(a) = f(b)$, i.e., $h(a\rho) = h(b\rho)$. Thus h is well-defined. Now we show that h is a bijective function. Let $a, b \in A$ such that $h(a\rho) = h(b\rho)$. Then $f(a) = f(b)$ and so $a \, \rho \, b$, i.e., $a\rho = b\rho$. Thus h is one-to-one. Again for any $c \in f(A)$, we have there exists $a \in A$ such that $f(a) = c$. So $c = h(a\rho)$ and hence h is onto. Therefore h is bijective.

Finally, define the inclusion map $i : f(A) \longrightarrow B$ by $i(c) = c$ for all $c \in B$ (note that $f(A) \subseteq B$). No doubt i is an injective function. Now for any $a \in A$, we have

$$(i \circ h \circ g)(a) = (i \circ h)(g(a)) = (i \circ h)(a\rho) = i(h(a\rho)) = i(f(a)) = f(a).$$

Thus we get

$$A \xrightarrow{g} A/\rho$$
$$f \downarrow \qquad \downarrow h$$
$$B \xleftarrow{i} f(A)$$

that is, $f = i \circ h \circ g$ where i is injective, h is bijective and g is surjective as we required.

Going ahead of ourselves, we would like to point out that this result plays the key role in the isomorphism theorems of groups and rings as we shall see in subsequent relevant chapters.

Worked-out Exercises

◊ **Exercise 1.4.1.** Determine and justify which of the following sets are functions from A to B:

(a) $f = \{(1,2),(1,3),(2,3),(3,4)\}$; $A = \{1,2,3\}, B = \{1,2,3,4\}$.

(b) $f = \{(a,b),(b,c),(c,d),(d,a)\}$; $A = B = \{a,b,c,d\}$.

(c) $f = \{(a,b),(b,c),(c,d)\}$; $A = B = \{a,b,c,d\}$.

Solution. (a) Here f is not a function, as image of $1(\in A)$ under f (i.e., $f(1)$) is not unique, (observe that $f(1) = 2$ and $f(1) = 3$ as well), whence the well-definedness of f is lost.

(b) Here domain of f is $\{a,b,c,d\} = A$. Further, it can easily be seen that f is well-defined, i.e., no element of A has more than one image under f. Consequently, f is a function from A to A.

(c) In this case, f is not a function from A to A. Indeed, the domain of this relation f is $\{a,b,c\} \subset A$.

◊ **Exercise 1.4.2.** Let $f, g : \mathbb{R} \to \mathbb{R}$ be two functions, given by $f(x) = |x| + x$ for all $x \in \mathbb{R}$ and $g(x) = |x| - x$, for all $x \in \mathbb{R}$. Find $f \circ g$ and $g \circ f$.

Solution. Here, $f(x) = |x| + x$.

$$\text{i.e.,} \quad f(x) \;=\; 2x \quad \text{if } x \geq 0$$
$$=\; 0 \quad \text{if } x < 0$$
$$\text{and} \quad g(x) \;=\; -2x \quad \text{if } x < 0$$
$$=\; 0 \quad \text{if } x \geq 0.$$

Now, let $x \geq 0$; then, $(f \circ g)(x) = f\big(g(x)\big) = f(0) = 0$

and $(g \circ f)(x) = g\big(f(x)\big) = g(2x) = 0.$

Again, let $x < 0$; then, $(f \circ g)(x) = f\big(g(x)\big) = f(-2x) = -4x$

and $(g \circ f)(x) = g\big(f(x)\big) = g(0) = 0.$

Consequently, we have $(g \circ f)(x) = 0$ for all $x \in \mathbb{R}$ and

$$f \circ g(x) \;=\; 0, \quad \text{if } x \geq 0$$
$$=\; -4x, \quad \text{if } x < 0.$$

◊ **Exercise 1.4.3.** Let $f, g : A \to B$ and $h, t : B \to C$ be functions. Prove that

(i) if $h \circ f = t \circ f$ and f is surjective, then $h = t$ and

(ii) if $h \circ f = h \circ g$ and h is injective, then $f = g$.

Solution. (i) Let $b \in B$. Since f is surjective, there exists some $a \in A$ such that $f(a) = b$. Now, $h(b) = h\big(f(a)\big) = (h \circ f)(a) = (t \circ f)(a) = t\big(f(a)\big) = t(b)$. Since this holds good for all $b \in B$, we conclude that $h = t$.

(ii) Let $a \in A$. Since $h \circ f = h \circ g$ we have, $(h \circ f)(a) = (h \circ g)(a)$, i.e., $h\big(f(a)\big) = h\big(g(a)\big)$. Now as h is injective, this gives $f(a) = g(a)$. Since a is an arbitrary element of A, we conclude that $f = g$.

◊ **Exercise 1.4.4.** For each of the function $f : \mathbb{Z} \to \mathbb{Z}$ given below, find:

(i) a left inverse of f, if it exists.

(a) $f(x) = 2x$;

(b) $f(x) = \frac{x}{2}$, if x is even;
= 7, if x is odd.

(ii) a right inverse of f, if it exists.

(a) $f(x) = x - 5$

(b) $f(x) = 2x$

Solution. (i)   Recall that a function has a left inverse if and only if it is injective.

(a)   Injectivity of f is immediate. Hence f has a left inverse. Let $g : \mathbb{Z} \to \mathbb{Z}$ be defined as

$$g(x) = \begin{cases} \frac{x}{2} & \text{when } x \text{ is even} \\ 1 & \text{when } x \text{ is odd.} \end{cases}$$

Now, $(g \circ f)(x) = g\big(f(x)\big) = g(2x) = x = i_{\mathbb{Z}}(x)$, whence $g \circ f = i_{\mathbb{Z}}$ and so g is a left inverse of f.

(b)   Observe that here, $f(3) = 7 = f(5)$ though $3 \neq 5$. This indicates that f is not injective and so f has no left inverse.

(ii)   Recall that a function has a right inverse if and only if it is surjective.

(a)   Note that for any $n \in \mathbb{Z}$, we have $n+5 \in \mathbb{Z}$ so that $f(n+5) = n+5-5 = n$, whence f is surjective and so f has a right inverse. Let us define $g : \mathbb{Z} \to \mathbb{Z}$ by $g(x) = x + 5$ for all $x \in \mathbb{Z}$. Then, $(f \circ g)(x) = f\big(g(x)\big) = f(x + 5) = x + 5 - 5 = x = i_{\mathbb{Z}}(x)$, whence $f \circ g = i_{\mathbb{Z}}$ shows that g is a right inverse of f.

(b)   Observe that for $5 \in \mathbb{Z}$, there does not exist any $x \in \mathbb{Z}$ such that $f(x) = 2x = 5$. Hence f is not surjective. So f has no right inverse.

$\diamond$ **Exercise 1.4.5.** Let $|X| = n$. Prove that there can be $n!$ different bijective functions on X.

Solution. Let $f : X \to X$ be a bijective function. For simplicity, let $X = \{a_1, a_2, \ldots, a_n\}$. Now, a bijective function f on X is to be defined by choosing the images of $a_1, a_2, \ldots, a_n$ under f. Suppose we choose it in the order $f(a_1), f(a_2), \ldots, f(a_n)$. Then $f(a_1)$ can be chosen in n ways and once it is chosen, then $f(a_2)$ can be chosen in $(n - 1)$ ways, $\ldots$ etc.; in general $f(a_k)$ can be chosen in $n - (k - 1)$ ways for all $1 \leq k \leq n$. Thus, f has $n(n - 1)(n - 2) \ldots 2 \cdot 1 = n!$ choices. Hence the number of bijective functions that can be defined on X is $n!$.

$\blacklozenge$ **Exercise 1.4.6.** Let A and B be two finite sets with $|A| = 5$ and $|B| = 3$. Show that the number of surjective functions from A onto B is 150.

Solution. Observe that since the set B has 3 elements and in a surjective function codomain is the same as range, if we find the number of different possible partitions of the set A into three subsets and assign to each such subset one element of B in all possible manners, then each such assignment will be a surjective function of A onto B. Now as $|A| = 5$, the number of different partitions of A into 3 subsets is given by $\phi(5, 3)$, which can be calculated to be equal to 25 [refer to Worked-out Exercise 1.2.7]. Again each of these partitions (into three subsets) can be assigned to three elements of B in $3!$ ways. Hence total number of possible surjective functions is $25 \times 3! = 25 \times 6 = 150$.

$\Diamond$ **Exercise 1.4.7.** Let $f : X \to Y$ be a function. Then prove that

  (i) if f is injective and $A, B \subseteq X$ then, $f(A \setminus B) \subseteq f(A) \setminus f(B)$;

  (ii) if $A, B \subseteq Y$ then, $f^{-1}(A \setminus B) = f^{-1}(A) \setminus f^{-1}(B)$

Solution. (i)   Let $x \in f(A \setminus B)$. Then $x = f(a)$ for some $a \in A$ such that $a \notin B$. Now, $a \in A$ implies that $f(a) \in f(A)$. Suppose $f(a) \in f(B)$. Then $f(a) = f(b)$ for some $b \in B$. But since f is injective $f(a) = f(b)$ implies that $a = b$ so that $a \in B$, which is a contradiction. Hence $f(a) \notin f(B)$. This implies that $x = f(a) \in f(A) \setminus f(B)$. Consequently, $f(A \setminus B) \subseteq f(A) \setminus f(B)$.

(ii)   Let $x \in f^{-1}(A) \setminus f^{-1}(B) \iff x \in f^{-1}(A)$ and $x \notin f^{-1}(B) \iff f(x) \in A$ and $f(x) \notin B \iff f(x) \in A \setminus B \iff x \in f^{-1}(A \setminus B)$. Hence we have $f^{-1}(A \setminus B) = f^{-1}(A) \setminus f^{-1}(B)$.

$\blacklozenge$ **Exercise 1.4.8.** Either prove the following statements or give counter examples to disprove:

  (i) The set $\mathbb{R}$ is equipotent with $\mathbb{R}^+$.

  (ii) The set $\mathbb{R}$ is equipotent with $S = \{x \in \mathbb{R} : 0 < x < 1\}$

  (iii) If $X = \{x \in \mathbb{R} : 0 \le x \le 1\}$ and $Y = \{x \in \mathbb{R} : 0 < x < 1\}$, then X and Y have the same cardinal number.

  (iv) Let A, B and C be nonempty sets and $f : A \to B$, $g : B \to C$ are functions.

      (a) if $g \circ f : A \to C$ is injective, then g is also injective.

      (b) if $g \circ f : A \to C$ is surjective, then f is also surjective.

  (v) Let $f : X \to Y$ be a function. Then f is injective if and only if $f(A \cap B) = f(A) \cap f(B)$ for all nonempty subsets A and B of X.

Solution. (i)   **True.** Define $f : \mathbb{R} \to \mathbb{R}^+$ by $f(x) = e^x$ for all $x \in \mathbb{R}$. Check that f is a bijective function from $\mathbb{R}$ onto $\mathbb{R}^+$.

(ii)   **True.** Define $f : S \to \mathbb{R}$ by $f(x) = \tan \pi(x - \frac{1}{2})$ for all $x \in S$. Check that f is a bijective function from S onto $\mathbb{R}$.

(iii)   **True.** Let $P = \{x \in \mathbb{R} : \frac{1}{4} \le x \le \frac{3}{4}\}$. Then $P \subseteq Y$. Let us define $f : X \to P$ by $f(x) = \frac{x}{2} + \frac{1}{4}$. Check that f is injective. Now let $x \in P$. Let $y = 2x - \frac{1}{2}$.

Now, as $\frac{1}{4} \leq x \leq \frac{3}{4}$, we see that $0 \leq 2x - \frac{1}{2} \leq 1$ and hence $y \in X$. Observe that, $f(y) = \frac{y}{2} + \frac{1}{4} = \frac{1}{2}(2x - \frac{1}{2}) + \frac{1}{4} = x$, whence f is surjective also and consequently a bijective function. Therefore $X \sim P$. Again, $Y \subseteq X$ and $Y \sim Y$. Now apply the Schröeder-Bernstein theorem to see that $X \sim Y$.

(iv) (a) **False.** Indeed, let $f, g : \mathbb{R} \to \mathbb{R}$ be defined by, $f(x) = e^x$ and $g(x) = x^2$ for all $x \in \mathbb{R}$. Note that, here $(g \circ f)(x) = g\big(f(x)\big) = g(e^x) = e^{2x}$ for all $x \in \mathbb{R}$, which is injective; but g is not injective as $-5 \neq 5$ but $g(-5) = (-5)^2 = 25 = (5)^2 = g(5)$.

(b) **False.** For example, let $A = \{1, \omega, \omega^2\}$ where $\omega^3 = 1$; let $f : \mathbb{N} \to \mathbb{N}$ be given by $f(n) = 5n$, for all $n \in \mathbb{N}$ and let $g : \mathbb{N} \to A$ be given by $g(n) = \omega^n$, for all $n \in \mathbb{N}$. Observe that $(g \circ f)(n) = g\big(f(n)\big) = g(5n) = \omega^{5n}$ for all $n \in \mathbb{N}$. Clearly, $g \circ f : \mathbb{N} \to A$ is a surjective function but f is not.

(v) **True.** Suppose f is injective and A, B be nonempty subsets of X. Let $y \in f(A \cap B)$; i.e., $y = f(x)$ for some $x \in A \cap B$. But as then $x \in A$ so, $y = f(x) \in f(A)$ and a similar argument shows that $y \in f(B)$, whence $y \in f(A) \cap f(B)$ and we get, $f(A \cap B) \subseteq f(A) \cap f(B)$. Now, let $y \in f(A) \cap f(B)$. Then $y \in f(A)$ and $y \in f(B)$, i.e., $y = f(a)$ for some $a \in A$ and $y = f(b)$ for some $b \in B$. Now, as f is injective and $f(a) = f(b)$, we conclude $a = b$, whence $a \in A \cap B$ so that $y = f(a) \in f(A \cap B)$. Hence, $f(A) \cap f(B) \subseteq f(A \cap B)$. Consequently, $f(A \cap B) = f(A) \cap f(B)$.

Conversely, suppose that $f(A \cap B) = f(A) \cap f(B)$ for all subsets A and B of X. Suppose that f is not injective. Then there must exist some $x, y \in X$ such that $x \neq y$ but $f(x) = f(y)$. Consider $A = \{x\}$ and $B = \{y\}$. Then $A \cap B = \emptyset$ and so $f(A \cap B) = \emptyset$. However, observe that $f(A) \cap f(B) = \{f(x)\} \neq \emptyset$. This gives $f(A \cap B) \neq f(A) \cap f(B)$, a contradiction. Hence f is injective.

$\diamond$ **Exercise 1.4.9.** Consider the map $f : \mathbb{Z}_{\geq 0} \times \mathbb{Z} \longrightarrow \mathbb{Z}$ given by $f(m, n) = 2^m(2n+1)$, where $\mathbb{Z}$ denotes the set of integers and $\mathbb{Z}_{\geq 0}$ denotes the set $\{0, 1, 2, 3, \ldots\}$. Pick the correct option.

(i) f is onto but not one-one.   (ii) f is one-one but not onto.

(iii) f is both one-one and onto.   (iv) f is neither one-one nor onto.

Solution. Let $a, b, c, d \in \mathbb{Z}_{\geq 0}$ such that $f(a, b) = f(c, d)$. Also, let $a \geq c$. Then $f(a, b) = f(c, d)$ implies $2^a(2b+1) = 2^c(2d+1)$, i.e., $2^{a-c}(2b+1) = 2^0(2d+1)$. Thus $a = c$ and $b = d$. Hence f is one-one. Here the element $0 \in \mathbb{Z}$ has no preimage, since neither factor can be zero. Thus f is not onto. Therefore, option (ii) is correct.

Exercises

1. Determine which of the following sets are functions from A to B. Justify your answer.

    (a) $f = \{(a,b),(a,c),(b,d),(c,a)\}$; $A = \{a,b,c\}$, $B = \{a,b,c,d\}$.

    (b) $f = \{(1,3),(2,2),(3,4)\}$; $A = \{1,2,3\}$ $B = \{1,2,3,4\}$.

    (c) $f = \{(a,p),(b,p),(c,q),(d,r)\}$; $A = \{a,b,c,d\}$ $B = \{p,q,r\}$.

    (d) $f = \{(a,b) \in \mathbb{Z} \times \mathbb{Z} \mid b = a+5\}$; $X = Y = \mathbb{Z}$.

    (e) $f = \{(a,b) \in \mathbb{R} \times \mathbb{R} \mid b = \sqrt{a}\}$; $X = Y = \mathbb{R}$.

    In case any of the above sets are functions, determine their nature as to injectivity, surjectivity or bijectivity.

2. If $A = \{a,b\}$ and $b = \{1,2\}$, find all the relations from A into B. Detect which of these relations are functions from A to B.

3. Show that the following functions are neither injective nor surjective.

    (a) $f : \mathbb{R} \to \mathbb{R}$ given by $f(x) = |x|$, $x \in \mathbb{R}$.

    (b) $f : \mathbb{R} \to \mathbb{R}$ given by $f(x) = \cos x$, $x \in \mathbb{R}$.

4. Show that the following functions are injective but not surjective.

    (a) $f : \mathbb{Z} \to \mathbb{Z}$ given by $f(x) = 2x$, $x \in \mathbb{Z}$.

    (b) $f : \mathbb{N} \to \mathbb{N}$ given by $f(x) = 2x + 5$, $x \in \mathbb{N}$.

5. Show that the following functions are surjective but not injective.

    (a) $f : \mathbb{Z} \to 2\mathbb{N}_0$ given by $f(x) = 2|x|$, $x \in \mathbb{Z}$.

    (b) $f : \mathbb{Z} \to \{1,-1\}$ given by $f(x) = (-1)^x$, $x \in \mathbb{Z}$.

6. Determine which of the following functions are surjective, injective or bijective.

    (a) $f : \mathbb{R} \to \mathbb{R}$ defined by $f(x) = |x|x$, for all $x \in \mathbb{R}$;

    (b) $f : \mathbb{R}^+ \to \mathbb{R}^+$ defined by $f(x) = \sqrt{x}$, for all $x \in \mathbb{R}^+$;

    (c) $f : \mathbb{R} \to \mathbb{R}$ defined by $f(x) = |x| + x$, for all $x \in \mathbb{R}$;

    (d) $f : \mathbb{Z} \to \mathbb{Q}$ defined by $f(x) = 2^x$, for all $x \in \mathbb{R}$;

    (e) $f : \mathbb{R}^* \to \mathbb{R}^*$ defined by $f(x) = \frac{1}{x}$, for all $x \in \mathbb{R}^*$;

    (f) $f : \mathbb{R} \to \mathbb{R}$ defined by $f(x) = 2x - 7$, for all $x \in \mathbb{R}$;

    (g) $f : \mathbb{R} \to \mathbb{R}$ defined by $f(x) = x^2 - 3x + 4$, for all $x \in \mathbb{R}$.

7. Let A be a finite set and let $f : A \to B$ be a surjective function. Show that the number of elements of B cannot be greater than that of A.

8. Suppose f and g are two functions from $\mathbb{R}$ into $\mathbb{R}$ such that $f \circ g = g \circ f$. Does it necessarily imply that $f = g$? Justify your answer.

9. Let $X = \{a,b,c\}$. Find all possible bijective functions from X into itself.

10. Let $f : A \to B$. Give suitable examples to show that the inverse relation $f^* = \{(y,x) \in B \times A : (x,y) \in f\}$ need not always be a function. Prove that f^* is a function from $Im(f)$ into A if and only if f is injective.

11. Let $f : A \to B$ be a bijective function. Prove that

    (a) inverse of f is a unique function which is also bijective;

    (b) $(f^{-1})^{-1} = f$, where f^{-1} denotes the unique inverse of f;

    (c) if further, $g : B \to C$ is another bijective function, then show that $(g \circ f)^{-1} = f^{-1} \circ g^{-1}$.

12. Find whether the following functions are bijective; if so, find their inverse.

    (a) Let $S = \{x \in \mathbb{R} : -1 < x < 1\}$ and $f : \mathbb{R} \to S$ be defined by $f(x) = \dfrac{x}{1 + |x|}$;

    (b) Let $P = \{x \in \mathbb{R} : 0 < x < 1\}$ and $f : P \to \mathbb{R}$ be defined by $f(x) = \dfrac{2x - 1}{1 - |2x - 1|}$.

13. † (a) Prove that the set of all integers is equipotent with the set of all rational numbers.

    (b) Prove that $3\mathbb{Z}$ and $5\mathbb{Z}$ are equipotent.

14. Let X and Y be nonempty sets and $f : X \to Y$ be a function of X into Y. If $A, A_1, A_2, A_\alpha \subseteq X$ and $B, B_1, B_2, B_\alpha \subseteq Y$ for all $\alpha \in \Gamma$ (where Γ is an index set), then prove the following:

    (i) $f(\emptyset) = \emptyset$, $\quad f^{-1}(\emptyset) = \emptyset$, $\quad f(X) \subseteq Y$, $\quad f^{-1}(Y) = X$;

    (ii) $A_1 \subseteq A_2 \Longrightarrow f(A_1) \subseteq f(A_2)$, $\quad B_1 \subseteq B_2 \Longrightarrow f^{-1}(B_1) \subseteq f^{-1}(B_2)$;

    (iii) $f(A_1 \cup A_2) = f(A_1) \cup f(A_2)$, $\quad f(A_1 \cap A_2) \subseteq f(A_1) \cap f(A_2)$;

    (iv) $f^{-1}(B_1 \cup B_2) = f^{-1}(B_1) \cup f^{-1}(B_2)$, $\quad f^{-1}(B_1 \cap B_2) = f^{-1}(B_1) \cap f^{-1}(B_2)$;

    (v) $f\left(\bigcup\limits_{\alpha \in \Gamma} A_\alpha\right) = \bigcup\limits_{\alpha \in \Gamma} f(A_\alpha)$, $\quad f^{-1}\left(\bigcup\limits_{\alpha \in \Gamma} B_\alpha\right) = \bigcup\limits_{\alpha \in \Gamma} f^{-1}(B_\alpha)$;

    (vi) $f\left(\bigcap\limits_{\alpha \in \Gamma} A_\alpha\right) \subseteq \bigcap\limits_{\alpha \in \Gamma} f(A_\alpha)$, $\quad f^{-1}\left(\bigcap\limits_{\alpha \in \Gamma} B_\alpha\right) = \bigcap\limits_{\alpha \in \Gamma} f^{-1}(B_\alpha)$;

    (vii) $f^{-1}(B') = \{f^{-1}(B)\}'$; where B' is the complement of B in Y;

    (viii) $A \subseteq f^{-1}\big(f(A)\big)$, $f\big(f^{-1}(B)\big) \subseteq B$;

    (ix) f is injective $\Longleftrightarrow A = f^{-1}\big(f(A)\big)$ is true for all $A \subseteq X$;

    (x) f is surjective $\Longleftrightarrow f\big(f^{-1}(B)\big) = B$ is true for all $B \subseteq Y$;

    (xi) f is surjective $\Longleftrightarrow \{f(A)\}' \subseteq f(A')$ is true for all $A \subseteq X$;

15. Let A be a nonempty set and ρ be an equivalence relation on A. Let B denote the set of all ρ-equivalent classes. Prove that there exists a surjective function from A onto B.

16. (a) Let $f, g : \mathbb{R} \to \mathbb{R}$ be defined by $f(x) = 3x^2 - 5$ and $g(x) = \dfrac{x}{x^2 + 1}$. Find $f \circ g$ and $g \circ f$.

    (b) Find $f^{-1}\big(\{70\}\big)$, $f\big(f^{-1}(\{70\})\big)$.

    (c) Show that $g^{-1}\big(g(\{2, 3\})\big) \neq \{2, 3\}$.

17. Suppose X and Y are two finite sets such that $|X| = 2$ and $|Y| = 3$. Find the number of functions that can be defined from (i) X into Y ; (ii) Y into X.

    [**Hint** : *For two finite sets A and B there are $|B|^{|A|}$ functions from A into B.*]

18. † Let A and B be two finite sets such that $|A| = n$ and $|B| = k$ with $1 \leq k \leq n$. Prove that the number of surjective functions from A onto B is $\phi(n, k) \times k!$ [Here $\phi(n, k)$ is as defined in Worked Out Exercise 1.2.7.]

1.5   Binary Operations

Right from our early school days, we are acquainted with the operations of 'addition', 'subtraction' or 'multiplication' among real numbers and hence we have a crude idea of what an *operation* may mean. Is it not the fact that by virtue of these operations, given any two numbers, we are always able to find a number, which may or may not be a new one ? For example, addition of two integers 7 and 2 is known to be 9 and multiplication of them yields the integer 14, whereas subtraction gives the integer 5. Analyzing these operations more closely, one finds that the order of appearance of the given numbers is sometimes important, as upon subtraction, 2 and 7 gives -5 and not 5. Further, the other well-known fundamental operation, viz., 'division' is not even defined for all possible pairs of numbers. Indeed, division of a number by zero is *undefined* in mathematics. However, excepting this case, division of any two numbers gives a number and here also the order of the given numbers cannot be neglected.

In the present section, we are going to furnish an *abstract* definition of an 'operation' by collecting the core of these basic ideas. The idea of abstraction, as it stands in mathematics, is to clearly examine an existing system and then to extract the object independent mathematical fact out of it and put it on a broader perspective, so that the existing system or systems may turn out to be mere example(s) of this more general setup. The following definition of a binary operation can surely be appreciated in this light.

Definition 1.5.1. Let A be a nonempty set. A ***binary operation*** $*$ on A is a function from $A \times A$ into A.

In other words, a binary operation $*$ on a set A is a rule of correspondence that assigns to each ordered pair $(a, b) \in A \times A$, some element of the set A. Note that, by considering the ordered pairs, we have taken into account the possibility that the element to be assigned with (a, b) may not be same as the element to be assigned with (b, a). Furthermore, watch carefully that the definition does not necessarily require a new element to be assigned with (a, b) as the outcome of the operation. As for example, under the operation of usual addition among real numbers, the pair $(3, 0)$ is assigned to 3 and under usual multiplication, the same ordered pair is assigned to 0. Hence there are two important aspects of the definition of a binary operation $*$ on a set A:

(I)   to each possible ordered pair in $A \times A$, exactly one element must be assigned; failing which the operation $*$ will not be *well-defined* as a function;

(II)   the element assigned to any ordered pair must again belong to A; failing which we say that the set A is not closed under $*$. We denote by $a * b$, the element of A assigned to the pair (a, b).

We now give several illustrations in favour of the above argument.

Example 1.5.2. (a) If we add any two integers, the outcome is again an integer; hence 'addition' $(+)$ is a binary operation on $\mathbb{Z}$. In a similar way 'subtraction'$(-)$ is a binary operation on $\mathbb{Z}$. However, since $\mathbb{N}$ is not closed under '$-$' [since, $(3, 5) \in \mathbb{N} \times \mathbb{N}$ but $3 - 5 = -2 \notin \mathbb{N}$], 'subtraction' is not a binary operation on $\mathbb{N}$.

(b) On $\mathbb{N}$, let us define $a * b = a$, i.e., $3 * 7 = 3$, $7 * 3 = 7, 7 * 7 = 7$ etc. Clearly, it is a binary operation on $\mathbb{N}$.

(c) On $\mathbb{N}$, define $a * b$ to be the quotient of a by b for all $a, b \in \mathbb{N}$. Observe that $\mathbb{N}$ is not closed under $*$ as $2 * 5 \notin \mathbb{N}$ and thus, $*$ is not a binary operation on $\mathbb{N}$.

(d) Let $\mathcal{C} = \{f \mid f : \mathbb{R} \to \mathbb{R}\}$, i.e., $\mathcal{C}$ be the set of all real valued functions defined on $\mathbb{R}$. Define $*$ on $\mathcal{C}$ by $f * g = h$ where $h(x) = f(x) + g(x)$ for all $x \in \mathbb{R}$, where $+$ is the usual addition of real numbers. We leave it to the reader to verify that $*$ is a binary operation on $\mathcal{C}$.

Definition 1.5.3. By a ***mathematical system***, we mean an ordered $(n + 1)$-tuple $(X, *_1, *_2, \ldots, *_n)$ where X is a nonempty set and $*_i$ is a binary operation on X, $i = 1, 2, 3 \ldots n$. The set X underlying the mathematical system is sometimes called the ***content*** of the system.

Definition 1.5.4. Let $(X, *)$ be a mathematical system of a single binary operation.[26] Then

(i) $*$ is called ***commutative*** if for all $x, y \in X, x * y = y * x$;

(ii) $*$ is called ***associative*** if for all $x, y, z \in X, x * (y * z) = (x * y) * z$.

We invite the reader to justify that when $*$ is associative, the expressions like $x * y * z * w$ without parentheses are unambiguous. Indeed, in whichever way you may put the parentheses for computation, the final results will always be the same. We shall take up this matter in a more formal manner at the end of this section.

Following are examples of some binary operations, some of which are commutative, some associative and some neither commutative nor associative.

Example 1.5.5. (a) Let $A \neq \emptyset$ and $X = \{f \mid f : A \to A\}$. Since composition of functions is again a function (vide 1.4.10) and such a composition is associative (vide

---

[26]$(X, *)$ is also called a ***groupoid***.

Theorem 1.4.13), we conclude that $(X, \circ)$ is an associative mathematical system. However, by virtue of Example 1.4.12, we may conclude that this system is noncommutative.

(b)   Consider the mathematical system $(\mathbb{R}, \cdot)$ where '$\cdot$' is the usual multiplication among real numbers. Since multiplication of reals are known to be commutative and associative, $(\mathbb{R}, \cdot)$ is a commutative and associative mathematical system.

(c)   Let $M_2(\mathbb{Z})$ denote the set of all 2×2 matrices over $\mathbb{Z}$, i.e.,

$$M_2(\mathbb{Z}) = \left\{ \begin{bmatrix} a & b \\ c & d \end{bmatrix} \ \middle|\ a, b, c, d \in \mathbb{Z} \right\}.$$

Let $\oplus$ denote the addition among matrices and $\odot$ denote the matrix multiplication. Taking for granted, the elementary knowledge about matrix addition and matrix multiplication, it can be shown by means of routine calculations, that $(M_2(\mathbb{Z}), \oplus)$ is a commutative and associative mathematical system, whereas $(M_2(\mathbb{Z}), \odot)$ is an associative mathematical system which is noncommutative.

(d)   Consider the mathematical system $(\mathbb{Z}, -)$, where '$-$' is the usual subtraction on $\mathbb{Z}$. Note that $3 - 2 = 1 \neq -1 = 2 - 3$ shows that the system is noncommutative. Now, $(5 - 4) - 3 = 1 - 3 = -2$ but $5 - (4 - 3) = 5 - 1 = 4$ and hence the system is not associative.

(e)   Let us recall $\mathbb{Z}_n$ as described in section 1.3. Define $\cdot_n$ on $\mathbb{Z}_n$ by $[a] \cdot_n [b] = [ab]$ for all $[a], [b] \in \mathbb{Z}_n$. Let us prove in detail that $(\mathbb{Z}_n, \cdot_n)$ is a commutative, associative mathematical system.

We begin by showing that $\cdot_n$ is a binary operation on $\mathbb{Z}_n$. Let $[a], [b], [c], [d] \in \mathbb{Z}_n$ and suppose that $[a] = [c]$ and $[b] = [d]$. Then $n | (a - c)$ and $n | (b - d)$, i.e., there exist integers p, q such that, $np = a - c$ and $nq = b - d$. By Theorem 1.3.7(ii), it follows that $[ab] = [cd]$. Hence $\cdot_n$ is well-defined and so $\cdot_n$ is a binary operation. Now, for all $[a], [b] \in \mathbb{Z}_n, ([a] \cdot_n [b]) = [ab] = [ba] = ([b] \cdot_n [a])$. Hence $\cdot_n$ is commutative. Again for all $[a], [b], [c] \in \mathbb{Z}_n, ([a] \cdot_n [b]) \cdot_n [c] = [ab] \cdot_n [c] = [(ab)c] = [a(bc)] = [a] \cdot_n [bc] = [a] \cdot_n ([b] \cdot_n [c])$. Hence $\cdot_n$ is associative. Consequently, $(\mathbb{Z}_n, \cdot_n)$ is a commutative associative mathematical system.

We enlist a few more examples to justify the independence of these two concepts as given below:

Example 1.5.6.

	Associative	Commutative	$(A, \star),\ A = \mathbb{Z}$
(i)	$\times$	$\times$	$a \star b = a - b$
(ii)	$\times$	$\checkmark$	$a \star b = \lvert a + b \rvert$
(iii)	$\checkmark$	$\times$	$a \star b = a$
(iv)	$\checkmark$	$\checkmark$	$a \star b = a + b$

Binary operations defined on a finite set can sometimes be conveniently expressed in terms of a table, called the **multiplication table**[27]. For example, let $A = \{1, \omega, \omega^2\}$ where ω is an imaginary cube root of unity. Consider the operation $*$ to be the complex multiplication. Then the multiplication table looks like

$$
\begin{array}{c|ccc}
* & 1 & \omega & \omega^2 \\
\hline
1 & 1 & \omega & \omega^2 \\
\omega & \omega & \omega^2 & 1 \\
\omega^2 & \omega^2 & 1 & \omega
\end{array}
$$

Note that the elements of the underlying set are to be listed across the top of the table in the same order as they are listed at the left; then the entry in the ij-th position of the table (i.e., the intersection of i-th row and j-th column) is given by the composition of the i-th entry on the left and j-th entry on the top of the table.

Observe that the binary operation is commutative if and only if the entries in the multiplication table are symmetric about the diagonal from top left to the bottom right corner.

Definition 1.5.7. A binary operation $\star$ on a nonempty set A is called **left cancellative** (or, said to satisfy the **left cancellation law**) if for any $a, b, c \in A$, $a \star b = a \star c$ implies that $b = c$. Similarly, $\star$ is called **right cancellative** (or, said to satisfy the **right cancellation law**), if for any $a, b, c \in A$, $b \star a = c \star a$ implies that $b = c$. If $\star$ is both left cancellative and right cancellative, then it is called **cancellative** (or, said to satisfy the **cancellation law**).

Example 1.5.8. In Example 1.5.6, the binary operations described in (i) and (iv) are cancellative and those described in (ii) and (iii) are not cancellative (verify!).

Example 1.5.9. Let $A = \mathbb{Z} \smallsetminus \{0\}$. Define $a \star b = \lvert a \rvert b$ for all $a, b \in A$. Then $\star$ is left cancellative but not right cancellative (verify!).

---

[27]It is merely a convenient terminology and not to be confused with the usual 'multiplication' defined among numbers.

Definition 1.5.10. Let $(A, *)$ be a mathematical system. An element $e_1 \in A$ is called a **left identity** of $(A, *)$ if for all $x \in A$, $e_1 * x = x$. Similarly, an element $e_2 \in A$ is called a **right identity** of $(A, *)$ if for all $x \in A$, $x * e_2 = x$. An **identity** is both left and right identity, i.e., $e \in A$ is called an identity of $(A, *)$ if for all $x \in A$, $ex = xe = x$.

Example 1.5.11. In Example 1.5.6, 0 is a right identity but not a left identity in case (i). In (ii) and (iii), A has no identity. In (iv), 0 is an identity.

Example 1.5.12. (a)   In Example 1.5.5(b), $1 \in \mathbb{R}$ is an identity of the mathematical system $(\mathbb{R}, \cdot)$; in Example 1.5.5(c), the matrices $\begin{bmatrix} 0 & 0 \\ 0 & 0 \end{bmatrix}$ and $\begin{bmatrix} 1 & 0 \\ 0 & 1 \end{bmatrix}$ are respectively the identity elements of $(M_2(\mathbb{Z}), \oplus)$ and $(M_2(\mathbb{Z}), \odot)$.

(b)   Consider the mathematical system $(2\mathbb{N}, +)$ where '+' denotes the usual addition in integers. Note that there is no identity element in this mathematical system.

Theorem 1.5.13. *An identity element of a mathematical system* $(A, *)$, *if exists, is unique.*

Proof. Let e, f be identities of $(A, *)$. Since e is an identity $e * x = x$ for all $x \in A$. In particular,

$$e * f = f. \tag{1.5.1}$$

Again, since f is an identity, $x * f = x$ for all $x \in A$. In particular,

$$e * f = e. \tag{1.5.2}$$

Combining (1.5.1) and (1.5.2) we get $e = e * f = f$ and consequently, an identity element (if it exists) is unique. $\square$

Definition 1.5.14. A **semigroup** is a mathematical system $(S, *)$, where S is a nonempty set and $*$ is an associative binary operation on S, i.e., $a * (b * c) = (a * b) * c$ for all $a, b, c \in S$.

Note that an element $a \in S$ is called **idempotent** if $a * a = a$. A semigroup $(S, *)$ is **commutative** if $*$ is commutative, i.e., $a * b = b * a$ for all $a, b \in S$, otherwise it is called **noncommutative**. Furthermore, if the semigroup has an identity element, then such a mathematical system is called a **monoid**.

Example 1.5.15. (a)   It can be easily seen that the set $\mathbb{N}$ of natural numbers endowed with the operation of *addition* is a semigroup which is not a monoid.

(b)   Let X be a nonempty set and S be the set of all mappings $f : X \to X$. If $\circ$ denotes the composition of mappings, then $(S, \circ)$ is a monoid, where the identity element is the identity mapping ι_X on X. Observe that the associativity of mapping composition follows from Theorem 1.4.13. Furthermore, this monoid is noncommutative (vide Example 1.4.12).

Definition 1.5.16. A mathematical system $(G, *)$ is called a **quasigroup**, if for any two elements $a, b \in G$, each of the equations $a * x = b$ and $y * a = b$ has a unique solution in G.

Example 1.5.17. $(\mathbb{Z}, -)$ is a natural example of a quasigroup, where $\mathbb{Z}$ is the set of integers. Indeed, for any $a, b \in \mathbb{Z}$, $a - x = b$ and $y - a = b$ have solutions $x = a - b$ and $y = a + b$, respectively.

Let $(S, *)$ be a semigroup and $a, b, c \in S$. Then by associative law, $a * (b * c) = (a * b) * c$. Recall that this virtually enables us to get rid of the parenthesis and to define $a * b * c = a * (b * c) = (a * b) * c$. In fact, this notion can be extended to more than three elements as the next definition shows.

Definition 1.5.18. Let $(G, *)$ be a semigroup and $a_1, a_2, \ldots, a_n \in G$ (not necessarily distinct). Define the **meaningful product** of $a_1, a_2, \ldots, a_n$ (in this order) as follows: If $n = 1$, then the meaningful product is a_1. If $n > 1$, then a meaningful product of $a_1, a_2, \ldots, a_n$ is any product of the form $(a_1 * a_2 * \ldots * a_m) * (a_{m+1} * a_{m+2} * \ldots * a_n)$, where $1 \leq m < n$ and $(a_1 * a_2 * \ldots * a_m)$ and $(a_{m+1} * a_2 * \ldots * a_n)$ are meaningful products of m and $n - m$ elements, respectively.

Definition 1.5.19. Let $(G, *)$ be a semigroup and $a_1, a_2, \ldots, a_n \in G, n \geq 1$. The **standard product** of $a_1, a_2, \ldots, a_n$ denoted by $(a_1 * a_2 * \ldots * a_n)$ is defined recursively as follows:
$$a_1 = a_1$$
$$(a_1 * a_2 * \ldots * a_n) = (a_1 * a_2 * \ldots * a_{n-1}) * a_n \text{ if } n > 1.$$

We now state the following theorem that establishes the equality between any meaningful product and standard product.

Theorem 1.5.20. *Let $(G, *)$ be a semigroup and $a_1, a_2, \ldots, a_n \in G, n \geq 1$. Then all possible meaningful products of $a_1, a_2, \ldots, a_n$ are equal to the standard product of $a_1, a_2, \ldots, a_n$ (the order of appearance of $a_1, a_2, \ldots, a_n$ in both products being same).*

Worked-out Exercises

◇ **Exercise 1.5.1.** Which of the following binary operations are associative and which are commutative?
(a) $(\mathbb{N}, *)$ where $a * b = a^b$ for all $a, b \in \mathbb{N}$.
(b) $(\mathbb{Z}, *)$ where $a * b = a + b - ab$ for all $a, b \in \mathbb{Z}$.
(c) $(\mathbb{R}, *)$ where $a * b = |a| + |b|$ for all $a, b \in \mathbb{R}$

Solution. (a) This binary operation is neither commutative nor associative. Indeed, $2 * 3 = 2^3 = 8 \neq 9 = 3^2 = 3 * 2$ proves the noncommutativity. Again, $(2 * 3) * 4 = 2^3 * 4 = (2^3)^4 = 2^{12}$ whereas $2 * (3 * 4) = 2 * 3^4 = 2 * 81 = 2^{81}$ and hence $2 * (3 * 4) \neq (2 * 3) * 4$. Consequently, $*$ is not associative.

(b) This binary operation is commutative. In fact, $a * b = a + b - ab = b + a - ba = b * a$ for all $a, b \in \mathbb{Z}$. Again, for all $a, b, c \in \mathbb{Z}, (a * b) * c = (a + b - ab) * c = (a + b - ab) + c - (a + b - ab)c = a + b + c - ab - bc - ac + abc = a + (b + c - bc) - a(b + c - bc) = a * (b + c - bc) = a * (b * c)$, and hence $*$ is associative.

(c) This binary operation is commutative. In fact, for all $a, b \in \mathbb{R}$, $a * b = |a| + |b| = |b| + |a| = b * a$ proves our claim. This operation is associative also. Indeed, for all $a, b, c \in \mathbb{R}, (a * b) * c = (|a| + |b|) * c = \left||a| + |b|\right| + |c| = (|a| + |b|) + |c| = |a| + (|b| + |c|) = |a| + \left||b| + |c|\right| = a * (|b| + |c|) = a * (b * c)$. Hence the claim is justified.

♦ **Exercise 1.5.2.** Let S be a finite set with $|S| = n$. How many different binary operations can be defined on S? How many of them are commutative ?

Solution. Since S is a finite set with $|S| = n$, to define a binary operation on S means to fill up the $n \times n$, i.e., n^2 places of the multiplication table by any of the available n elements of the set S. Since each place of the multiplication table can be filled up in n ways, total number of ways in which n^2 places can be filled up is $n^{(n^2)}$. Hence the number of binary operations that can be defined on S is $n^{(n^2)}$.

Now to be commutative, the multiplication table of a binary operation on a finite set must have to be symmetric about the diagonal of the table, from top left to bottom right corner (Fig. 9). This means that the ij-th entry $(i \neq j)$ of the table must be the same as the ji-th entry. So for a commutative binary operation, it is sufficient to fill up only the upper triangular part of the table comprising of $\frac{n^2 - n}{2}$ entries together with n entries in the diagonal, i.e., to fill up altogether $\frac{n^2 - n}{2} + n = \frac{n^2 + n}{2}$ entries, each of which can be filled up by any of the n elements of S.

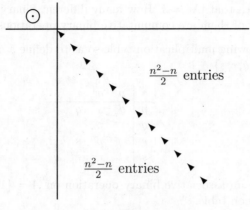

$\frac{n^2-n}{2}$ entries

$\frac{n^2-n}{2}$ entries

Fig. 9

Consequently, the total number of ways this can be done is $n^{\frac{n^2+n}{2}}$, i.e., $n^{\frac{n(n+1)}{2}}$. So the required number of different commutative binary operations on the set S with n elements is $n^{\frac{n(n+1)}{2}}$.

$\Diamond$ **Exercise 1.5.3.** Define $C(a) = \{x \in S \mid x \star a = a \star x\}$, where $(S, \star)$ is a semigroup and $a \in S$. Show that $C(a)$ is nonempty and is closed under $\star$. Hence prove that $\big(C(a), \star\big)$ is also a semigroup.

Solution. Certainly $a \in C(a)$ and so $C(a) \neq \emptyset$. Let $x, y \in C(a)$. Then $x \star a = a \star x$ and $y \star a = a \star y$. Therefore we have $(x \star y) \star a = x \star (y \star a) = x \star (a \star y) = (x \star a) \star y = (a \star x) \star y = a \star (x \star y)$. This implies that $x \star y \in C(a)$, proving that $C(a)$ closed under $\star$. Also since all elements of $C(a)$ are elements of S, any three of them must satisfy the associative law. Therefore $\big(C(a), \star\big)$ is a semigroup.

Exercises

1. Which of the following are associative binary operations? Also find which of these are commutative?
   (a) $(\mathbb{N}, *)$ where $a * b = \mathrm{lcm}(a, b)$ for all $a, b \in \mathbb{N}$.
   (b) $(\mathbb{R}, *)$ where $a * b = \min(a, b)$ for all $a, b \in \mathbb{R}$.
   (c) $(\mathbb{Z}, *)$ where $a * b = a + b + 2$ for all $a, b \in \mathbb{Z}$.
   (d) $(\mathbb{Z}, *)$ where $a * b = a|b|$ for all $a, b \in \mathbb{Z}$.
   (e) $(\mathbb{Z}, *)$ where $a * b = |a|b$ for all $a, b \in \mathbb{Z}$.
   (f) $(\mathbb{R}, *)$ where $a * b = |a + b|$ for all $a, b \in \mathbb{R}$.
   (g) $(\mathbb{N}, *)$ where $a * b = \gcd(a, b)$ for all $a, b \in \mathbb{N}$.
   (h) $(\mathbb{Z}^+, *)$ where $a * b = 2^{ab}$ for all $a, b \in \mathbb{Z}^+$.
   (i) $(\mathbb{Q}, *)$ where $a * b = ab + 3$ for all $a, b \in \mathbb{Q}$.
   (j) $(\mathbb{R}, *)$ where $a * b = \max(a, b)$ for all $a, b \in \mathbb{R}$.

2. Find the identity element, if it exists, of each of the mathematical systems given in the above exercise.

3. Let X be a set such that $|X| = 3$. How many different binary operations can be defined on X? How many of them are commutative binary operations?

4. Complete the following multiplication table so as to define a commutative binary operation $*$ on $A = \{p, q, r, s\}$.

$*$	p	q	r	s
p	q	s	q	p
q		p		
r		p	s	
s		r	r	q

5. Assuming $*$ to be an associative binary operation on $A = \{1, 2, 3, 4\}$, complete the following multiplication table:

$*$	1	2	3	4
1	1	2	3	4
2	2	1	3	4
3	3	4	3	4
4				

6. Let $\mathcal{P}(S)$ be the set of all subsets of a set S. Show that $\bigl(\mathcal{P}(S), *\bigr)$ is a semigroup with an identity where $*$ is defined by $A * B = A \cap B$ for all $A, B \in \mathcal{P}(S)$.

Chapter 2

Integers

Integers are by and large the building blocks of mathematics[1], particularly of abstract algebra. In fact, many algebraic abstractions come from the set of integers. Throughout this book the set $\mathbb{Z}$ of all integers[2] will be used as a major source of example of different algebraic systems. In this section we do not intend to give an axiomatic development of the integers. We rather assume that the reader is familiar with the set $\mathbb{N} = \{1, 2, \ldots\}$ of all positive integers (i.e., natural numbers[3]) and the set $\mathbb{N}_0 = \{0, 1, 2, \ldots\}$ of all nonnegative integers, together with the properties of the two fundamental operations, viz., *addition* and *multiplication* along with the usual *order* prevailing among these numbers. In particular, for all $a, b, c \in \mathbb{Z}$, we have

- **Commutative laws :** $a + b = b + a, a \cdot b = b \cdot a$;
- **Associative laws :** $(a + b) + c = a + (b + c), (a \cdot b) \cdot c = a \cdot (b \cdot c)$;
- **Distributive law :** $a \cdot (b + c) = a \cdot b + a \cdot c$;
- **Identity elements :** $a + 0 = a, a \cdot 1 = a$ for any a.
- **Additive inverse :** For each a there exists b such that $a + b = 0$; this integer b is called the additive inverse of a and is denoted by $-a$. We write $a - b$ for $a + (-b)$.
- **No zero divisors:**[4] If $a \cdot b = 0$, then either $a = 0$ or $b = 0$.

---

[1] "The primary source of all mathematics is the integers"-Herman Minkowski.

[2] Numbers in German is called 'Zählen', hence the symbol.

[3] These numbers are believed to be created naturally with the development of early human civilization, as an abstraction of the process of counting tangible objects. Kronecker once remarked "God created the natural numbers; everything else is man's handiwork."

[4] The term *zero divisors* is a jargon about which you will come to know in greater details in the chapter on Ring in Definition 12.2.1.

2.1   Divisibility

The following theorem on integers can be proved using the aforesaid basic properties.

Theorem 2.1.1. *(i) Let a, b and c be integers. Then (a) $b + a = c + a$ implies $b = c$ and (b) $a + b = a + c$ implies $b = c$.*

  (ii) For any integer a, $a \cdot 0 = 0 \cdot a = 0$.

  (iii) For any integer a, $-(-a) = a$.

Proof. (i)   (a) : Suppose a, b and c are integers such that $b + a = c + a$. Then,
$$(b + a) - a = (c + a) - a,$$
  i.e., $b + (a - a) = c + (a - a)$ (by associative law)

  i.e., $b + 0 = c + 0$ (by additive inverse law)

  i.e., $b = c$ (since 0 is an additive identity).

  Hence $b + a = c + a$ implies that $b = c$.

  (b)   Suppose $a + b = a + c$. Then by commutative law, $b + a = c + a$. Hence from i(a) above, we find that $b = c$.

  (ii)   For any integer a,
$$a \cdot 0 + 0 = a \cdot 0,$$ (since 0 is additive identity)

  i.e., $a \cdot 0 + 0 = a \cdot (0 + 0)$ (since 0 is additive identity)

  i.e., $a \cdot 0 + 0 = a \cdot 0 + a \cdot 0$ (by distributive law).

  Hence from (i), $a \cdot 0 = 0$. Now by commutative law, $0 \cdot a = 0$.

  (iii)   From the inverse property, we find $a + (-a) = 0$. Hence by commutative property, $(-a) + a = 0$. But $(-a) + (-(-a)) = 0$. Hence by (i), $-(-a) = a$.   □

Definition 2.1.2. Let a and b be any two integers. a is said to be **greater than** b, denoted by $a > b$, if $a - b$ is a positive integer. If $a > b$, one may also write $b < a$.

Theorem 2.1.3. *Let a and b be any two integers such that $a > b$. Then*
(i) $a + c > b + c$ for any integer c, and
(ii) $ad > bd$, for any positive integer d.

Proof. Left as an exercise.   □

Theorem 2.1.4. (Cancellation law) *If a, b, c are integers such that $a \neq 0$ and $a \cdot b = a \cdot c$, then $b = c$.*

Proof. Suppose that $a \neq 0$ and $a \cdot b = a \cdot c$. We show that both $b > c$ and $b < c$ can be ruled out. Indeed, if $b > c$, then $b = c + k$, for some $k(\neq 0) \in \mathbb{Z}$, whence $a \cdot (c + k) = a \cdot c$ implies $a \cdot k = 0$, (by distributive law and Theorem 2.1.1 (i)), whence by non existence of zero divisors in $\mathbb{Z}$, either $a = 0$ or $k = 0$, each of which is a contradiction. The other case is similar. $\square$

Now we assume a property of $\mathbb{Z}$ which is intuitively clear, as a basic axiom.

Well-ordering Axiom (Principle of well-ordering): Any nonempty subset of non-negative integers has a least element, i.e., if S is a nonempty set of nonnegative integers, then there exists $n \in S$ such that $n \leq m$ for all $m \in S$.

Using this axiom, we now prove the following theorem:

Theorem 2.1.5. (The Division Algorithm) *Let a and $b(\geq 1)$ be integers; then there exist unique integers q and r such that $a = qb + r$ with $0 \leq r < b$.*

Proof. Consider the set

$$S = \{a - tb \mid t \in Z, a - tb \geq 0\}.$$

We show that S is nonempty. In fact, if $a \geq 0$, then $a = a - 0b \geq 0$ shows that a is in S and if $a < 0$, then $a - ab = a(1 - b) \geq 0$, whence $a - ab \in S$. It follows that S is a nonempty set of nonnegative integers. Hence by well-ordering principle, S has a least element, say r. Then $r = a - qb$ for some integer q. So we find that $a = qb + r$ such that $r \geq 0$. It remains to show that $r < b$. If $r \geq b$, then $a - (q+1)b = (a - qb) - b \geq 0$ shows that $a - (q+1)b \in S$, i.e., $r - b \in S$. But $r - b < r$, which contradicts the choice of r as the least element of S. Hence $r < b$.

To show the uniqueness of q and r, suppose that there exist integers q_1, q_2, r_1, r_2 such that $a = q_1 b + r_1, a = q_2 b + r_2$ and $0 \leq r_1 < b, 0 \leq r_2 < b$. Then $q_1 b + r_1 = q_2 b + r_2$ which implies that $(q_1 - q_2)b = r_2 - r_1$. This implies that b divides $r_2 - r_1$. But $-b < r_2 - r_1 < b$. Hence $r_2 - r_1 = 0$. So we find that $r_2 = r_1$. Then $q_1 b + r_1 = q_2 b + r_2$ implies that $(q_1 - q_2)b = 0$. Since $b > 0$, it follows that $q_1 = q_2$. $\square$

Corollary 2.1.6. *If a and b be two integers with $b \neq 0$, then there exist unique integers q and r such that $a = qb + r$ where $0 \leq r < |b|$.*

Proof. **Case I**: Suppose $b > 0$. In this case, the corollary follows from Theorem 2.1.5 above.

Case II: Suppose $b < 0$. Then $|b| = -b > 0$. Hence from the above Theorem 2.1.5, it follows that there exist unique integers q_1 and r such that $a = q_1(-b) + r$ and $0 \leq r < |b|$. Let $-q_1 = q$. Hence there exist unique integers q and r such that $a = qb + r$, where $0 \leq r < |b|$. $\square$

Definition 2.1.7. Let a and b be two integers such that $a \neq 0$. If there exists an integer c such that $b = ac$, then a is said to **divide** b or a is said to be a **divisor** of b and we write $a \mid b$.

Whenever we write $a \mid b$, we mean $a \neq 0$ and a divides b. The notation $a \nmid b$ means that a does not divide b. Clearly, $1 \mid a$ and if $b \neq 0$, then $b \mid 0$ and $b \mid b$. In the following theorem, we enlist some basic properties of divisibility:

Theorem 2.1.8. *Let* a, b, c *be integers such that* $a \neq 0$, $b \neq 0$.

(i)   *If* $a \mid b$, $b \mid c$, *then* $a \mid c$.

(ii)   *If* $b \mid a$, $c \neq 0$, *then* $cb \mid ca$.

(iii) *If* $a \mid b$ *and* $a \mid c$, *then* $a \mid (bx + cy)$ *for any integers* x, y.

(iv)   *If* $a \mid b$ *and* $b \mid a$, *then* $a = \pm b$.

Proof. (i)   If $a \mid b$ and $b \mid c$, then there exist integers m and n such that $b = na$ and $c = mb$. Hence $c = mb = m(na) = (mn)a$. This implies that $a \mid c$.

(ii)   The proof is left to the reader.

(iii) Suppose $a \mid b$ and $a \mid c$. Then there exist integers n and m such that $b = an$ and $c = am$. Hence $bx + cy = anx + amy = a(nx + my)$, and this implies that a divides $bx + cy$.

(iv)   Suppose $a \mid b$ and $b \mid a$. Then there exist integers m and n such that $b = ma$ and $a = nb$, Then $a = nma$. This implies that $nm = 1$. As m and n are integers, we conclude that either $n = m = 1$ or $n = m = -1$ and so $a = b$ or $a = -b$. $\square$

Definition 2.1.9. A nonzero integer d is said to be a **common divisor** of integers m and n if $d \mid m$ and $d \mid n$. A nonzero integer d is said to be a **greatest common divisor** of m and n if

(i) d is a common divisor of m and n and

(ii)   if c is a common divisor of m and n, then c is a divisor of d.

Let d and d_1 be the two greatest common divisors of integers m and n. Then from (ii) of Definition 2.1.9, we find that $d \mid d_1$ and $d_1 \mid d$. Hence from Theorem 2.1.8 (iv), $d = \pm d_1$. So it follows that two different gcd's of m and n, differ in their sign only. Of the two gcd's of m and n, the positive one is denoted by $gcd(m, n)$. For example, 4 and -4 are the gcd's of 8 and 12. But we write $gcd(8, 12) = 4$. In the next theorem, we show using the well-ordering principle that gcd of two integers, which are not both zero, exists.

Theorem 2.1.10. [**Bézout's Identity**] *Let m and n be integers, not both zero. Then $gcd(m, n)$ exists and if $d = gcd(m, n)$, then there exist integers s and t such that $d = sm + tn$.*

Proof. Let $S = \{km + ln \mid l, k \in \mathbb{Z} \text{ and } km + ln \geq 1\}$. Since m and n are not both zero, $m^2 + n^2 \geq 1$ and hence $m^2 + n^2 \in S$. Thus we see that S is nonempty, so by the well-ordering principle, S has a smallest element, say d. Then $1 \leq d \leq x$ for any $x \in S$ and $d = sm + tn$ for some integers s and t. The equality $d = sm + tn$ implies that any common divisor of m and n is also a divisor of d. It remains to show that $d \mid m$ and $d \mid n$. By division algorithm, (see Theorem 2.1.5) there exist integers q and r such that $m = qd + r$ and $0 \leq r < d$. Then,

$$r = m - qd = m - q(sm + tn) = (1 - qs)m + (-qt)n.$$

If $r > 0$, then $r \in S$, contradicting the fact that d is the smallest integer in S. Hence $r = 0$. Thus we find that d divides m. Similarly it can be shown that d divides n. Hence $d = gcd(m, n)$. $\square$

The above theorem proves that for any two integers m, n which are not both zero, there exists $gcd(m, n)$. But how do we compute $gcd(a, b)$ in general? There is an efficient procedure for computing $gcd(a, b)$. Towards this, we first prove the following lemma:

Lemma 2.1.11. *If m and n are two positive integers and $m = qn + r$, $0 \leq r < n$, then $gcd(m, n) = gcd(n, r)$.*

Proof. Let $d = gcd(m, n)$ and $e = gcd(n, r)$. Then d divides m and d divides n. Hence d divides qn, which implies that d divides $m - qn = r$. So d is a common divisor of n and r and hence d divides e. Similarly we can show that e divides d. Now d and e are positive integers. Consequently, $d = e$. $\square$

We now describe the procedure for computing $d = gcd(m, n)$, often referred to as ***Euclidean algorithm***; in addition, we describe how to express d in the form $d = sm + nt$. This procedure is known as ***extended Euclidean algorithm***[5].

---

[5]The present day algorithm for finding GCD of two integers by division is known as **Euclid's algorithm**, though Euclid described it by successive subtraction, as it is found in the 7th volume of his compiled book *Elements*(c.300 BC). The so called extended Euclidean algorithm has got nothing to do with Euclid historically and it was first published by N. Saunderson (1682-1739), who attributed the result to Roger Cotes(1682-1716). Amazingly, it is found in Āryabhaṭiya, the works of Indian mathematician-astronomer Āryabhaṭa (476-550 A.D.), whose commentator Bhaskara I (c.600-680) gave the detailed algorithm and called it 'kuṭṭaka', which means 'pulverization'.

Consider two positive integers a and b. By division algorithm, there exist integers q_1 and r_1 such that $a = q_1 b + r_1$, $0 \le r_1 < b$. If $r_1 \neq 0$, then by division algorithm there exist integers q_2 and r_2 such that $b = q_2 r_1 + r_2$, $0 \le r_2 < r_1$. If $r_2 \neq 0$, we repeat the process. Hence by repeated use of division algorithm, we have the following:

$$a = q_1 b + r_1, \qquad 0 \le r_1 < b;$$
$$\text{if } 0 < r_1, \quad b = q_2 r_1 + r_2, \quad 0 \le r_2 < r_1;$$
$$\text{if } 0 < r_2, \quad r_1 = q_3 r_2 + r_3, \quad 0 \le r_3 < r_2;$$
$$\text{if } 0 < r_3, \quad r_2 = q_4 r_3 + r_4, \quad 0 \le r_4 < r_3;$$
$$\cdots\cdots \qquad \cdots\cdots\cdots \qquad \cdots\cdots\cdots$$
$$\cdots\cdots \qquad \cdots\cdots\cdots \qquad \cdots\cdots\cdots$$

Now the remainders form a decreasing sequence of nonnegative integers $b > r_1 > r_2 > r_3 \ldots \ge 0$. Since b is a fixed positive integer, we must encounter the remainder 0 after a finite number of steps. Hence the process terminates after some steps. If this process terminates after $(k+1)$th step, then we get

$$0 < r_{k-1}, r_{k-2} = q_k r_{k-1} + r_k, 0 \le r_k < r_{k-1}$$

$$0 < r_k, \quad r_{k-1} = q_{k+1} r_k + 0.$$

Now the repeated application of the result of Lemma 2.1.11 gives

$$
\begin{aligned}
gcd(a,b) &= gcd(b, r_1) \\
&= gcd(r_1, r_2) \\
&= gcd(r_2, r_3) \\
&\quad\vdots \\
&= gcd(r_{k-1}, r_k).
\end{aligned}
$$

Since $r_{k-1} = q_{k+1} r_k$, it follows that $gcd(r_{k-1}, r_k) = r_k$. Hence $gcd(a,b) = r_k$.

We now find integers s and t such that

$$gcd(a,b) = sa + tb.$$

From above,

$$
\begin{aligned}
r_k &= r_{k-2} - q_k r_{k-1} \\
&= r_{k-2} + r_{k-1}(-q_k) \\
&= r_{k-2} + [r_{k-3} + r_{k-2}(-q_{k-1})](-q_k) \\
&= r_{k-2}[1 + q_{k-1} q_k] + r_{k-3}(-q_k).
\end{aligned}
$$

We now substitute $r_{k-4} + r_{k-3}(-q_{k-2})$ for r_{k-2}. We repeat this back substitution process until we reach $r_k = sa + tb$, where s and t are integers.

Finally we note that for any integers m and n which are not both zero, we can show that $gcd(m, n) = gcd(m, -n) = gcd(-m, n) = gcd(-m, -n)$. Moreover, $d = sm + tn = (-s)(-m) + tn = sm + (-t)(-n) = (-s)(-m) + (-t)(-n)$.

We illustrate the above procedure for finding the gcd and integers s and t by the following example:

Example 2.1.12. Consider the integers 475 and 120.

By repeated application of division algorithm, we get

$$
\begin{aligned}
475 &= 3.120 + 115 \\
120 &= 1.115 + 5 \\
115 &= 23.5 + 0
\end{aligned}
$$

Hence $gcd(475, 120) = 5$ and

$$
\begin{aligned}
5 &= 120 - 1.115 \\
&= 120 - 1.(475 - 3.120) \\
&= 120 + 3.120 + (-1)475 \\
&= (-1)475 + 4.120
\end{aligned}
$$

Definition 2.1.13. Two integers m and n such that $gcd(m, n) = 1$, are said to be *relatively prime*.

Example 2.1.14. The integers 7 and 20 are relatively prime. 1 is relatively prime to every integer n. Note that any prime integer is mutually prime to every other integer.

Theorem 2.1.15. *Let m and n be two integers not both zero, then m and n are relatively prime if $1 = rm + tn$ for some integers r and t.*

Proof. Suppose $gcd(m, n) = 1$. Then by extended Euclidean algorithm, there exist integers r and t such that $1 = rm + tn$.

Conversely, assume that $1 = rm + tn$ for some integers r and t. Let $d = gcd(m, n)$. Then $d \mid m$ and $d \mid n$. Hence $d \mid 1$. Since $d > 0$, it follows that $d = 1$, hence m and n are relatively prime. $\qquad \square$

Worked-out Exercises

◊ **Exercise 2.1.1.** Let a, b and c be three consecutive integers. Show that 3 divides one of these.

Solution. Since a, b and c are consecutive integers, there exists an integer n such that $a = n - 1$, $b = n$ and $c = n + 1$. By division algorithm, there exist integers q and r such that $n = 3q + r$ where $0 \leq r < 3$. If $r = 0$, then $b = 3q$ and hence $3 \mid b$. If $r = 1$, then $a = 3q$ which is divisible by 3. Finally, if $r = 2$, then $c = 3q + 2 + 1 = 3(q + 1)$ and hence $3 \mid c$. So we find that 3 divides one of a, b, c.

◊ **Exercise 2.1.2.** Let m, n and r be integers such that $m \neq 0$, $m \mid n$ and $m \mid n + r$. Then $m \mid r$.

Solution. There exist integers s and k such that $n = sm$ and $n + r = km$. Hence $sm + r = km$. This implies that $(k - s)m = r$. Hence $m \mid r$.

◊ **Exercise 2.1.3.** For any integer n, show that $3n + 1$ and $13n + 4$ are relatively prime.

Solution. Let $gcd(3n + 1, 13n + 4) = d$. Then $d \mid 3n + 1$ and $d \mid 13n + 4$. Now $13n + 4 = 4(3n + 1) + n$ implies that $d \mid n$. Then from $d \mid 3n + 1$ and $d \mid n$ we find that $d = 1$. Hence $3n + 1$ and $13n + 4$ are relatively prime.

◊ **Exercise 2.1.4.** Let m, n, r and t be integers such that $(m - r)$ divides $mn + rt$. Then prove that $m - r$ divides $mt + nr$.

Solution. $(mt + nr) - (mn + rt) = (m - r)t - (m - r)n = (m - r)(t - n)$. This implies that $m - r$ divides $(mt + nr) - (mn + rt)$. But $m - r$ divides $mn + rt$. Hence $m - r$ divides $mt + nr$.

◊ **Exercise 2.1.5.** Let m, n be two integers not both zero. Prove that $gcd(km, kn) = k \cdot gcd(m, n)$ for any positive integer k.

Solution. Let $gcd(m, n) = d_1$, $gcd(km, kn) = d_2$. Then there exist integers s and t such that $d_1 = ms + nt$. Then $kd_1 = kms + knt$. Now d_2 divides km and kn. Hence d_2 divides $kms + knt$, i.e., d_2 divides kd_1. On the other hand, d_1 divides m and n; hence kd_1 divides km and kn. But d_2 is the gcd of km and kn. Consequently, kd_1 divides d_2. Hence $gcd(km, kn) = d_2 = kd_1 = k \cdot gcd(m, n)$.

◊ **Exercise 2.1.6.** If a, b and c are integers such that $gcd(a, b) = 1$ and $gcd(a, c) = 1$, then prove that $gcd(a, bc) = 1$.

Solution. There exist integers p, q, r and s such that $ap + bq = 1$ and $ar + cs = 1$. Hence $(ap + bq)(ar + cs) = 1$. Then,

$$apar + apcs + bqar + bqcs = 1,$$
$$\text{i.e., } a(par + pcs + bqr) + bc(qs) = 1.$$

Hence there exist integers x and y such that $ax + bcy = 1$. This implies that $gcd(a, bc) = 1$.

◊ **Exercise 2.1.7.** If a, b and c are integers such that $a \neq 0$ and $gcd(a, bc) = 1$, then prove that $gcd(a, b) = 1 = gcd(a, c)$.

Solution. Since $gcd(a, bc) = 1$, there exist integers s and t such that $as + bct = 1$. Hence $as + b(ct) = 1$. This shows that $gcd(a, b) = 1$. Similarly, $gcd(a, c) = 1$.

◊ **Exercise 2.1.8.** Show that $gcd(a^2, b^2) = \left(gcd(a, b)\right)^2$ for positive integers a, b.

Solution. Let $d = gcd(a, b)$. Then $gcd\left(\frac{a}{d}, \frac{b}{d}\right) = 1$. Then, $gcd\left(\frac{a^2}{d^2}, \frac{b}{d}\right) = 1$, by Worked-out Exercise 2.1.6. Again applying the same exercise, we have

$$gcd\left(\frac{a^2}{d^2}, \frac{b^2}{d^2}\right) = 1.$$

Now,

$$
\begin{aligned}
gcd(a^2, b^2) &= gcd\left(d^2 \frac{a^2}{d^2}, d^2 \frac{b^2}{d^2}\right) \\
&= d^2 \, gcd\left(\frac{a^2}{d^2}, \frac{b^2}{d^2}\right) \quad \text{[by Worked-out Exercise 2.1.5]} \\
&= d^2 \\
&= \left(gcd(a, b)\right)^2.
\end{aligned}
$$

◊ **Exercise 2.1.9.** Find gcd of 615 and 1080 and find integers s and t such that $gcd(615, 1080) = 615s + 1080t$.

Solution. By division algorithm we get,

$$
\begin{aligned}
1080 &= 1 \cdot 615 + 465 \\
615 &= 1 \cdot 465 + 150 \\
465 &= 3 \cdot 150 + 15 \\
150 &= 10 \cdot 15
\end{aligned}
$$

Hence $gcd(615, 1080) = 15$.

Now,

$$
\begin{aligned}
15 &= 465 - 3 \cdot 150 \\
&= 465 - 3 \cdot (615 - 1 \cdot 465) \\
&= 4 \cdot 465 - 3 \cdot 615 \\
&= 4 \cdot (1080 - 1 \cdot 615) - 3 \cdot 615 \\
&= 615(-7) + 1080(4)
\end{aligned}
$$

This shows that $s = -7$ and $t = 4$.

Exercises

1. For any integer n, prove that
   (i) 3 divides one of the integers $n, n+1, 2n+1$.
   (ii) 3 divides one of $n, n+2, n+4$.

2. Show that for any integer n, $5 \mid (n^5 - n)$ and $3 \mid (n^5 - n)$.

3. Let a, b, c and d be integers such that $a \neq 0$, $b \neq 0$. Prove the following:
   (i) If $a \mid b$, then $a \mid bc$.
   (ii) If $a \mid b$ and $a \mid c$, then $a^2 \mid bc$.
   (iii) $a \mid b$ if and only if $ac \mid bc$, where $c \neq 0$.
   (iv) If $a > 0, b > 0$ with $a \mid b$ and $b \mid a$, then $a = b$.
   (v) If $a \mid c$ and $b \mid d$, then $ab \mid cd$.

4. If m and n are two integers such that $m \neq 0$ and $m \mid n$, then prove that $m^k \mid n^k$ for any positive integer k.

5. Let a, b be integers not both zero.
   (i) If $gcd(a, b) = 1$, then prove that $gcd(a+b, a-b) = 1$ or 2.
   (ii) If $gcd(a, 4) = 2 = gcd(b, 4)$, prove that $gcd(a+b, 4) = 4$.
   (iii) Prove that $gcd(a, b) = gcd(a, b+ac)$, for any integer c.

6. If d is a positive integer such that $d \mid 13n+6, d \mid 12n+5$ for some integer n, then $d = 1$ or 7.

7. Let m and n be integers not both zero and $gcd(m, n) = d$. Prove that the integers $\frac{m}{d}$ and $\frac{n}{d}$ are relatively prime.

8. If m, n, p and q are positive integers such that $m \mid p$ and $n \mid q$, then prove that $gcd(m, n)$ divides $gcd(p, q)$.

9. For any integer n, show that $2n+1$ and $13n+6$ are relatively prime.

10. If a, b are two integers such that a and b are relatively prime, then prove that a^2 and b^2 are relatively prime.

11. Find the gcd of the integers 4235 and 315 and find s and t such that $gcd(4235, 315) = 4235s + 315t$.

12. Find the $gcd(360, 125)$ and express it in the form $360s + 125t$, where s and t are integers.

13. † If n is a positive integer greater than 1, then prove that $1 + \frac{1}{2} + \frac{1}{3} + \ldots + \frac{1}{n}$ is not an integer.

14. Let a, b and c be three positive integers. Prove that $gcd\left(a^b - 1, a^c - 1\right) = a^{gcd\,(b,c)} - 1$.

15. † If $a_n = n^2 + 20$, $d_n = gcd\left(a_n, a_{n+1}\right)$, for all $n \in \mathbb{N}$ then prove that $d_n \mid 81$.

2.2 Mathematical Induction

Suppose we are asked to prove

$$1^2 + 2^2 + 3^2 + \ldots + n^2 = \frac{n(n + 1)(2n + 1)}{6} \tag{2.2.1}$$

for all positive integers n. We denote this mathematical statement by $P(n)$. If $n = 1$, then we find that $\frac{1(1+1)(2.1+1)}{6} = \frac{6}{6} = 1^2$. Hence the above statement is true for $n = 1$. Suppose $n = 2$. Then $1^2 + 2^2 = 5$ and $\frac{2(2+1)(2.2+1)}{6} = 5$. So we find that the statement is true for $n = 2$. Thus, it is not difficult to verify that $P(n)$ is true for $n = 1, 2, 3$ or 4. But it is not possible to verify that the above statement is true for *all* positive integers. To prove that the above statement $P(n)$ is true for all positive integers, we generally follow a method of proof, which is known as proof by the *principle of mathematical induction* or simply proof by mathematical induction. For this we *assume* the following important property of integers.

Principle of Mathematical Induction : Let $P(n)$ be a mathematical statement about nonnegative integer n and n_0 be a fixed nonnegative integer.

(1)   Suppose $P(n_0)$ is true (i.e., $P(n)$ is true for $n = n_0$).

(2)   Whenever k is an integer such that $k \geq n_0$ and $P(k)$ is true, then $P(k+1)$ is true.

Then $P(n)$ is true for all integers $n \geq n_0$.

Note that the above property of integers is also called the *first principle of mathematical induction*. We now show the proof of (2.2.1) for all integers $n \geq 1$, by the principle of mathematical induction.

Let $P(n)$ denote the statement (2.2.1), for all integers $n \geq 1$. For $n = 1$, we have already seen that $P(1)$ is true. Let k be an integer such that $k \geq 1$. Assume that $P(k)$ is true.

Now,

$$1^2 + 2^2 + 3^2 + \ldots + k^2 + (k+1)^2$$
$$= \quad (1^2 + 2^2 + 3^2 + \ldots + k^2) + (k+1)^2$$
$$= \quad (k+1)\left(\frac{k(2k+1)}{6} + (k+1)\right) \qquad \text{(since } P(k) \text{ is true)}$$

$$= \quad (k+1)\left(\frac{2k^2 + 7k + 6}{6}\right)$$

$$= \quad \frac{(k+1)(k+2)(2k+3)}{6}.$$

Thus we find that $P(k+1)$ is true. Hence by the principle of mathematical induction, it follows that $P(n)$ is true for all integers $n \geq 1$. □

From the above proof, we find that a proof of some mathematical statement by the principle of mathematical induction consists of three steps.

Step 1. (*Basis step*) To show that $P(n_0)$ is true.

Step 2. (*Inductive hypothesis*) To write the inductive hypothesis : Let k be an integer such that $k \geq n_0$ and $P(k)$ is true.

Step 3. (*Inductive step*) To show that $P(k+1)$ is true.

We have an equivalent statement of the principle of mathematical induction which is often very useful. This equivalent statement is called *strong* induction or the second principle of mathematical induction, in contrast with the previous one, which is often referred to as *weak* induction.

Second Principle of Mathematical Induction : Let $P(n)$ be a mathematical statement about nonnegative integers n and n_0 be a fixed nonnegative integer. Suppose $P(n_0)$ is true. If for any integer $k \geq n_0$, '$P(n_0), P(n_0+1), P(n_0+2), \ldots, P(k)$ are true' implies that '$P(k+1)$ is true', then $P(n)$ is true for all $n \geq n_0$.

Though the nomenclatures seem to suggest otherwise, it can be proved that *the first principle of mathematical induction (i.e. weak induction) holds if and only if the second principle of mathematical induction (strong induction) holds.*

Let us now show some applications of this principle. For this we consider the *Fibonacci sequence*[6] $f_1, f_2, f_3, \ldots$, where $f_1 = 1, f_2 = 1$ and $f_n = f_{n-1} + f_{n-2}$ for $n \geq 3$.

---

[6]It is named after the Italian mathematician Leonardo Pisano (1175-1250 A.D.), who was a son of certain Bonaccio, and hence nicknamed Fibonacci. Through his book Liber Abaci (1202 A.D.), Europe came to know about the decimal place-value system with 0 and other Hindu-Arabic numerals. Amazingly, this sequence was known to Indians earlier through a Sanskrit work regarding patterns of one-bit and two-bit notes in music by a Jain scholar Hemachandra (c.1150 A.D.). Interested readers may watch the Youtube video of Fields Medalist Prof. Manjul Bhargava in this regard.

Then

$$f_3 = f_1 + f_2 = 1 + 1 = 2,$$
$$f_4 = f_2 + f_3 = 1 + 2 = 3,$$
$$f_5 = f_3 + f_4 = 2 + 3 = 5,$$
$$f_6 = f_4 + f_5 = 3 + 5 = 8, \quad \text{and so on.}$$

Example 2.2.1. We now show by strong induction that

$$f_n \geq u^{n-2} \text{ for } n \geq 3, \quad \text{where } u = \frac{1 + \sqrt{5}}{2}$$

and (f_n) is the Fibonacci sequence. Let $P(n)$ be the statement

$$f_n \geq u^{n-2} \text{ for } n \geq 3, \quad \text{where } u = \frac{1 + \sqrt{5}}{2}.$$

Basis step. For $n = 3$, we have $u = \frac{1+\sqrt{5}}{2} < 2$ and $f_3 = 2$ and hence $f_3 \geq u^{3-2}$.

Inductive hypothesis. Assume that $P(n)$ is true for all n such that $3 \leq n < k$, where k is a positive integer.

Inductive step. In this step we show that $P(k)$ is true. Now $u = \frac{1+\sqrt{5}}{2}$ shows that u is a solution of $x^2 - x - 1 = 0$. Then $u^2 = u + 1$. Hence,

$$
\begin{aligned}
u^{k-2} &= u^2 \cdot u^{k-4} \\
&= (u + 1) \cdot u^{k-4} \\
&= u^{k-3} + u^{k-4} \\
&\leq f_{k-1} + f_{k-2} \quad \text{(by inductive hypothesis).}
\end{aligned}
$$

But $f_{k-1} + f_{k-2} = f_k$ for $k \geq 3$. Hence $f_k \geq u^{k-2}$. Consequently, from the second principle of induction, it follows that $f_n \geq u^{n-2}$ for all $n \geq 3$.

Remark 2.2.2. Since the first and the second principles of mathematical induction are equivalent, we shall henceforth talk about mathematical induction only. We would like to point out here that either the principle of mathematical induction or the well-ordering principle can be proved as a theorem, given the other principle and properties of integers; in other words, we can say that these two principles are equivalent. Another point to be noted is that, it is not at all mandatory that the induction must begin from $n = 0$; indeed it can start from any $n \in \mathbb{N}$ (and for that matter, it's scope can be extended to begin from any $n \in \mathbb{Z}$ as well). However, its impact on the statement $P(n)$ must always be for all integers $\geq n$.

Worked-out Exercises

$\Diamond$ **Exercise 2.2.1.** Let A be a set with n elements. Show that the number of subsets of A is 2^n.

Solution. We prove it by induction on n.

Basis step. Suppose $n = 0$. Then A is empty and hence empty set is the only subset of A. We find that the number of subsets of A is $1 = 2^0$.

Inductive hypothesis. Let n be a positive integer. Suppose for any set A with m elements where $0 \leq m < n$, the number of subsets of A is 2^m.

Inductive step. Let A be a set with $n \geq 1$ elements. Since $n \geq 1$, A contains at least one element a. Let $B = A \setminus \{a\}$. Then the number of elements of B is $n - 1$. By inductive hypothesis, the number of subsets of B is 2^{n-1}. Let

$$T_1 = \{D \in \mathcal{P}(A) \,|\, a \notin D\}.$$

Now $T_1 = \mathcal{P}(B)$. Let

$$T_2 = \{D \in \mathcal{P}(A) \,|\, a \in D\}.$$

Then,

$$T_2 = \{D \in \mathcal{P}(A) \,|\, D \setminus \{a\} \in T_1\}.$$

Hence T_1 and T_2 have 2^{n-1} elements. Since

$$\mathcal{P}(A) = T_1 \cup T_2 \quad \text{and} \quad T_1 \cap T_2 = \emptyset,$$

we find that

$$|\mathcal{P}(A)| = |T_1| + |T_2| = 2^{n-1} + 2^{n-1} = 2 \cdot 2^{n-1} = 2^n.$$

Hence by mathematical induction, the result follows.

$\blacklozenge$ **Exercise 2.2.2.** Let S be a set containing n elements, where n is a positive integer. If r is an integer such that $0 \leq r \leq n$, then show that the number of subsets of S containing exactly r elements is

$$\frac{n!}{r! \, (n-r)!}.$$

Solution. We prove this by induction on n.

Let $P(n)$ be the statement : If S is a set containing $n (> 0)$ elements then the number of subsets of S containing exactly r elements $(0 \leq r \leq n)$ is $\frac{n!}{r! \, (n-r)!}$.

Basis step. Suppose $n = 1$. Then S has only one element, say a. Then $\emptyset$ and $\{a\}$ are the only subsets of S. Hence if $r = 0$, then $\emptyset$ is the only subset with 0 element. Hence,

$$1 = \frac{1!}{0!\,(1-0)!}.$$

Again for $r = 1$, $\{a\}$ is the only subset with 1 element. So,

$$1 = \frac{1!}{1!\,(1-1)!}.$$

Hence we see that the statement is true for $n = 1$.

Inductive hypothesis. Suppose k is a positive integer. Assume that $P(k)$ holds for any set with k elements.

Inductive step. Let S be a set with $k + 1(k \geq 1)$ elements, say $S = \{a_1, a_2, \ldots, a_n, a_{k+1}\}$. We now find the number of subsets of S containing exactly r elements where $0 \leq r \leq k + 1$. If $r = 0$, then the empty set $\emptyset$ is the only subset with zero element and for $r = k + 1$, the set S is the only subset with $k + 1$ elements. In both these cases, $P(k+1)$ holds, since

$$1 = \frac{(k+1)!}{0!\left((k+1) - 0\right)!} \quad \text{and} \quad 1 = \frac{(k+1)!}{(k+1)!\,(k+1-k-1)!}.$$

Now, let A be any subset with exactly r elements, where $0 < r < k + 1$. There are two cases to consider.

Case 1. $a_{k+1} \notin A$. In this case, A is a subset of $\{a_1, a_2, \ldots, a_k\}$ with r elements. By inductive hypothesis, the number of such subsets is

$$\frac{k!}{r!\,(k-r)!}.$$

Case 2. $a_{k+1} \in A$. In this case, if we remove a_{k+1} from A, then $A \setminus \{a_{k+1}\}$ is a subset of $\{a_1, a_2, \ldots, a_k\}$ with $r - 1$ elements. By inductive hypothesis, there are

$$\frac{k!}{(r-1)!\left(k - (r-1)\right)!}$$

subsets like this. Now from case 1 and case 2, we find that the total number of subsets A of S with r elements is

$$\frac{k!}{r!\,(k-r)!} + \frac{k!}{(r-1)!\,(k-r+1)!} = \frac{k!(k-r+1) + k!\,r}{r!\,(k-r+1)!} = \frac{(k+1)!}{r!\,(k+1-r)!}.$$

Hence $P(k+1)$ holds for any set with $(k+1)$ elements. This completes the induction.

Exercises

1. Use mathematical induction to prove the following:

   (a) $1 \mid (13^n - 1)$ for all positive integers n.

   (b) $4 \mid 6 \cdot 7^n + 2 \cdot 3^n$ for all nonnegative integers n.

   (c) $8 \mid 7^n + 3^n - 2$ for all positive integers n.

   (d) $4 \mid 5^n + 3$ for all integers $n \geq 0$.

   (e) $7 \mid 3^{2n+1} + 2^{n+2}$ for any positive integer n.

2. Use mathematical induction to prove the following:

   (a) $1 + 2 + 3 + \ldots + n = \frac{n(n+1)}{2}$ for all positive integers n.

   (b) $1^3 + 2^3 + 3^3 + \ldots + n^3 = \left(\frac{n(n+1)}{2}\right)^2$ for all positive integers n.

   (c) $1 \cdot 2 + 2 \cdot 3 + 3 \cdot 4 + \ldots + n(n+1) = \frac{n(n+1)(n+2)}{3}$ for any positive integer n.

   (d) $1^2 - 2^2 + 3^2 - \ldots + (-1)^{n-1}n^2 = (-1)^{n-1}\frac{n(n+1)}{2}$ for any positive integer n.

   (e) $1 + 3 + 5 + \ldots + (2n - 1) = n^2$ for any positive integer n.

   (f) $1(1!) + 2(2!) + \ldots + n(n!) = (n+1)! - 1$ for all positive integers n.

3. Prove the following inequalities by induction on n:

   (a) $3^n < n!$ for all integers $n \geq 7$.

   (b) $n < 2^n$ for all integers $n \geq 0$.

   (c) $\frac{1}{1^2} + \frac{1}{2^2} + \ldots + \frac{1}{n^2} \leq 2 - \frac{1}{n}$ for all positive integers n.

   (d) $n^2 < n!$ for all integers $n \geq 4$.

   (e) $2^{n+1} < 1 + (n+1)2^n$ for all integers $n \geq 1$.

   (f) $n^2 < 2^n$ for all integers $n \geq 5$.

4. Show that $9^n - 8n - 1$ is divisible by 64, for all integers $n \geq 0$.

5. If a and r are real numbers such that $r \neq 1$, then prove by induction on n that

$$a + ar + ar^2 + \ldots + ar^n = \frac{ar^{n+1} - a}{r - 1}$$

   for all integers $n \geq 1$.

6. † If n straight lines are drawn on a plane such that no two are parallel and no three pass through the same point, then prove by induction that these n straight lines divide the plane into $\frac{1}{2}(n^2 + n + 2)$ distinct regions.

2.3   Prime Numbers

Among the positive integers $1, 2, 3, 4, 5, 6, \ldots$, some integers have only two positive divisors and the others (except 1) have more than two. The integer 1 has just one positive divisor.

Definition 2.3.1. An integer $p > 1$ is called a ***prime number*** or simply a prime if the only positive divisors of p are 1 and p. An integer $q > 1$ which is not a prime is called ***composite***.

The integers $2, 3, 5, 7$ are all prime numbers and the integers $4, 6, 8, 9$ are composite. Among all even integers, only 2 is prime and all others are composite.

Theorem 2.3.2. *An integer $p > 1$ is a prime number if and only if p divides ab implies, either p divides a or p divides b, where a, b are any two integers.*

Proof. Suppose p is a prime and a, b are two integers such that $p \mid ab$. If p divides a, then we are done. Assume that $p \nmid a$. Since only positive divisors of p are 1 and p, it follows that $gcd(p, a) = 1$. Hence there exist integers r and t such that $1 = rp + ta$. Then $b = brp + tab$. Now p divides brp and p divides $t(ab)$. Hence p divides b.

Conversely, suppose that the integer p satisfies the condition. Let q be a positive divisor of p such that $q < p$. There exists an integer r such that $p = qr$. Since p divides p, we find that p divides qr. Hence either p divides q or p divides r. Since $0 < q < p$, p does not divide q. Therefore, p divides r. Then $r = pt$ for some integer t. Hence $p = qr = qpt$. This implies $qt = 1$. Hence $q = 1$. So we conclude that 1 and p are the only positive divisors of p. Hence p is prime. $\square$

Corollary 2.3.3. *Let p be a prime number. For any integer $n \geq 2$, if p divides $a_1 a_2 \ldots a_n$, then p divides one of the integers $a_1, a_2, \ldots, a_n$.*

Proof. We prove this result by induction on n. For $n = 2$, the result follows from Theorem 2.3.2. Suppose as induction hypothesis that for some positive integer $n \geq 2$, if p divides a product of n integers, then p divides at least one of these integers. Consider now the product $a_1 a_2 \ldots a_n a_{n+1}$ of $n+1$ integers and assume p divides $a_1 a_2 \ldots a_n a_{n+1}$. Then p divides $(a_1 a_2 \ldots a_n) a_{n+1}$. According to Theorem 2.3.2, either p divides $a_1 a_2 \ldots a_n$ or p divides a_{n+1}. If p divides $a_1 a_2 \ldots a_n$, then the induction hypothesis ensures that p divides one of $a_1, a_2, \ldots, a_n$. In any case, p divides one of $a_1, a_2, \ldots, a_n, a_{n+1}$. Hence by induction the result follows. $\sqcup$

Example 2.3.4. Consider the integer 6. Now 6 divides $20 \cdot 3$ but neither 20 nor 3 is divisible by 6. Hence 6 is not a prime.

Let us now consider the integers $20, 21, 23, 35$. Observe that $5 \mid 20$, $7 \mid 21$, $23 \mid 23$, $5 \mid 35$. So we find that each of these integers has a prime factor. We prove this fact for any integer $n \geq 2$.

Theorem 2.3.5. *Every integer $n \geq 2$ has a prime factor.*

Proof. We prove this result by the *second principle* of mathematical induction.

Basis step: For $n = 2$, note that 2 is a prime factor of itself. Hence the result holds for $n = 2$.

Induction hypothesis: Suppose n is a positive integer such that $n \geq 2$. Assume that each of the integers $2, 3, 4, \ldots, n - 1$ has a prime factor.

Induction step: Consider now the integer $n > 2$. If n is itself a prime, then n has a prime factor, which is itself. If n is composite, then there exist integers r and s such that $n = rs$, where $1 < r < n$ and $1 < s < n$. Then by induction hypothesis, r has a prime factor which is also a prime factor of n. So, by mathematical induction, every integer $n \geq 2$ has a prime factor. $\square$

The next theorem, which is more than two thousand years old, shows that the number of primes is not finite.[7] It was proved by Euclid (around 300 B.C.) and till date it is considered to be one of the most elegant proofs in mathematics that uses the method of *reductio ad absurdum* (i.e., the so called *method of negation*).

Theorem 2.3.6. *There are infinitely many primes.*

Proof. Assume on the contrary, that there are only finite number of distinct primes and let the number of primes be n. Further, let $p_1 = 2, p_2 = 3, p_3 = 5, p_4 = 7, \ldots, p_n$ be the complete list of all prime integers. Now let us consider the number $m = p_1 p_2 p_3 p_4 \cdots p_n + 1$. Obviously, $m > 1$. Then by Theorem 2.3.5, we see that m must have a prime factor, say p. Hence p must be one of $p_i, i = 1, 2, \ldots, n$. Then $p \mid p_1 p_2 p_3 \cdots p_n$ and $p \mid (p_1 p_2 p_3 \cdots p_n + 1)$ together imply that $p \mid 1$. There we arrive at a contradiction, since $p > 1$. Hence our initial assumption was wrong. So the number of primes cannot be finite. $\square$

Theorem 2.3.7. *Any composite integer n must have a prime factor less than or equal to $\sqrt{n}$.*

Proof. If n is composite, then there exist integers r and t such that $1 < r \leq t < n$ and $n = rt$. We must have $r \leq \sqrt{n}$. For if $r > \sqrt{n}$, then $t \geq r > \sqrt{n}$ implies that $n = rt > \sqrt{n}\sqrt{n} = n$ and this leads to a contradiction. From Theorem 2.3.5, we find that r has a prime factor p (say), which is also a prime factor of n. Clearly, $p \leq \sqrt{n}$. $\square$

---

[7]Number theory is one of the oldest areas of mathematics, and in a sense, the most fundamental. Numbers are universal building blocks of mathematics, yet many simple looking questions about them are still unsolved. A brief account of some interesting problems involving prime numbers are given in the Appendix C.

Given a particular integer, how can we determine whether it is prime or composite? We now give an algorithm[8] towards this determination.

Algorithm to test whether an integer $n > 1$ is a prime.

Step I. Check whether n is 2. If n is 2, n is prime; if not, go to step II.

Step II. Check whether 2 divides n. If 2 divides n, then n is not a prime. If 2 does not divide n, then go to step III.

Step III. Find all odd primes $p \leq \sqrt{n}$. If there is no such odd prime, then n is prime. Otherwise go to step IV.

Step IV. Check whether p divides n, where p is a prime obtained in step III. If p divides n, then n is not a prime. If p does not divide n for any prime p obtained in step III, then n is a prime.

Example 2.3.8. Consider the integer 137. Observe that 2 does not divide 137. We now find all odd primes p such that $p^2 \leq 137$. These primes are $3, 5, 7, 11$. Now none of $3, 5, 7, 11$ divide 137. Hence 137 is a prime.

Next consider the integer 287. The primes 2, 3, 5, 7, 11, 13 are the only primes p such that $p^2 \leq 287$. None of 2, 3, 5 divide 287. But 7 divides 287. Hence 287 is a composite integer.

We now show how to find all primes less than or equal to a fixed positive integer $n > 1$. Let us take $n = 100$. First we find all primes p such that $p^2 \leq 100$. These primes are $2, 3, 5, 7$. So to find all primes less than or equal to 100, we need only to find those numbers which are not divisible by 2,3,5 and 7. For this we go through the following steps:

Step I. List all integers from 2 to 100.

Step II. Cross out all multiples of 2 which are greater than 2 and less than 100.

Step III. Cross out those integers remaining in the list that are multiples of 3, other than 3.

Step IV. Cross out those integers remaining in the list that are multiples of 5, other than 5.

Step V. Cross out those integers remaining in the list that are multiples of 7, other than 7.

---

[8]An *algorithm* is a specified set of rules for obtaining a desired result from a set of inputs. The term has been derived out of the distorted name of the Arab mathematician **Al Khwarizmi** (c.780-850 A.D.), from the court of Abbasid Calip Al-Ma'mun. His book **Al-Jabr wa'l Muqabalah**, gave birth to the word *Algebra* during its Latinization in Europe.

All remaining integers in the list must be prime.[9]

The table below shows the result of this process. The multiples of 2 are crossed out by /, the multiples of 3 are crossed out by −, the multiples of 5 are crossed out by × and the multiples of 7 are crossed out by \.

$$
\begin{array}{cccccccccc}
2 & 3 & 4 & 5 & 6 & 7 & 8 & 9 & 10 \\
11 & 12 & 13 & 14 & 15 & 16 & 17 & 18 & 19 & 20 \\
21 & 22 & 23 & 24 & 25 & 26 & 27 & 28 & 29 & 30 \\
31 & 32 & 33 & 34 & 35 & 36 & 37 & 38 & 39 & 40 \\
41 & 42 & 43 & 44 & 45 & 46 & 47 & 48 & 49 & 50 \\
51 & 52 & 53 & 54 & 55 & 56 & 57 & 58 & 59 & 60 \\
61 & 62 & 63 & 64 & 65 & 66 & 67 & 68 & 69 & 70 \\
71 & 72 & 73 & 74 & 75 & 76 & 77 & 78 & 79 & 80 \\
81 & 82 & 83 & 84 & 85 & 86 & 87 & 88 & 89 & 90 \\
91 & 92 & 93 & 94 & 95 & 96 & 97 & 98 & 99 & 100
\end{array}
$$

The remaining integers are $2, 3, 5, 7, 11, 13, 17, 19, 23, 29, 31, 37, 41, 43, 47, 53, 59,$ $61, 67, 71, 73, 79, 83, 89, 97$. These are the prime numbers less than 100.

Though with the help of this process we can determine all primes less than or equal to a fixed positive integer $n > 1$, this process is neither suitable nor time efficient for large integers. There are better methods for finding out whether a given integer is prime or not. But these methods are out of scope of discussion of this book.

The following theorem has a far-reaching consequence in abstract algebra.

Theorem 2.3.9. [Fundamental Theorem of Arithmetic] *Every integer $n \geq 2$ can be expressed uniquely as a product of (one or more) primes, upto the order of the factors. More precisely, any integer $n \geq 2$ can be expressed as $n = p_1 p_2 \ldots p_r$ where $p_1, p_2, \ldots, p_r$ are primes. Moreover, if $n = p_1 p_2 \ldots p_t$ and $n = q_1 q_2 \ldots q_r$ be two factorizations of n as a product of primes, then $t = r$ and the primes q_j can be relabeled so that $p_i = q_i$ for all $i = 1, 2, \ldots, r$.*

Proof. Let $P(n)$: *every integer $n \geq 2$ can be expressed as a product of primes.* If $n = 2$, then $P(2)$ is true because 2 is a prime. Assume that k is a positive integer, $k \geq 2$ and

---

[9]This process of finding all primes less than a fixed number goes back to antiquity and is known as the *Sieve of Eratosthenes* after the Greek mathematician Eratosthenes (276 - 194 B.C.) from Alexandria. Amazingly, modern sieve theory, pioneered by the work of Goldston-Pintz-Yildirim (2005) and steered ahead during 2013-2014 by Yitang Zhang, Terrence Tao, James Maynard among others, happens to be one of the most powerful tools known till date to attack and tackle, if only partially, some of the most difficult problems in number theory, some of which are age old. See Appendix C for further information.

each of the integers $2, 3, 4, \ldots, k-1, k$ can be expressed as a product of primes. We now show that the integer $(k + 1)$ can be expressed as a product of primes. If $(k + 1)$ itself is a prime, then there is nothing to prove further; otherwise there exist integers r and s such that $k + 1 = rs$ where $2 \leq r \leq k$ and $2 \leq s \leq k$. Then by induction hypothesis, both r and s can be expressed as a product of primes. This completes induction. Hence any integer $n \geq 2$ can be expressed as a product of primes.

Now to show the *uniqueness of the representation* of n as a product of primes, we assume that n can be expressed as a product of primes in two ways; say,

$$n = p_1 p_2 \ldots p_t = q_1 q_2 \ldots q_r, \qquad (2.3.1)$$

where p_i and q_j are primes. Rearranging the prime factors of (2.3.1) if necessary, we assume that

$$p_1 \leq p_2 \leq \ldots \leq p_t \text{ and } q_1 \leq q_2 \leq \ldots \leq q_r.$$

Suppose $t < r$. Now p_1 divides n. Hence p_1 divides $q_1 q_2 \ldots q_r$. Then by Corollary 2.3.3, p_1 divides one of $q_1, q_2, \ldots, q_r$, say, p_1 divides q_k. But then $p_1 = q_k \geq q_1$ (as p_1 and q_k both are primes). Hence $p_1 \geq q_1$. Similarly, we can show that $q_1 \geq p_1$. Hence $p_1 = q_1$. We cancel this common factor from the equality (2.3.1) and obtain

$$p_2 p_3 \ldots p_t = q_2 q_3 \ldots q_r. \qquad (2.3.2)$$

We repeat the above process and obtain $p_2 = q_2$. Now cancel this factor from the equality (2.3.2) and write

$$p_3 p_4 \ldots p_t = q_3 q_4 \ldots q_r. \qquad (2.3.3)$$

Continuing this way, we obtain

$$1 = q_{t+1} q_{t+2} \ldots q_r$$

which is not true since $q_i > 1$, for all $i = t + 1, t + 2, \ldots, r$.

Hence $t \not< r$. Similarly we can show that $r \not< t$. Thus we find that $t = r$ and $p_1 = q_1, p_2 = q_2, \ldots, p_r = q_r$. So we conclude that n can be expressed as a product of primes uniquely.   □

Note.   Theorem 2.3.5 follows from the above theorem.

Remark 2.3.10. At the outset of this section we have clearly defined a prime number *as an integer greater than 1* as per the present tradition. Amazingly, for a very long period in the history of Mathematics, many great mathematicians till about the first quarter of 20th century used to consider 1 as a prime. It is worth pointing out that, while definition in Mathematics may be a matter of choice, yet they are never made at random. So, what ultimately motivated this paradigm shift? Indeed, an elementary reason is that the inclusion of 1 in the list of primes would jeopardize the much cherished 'uniqueness' in the factorization of integers via fundamental theorem.[10] For example, say 6 can then be written as 2×3 or as $2 \times 3 \times 1$ or for that matter, as $2 \times 3 \times 1^n$, for any positive integer n.

Worked-out Exercises

◇ **Exercise 2.3.1.** Determine which of the following integers are prime:
   (a) 293   (b) 493.

Solution. (a) We first find all primes p such that $p^2 \leq 293$. These primes are $2, 3, 5, 7, 11, 13, 17$. Now none of these primes divide 293. Hence 293 is a prime.

(b) We find all primes p such that $p^2 \leq 493$. These primes are $2, 3, 5, 7, 11, 13, 17$. None of $2, 3, 5, 7, 11, 13$ divide 493. But 17 divides 493. Hence 493 is not a prime.

◇ **Exercise 2.3.2.** Find all prime divisors of 50!

Solution. Since 50! is the product of all integers from 1 to 50, the prime divisors of 50! are those primes which are less than 50. Hence $2, 3, 5, 7, 11, 13, 17, 19, 23, 29, 31, 37, 41, 43, 47$ are the only prime divisors of 50!

◇ **Exercise 2.3.3.** Show that the number of primes of the form $4n + 3$ is infinite.

Solution. $3, 7, 11$ are primes of the form $4n + 3$. Suppose there exist only a finite number of primes of the form $4n + 3$. Let $p_1, p_2, p_3, \ldots, p_k$ be the complete list of all primes of the form $4n + 3$. Consider the integer, $m = 4p_1 p_2 \ldots p_k - 1$. Observe that none of the primes $p_1, p_2, p_3, \ldots, p_k$ and 2 divide m. Since $m > 1$, we find that m has an odd prime factor. Now any odd prime is either of the form $4n + 1$ or of the form $4n + 3$ (Justify!). Since the product of any two integers of the form $4n + 1$ is again an integer of the form $4n + 1$, it follows that all the prime factors of m cannot be of

---

[10]Of course there were much deeper reasons involved. From the structural perspectives of ring theory in abstract algebra, it was gradually appreciated that it is better to look at 1 in the ring of integers, not as a 'prime element', but rather as a 'unit' or an invertible element. This approach played an important role to segregate the concept of 'primality' from that of 'irreducibility' in certain classes of rings and ultimately forced the general acceptance of current definition of prime.

the form $4n + 1$. Hence, m has a prime factor of the form $4n + 3$ which must be one of $p_1, p_2, p_3, \ldots, p_k$. This contradicts that none of p_i divides m. Hence the number of primes of the form $4n + 3$ is infinite.

◊ **Exercise 2.3.4.** Justify that for any positive integer n, $f(n) = n^2 + n + 13$ may not always be prime.

Solution. Since $f(13) = 13^2 + 13 + 13 = 13(13 + 1 + 1) = 13 \cdot 15$, it follows that $f(13)$ is not a prime.

◊ **Exercise 2.3.5.** If n is a positive integer and $n^3 - 1$ is a prime, then prove that $n = 2$.

Solution. Suppose n is a positive integer and $n^3 - 1 = (n-1)(n^2 + n + 1)$. Since $n^3 - 1$ is prime, either $n - 1 = 1$ or, $n^2 + n + 1 = 1$. Since $n \geq 1$, so $n^2 + n + 1 \neq 1$. Hence $n - 1 = 1$. This implies that $n = 2$.

◊ **Exercise 2.3.6.** If $2^n - 1$ is a prime, then prove that n is also prime.

Solution. We prove this by contrapositive argument. Suppose that n is composite. Then there exist integers m, k such that $1 < m, k < n$ and $n = mk$.

Now,
$$2^n - 1 = 2^{mk} - 1 = (2^m - 1)(2^{m(k-1)} + 2^{m(k-2)} + \ldots + 2^m + 1).$$
Since $m > 1$, we find that $2^m - 1 > 1$; also $k > 1$, so we have

$$2^{m(k-1)} + 2^{m(k-2)} + \ldots + 2^m + 1 > 1.$$

Thus, $2^n - 1$ is expressed as the product of two integers both of which are greater than one. Hence $2^n - 1$ is not prime.

So we have proved that if n is not a prime (i.e., a composite), then $2^n - 1$ is also not a prime. Then by the contrapositive logic it follows that if $2^n - 1$ is a prime, then n is also a prime.

◊ **Exercise 2.3.7.** If p_n is the nth prime, then prove that

$$\frac{1}{p_1} + \frac{1}{p_2} + \ldots + \frac{1}{p_n}$$

is not an integer.

Solution. If p_i is the ith prime, where $1 \le i \le n-1$, then p_i divides $p_1 p_2 \cdots p_i \cdots p_{n-1}$.

Hence $\dfrac{p_1 p_2 \cdots p_i \cdots p_{n-1}}{p_i}$ is an integer. Suppose $\dfrac{1}{p_1} + \dfrac{1}{p_2} + \ldots + \dfrac{1}{p_n}$ is an integer. Let

$$\frac{1}{p_1} + \frac{1}{p_2} + \ldots + \frac{1}{p_n} = t.$$

Then,

$$p_1 p_2 \cdots p_{n-1} \left(\frac{1}{p_1} + \frac{1}{p_2} + \ldots + \frac{1}{p_{n-1}} \right) + \frac{p_1 p_2 \cdots p_{n-1}}{p_n} = p_1 p_2 \cdots p_{n-1} t. \quad \ldots (*)$$

Now,

$$p_1 p_2 \cdots p_{n-1} \left(\frac{1}{p_1} + \frac{1}{p_2} + \ldots + \frac{1}{p_{n-1}} \right)$$
$$= \left(\frac{p_1 p_2 \cdots p_{n-1}}{p_1} + \frac{p_1 p_2 \cdots p_{n-1}}{p_2} + \ldots + \frac{p_1 p_2 \cdots p_{n-1}}{p_{n-1}} \right)$$

is the sum of integers and hence an integer itself. Again R.H.S. of $(*)$ is an integer. So, it follows that $\dfrac{p_1 p_2 \cdots p_{n-1}}{p_n}$ is an integer. Hence p_n divides one of the $p_1, p_2, \ldots, p_{n-1}$. But for all $i = 1, 2, \ldots, n-1$, $p_i < p_n$. Hence p_n cannot divide p_i. Thus we arrive at a contradiction. Consequently,

$$\frac{1}{p_1} + \frac{1}{p_2} + \ldots + \frac{1}{p_n}$$

is not an integer.

Exercises

1. Determine which of the following integers are primes: (a) 287 (b) 1999 (c) 10933.

2. Find all prime numbers p such that $100 \le p \le 140$.

3. If p is a prime integer such that $p = n^2 - 9$ for some integer n, then show that $p = 7$.

4. If n is a positive integer such that $n^3 + 1$ is prime, then show that $n = 1$.

5. Find all prime factors of 30!

6. If $a > 0$, $n \ge 2$ are integers such that $a^n - 1$ is prime, then show that $a = 2$.

7. If p_n is the nth prime, prove that $p_{n+1} \le p_1 p_2 \cdots p_n + 1$ and hence show that $p_n \le 2^{2^{n-1}}$.

8. Let k be a positive integer. Prove that the following integers

$$(k+1)! + 2, \, (k+1)! + 3, \ldots, (k+1)! + k, (k+1)! + (k+1)$$

are k consecutive composite integers.

9. Find seven consecutive composite integers.

10. Prove that any prime p of the form $7k + 1$ is also of the form $14t + 1$.

11. Prove that there are infinitely many primes of the form $4n - 1$.

12. Let a, b be two integers such that $3 \mid a^2 + b^2$. Then prove that $3 \mid a$ and $3 \mid b$.

13. Let p be a prime number and a, b be any two integers such that $p^5 \mid a^2$ and $p^2 \mid a^7 + b^2$. Then show that $p \mid b$.

2.4 Linear Diophantine Equations

Diophantus of Alexandria (around A.D. 250) carried out extensive studies on problems relating to indeterminate equations, which are found in *Arithmetica*, six of the thirteen volumes of which still survive through Arabic translations. A *Diophantine equation* is an algebraic equation in one or more unknowns with *integer* coefficients, for which *integer* solutions are sought. Such an equation may have no solution, a finite number, or an infinite number of solutions[11]. It is worth pointing out that admissible solutions of a Diophantine equation must be integral.

In this section, we consider *linear* Diophantine equations only and discuss the necessary and sufficient conditions for such an equation to admit integral solutions.

Definition 2.4.1. A linear equation of the form $ax + by = c$, where a, b, c are integers and x, y are variables such that the solutions are restricted to integers, is called a ***linear Diophantine equation*** in two variables.

Let $ax + by = c$ be a linear Diophantine equation. If (x_0, y_0) be a pair of integers such that $ax_0 + by_0 = c$, then (x_0, y_0) is said to be an integral solution of this equation.

Consider the Diophantine equation $8x + 12y = 13$. Suppose this equation has a solution (x_0, y_0). Then $8x_0 + 12y_0 = 13$. Now 4 divides $8x_0 + 12y_0$. Hence 4 divides 13, which is not true. So we find that a Diophantine equation may not automatically have a solution. we merely state the next theorem which tells us when a Diophantine equation has a solution.

Theorem 2.4.2. *The linear Diophantine equation $ax + by = c$ with $a \neq 0, b \neq 0$ has a solution if and only if d divides c, where $d = \gcd(a, b)$. Moreover, if $x = x_0, y = y_0$ is a particular solution of this equation, then all integral solutions of this equation are given by*

$$x = x_0 + \frac{b}{d}n, \ y = y_0 - \frac{a}{d}n,$$

where n is any integer.

---

[11]In his famous address to the 1900 ICM (International Congress of Mathematicians) David Hilbert posed 23 problems of mathematics, the solutions to which, he believed were of utmost importance for future development of the subject. His tenth problem was to find whether there exists a general algorithm for testing a Diophantine equation for a solution. In 1970, Russian Mathematician Yuri Mattijasevic found the answer in the negative.

Worked-out Exercises

◊ **Exercise 2.4.1.** Find all the integral solutions of the equation $5x + 4y = 9$.

Solution. $gcd(5, 4) = 1$ and 1 divides 9. Hence $5x + 4y = 9$ has an integral solution. Now, $1 = 5 \cdot 1 + 4(-1)$. Upon multiplying this equality by 9, we arrive at $5 \cdot 9 + 4(-9) = 9$ so that $x = 9$ and $y = -9$ is an integral solution of the given equation. All integral solutions of the given equations are given by

$$x = 9 + \frac{4}{1}n \text{ and } y = -9 - \frac{5}{1}n \text{ for any integer } n,$$

i.e., $x = 9 + 4n, y = -9 - 5n$ for any integer n.

◊ **Exercise 2.4.2.** Which of the following linear equations cannot be solved in integers?
  (a) $24x + 16y = 2$; (b) $51x + 6y = 8$ (c) $28x + 35y = 14$.

Solution. (a) $gcd(24, 16) = 8$ and 8 does not divide 2. Hence this equation has no integral solution.

  (b) $gcd(51, 6) = 3$ and 3 does not divide 8. This implies that the given equation has no solution in integers.

  (c) $gcd(28, 35) = 7$ and 7 divides 14. Hence the given equation has integral solutions.

◊ **Exercise 2.4.3.** Find all positive integral solutions of $9x + 7y = 200$.

Solution. The $gcd(9, 7) = 1$ and 1 divides 200. Hence $9x + 7y = 200$ has integral solutions.

  By division algorithm

$$9 = 7 \cdot 1 + 2$$
$$7 = 2 \cdot 3 + 1$$

  Then

$$1 = 7 - 2 \cdot 3 = 7 - 3[9 - 7 \cdot 1] = 7 \cdot 4 + 9(-3)$$

This implies that

$$200 = 9(-600) + 7 \cdot 800.$$

Thus an integral solution of the given equation is $x = -600, y = 800$. All integral solutions of the given equation are given by

$$x = -600 + 7n, \ y = 800 - 9n$$

for all integers n.

When the solutions are positive, then

$$-600 + 7n > 0, \quad \text{and} \quad 800 - 9n > 0.$$

The integer n must satisfy

$$\frac{600}{7} < n < \frac{800}{9}.$$

Therefore, $n = 86, 87$ and 88. The equation $9x + 7y = 200$ has exactly three positive integral solutions and these are

$$x = -600 + 7 \cdot 86 = 2, \; y = 800 - 9 \cdot 86 = 26,$$

$$x = -600 + 7 \cdot 87 = 9, \; y = 800 - 9 \cdot 87 = 17,$$

and

$$x = -600 + 7 \cdot 88 = 16, \; y = 800 - 9 \cdot 88 = 8.$$

$\Diamond$ **Exercise 2.4.4.** A man pays Rs. 839 for some bags and boxes. If each bag costs Rs. 18 and each box costs Rs. 25, how many of each did he buy?

Solution. Suppose he bought x bags and y boxes. Then

$$18x + 25y = 839 \qquad \qquad \dots (*)$$

Now $gcd(18, 25) = 1$ and

$$25 = 1.18 + 7,$$
$$18 = 2.7 + 4,$$
$$7 = 1.4 + 3,$$
$$4 = 1.3 + 1.$$

Hence,

$$1 = 4 - 1.3 = 4 - 1(7 - 1.4) = 2.4 - 1.7 = 2(18 - 2.7) - 1.7$$

$$= -5.7 + 2.18 = -5(25 - 1.18) + 2.18 = 18.7 + 25(-5).$$

Then,

$$839 = 18(5873) + 25(-4195).$$

This implies that $x = 5873$ and $y = -4195$ is an integral solution of $(*)$. Hence all integral solutions of $(*)$ are given by

$$x = 5873 + 25n, \; y = -4195 - 18n, \text{ for any integer } n.$$

Since we must have $x > 0, y > 0$, we find that

$$5873 + 25n > 0, \quad \text{and} \quad -4195 - 18n > 0.$$

Hence

$$-\frac{5873}{25} < n < -\frac{4195}{18}$$

i.e.,

$$-234\frac{23}{25} < n < -233\frac{1}{18}.$$

Hence, $n = -234$. This implies that

$$x = 5873 + 25(-234) = 23 \text{ and } y = -4195 - 18(-234) = 17.$$

Hence the number of bags is 23 and the number of boxes is 17.

Exercises

1. Which of the following Diophantine equations cannot be solved?
   (a) $6x + 4y = 91$; (b) $158x - 57y = 7$; (c) $621x + 736y = 46$.

2. Solve the following Diophantine equations:
   (a) $158x - 47y = 9$; (b) $29x - 19y = 114$; (c) $101x + 12y = 1$;
   (d) $25x + 65y = 50$; (e) $3x + 4y = 9$; (f) $7x - 5y = 100$.

3. Find a positive integral solution (if any):
   (a) $17x + 15y = 145$; (b) $61x + 56y = 7643$; (c) $2x + 3y = 50$;
   (d) $120x + 41y = 11$; (e) $5x + 7y = 100$; (f) $14x + 21y = 400$.

4. A retailer wants to order pens and pencils for Rs.213. If a pen costs Rs. 19 and a pencil Rs. 7, find in how many ways he can place his order.

5. A fruit-seller orders mangoes and oranges for Rs. 1000. If one basket of mangoes costs Rs. 20 and one basket of oranges costs Rs. 172, how many baskets of each type does he order?

6. A certain housing complex contains rental apartments of two types: A and B. The monthly rent of each apartment of type A is Rs. 1230 and that of type B is Rs. 870. When all the apartments are rented, the total income is Rs. 87,300 per month. Find the number of apartments of each type.

2.5   Arithmetic Functions

An **arithmetic function** in general, is a function $f : \mathbb{N} \to \mathbb{C}$, from the set of natural numbers to the set of complex numbers. In other words, it may be looked upon as a sequence $\{a_n\}_n$ of complex numbers, where $f(n) = a_n$. However, this definition is too wide to be interesting and in what follows, we shall discuss only certain arithmetic functions that have some interesting number theoretic properties. Following is a list of some important arithmetic functions.

Example 2.5.1. For a positive integer n,

$$\pi(n) = \text{the number of primes} \leq n$$
$$\tau(n) = \text{the number of positive divisors of } n$$
$$\sigma(n) = \text{the sum of the positive divisors of } n$$
$$p(n) = \text{the product of positive divisors of } n$$
$$s(n) = \text{the sum of the positive } proper \text{ divisors of } n$$
$$\sigma_k(n) = \text{the sum of the } k\text{th powers of the positive divisors of } n$$
$$\omega(n) = \text{the number of distinct primes dividing } n$$
$$\phi(n) = \text{the number of positive integers} \leq n \text{ and relatively prime to } n$$

Remark 2.5.2. We shall not take up all these functions for detailed discussion here. Our main focus in the present volume will be on $\tau(n)$ and $\sigma(n)$, often called **divisor functions**[12] and also $\phi(n)$, known as *Euler Totient* or simply *Euler phi function*. Following form of definitions for $\tau(n)$, $\sigma(n)$ and $\sigma_k(n)$ are more handy for further mathematical computations.

$$\tau(n) = \sum_{d|n} 1; \quad \sigma(n) = \sum_{d|n} d; \quad \sigma_k(n) = \sum_{d|n} d^k.$$

It is interesting to note that $\sigma_0(n) = \tau(n)$, $\sigma_1(n) = \sigma(n)$ and $s(n) = \sigma(n) - n$. If $s(n) = n$, i.e., if n is equal to the sum of its proper divisors, then n is called a *perfect number*. Clearly, for a perfect number n we see that $\sigma(n) = 2n$. First three perfect numbers are 6, 28 and 496. Some interesting information on perfect numbers are given in *Appendix C*.

Before any further discussion, let us calculate the values of the functions in Example 2.5.1, directly from their definitions, for some particular n.

Example 2.5.3. For the positive integer 10,

---

[12]Some authors prefer to write $d(n)$ or, $\nu(n)$ for $\tau(n)$ (German *Teiler* means *divisor*). This function is not to be confused with the celebrated *Ramanujan's tau function*. Function $s(n)$ is also called the sum of *aliquot parts* as in Latin *aliquot* means dividing without remainder.

Function	Value	Computation	
$\pi(10) =$	4	2,3,5,7	[primes ≤ 10]
$\tau(10) =$	4	1,2,5,10	[positive divisors of 10]
$\sigma(10) =$	18	1+2+5+10	[sum of the positive divisors of 10]
$p(10) =$	100	$1 \cdot 2 \cdot 5 \cdot 10$	[product of the positive divisors of 10]
$s(10) =$	8	$(1+2+5+10) - 10$	[sum of the proper divisors of 10]
$\sigma_2(10) =$	130	$1^2 + 2^2 + 5^2 + 10^2$	[sum of the square of the divisors of 10]
$\omega(10) =$	2	2,5	[distinct primes dividing 10]
$\phi(10) =$	4	1,3,7,9	[positive integers ≤ 10 and relatively prime to 10]

Example 2.5.4. It is not difficult to see that for any *prime q*, $\tau(q) = 2$, as only divisors of q are 1 and q. clearly, $\sigma(q) = q + 1$, $p(q) = q$, $s(q) = 1$, $\sigma_k(q) = 1 + q^k$, $\omega(q) = 1$ and $\phi(q) = q - 1$, as all integers less than a prime is relatively prime to it. However, no such simple formula exists for $\pi(q)$. Note that,

$$\sum_{d|10} \phi(d) = \phi(10) + \phi(5) + \phi(2) + \phi(1) = 4 + 4 + 1 + 1 = 10.$$

Definition 2.5.5. An arithmetic function f is said to be ***multiplicative***[13] if
(i) $f(1) \neq 0$;
(ii) for all positive integers m, n with $(m, n) = 1$, $f(mn) = f(m)f(n)$.

Successive application of the above Definition 2.5.5 immediately leads us to the following theorem.

Theorem 2.5.6. *Let $n \geq 2$ be an integer*[14] *such that $n = p_1^{r_1} p_2^{r_2} \cdots p_k^{r_k}$, where $p_1, p_2,$ ..., p_k are distinct prime integers. Then*

$$f(n) = \prod_{i=1}^{k} f(p_i^{r_i}).$$

Remark 2.5.7. Theorem 2.5.6 actually tells that a multiplicative arithmetic function is completely determined by the values it takes on the prime powers like p^r. Since the divisors of p^r are $1, p, p^2, \ldots, p^r$, we have the following.

Corollary 2.5.8. $\tau(p^r) = r + 1$ *and* $\sigma(p^r) = \dfrac{p^{r+1} - 1}{p - 1}.$

---

[13]If the condition that $(m, n) = 1$ be dropped from the defintion, then f is called *completely* multiplicative. However, since none of the arithmetic functions of our interest in this volume is completely multiplicative, we are not going to treat it in any further detail.

[14]If one drops the condition $n \geq 2$, then one has to adopt the convention that for $n = 1$, $k = 0$ and a product over *zero terms* is declared to be 1.

We now state the following lemma, and invite the reader to prove it directly from the relevant definitions.

Lemma 2.5.9. *The divisor functions τ and σ are multiplicative.*

This lemma along with the fundamental theorem of arithmetic immediately lead us to explicit formulae for computing $\tau(n)$ and $\sigma(n)$ for any $n \geq 2$.

Theorem 2.5.10. *If $n = p_1^{r_1} p_2^{r_2} \cdots p_k^{r_k}$, be the usual prime factorization of n, then*

$$\tau(n) = \prod_{i=1}^{k}(r_i + 1) \quad \text{and} \quad \sigma(n) = \prod_{i=1}^{k}\Big(\frac{p_i^{r_i+1} - 1}{p_i - 1}\Big).$$

Though we have already described the *phi* or totient function, we prefer to define it formally here.

Definition 2.5.11. Let n be a positive integer. The ***Euler phi function*** defined by

$$\phi(n) = \#\{1 \leq m \leq n \mid \gcd(m,n) = 1\}$$

is the number of positive integers not exceeding n and relatively prime to n.

Lemma 2.5.12. *If p is a prime and n is a positive integer, then $\phi(p^n) = p^n(1 - \frac{1}{p})$.*

Proof. Let us arrange the integers from 1 to p^n in the following way:

$1,$	$2,$	$3,$	$\ldots$	$(p-1),$	$p,$
$(p+1),$	$(p+2),$	$(p+3),$	$\ldots$	$p+(p-1),$	$2p,$
$(2p+1),$	$(2p+2),$	$(2p+3),$	$\ldots$	$2p+(p-1),$	$3p,$

$$\vdots$$

$(p^{n-1}-1)p+1, \quad (p^{n-1}-1)p+2, \quad (p^{n-1}-1)p+3, \quad \ldots \quad (p^{n-1}-1)p+(p-1), \quad p^{n-1}p.$

From the above table we find that if $q \leq p^n$ is a positive integer, then $\gcd(q, p^n) \neq 1$ if and only if q is one of

$$p, 2p, 3p, \ldots, p^{n-1}p.$$

The number of such integers is p^{n-1}.

Hence among the integers from 1 to p^n there are p^{n-1} integers which are not relatively prime to n. So,

$$\phi(p^n) = p^n - p^{n-1} = p^n(1 - \frac{1}{p}).$$

This completes the proof. $\qquad\qquad\qquad\qquad\qquad\qquad\qquad\qquad\qquad\qquad\qquad\square$

We leave the proof of the following lemma as a non-trivial exercise.

Lemma 2.5.13. *If a and b are positive integers such that $\gcd(a, b) = 1$, then*

$$\phi(ab) = \phi(a)\phi(b).$$

i.e., Euler totient is multiplicative.

The following theorem shows how to determine $\phi(n)$ for any positive integer n.

Theorem 2.5.14. *Let n be an integer greater than 1 such that $n = p_1^{r_1} p_2^{r_2} \cdots p_k^{r_k}$, where $p_1, p_2, \ldots, p_k$ are distinct prime integers. Then*

$$\phi(n) = n(1 - \frac{1}{p_1})(1 - \frac{1}{p_2}) \cdots (1 - \frac{1}{p_k}).$$

Proof. We have, by Lemma 2.5.13

$$
\begin{aligned}
\phi(n) &= \phi(p_1^{r_1} p_2^{r_2} \cdots p_k^{r_k}) \\
&= \phi(p_1^{r_1})\phi(p_2^{r_2} \cdots p_k^{r_k}),
\end{aligned}
$$

because $\gcd(p_1^{r_1}, p_2^{r_2} \cdots p_k^{r_k}) = 1$. Proceeding in this way, we ultimately obtain

$$\phi(n) = \phi(p_1^{r_1})\phi(p_2^{r_2}) \cdots \phi(p_k^{r_k}).$$

By Lemma 2.5.12, we have, for each $i = 1, 2, \ldots, k$

$$\phi(p_i^{r_i}) = p_i^{r_i}(1 - \frac{1}{p_i}).$$

Hence,

$$
\begin{aligned}
\phi(n) &= p_1^{r_1}(1 - \frac{1}{p_1})p_2^{r_2}(1 - \frac{1}{p_2}) \cdots p_k^{r_k}(1 - \frac{1}{p_k}) \\
&= p_1^{r_1} p_2^{r_2} \cdots p_k^{r_k}(1 - \frac{1}{p_1})(1 - \frac{1}{p_2}) \cdots (1 - \frac{1}{p_k}) \\
&= n(1 - \frac{1}{p_1})(1 - \frac{1}{p_2}) \cdots (1 - \frac{1}{p_k}).
\end{aligned}
$$

$\square$

Worked-out Exercises

$\Diamond$ **Exercise 2.5.1.** If f is multiplicative, show that $f(1) = 1$.

Solution. Since f is multiplicative, we have, $f(mn) = f(m)f(n)$ for all $m, n \in \mathbb{N}$. Putting $m = n = 1$ we get $f(1 \cdot 1) = f(1)f(1)$ i.e., $f(1) = f(1)^2$. Since $f(1) \neq 0$, we have $f(1) = 1$.

$\Diamond$ **Exercise 2.5.2.** Find (i) $\tau(2400)$; (ii) $\sigma(2400)$; (iii) $\phi(2400)$.

Solution. Here, $2400 = 2^5 \cdot 5^2 \cdot 3$.

(i) Hence, $\tau(2400) = \tau(2^5 \cdot 5^2 \cdot 3) = (5+1)(2+1)(1+1) = 6 \cdot 3 \cdot 2 = 36$.

(ii) Again $\sigma(2400) = \sigma(2^5 \cdot 5^2 \cdot 3) =$

$$\left(\frac{2^{5+1}-1}{2-1}\right)\left(\frac{5^{2+1}-1}{5-1}\right)\left(\frac{3^{1+1}-1}{3-1}\right) = 63 \cdot 31 \cdot 4 = 7812.$$

(iii) Now,

$$\begin{aligned}
\phi(2400) &= \phi(2^5 \cdot 5^2 \cdot 3) \\
&= 2400(1 - \tfrac{1}{2})(1 - \tfrac{1}{5})(1 - \tfrac{1}{3}) \\
&= 2400 \cdot \tfrac{1}{2} \cdot \tfrac{4}{5} \cdot \tfrac{2}{3} \\
&= 640.
\end{aligned}$$

$\Diamond$ **Exercise 2.5.3.** Let $n > 2$ be an integer. Show that $\phi(n)$ is even.

Solution. Let

$$n = p_1^{r_1} p_2^{r_2} \cdots p_k^{r_k},$$

where $p_1, p_2, \ldots, p_k$ are distinct primes and $r_1, r_2, \ldots, r_k$ are positive integers. Now

$$\phi(p_i^{r_i}) = p_i^{r_i}(1 - \frac{1}{p_i}) = p_i^{r_i - 1}(p_i - 1).$$

Hence, if p_i is an odd prime, then $p_i - 1$ is even. This implies that $\phi(p_i^{r_i})$ is even. So we find that if one of p_is is odd, then $\phi(n)$ is even. Suppose there is no odd prime factor of n. Then $n = 2^r$. Because $n > 2$, we find that $r > 1$. Hence,

$$\phi(n) = \phi(2^r) = 2^r(1 - \frac{1}{2}) = 2^{r-1}.$$

Because $r > 1$, $r - 1 > 0$. Hence, $\phi(n)$ is even. Thus, for any integer $n > 2$, $\phi(n)$ is even.

$\Diamond$ **Exercise 2.5.4.** Prove that if n is a square number, then $\sigma(n)$ is an odd integer and if n is non-square odd integer, then $\sigma(n)$ is even.

Solution. Let

$$n = p_1^{2r_1} p_2^{2r_2} \cdots p_k^{2r_k},$$

where p_i are distinct primes and $r_i > 0$. Then

$$\sigma(n) = (1 + p_1 + \ldots + p_1^{2r_1}) \ldots (1 + p_k + \ldots + p_k^{2r_k}).$$

Since any factor $(1+p_i+\ldots+p_i^{2r_i})$ is the sum of an odd number of integers, irrespective of p_i being odd or even, it must be odd, whence $\sigma(n)$ must be odd.

If n is not a perfect square, say $n = p_1^{r_1} p_2^{r_2} \cdots p_k^{r_k}$, then all the r_is can not be even, say r_1 be odd; then $\sigma(n)$ is even, since $(1 + p_1 + \ldots + p_1^{r_1})$ is even.

◊ **Exercise 2.5.5.** Prove that $\sqrt{n^{\tau(n)}} = \prod\limits_{d|n} d.$

Solution. For every divisor d of n, there exists some quotient q (say), which can play the role of divisor as well, with d as corresponding quotient, whence $n = d \cdot q$. Now, if d is allowed to vary, i.e., it runs through all possible divisors of n, then corresponding q will vary as well, whence

$$\prod_{d|n} d = \prod_{d \cdot q = n} q.$$

Now when d runs through all the $\tau(n)$ number of divisors of n, we have $\tau(n)$ number of equalities like $n = d \cdot q$. Multiplying all these equalities sidewise, we have

$$n^{\tau(n)} = \left(\prod_{d|n} d\right) \cdot \left(\prod_{d \cdot q = n} q\right) = \left(\prod_{d|n} d\right)^2.$$

Since all the numbers under consideration are positive, taking square root on both the sides we get the required identity.

◊ **Exercise 2.5.6.** Prove that the geometric mean of the set of divisors of the number n is $\sqrt{n}$.

Solution. Let $\tau(n) = k$, so that the geometric mean is $\sqrt[k]{\prod_{d|n} d}$. From Exercise 2.5.5 above, we have $\sqrt{n^{\tau(n)}} = \prod\limits_{d|n} d$. Hence,

$$\sqrt[k]{\prod_{d|n} d} = \left(\prod_{d|n} d\right)^{\frac{1}{k}} = \left(\sqrt{n^k}\right)^{\frac{1}{k}} = \sqrt{n}.$$

◊ **Exercise 2.5.7.** For a multiplicative function f, it is given that the arithmetic function F defined by $F(n) = \sum_{d|n} f(d)$ is also multiplicative. Use it to prove the **Gauss Identity** that, for all $n \in \mathbb{N}$, $\sum\limits_{d|n} \phi(d) = n$.

Solution. The result is trivial for $n = 1$. For $n > 1$, define $F(n) = \sum\limits_{d|n} \phi(d)$. Since ϕ is multiplicative, so will be F. Hence for the usual prime factorization $n = p_1^{r_1} p_2^{r_2} \cdots p_k^{r_k}$, we have

$$F(n) = F(p_1^{r_1}) F(p_2^{r_2}) \cdots F(p_k^{r_k}).$$

For each i,

$$F(p_i^{k_i}) = \sum_{d|p_i^{k_i}} \phi(d)$$

$$= \phi(1) + \phi(p_i) + \phi(p_i^2) + \phi(p_i^3) + \ldots \phi(p_i^{k_i})$$

$$= 1 + (p_i - 1) + (p_i^2 - p_i) + (p_i^3 - p_i^2) + \ldots (p_i^{k_i} - p_i^{k_i-1})$$

$$= p_i^{k_i}$$

Clearly,

$$F(n) = p_1^{r_1} p_2^{r_2} \cdots p_k^{r_k} = n,$$

whence $\sum_{d|n} \phi(d) = n$.

Exercises

1. Find (a) $\sigma_0(140)$ (b) $\sigma_1(140)$ (c) $\tau(12)$ (d) $\sigma(12)$ (e) $s(12)$

2. Find (a) $\phi(1999)$ (b) $\phi(2101)$ (c) $\phi(4245)$ (d) $\phi(1991)$.

3. Show by direct computation that $\sum_{d|120} \phi(d) = 120$.

4. Prove that $\phi(5n) = 5\phi(n)$ if and only if 5 divides n.

5. Show that if the condition $f(1) \neq 0$ be dropped from the definition of arithmetic function f, then f may become identically zero.

6. Show that for a prime power p^α the sum of its divisors $\sigma(p^\alpha) = \frac{p^{\alpha+1}-1}{p-1}$. Hence show that $\sigma(p) = p + 1$.

7. †Show that the function σ_k for all $k \in \mathbb{N}$ is multiplicative.

2.6   More on Congruence

It is well known from elementary algebra that the equation $ax = b$, where $a, b \in \mathbb{Z}$ and $a \neq 0$, has a solution in $\mathbb{Z}$ if and only if a divides b in $\mathbb{Z}$. We shall now discuss the solution of congruence $ax \equiv b \pmod{m}$ in $\mathbb{Z}$.

Definition 2.6.1. A congruence of the form $ax \equiv b \pmod{m}$, where $a, b \in \mathbb{Z}$, m is a positive integer and x is an unknown integer, is called a ***linear congruence in one variable*** x. An integer x_0 is called a ***solution*** of the linear congruence $ax \equiv b \pmod{m}$ if $ax_0 \equiv b \pmod{m}$.

Example 2.6.2. Consider the linear congruence $6x \equiv 1 \pmod{13}$ in one variable. Now $6 \cdot 11 \equiv 1 \pmod{13}$ and so it follows that 11 is a solution of this congruence. Note that $6 \cdot 24 \equiv 1 \pmod{13}$. Therefore, 24 is also a solution of $6x \equiv 1 \pmod{13}$. In fact, we can show that if x_0 is an integer such that $x_0 \equiv 11 \pmod{13}$, then x_0 is also a solution of the congruence.

Theorem 2.6.3. *Let a, b, m be integers with $m > 0$. Suppose that x_0 is a solution of the linear congruence $ax \equiv b \pmod{m}$. Then any integer x_1 satisfying the congruence $x_1 \equiv x_0 \pmod{m}$ is also a solution of this linear congruence.*

Proof. As x_0 is a solution of $ax \equiv b \pmod{m}$ we must have $ax_0 \equiv b \pmod{m}$. Suppose x_1 is an integer such that $x_1 \equiv x_0 \pmod{m}$. This implies that $ax_1 \equiv ax_0 \pmod{m}$. Now $ax_0 \equiv b \pmod{m}$ and $ax_1 \equiv ax_0 \pmod{m}$ together imply that $ax_1 \equiv b \pmod{m}$. So we find that x_1 is also a solution of this congruence. $\qquad\square$

Consider the following example which will show that a linear congruence may not have an integral solution.

Example 2.6.4. Consider the linear congruence $5x \equiv 6 \pmod{10}$. Suppose that this linear congruence has a solution, say $x_0 \in \mathbb{Z}$. This implies that $5x_0 \equiv 6 \pmod{10}$. Now

$$5x_0 \equiv 6 \pmod{10}$$
$$\Rightarrow \quad 10 \text{ divides } 5x_0 - 6$$
$$\Rightarrow \quad 5x_0 - 6 = 10t \text{ for some integer } t$$
$$\Rightarrow \quad -6 = 10t - 5x_0$$
$$\Rightarrow \quad -\tfrac{6}{5} = 2t - x_0 \in \mathbb{Z},$$

which is not true. Hence, the linear congruence $5x \equiv 6 \pmod{10}$ has no integral solutions.

Example 2.6.5. Consider the congruence $13x \equiv 5 \pmod{6}$.

Now $\gcd(13, 6) = 1$. Thus, by Theorem 2.1.10, there exist integers u and t (for example $u = 1$ and $t = -2$) such that $13u + 6t = 1$. This implies that $13 \cdot 5u + 6 \cdot 5t = 5$. Thus, $13 \cdot 5u - 5 = 6(-5t)$ and hence, $13 \cdot 5u \equiv 5 \pmod{6}$, whence $5u$ is a solution of this congruence.

The previous example implies that a congruence $ax \equiv b \pmod{m}$ with $\gcd(a, m) = 1$ has a solution. Indeed, the following theorem proves that this is the case in general.

Theorem 2.6.6. *Let a, b, m be integers with $m > 0$ and $\gcd(a, m) = 1$. Then the congruence $ax \equiv b \pmod{m}$ has a solution. Further if x_0 is such a solution, then any integer x_1 is also a solution if and only if $x_1 \equiv x_0 \pmod{m}$. In this sense, we say that the **solution is unique modulo** m.*

Proof. Because $\gcd(a,m) = 1$, by Theorem 2.1.10, there exist integers u and t such that $au + mt = 1$. This implies that $aub + mtb = b$. Thus, $aub - b = m(-tb)$ and so we find that

$$aub \equiv b(\text{mod } m).$$

Hence $x_0 = ub$ is a solution of $ax \equiv b(\text{mod } m)$.

Suppose x_0 is a solution of the given congruence. Let x_1 be another solution of $ax \equiv b(\text{mod } m)$. Then $ax_1 \equiv b(\text{mod } m)$.

Now $ax_1 \equiv b(\text{mod } m)$ and $ax_0 \equiv b(\text{mod } m)$, i.e., $ax_1 \equiv b(\text{mod } m)$ and $b \equiv ax_0(\text{mod } m)$. Hence, $ax_1 \equiv ax_0(\text{mod } m)$. Because $\gcd(a,m) = 1$, it follows from Theorem 1.3.9(ii) that $x_1 \equiv x_0(\text{mod } m)$. Converse part follows from Theorem 2.6.3 above. □

Corollary 2.6.7. *Let a, b and p be integers such that p is prime and $p \nmid a$. Then the congruence $ax \equiv b(\text{mod } p)$ has a solution which is unique modulo p.*

Proof. Because $p \nmid a$, $\gcd(a,p) = 1$. Hence, it follows from Theorem 2.6.6. □

Definition 2.6.8. Let m be a positive integer. For any integer a with $\gcd(a,m) = 1$, an integer b is called an ***inverse*** of a modulo m if $ab \equiv 1(\text{mod } m)$.

From the above Definition, it follows that b is an inverse of a modulo m if and only if b is a solution of $ax \equiv 1(\text{mod } m)$.

Example 2.6.9. 8 is an inverse of 5 modulo 3, because $8 \cdot 5 \equiv 1(\text{mod } 3)$.

We now extend Theorem 2.6.6 to the linear congruence $ax \equiv b(\text{mod } m)$, where $\gcd(a,m) = d \geq 1$, without proof.

Theorem 2.6.10. *Let a, b, and m be integers with $m > 0$ and $\gcd(a,m) = d$. Then $ax \equiv b(\text{mod } m)$ has no solutions when d does not divide b; but if d divides b, then there are exactly d solutions [15] modulo m.*

The following theorem deals with the solution of simultaneous congruences. The Chinese mathematician Sunzi considered this theorem in his book *Sunzi Suanjing* the third century AD.

---

[15]The words 'exactly d solutions modulo m' mean that there are d distinct integers $a_1, a_2, \ldots, a_d$ such that $aa_i \equiv b(\text{mod } m)$ for $i = 1, 2, \ldots, d$, $a_i \not\equiv a_j(\text{mod } m)$ if $i \neq j$, and if u is an integer such that $au \equiv b(\text{mod } m)$, then $u \equiv a_i(\text{mod } m)$ for some i, where $1 \leq i \leq d$. It can be shown that if x_0 is a solution of $ax \equiv b(\text{mod } m)$, then **all the d solutions** of this congruence are given by

$$x \equiv (x_0 + \frac{m}{d}i)(\text{mod } m)$$

where $i = 0, 1, 2, \ldots, d-1$.

Theorem 2.6.11. [**Chinese Remainder Theorem**] *Let* m_1, m_2, ..., m_k *be positive integers such that* $\gcd(m_i, m_j) = 1$ *for* $i \neq j$. *Then for any integers* a_1, a_2, ..., a_k, *the system of congruences*

$$x \equiv a_1(\text{mod } m_1)$$
$$x \equiv a_2(\text{mod } m_2)$$
$$\vdots$$
$$x \equiv a_k(\text{mod } m_k)$$

has a solution. Furthermore, any two solutions of the system are congruent modulo $m_1 m_2 \cdots m_k$.

Proof. Let $M = m_1 m_2 \cdots m_k$ and $N_i = \frac{M}{m_i}$, where $i = 1, 2, \ldots, k$. Since for $i \neq j$, $\gcd(m_i, m_j) = 1$, we find that $\gcd(N_i, m_i) = 1$.

Then by Theorem 2.6.6, the linear congruence $N_i x \equiv 1(\text{mod } m_i)$ has a unique solution, say b_i modulo m_i. Let $x_0 = a_1 b_1 N_1 + a_2 b_2 N_2 + \cdots + a_k b_k N_k$. We show that the integer x_0 is a solution of the given system of congruences.

We first observe that $N_i = \frac{M}{m_i} = m_1 m_2 \cdots m_{i-1} m_{i+1} \cdots m_k \equiv 0(\text{mod } m_j)$ for $j = 1, 2, \ldots, i-1, i+1, \ldots, k$. Thus $x_0 \equiv a_i b_i N_i(\text{mod } m_i)$ for $i = 1, 2, \ldots, k$. But $N_i b_i \equiv 1(\text{mod } m_i)$ and this implies that $N_i b_i a_i \equiv a_i(\text{mod } m_i)$. Hence, $x_0 \equiv a_i(\text{mod } m_i)$. This shows that x_0 is a solution of the given system of congruences.

Next, let x_1 be a solution of the given system of congruences. Then $x_1 \equiv a_i(\text{mod } m_i)$ for $i = 1, 2, \ldots, k$. Because $\gcd(m_i, m_j) = 1$ for $i \neq j$, it follows that $m_1 m_2 \cdots m_k$ divides $x_1 - x_0$. Thus, we find that $x_1 \equiv x_0(\text{mod } m_1 m_2 \cdots m_k)$. This completes the proof. $\qquad\square$

Following theorem by Fermat, popularly known as **Fermat's little theorem**, in contrast with his famous *last theorem* (FLT), is an important landmark in number theory, which has been proved to be a powerful tool in *Cryptology*, the modern science of ciphering and deciphering messages[16]. Though the theorem can be proved by purely number theoretic method, we prefer to simply state it here and give a formal group theoretic proof in Theorem 5.3.13 later.

Theorem 2.6.12. [**Fermat**] *If* p *is a prime and* a *is an integer such that* p *does not divide* a, *then*

$$a^{p-1} \equiv 1(\text{mod } p).$$

---

[16] As an immediate application of this result, as well as its generlization by Euler, we invite the reader to check out the RSA cryptosystem and Digital signature discussed in **Appendix F**.

As an immediate consequence of Fermat's little theorem, we have the following corollary.

Corollary 2.6.13. *If p is a prime and a is any integer, then $a^p \equiv a(\bmod\ p)$.*

Proof. First suppose p does not divide a. Then by Fermat's little theorem, $a^{p-1} \equiv 1(\bmod\ p)$. Then $a \cdot a^{p-1} \equiv a \cdot 1(\bmod\ p)$, i.e., $a^p \equiv a(\bmod\ p)$. Otherwise, p divides a and hence $a \equiv 0(\bmod\ p)$ which implies $a^p \equiv 0(\bmod\ p)$. Thus we get $a^p \equiv a(\bmod\ p)$, as required. $\square$

For any prime p, we know that Euler's Totient $\phi(p) = p - 1$, whence Fermat's little theorem can be reformulated as follows:

Corollary 2.6.14. *If a is a positive integer and p is a prime such that $\gcd(a, p) = 1$, then*

$$a^{\phi(p)} \equiv 1(\bmod\ p).$$

The next theorem is another cornerstone of number theory, known as the *Euler's generalization of Fermat's Little Theorem*. We merely state it here and a formal group theoretic proof is given later in Theorem 5.3.14.

Theorem 2.6.15 (Euler). *Let a and n be integers such that $n > 0$ and $\gcd(a, n) = 1$. Then*

$$a^{\phi(n)} \equiv 1(\bmod\ n).$$

Worked-out Exercises

$\Diamond$ **Exercise 2.6.1.** Find all solutions of the congruence $19x \equiv 8(\bmod 32)$.

Solution. Let $19x \equiv 8(\bmod 32)$ ...(1) Here $\gcd(19, 32) = 1$. Therefore, (1) has a unique solution (modulo 32). We now express $1 = 19u + 32v$ for some integer u and v.

Note that,

$$
\begin{aligned}
32 &= 1 \cdot 19 + 13 \\
19 &= 1 \cdot 13 + 6 \\
13 &= 2 \cdot 6 + 1.
\end{aligned}
$$

Hence

$$1 = 13 - 2 \cdot 6$$
$$= 13 - 2 \cdot (19 - 1 \cdot 13)$$
$$= -2 \cdot 19 + 3 \cdot 13$$
$$= -2 \cdot 19 + 3(32 - 19) = -5 \cdot 19 + 3 \cdot 32$$

Consequently, $8 = 19 \cdot (-40) + 32 \cdot 24$ .This implies, $19 \cdot (-40) \equiv 8 (\mathrm{mod}\, 32)$. Hence, $x_0 = -40$ is a solution of (1). Now $-40 \equiv 24 (\mathrm{mod}\, 32)$. Therefore, the given congruence has the solution $x \equiv 24 (\mathrm{mod}\, 32)$.

$\Diamond$ **Exercise 2.6.2.** Find an inverse of 13 modulo 60, if it exists.

Solution. Consider the congruence $13x \equiv 1 (\mathrm{mod}\, 60)$. Because $\gcd(13, 60) = 1$, it follows that the congruence has a solution, whence there exists an inverse of 13 modulo 60. Let us now express $1 = 60u + 13v$ for some integer u and v.

Note that,

$$60 = 4 \cdot 13 + 8$$
$$13 = 1 \cdot 8 + 5$$
$$8 = 1 \cdot 5 + 3$$
$$5 = 1 \cdot 3 + 2$$
$$3 = 1 \cdot 2 + 1.$$

Hence

$$1 = 3 - 1 \cdot 2 \qquad = 3 - 1 \cdot (5 - 1 \cdot 3)$$
$$= 2 \cdot 3 - 1 \cdot 5 \qquad = 2(8 - 1 \cdot 5) - 1 \cdot 5$$
$$= 2 \cdot 8 - 3 \cdot 5 \qquad = 2 \cdot 8 - 3(13 - 1 \cdot 8)$$
$$= 5 \cdot 8 - 3 \cdot 13 \qquad = 5(60 - 4 \cdot 13) - 3 \cdot 13$$
$$= 5 \cdot 60 - 23 \cdot 13.$$

Consequently, $13 \cdot (-23) \equiv 1 (\mathrm{mod}\, 60)$. Hence, $x_0 = -23$ is a solution of the congruence $13x \equiv 1 (\mathrm{mod}\, 60)$. Now $-23 \equiv 37 (\mathrm{mod}\, 60)$. Therefore, the inverse of 13 modulo 60 is 37.

$\Diamond$ **Exercise 2.6.3.** Solve the congruence $6x \equiv 4 (\mathrm{mod}\, 8)$.

Solution. Because $\gcd(6, 8) = 2$, and 2 divides 4, the congruence has exactly two solutions modulo 8. To solve this congruence, we must first solve the Diophantine equation $6x + 8y = 4$. Observe that, $6 \cdot (-2) + 8 \cdot (2) = 4$. Hence, the equation has a solution $(-2, 2)$. Hence, all solutions of $6x \equiv 4 (\mathrm{mod}\, 8)$ are given by

$$x \equiv (-2 + \frac{8}{2}i)(\mathrm{mod}\ 8)$$
$$\text{i.e., } x \equiv (-2 + 4i)(\mathrm{mod}\ 8),$$

where $i = 0$ and 1. Hence, the two solutions of the congruence $6x \equiv 4(\text{mod } 8)$ are as follows: $x \equiv -2(\text{mod } 8)$, $x \equiv 2(\text{mod } 8)$.

◊ **Exercise 2.6.4.** Solve the following system of congruences

$$x \equiv 2(\text{mod } 7),$$
$$x \equiv 3(\text{mod } 9),$$
$$x \equiv 2(\text{mod } 11).$$

Solution. We use Chinese remainder theorem, to solve this system of congruences.

Let $M = 7 \cdot 9 \cdot 11$. Consider the congruences

$$\frac{M}{7}x \equiv 1(\text{mod } 7),$$
$$\frac{M}{9}x \equiv 1(\text{mod } 9),$$
$$\frac{M}{11}x \equiv 1(\text{mod } 11),$$

i.e.,

$$99x \equiv 1(\text{mod } 7)$$
$$77x \equiv 1(\text{mod } 9)$$
$$63x \equiv 1(\text{mod } 11),$$

i.e.,

$$(98 + 1)x \equiv 1(\text{mod } 7)$$
$$(72 + 5)x \equiv 1(\text{mod } 9)$$
$$(66 - 3)x \equiv 1(\text{mod } 11).$$

These congruences naturally boil down respectively to the following congruences;

$$x \equiv 1(\text{mod } 7).....(i)$$
$$5x \equiv 1(\text{mod } 9).....(ii)$$
$$-3x \equiv 1(\text{mod } 11).....(iii)$$

Note that $x = 8$ is a solution of (i), $x = 2$ is a solution of (ii), $x = -4$ is a solution of (iii). Hence,

$$99x \equiv 1(\text{mod } 7) \text{ is satisfied by } x = 8,$$

$$77x \equiv 1(\text{mod } 9) \text{ is satisfied by } x = 2,$$

$$63x \equiv 1(\text{mod } 11) \text{ is satisfied by } x = -4.$$

Hence, a solution of the given system is given by

$$x_0 = 2 \cdot 8 \cdot 99 + 3 \cdot 2 \cdot 77 + 2 \cdot (-4) \cdot 63 = 1542$$

and the unique solution (modulo $7 \cdot 9 \cdot 11$) is given by

$$x \equiv 1542(\text{mod } 7 \cdot 9 \cdot 11),$$

i.e.,

$$x \equiv 1542(\text{mod } 693),$$

i.e.,

$$x \equiv 156(\text{mod }\ 693).$$

$\Diamond$ **Exercise 2.6.5.** A certain integer between 1 and 1000 leaves the remainder $1, 2, 7$ when divided by $8, 11, 15$ respectively. Find the integer.

Solution. The required integer is a solution of the following system of linear congruences.

$$x \equiv 1(\text{mod } 8)$$
$$x \equiv 2(\text{mod } 11)$$
$$x \equiv 7(\text{mod } 15).$$

Let $M = 8 \cdot 11 \cdot 15$. Consider the congruences

$$15 \cdot 11x \equiv 1(\text{mod } 8)$$
$$8 \cdot 15x \equiv 1(\text{mod } 11)$$
$$8 \cdot 11x \equiv 1(\text{mod } 15).$$

That is,

$$165x \equiv 1(\text{mod } 8)$$
$$120x \equiv 1(\text{mod } 11)$$
$$88x \equiv 1(\text{mod } 15),$$

or

$$(160 + 5)x \equiv 1(\text{mod } 8)$$
$$(110 + 10)x \equiv 1(\text{mod } 11)$$
$$(90 - 2)x \equiv 1(\text{mod } 15).$$

Hence, we consider the congruences,

$$5x \equiv 1(\text{mod } 8)$$

$$10x \equiv 1(\text{mod } 11)$$

$$-2x \equiv 1(\text{mod } 15).$$

Observe that, $x = -3$ is a solution of $5x \equiv 1(\text{mod } 8)$. Hence, $x = -3$ is a solution of $165x \equiv 1(\text{mod } 8)$. Similarly, $x = -1$ is a solution of $120x \equiv 1(\text{mod } 11)$ and $x = 7$ is a solution of $88x \equiv 1(\text{mod } 15)$.

Hence, a solution of the initial system of congruences is given by

$$x_0 = 165 \cdot (-3) \cdot 1 + 120 \cdot (-1) \cdot 2 + 88 \cdot 7 \cdot 7 = 3577$$

and the unique solution is given by

$$x \equiv 3577 (\bmod \ 1320),$$

i.e.,

$$x \equiv 937 (\bmod \ 1320).$$

Hence, the required integer is 937.

◊ **Exercise 2.6.6.** Find the remainder when 12^{201} is divided by 7.

Solution. If we find an integer r such that $0 \le r < 7$ and $12^{201} \equiv r (\bmod \ 7)$, then r will be the required remainder.

Now $\gcd(12, 7) = 1$, then, by Fermat's theorem $12^{7-1} \equiv 1 (\bmod \ 7)$, i.e.,

$$12^6 \equiv 1 (\bmod \ 7).$$

Note that $201 = 6 \cdot 33 + 3$. Hence, from the congruence, $(12^6)^{33} \equiv 1^{33} (\bmod \ 7)$, i.e.,

$$12^{198} \equiv 1 (\bmod \ 7)$$
$$\Rightarrow 12^{198} \cdot 12^3 \equiv 12^3 (\bmod \ 7)$$

Again, $12 \equiv -2 (\bmod \ 7)$. Then

$$12^3 \equiv -8 (\bmod \ 7)$$
$$\equiv 6 (\bmod \ 7)$$
$$\Rightarrow 12^{198} \cdot 12^3 \equiv 6 (\bmod \ 7).$$

Hence, $12^{201} \equiv 6 (\bmod \ 7)$. Therefore, the required remainder is 6.

◊ **Exercise 2.6.7.** Show that for any positive integer n, $\frac{n^{29}}{29} + \frac{n^{11}}{11} + \frac{279n}{319}$ is an integer.

Solution. We have $n^{29} \equiv n (\bmod \ 29)$ and $n^{11} \equiv n (\bmod \ 11)$. Hence, there exist integers r and t such that

$$n^{29} - n = 29r \text{ and } n^{11} - n = 11t.$$

Hence,

$$\begin{aligned}
\frac{n^{29}}{29} + \frac{n^{11}}{11} + \frac{279n}{319} &= \frac{29r+n}{29} + \frac{11t+n}{11} + \frac{279n}{319} \\
&= (r+t) + \frac{n}{29} + \frac{n}{11} + \frac{279n}{319} \\
&= (r+t) + \frac{11n+29n+279n}{319} \\
&= (r+t) + \frac{319n}{319} \\
&= (r+t) + n,
\end{aligned}$$

which is an integer.

$\Diamond$ **Exercise 2.6.8.** Find the integer in the unit place of 7^{316}.

Solution. 7^{316} can be expressed uniquely as

$$7^{316} = a_k 10^k + a_{k-1} 10^{k-1} + \cdots + a_1 10 + a_0,$$

where a_i's are integers and $0 \le a_i < 10$.

Now a_0 is the digit in the unit place of 7^{316} and a_0 satisfies

$$7^{316} \equiv a_0 (\text{mod } 10).$$

Now from Euler's theorem we have $7^{\Phi(10)} \equiv 1 (\text{mod } 10)$. But $\Phi(10) = 4$. Hence $7^4 \equiv 1 (\text{mod } 10)$. This implies that $7^{316} \equiv 1 (\text{mod } 10)$. Therefore, the integer in the unit place of 7^{316} is 1.

$\Diamond$ **Exercise 2.6.9.** Find the integer in the unit place of 32^{631}.

Solution. 32^{631} can be expressed uniquely as

$$32^{631} = a_k 10^k + a_{k-1} 10^{k-1} + \cdots + a_1 10 + a_0 \ldots \ldots (i)$$

where a_i s are integers such that $a_k \neq 0$ and $0 \le a_i < 10$.

Here a_0 is the digit in the unit place. From (i), we find that the integer a_0 satisfies the congruence

$$32^{631} \equiv a_0 (\text{mod } 10).$$

Now,

$$32 \equiv 2 (\text{mod } 10).$$

Hence,

$$(32)^5 \equiv 2^5 (\text{mod } 10),$$

and

$$2^5 = 32 \equiv 2 (\text{mod } 10) \ldots \ldots (ii)$$

Then

$$(32)^5 \equiv 2 (\text{mod } 10) \ldots \ldots (iii)$$

Notice that $631 = 5 \cdot 126 + 1$. Hence, from (iii)

$$(32)^{5 \cdot 126} \equiv 2^{126} (\text{mod } 10) \ldots \ldots (iv)$$

Thus from (iii),

$$(2^{25})^5 \equiv 2^5 (\text{mod } 10) \equiv 2 (\text{mod } 10),$$

i.e.,

$$2^{125} \equiv 2(\text{mod } 10).$$

This implies that

$$2^{125} \cdot 2^1 \equiv 2 \cdot 2(\text{mod } 10),$$

i.e.,

$$2^{126} \equiv 4(\text{mod } 10)$$

Hence, from (iv),

$$(32)^{5 \cdot 126} \equiv 4(\text{mod } 10).$$

Thus,

$$(32)^{5 \cdot 126} \cdot 32 \equiv 4 \cdot 32(\text{mod } 10),$$

i.e.,

$$(32)^{5 \cdot 126 + 1} \equiv 128(\text{mod } 10).$$

Because $128 \equiv 8(\text{mod } 10)$. Hence, $(32)^{5 \cdot 126 + 1} \equiv 8(\text{mod } 10)$. Therefore, the integer in the unit place of 32^{631} is 8.

◊ **Exercise 2.6.10.** Determine the integer in the unit place of $7^{7^{14}}$.

Solution. $7^{7^{14}}$ can be expressed uniquely as

$$7^{7^{14}} = a_k 10^k + a_{k-1} 10^{k-1} + \cdots + a_1 10 + a_0 \ldots \ldots (i)$$

where a_is are integers such that $a_k \neq 0$ and $0 \leq a_i < 10$.

Here a_0 is the digit in the unit place. From (i), we find that the integer a_0 satisfies the congruence

$$7^{7^{14}} \equiv a_0(\text{mod } 10).$$

We first note that $7 \equiv -1(\text{mod } 4)$. Hence, $7^{14} \equiv (-1)^{14}(\text{mod } 4)$ or $7^{14} \equiv 1(\text{mod } 4)$. This implies that $7^{14} = 4m + 1$ for some integer m.

Again $7^2 \equiv -1(\text{mod } 10) \implies 7^4 \equiv 1(\text{mod } 10) \implies 7^{4m} \equiv 1(\text{mod } 10)$.

Thus,

$$7^{4m+1} \equiv 7(\text{mod } 10).$$

This implies that

$$7^{7^{14}} \equiv 7(\text{mod } 10).$$

Hence, the digit in the unit place of $7^{7^{14}}$ is 7.

◊ **Exercise 2.6.11.** Find the remainder when $3^{1000000}$ is divided by 17.

Solution. Suppose r is the remainder when $3^{1000000}$ is divided by 17. Then we must have $0 \leq r < 17$ and

$$3^{1000000} \equiv r(\text{mod } 17).$$

Now 17 is a prime and $\gcd(17,3) = 1$. Hence,

$$3^{17-1} \equiv 1(\text{mod } 17),$$

i.e.,

$$3^{16} \equiv 1(\text{mod } 17)\ldots\ldots(i)$$

Note that $1000000 = 62500 \cdot 16$. Hence, (i) implies that

$$(3^{16})^{62500} \equiv 1(\text{mod } 17),$$

i.e.,

$$3^{1000000} \equiv 1(\text{mod } 17).$$

Therefore, the remainder is 1.

◊ **Exercise 2.6.12.** Find the remainder when 53^{49} is divided by 36.

Solution. Suppose r is the remainder when 53^{49} is divided by 36. Hence, $0 \leq r < 36$ and $53^{49} \equiv r(\text{mod } 36)$.

Because $\gcd(53,36) = 1$, by Euler's Theorem

$$53^{\phi(36)} \equiv 1(\text{mod } 36).$$

Now

$$\phi(36) = \phi(2^2 \cdot 3^2) = 36(1 - \frac{1}{2})(1 - \frac{1}{3}) = 36 \cdot \frac{1}{2} \cdot \frac{2}{3} = 12.$$

This implies that

$$53^{12} \equiv 1(\text{mod } 36).$$

Hence,

$$(53^{12})^4 \equiv 1^4(\text{mod } 36)$$

and so

$$53^{48} \equiv 1(\text{mod } 36).$$

It now follows that

$$53^{48} \cdot 53 \equiv 53(\text{mod } 36),$$

i.e.,

$$53^{49} \equiv 53(\text{mod } 36).$$

Because $53 \equiv 17(\text{mod } 36)$, we have $53^{49} \equiv 17(\text{mod } 36)$. Therefore, the remainder is 17.

Exercises

1. Find all solutions of the following linear congruences.
   (a) $6x \equiv 9 \pmod{15}$. (b) $15x \equiv 3 \pmod{26}$. (c) $12x \equiv 9 \pmod{15}$.
   (d) $18x \equiv 5 \pmod{7}$. (e) $6x \equiv 5 \pmod{19}$. (f) $6x \equiv 3 \pmod{9}$.
   (g) $17x \equiv 4 \pmod{36}$.

2. If it exists, find an inverse of
   (a) 8 modulo 13,
   (b) 16 modulo 20,
   (c) 15 modulo 17
   (d) 11 modulo 21.

3. Solve the following system of congruences.
   (a) $x \equiv 3 \pmod 5$ (b) $x \equiv 6 \pmod 7$ (c) $x \equiv 2 \pmod 5$
        $x \equiv 4 \pmod 7$. $x \equiv 2 \pmod 4$. $x \equiv 9 \pmod{11}$
                                                                  $x \equiv 7 \pmod{12}$.

   (d) $x \equiv 1 \pmod 5$ (e) $x \equiv 4 \pmod{13}$ (f) $x \equiv 2 \pmod 3$
        $x \equiv 2 \pmod 6$ $x \equiv 5 \pmod{11}$ $x \equiv 3 \pmod 5$
        $x \equiv 3 \pmod 7$. $x \equiv 11 \pmod{15}$. $x \equiv 2 \pmod{11}$.

4. A certain integer between 1 and 1000 leaves the remainder $1, 2, 6$ when divided by $9, 11$, and 13, respectively. Find the integer.

5. Find the smallest positive integer that leaves the remainder $1, 8, 10$ when divided by $4, 9$, and 25, respectively.

6. Find the smallest integer greater than 60 (if any) that leaves the remainder $3, 5, 4$ when divided by $7, 9$, and 5 respectively.

7. Find the smallest integer greater than 100 which is divisible by 3 but leaves the remainder $1, 5$ when divided by 4 and 7, respectively.

8. Find the smallest positive integer that leaves the remainder $3, 1, 17$ when divided by $4, 3$, and 25, respectively

9. (From Brahmagupta's *Brahmasphuta Siddhanta*) If eggs are taken out from a basket, two, three, four, five, and six at a time, there are left over, respectively, one, two, three, four, and five eggs. If they are taken out seven at a time, there are no eggs left over. What is the minimum number of eggs in the basket?

10. Find the respective remainders when
    (a) 17^{250} is divided by 11,
    (b) 20^{41} is divided by 7,
    (c) $5^{16} \cdot 3^{12}$ is divided by 13.

11. Find the integer in the unit place of 3^{25}.

12. Find the remainder when $7^{1000000}$ is divided by 19.

13. Find the remainder when 25^{43} is divided by 22.

14. Find the digit in the unit place of (a) 77^{213}; (b) 7^{2000}.

15. Determine the integer in the unit place of $13^{13^{13}}$.

16. Show that for any integer n,

  (a) $\frac{n^{19}}{19} + \frac{n^7}{7} + \frac{107n}{133}$ is an integer;

  (b) $\frac{n^7}{7} + \frac{n^3}{3} + \frac{11n}{21}$ is an integer.

17. For any positive integer n, show that $n^7 - n$ is divisible by 42.

18. Prove that $n^{16} - a^{16}$ is divisible by 17, where n and a are positive integers such that $\gcd(n, 17) = 1 = \gcd(a, 17)$.

19. Show that if p and q are distinct primes, then $p^{q-1} + q^{p-1} \equiv 1 \pmod{pq}$.

20. If n is a positive integer such that $(n-1)! \equiv -1 \pmod{n}$, then prove that n is a prime.

21. Prove that 42 divides $7^2 + 6^6 - 1$.

22. Prove that
$$1 + 20 + 20^2 + 20^3 + \cdots + 20^{21} \equiv 0 \pmod{23}.$$

23. Prove that $2^{145} \cdot 14^{10} + 1$ is divisible by 11.

24. If $f(x) = 14x^5 - 9x^4 + 7x^2 - 3$, find the remainder when $f(16)$ is divided by 5.

Chapter 3

Groups

The theory of groups, which occupies a central position in Modern Algebra[1], is one of the oldest branches of abstract algebra. Group theory arose mainly from attempts to find the roots of a polynomial in terms of its coefficients. Though the first effective use of the concept of groups can be found in early nineteenth century works of Augustin Louis Cauchy (1789-1857) and Evariste Galois (1811-1832) towards describing the effect of permutations of roots of a polynomial equation, the core idea of group theory was used as early as 1770 by Lagrange (1736-1813) for the investigation of the roots of a polynomial. Around 1829, Galois, an eighteen year old genius[2] from France, who is now considered the pioneer of the modern approach to algebra, left behind the path of endlessly complicated calculations, changed the character of the then existing notions of algebra radically by extending Lagrange's work and first introduced the term *group*. But this concept of group was not based on the present day axiomatic approach. In fact, Arthur Cayley (1821-1895) in 1854, gave the first postulates for a (finite) group, which somehow went unnoticed by the contemporary mathematical world. In 1870, Camille Jordan (1838-1922) clarified Galois' work in his book. Finally, it was Walther

---

[1]In contrast with Classical Algebra, where every single problem was a different war-front, this relatively new branch approaches the problem at the deep structure level, and this is precisely the modernity of approach.

[2]It is worthy to mention one of the innumerable tributes to this child prodigy. Herman Weyl, himself a great mathematician once remarked, "*Galois' ideas, which......later exerted a more and more profound influence upon the whole development of mathematics, are contained in a farewell letter written to a friend on the eve of his death, which he met in a silly duel at the age of twenty-one. This letter, if judged by the novelty and profundity of ideas it contains, is perhaps the most substantial piece of writing in the whole literature of mankind*". These works came to light only in 1846, fourteen years after his death. Interested readers may find the exact letter, (written on May 29, 1832) translated into English in "A Source Book in Mathematics" by D.E.Smith; Dover Publications.

Von Dyck (1856-1934), who set down the axioms for an abstract group in 1883, in the present day language.

3.1   Elementary Properties

In this section, we will be concerned with a particular mathematical system, called group, which is composed of a nonempty set together with a binary operation defined on it, such that certain properties hold. From these properties, results concerning the system can be derived. Indeed, this axiomatic approach to an abstract algebraic structure is common to a great variety of examples.

As mentioned earlier, the notion of a group arose from the study of one-to-one functions on the set of roots of a polynomial equation. We know that the set S of all one-one functions from a set X onto itself satisfies the following properties:

(i)   composition of functions, $\circ$, is a binary operation on S.

(ii)   for all $f, g, h \in S$, $f \circ (g \circ h) = (f \circ g) \circ h$.

(iii)   there exists $\iota \in S$ such that $f \circ \iota = f = \iota \circ f$ for all $f \in S$.

(iv)   for all $f \in S$, there exists an element $f^{-1} \in S$ such that $f \circ f^{-1} = \iota = f^{-1} \circ f$.

These properties lead us to define an abstract group.

Definition 3.1.1. A *group* is an ordered pair $(G, *)$, where G is a nonempty set and $*$ *is a binary operation on* G such that the following properties hold:

(G1)   for all $a, b, c, \in G, a * (b * c) = (a * b) * c$ (**associative law**).

(G2)   there exists $e \in G$ such that, for any $a \in G, a * e = a = e * a$
(**existence of an identity**).

(G3)   for each $a \in G$, there exists $b \in G$ such that $a * b = e = b * a$
(**existence of an inverse**).

Thus, a group is a mathematical system $(G, *)$ satisfying axioms G1 to G3.

Let us first observe the following important properties of groups.

Theorem 3.1.2. *Let* $(G, *)$ *be a group.*

(i)   *There exists a unique element* $e \in G$ *such that for any* $a \in G, e * a = a = a * e$.

(ii)   *For each* $a \in G$, *there exists a unique* $b \in G$ *such that* $a * b = e = b * a$.

Proof. (i)   Follows from Theorem 1.5.13.

(ii)   Let $a \in G$. By G3, there exists $b \in G$ such that $a * b = e = b * a$. Suppose there exists $c \in G$ such that $a * c = e = c * a$. We show that $b = c$. Now,

$$
\begin{aligned}
b &= b * e \\
&= b * (a * c) \quad \text{(substituting } e = a * c) \\
&= (b * a) * c \quad \text{(using the associativity of } *) \\
&= e * c \quad\quad\; \text{(since } b * a = e) \\
&= c.
\end{aligned}
$$

Thus b is unique. $\qquad\square$

The unique element $e \in G$ that satisfies G2 is called the **identity** element of the group $(G, *)$. Let $a \in G$. Then the unique element $b \in G$ that satisfies G3 is called the **inverse** of a in G and is denoted by a^{-1}.

A group $(G, *)$ is called **commutative** or **Abelian** if $a * b = b * a$ for all $a, b \in G$. A group $(G, *)$ that is not commutative is called **noncommutative**. If $(G, *)$ is a group such that the number of elements of G is some positive integer n, then the group $(G, *)$ is said to be a **finite group** and n is called the **order** of the group G. It is denoted as $|G| = n$. If G is not finite, then the group $(G, *)$ is said to be an **infinite group**.

We now present several examples of groups from a variety of areas.

Example 3.1.3. Consider the ordered pair $(\mathbb{Z}, +)$, where $\mathbb{Z}$ is the set of all integers and $+$ is the usual addition. We know that $+$ is associative. Now $0 \in \mathbb{Z}$ and for all $a \in \mathbb{Z}$, $a + 0 = a = 0 + a$ and so 0 is the identity. Also for all $a \in \mathbb{Z}, -a \in \mathbb{Z}$ and $a + (-a) = 0 = (-a) + a$. That is, $-a$ is the inverse of a. Hence, $(\mathbb{Z}, +)$ is a group. Since $a + b = b + a$ for all $a, b \in \mathbb{Z}$, $(\mathbb{Z}, +)$ is a commutative group.

Similarly, it can be shown that $(\mathbb{Q}, +)$, $(\mathbb{R}, +)$, $(\mathbb{C}, +)$, $(\mathbb{Q} \smallsetminus \{0\}, \cdot)$, $(\mathbb{R} \smallsetminus \{0\}, \cdot)$, $(\mathbb{C} \smallsetminus \{0\}, \cdot)$ are all examples of commutative groups, where $+$ is the usual addition and $\cdot$ is the usual multiplication. Note that for each of the groups $(\mathbb{Q}, +), (\mathbb{R}, +)$ and $(\mathbb{C}, +)$, the identity element is 0 and for the groups $(\mathbb{Q} \smallsetminus \{0\}, \cdot), (\mathbb{R} \smallsetminus \{0\}, \cdot)$ and $(\mathbb{C} \smallsetminus \{0\}, \cdot)$, the identity element is 1. In the first three groups, the inverse of an element a is $-a$ and in the last three groups, the inverse of an element a is $\frac{1}{a}$.

Example 3.1.4. Let a be any fixed integer. Let $G = \{na \,|\, n \in \mathbb{Z}\}$. Then $(G, +)$ is a commutative group, where $+$ is the usual addition of integers. Note that $0 = 0 \cdot a$ and $-(na) = (-n)a$ are members of G.

The next two examples are due to Gauss, whose pioneering work paved the path towards many new directions of research in commutative groups.

Example 3.1.5. Let n be a positive integer. Consider the set $\mathbb{Z}_n$ of all congruence classes of integers modulo n. Define addition $+$ of the congruence classes $[a], [b] \in \mathbb{Z}_n$ by

$$[a] + [b] = [a + b]$$

for all $[a], [b] \in \mathbb{Z}_n$.

We first prove that $+$ is a binary operation on $\mathbb{Z}_n$. Let $[a], [b], [c], [d] \in \mathbb{Z}_n$. Suppose $[a] = [c]$ and $[b] = [d]$. Then $n \mid (a-c)$ and $n \mid (b-d)$. This implies that $n \mid \big((a-c)+(b-d)\big)$. Hence $(a+b) \equiv (c+d) \pmod n$, whence $[a+b] = [c+d]$. As a result, $+$ is well-defined and so $+$ is a binary operation on $\mathbb{Z}_n$. For all $[a], [b], [c] \in \mathbb{Z}_n$, $([a]+[b])+[c] = [a+b]+[c] = [(a+b)+c] = [a+(b+c)] = [a]+[b+c] = [a]+([b]+[c])$. Hence $+$ is associative. Now, $[0] \in \mathbb{Z}_n$ and for all $[a] \in \mathbb{Z}_n$,

$$[a] + [0] = [a + 0] = [a] = [0 + a] = [0] + [a].$$

This shows that $[0]$ is the identity element. Also, for all $[a] \in \mathbb{Z}_n$, $[-a] \in \mathbb{Z}_n$ and

$$[a] + [-a] = [a - a] = [0] = [-a + a] = [-a] + [a].$$

Thus, $[-a]$ is the inverse of $[a]$. Finally, for all $[a], [b] \in \mathbb{Z}_n$,

$$[a] + [b] = [a + b] = [b + a] = [b] + [a]$$

and so $\mathbb{Z}_n$ is commutative. Hence, $(\mathbb{Z}_n, +)$ is a commutative group.

In $\mathbb{Z}_n$, $[0], [1], [2], \ldots [n-1]$ are n distinct congruence classes and any congruence class $[a] \in \mathbb{Z}_n$ is equal to one of these. Hence $|\mathbb{Z}_n| = n$ and so $(\mathbb{Z}_n, +)$ is a finite group of order n.

Example 3.1.6. In this example we again consider $\mathbb{Z}_n$, the set of all congruence classes modulo a positive integer n. Define multiplication $\cdot$ on $\mathbb{Z}_n$ by

$$[a] \cdot [b] = [ab]$$

for all $[a], [b] \in \mathbb{Z}_n$. It can be readily seen from Example 1.5.5(e) that, '$\cdot$' is a binary operation on $\mathbb{Z}_n$ and '$\cdot$' is associative. Now $[1] \in \mathbb{Z}_n$ and for all $[a] \in \mathbb{Z}_n$,

$$[a] \cdot [1] = [a \cdot 1] = [a] = [1 \cdot a] = [1] \cdot [a].$$

This implies that $[1]$ is the identity element. We claim that if $[a] \in \mathbb{Z}_n$ and $[a] \neq [0]$, then there exists an element $[b]$ in $\mathbb{Z}_n$ such that $[a] \cdot [b] = [b] \cdot [a] = [1]$ if and only if $\gcd(a, n) = 1$.

Let $[a] \in \mathbb{Z}_n$ and $[a] \neq [0]$. Suppose $\gcd(a, n) = 1$. Then there exist $b, r \in \mathbb{Z}$ such that $ab + nr = 1$, i.e., n divides $ab - 1$. This implies that $ab \equiv 1 \,(\mathrm{mod}\, n)$ and $[ab] = [1]$ or, $[a] \cdot [b] = [1]$. Since $ab = ba$, we also have $[b] \cdot [a] = [ba] = [ab] = [1]$. Thus, there exists $[b] \in \mathbb{Z}_n$ such that $[a][b] = [1] = [b][a]$. Conversely, suppose $[a] \in \mathbb{Z}_n$, $[a] \neq [0]$ and there exists an element $[b]$ in $\mathbb{Z}_n$ such that $[a][b] = [b][a] = [1]$. Then $[ab] = [1]$ and this implies that $n|(ab-1)$ and so $ab - 1 = nr$ for some $r \in \mathbb{Z}$. Thus $ab + nr = 1$ and hence by Theorem 2.1.15, $\gcd(a, n) = 1$. This proves our claim.

Let U_n be the set of all elements $[a]$ of $\mathbb{Z}_n \setminus \{[0]\}$ such that $\gcd(a, n) = 1$ i.e.,

$$U_n = \{[a] \in \mathbb{Z}_n \setminus \{[0]\} \mid \gcd(a, n) = 1\}.$$

Note that for $n = 8$,

$$U_8 = \{[1], [3], [5], [7]\}$$

and for $n = 7$,

$$U_7 = \{[1], [2], [3], [4], [5], [6]\} = \mathbb{Z}_7 \setminus \{[0]\}.$$

Define the operation of multiplication in U_n by

$$[a] \star [b] = [ab] \tag{3.1.1}$$

We prove that the multiplication given by (3.1.1) is a binary operation on U_n. Let $[a]$ and $[b]$ be two elements of U_n. Then $\gcd(a, n) = 1$ and $\gcd(b, n) = 1$. Hence by Worked-out Exercise 2.1.6, $\gcd(ab, n) = 1$. So, we find that $[ab] \in U_n$. Next we show that $[ab]$ is unique for $[a], [b] \in U_n$. To establish this, let $[a] = [c]$ and $[b] = [d]$ in U_n. There exist r and t such that $a - c = rn$ and $b - d = tn$. Then $ab - cb = brn$ and $cb - cd = ctn$. This implies that $ab - cd = (ab - cb) + (cb - cd) = (br + ct)n$. As a result, $ab \equiv cd \,(\mathrm{mod}\, n)$ and then $[ab] = [cd]$. So there exists a unique class $[ab]$ such that $[a][b] = [ab]$ and if we define $[a] \star [b] = [a][b] = [ab]$, then $\star$ is a well-defined binary operation on U_n. It is easy to verify that this binary operation is associative and commutative. Since $\gcd(1, n) = 1$, $[1] \in U_n$. Clearly $[1]$ is the identity element for the above binary operation in U_n. Finally, we show that for each $[a] \in U_n$, there exists an element $[b]$ in U_n such that $[b] \star [a] = [1]$. If $[a] \in U_n$, then there exist integers b and t such that $1 = ba + tn$. This implies that $\gcd(b, n) = 1$ and also $1 \equiv ba \,(\mathrm{mod}\, n)$. Hence $[b] \in U_n$ such that $[b] \star [a] = [ba] = [1]$. Thus, we find that $(U_n, \star)$ is a commutative group. Generally, we say that U_n is a group under multiplication, which is defined as $[a][b] = [ab]$. Clearly $|U_n| = \phi(n)$, as is evident from the Definition 2.5.11 of Euler phi-function.

Example 3.1.7. Let $n = 6$. Then $\mathbb{Z}_6$ consists of six distinct elements $[0], [1], [2], [3], [4]$ and $[5]$. If m is any integer, then $[m]$ is equal to one of these classes, for example

$[13] = [1]$ since $6 \mid (13 - 1)$, $[202] = [4]$, since $6 \mid (202 - 4)$. Now in $\mathbb{Z}_6$, $[a] + [b] = [a + b]$ for all $[a], [b] \in \mathbb{Z}_6$. For example, $[2] + [5] = [2 + 5] = [7] = [1]$. $(\mathbb{Z}_6, +)$ is a group with 6 elements. The Cayley table for this group is given below:

+	[0]	[1]	[2]	[3]	[4]	[5]
[0]	[0]	[1]	[2]	[3]	[4]	[5]
[1]	[1]	[2]	[3]	[4]	[5]	[0]
[2]	[2]	[3]	[4]	[5]	[0]	[1]
[3]	[3]	[4]	[5]	[0]	[1]	[2]
[4]	[4]	[5]	[0]	[1]	[2]	[3]
[5]	[5]	[0]	[1]	[2]	[3]	[4]

Now, we describe U_6. Note that $U_6 = \{[a] \in \mathbb{Z}_6 \smallsetminus \{[0]\} \mid \gcd(a, 6) = 1\}$. Since $\mathbb{Z}_6 = \{[0], [1], [2], [3], [4], [5]\}$, we find that $U_6 = \{[1], [5]\}$. Hence $(U_6, \cdot)$ is a group with two elements and the Cayley table for the group is given below:

$\star$	[1]	[5]
[1]	[1]	[5]
[5]	[5]	[1]

Example 3.1.8. Let $\mathbb{Q}[\sqrt{2}] = \{a + b\sqrt{2} \mid a, b \in \mathbb{Q}\}$. Then the groups $(\mathbb{Q}[\sqrt{2}], +)$ and $(\mathbb{Q}[\sqrt{2}] \smallsetminus \{0\}, \cdot)$ are commutative, where $+$ is the usual addition and $\cdot$ is the usual multiplication. The identity of $(\mathbb{Q}[\sqrt{2}], +)$ is $0 + 0\sqrt{2}$ and the inverse of $a + b\sqrt{2}$ in $(\mathbb{Q}[\sqrt{2}], +)$ is $-a + (-b)\sqrt{2}$. The identity of $(\mathbb{Q}[\sqrt{2}] \smallsetminus \{0\}, \cdot)$ is $1 = 1 + 0\sqrt{2}$ and the inverse of $a + b\sqrt{2} \neq 0$ in $(\mathbb{Q}[\sqrt{2}] \smallsetminus \{0\}, \cdot)$ is $\frac{a}{a^2 - 2b^2} - \frac{b}{a^2 - 2b^2}\sqrt{2}$.

Example 3.1.9. Let $\mathcal{P}(X)$ be the power set of a set X. Consider the operation Δ (symmetric difference) on $\mathcal{P}(X)$. Then for all $A, B \in \mathcal{P}(X)$,

$$A\Delta B = (A \smallsetminus B) \cup (B \smallsetminus A).$$

$\left(\mathcal{P}(X), \Delta\right)$ is a commutative group. The empty set $\emptyset$ is the identity of $\left(\mathcal{P}(X), \Delta\right)$ and every element of $\mathcal{P}(X)$ is its own inverse. We warn the reader that verification of the associative law is tedious.

Example 3.1.10. Let X be a set and S_X be the set of all bijective mappings of X onto X. Since i_X, the identity mapping on X, is bijective, $i_X \in S_X$. Thus $S_X \neq \emptyset$. Define a binary operation $*$ on S_X by $f * g = f \circ g$ for all $f, g \in S_X$, where $f \circ g$ is the composition of the mappings f and g. From the Theorem 1.4.14(v), we find that $f * g \in S_X$. Already we know (Theorem 1.4.13) that $(f \circ g) \circ h = f \circ (g \circ h)$ for all $f, g \in S_X$. Also for all $f \in S_X, f^{-1} \in S_X$ and $f \circ f^{-1} = i_x = f^{-1} \circ f$. Consequently, $(S_X, *)$ is a group. However, $(S_X, \circ)$ is not necessarily commutative. For example, let $X = \{a, b, c\}$. Let $f, g \in S_X$ be defined by $f(a) = a, f(b) = c, f(c) = b$; $g(a) = b, g(b) = a, g(c) = c$. Then, $(f * g)(a) = f(g(a)) = f(b) = c$ and $(g * f)(a) = g(f(a)) = g(a) = b$. Hence $f * g \neq g * f$. Thus, $(S_X, *)$ is not commutative.

Example 3.1.11. Let $G = \left\{ \begin{bmatrix} a & b \\ c & d \end{bmatrix} \mid a, b, c, d \in \mathbb{R}, ad - bc \neq 0 \right\}$, the set of all 2×2 real matrices having a nonzero determinant. Define a binary operation $*$ on G by

$$\begin{bmatrix} a & b \\ c & d \end{bmatrix} * \begin{bmatrix} u & v \\ w & s \end{bmatrix} = \begin{bmatrix} au + bw & av + bs \\ cu + dw & cv + ds \end{bmatrix}$$

for all $\begin{bmatrix} a & b \\ c & d \end{bmatrix}, \begin{bmatrix} u & v \\ w & s \end{bmatrix} \in G$. This binary operation is the usual matrix multiplication. Since matrix multiplication is associative, we have $*$ is associative. The element $\begin{bmatrix} 1 & 0 \\ 0 & 1 \end{bmatrix} \in G$ is the identity element for the above operation. Let $\begin{bmatrix} a & b \\ c & d \end{bmatrix} \in G$. Then $ad - bc \neq 0$. Consider the matrix $\begin{bmatrix} \frac{d}{ad-bc} & \frac{-b}{ad-bc} \\ \frac{-c}{ad-bc} & \frac{a}{ad-bc} \end{bmatrix}$. Since

$$\frac{d}{ad - bc} \cdot \frac{a}{ad - bc} - \frac{-b}{ad - bc} \cdot \frac{-c}{ad - bc} = \frac{1}{ad - bc} \neq 0,$$

we have

$$\begin{bmatrix} \frac{d}{ad-bc} & \frac{-b}{ad-bc} \\ \frac{-c}{ad-bc} & \frac{a}{ad-bc} \end{bmatrix} \in G.$$

Now,

$$\begin{bmatrix} a & b \\ c & d \end{bmatrix} * \begin{bmatrix} \frac{d}{ad-bc} & \frac{-b}{ad-bc} \\ \frac{-c}{ad-bc} & \frac{a}{ad-bc} \end{bmatrix} = \begin{bmatrix} 1 & 0 \\ 0 & 1 \end{bmatrix}$$

and

$$\begin{bmatrix} \frac{d}{ad-bc} & \frac{-b}{ad-bc} \\ \frac{-c}{ad-bc} & \frac{a}{ad-bc} \end{bmatrix} * \begin{bmatrix} a & b \\ c & d \end{bmatrix} = \begin{bmatrix} 1 & 0 \\ 0 & 1 \end{bmatrix}.$$

Thus, $\begin{bmatrix} \frac{d}{ad-bc} & \frac{-b}{ad-bc} \\ \frac{-c}{ad-bc} & \frac{a}{ad-bc} \end{bmatrix}$ is the inverse of $\begin{bmatrix} a & b \\ c & d \end{bmatrix}$. Hence, G is a group. Now

$$\begin{bmatrix} 1 & 1 \\ 0 & 1 \end{bmatrix}, \begin{bmatrix} 1 & 0 \\ 1 & 1 \end{bmatrix} \in G$$

and

$$\begin{bmatrix} 1 & 1 \\ 0 & 1 \end{bmatrix} * \begin{bmatrix} 1 & 0 \\ 1 & 1 \end{bmatrix} = \begin{bmatrix} 2 & 1 \\ 1 & 1 \end{bmatrix} \neq \begin{bmatrix} 1 & 1 \\ 1 & 2 \end{bmatrix} = \begin{bmatrix} 1 & 0 \\ 1 & 1 \end{bmatrix} * \begin{bmatrix} 1 & 1 \\ 0 & 1 \end{bmatrix}.$$

Hence, G is a noncommutative group.

This group is known as the **general linear group of degree 2 over** $\mathbb{R}$ and is denoted by $GL(2, \mathbb{R})$. Indeed, the elements of this group are non singular 2×2 real matrices. If instead, we take only those 2×2 real matrices that have their determinant equal to 1, (i.e., $ad - bc = 1$), they also form a group under matrix multiplication. (see Problem 5(c) of Exercise 3.1) This group is known as **special linear group of degree 2 over** $\mathbb{R}$ and is denoted by $SL(2, \mathbb{R})$.

Example 3.1.12. (a) It is easy to check that $\left\{ A = \begin{bmatrix} a & b \\ c & d \end{bmatrix} \in GL(2, \mathbb{R}) : A^T A = I_2 \right\}$ is a group. This group of real orthogonal matrices is known as the 2-dimensional **Orthogonal group**, denoted by $O(2, \mathbb{R})$.

(b) Again, let $G = \left\{ R_\theta = \begin{bmatrix} \cos\theta & -\sin\theta \\ \sin\theta & \cos\theta \end{bmatrix} \,\middle|\, \theta \in \mathbb{R} \right\}$. Then G is a commutative group under matrix multiplication. Indeed it is routine to check that $R_\alpha R_\beta = R_{\alpha+\beta} = R_\beta R_\alpha$. Associativity of matrix multiplication is known. Clearly the matrix $R_0 = I_2$ is the identity here and inverse for R_θ is $R_{-\theta}$. This group[3] is known as the **special orthogonal group of degree 2 over** $\mathbb{R}$ and is denoted by $SO(2, \mathbb{R})$. Note that here the matrices are orthogonal with determinant value 1.

Remark 3.1.13. Certain examples of group, like *symmetric group* (Example 4.1.4), *quaternion group* (Problem no.6(a) of Exercise 3.1), *dihedral group* (Problem no.6(b) of Exercise 3.1), *Klein's four-group* (Example 5.2.5) etc., abstract as they are, do still have some fascinating geometrical representations. In this regard, group of *symmetries* of an equilateral triangle (Example 8.3.6) or that of a square (Example 8.3.8) are most instructive at this level. We shall take them up at length, at a later stage of development in Chapter 8 on symmetry.

We now prove some elementary properties of a group in the following theorem:

Theorem 3.1.14. *Let* $(G, *)$ *be a group.*

(i)   *For all* $a \in G$, $(a^{-1})^{-1} = a$.

(ii)   *For all* $a, b \in G$, $(a * b)^{-1} = b^{-1} * a^{-1}$.

(iii)   *For all* $a, b, c \in G$, *if either* $a * c = b * c$ *or* $c * a = c * b$,
       then $a = b$.(**cancellation law**)

(iv)   *For all* $a, b \in G$, *the equations* $a * x = b$ *and* $y * a = b$ *have*
       unique solutions in G *for* x *and* y.

---

[3]This group has a beautiful geometric interpretation. It depicts the rotations in a plane and hence is also known as the **rotation group**. Indeed the matrix R_θ represents the anticlockwise rotation through θ degree about the origin in a plane. Seen from this light, the commutativity of their composition, significance of the identity element R_0 as a rotation through 0 degree and inverse $R_{-\theta}$ as a rotation through same angle θ but in opposite (i.e. clockwise) orientation, becomes immediate.

Proof. (i)   In a group, each element has a unique inverse. Hence for $a \in G$, a^{-1} has a unique inverse $(a^{-1})^{-1}$ in G. Now $a^{-1} * a = a * a^{-1} = e$ implies that a is the inverse of a^{-1}. Since the inverse of a^{-1} is unique, we must have $a = (a^{-1})^{-1}$.

(ii)   Let $a, b \in G$. Then

$$
\begin{aligned}
(a * b) * (b^{-1} * a^{-1}) &= \left((a * b) * b^{-1}\right) * a^{-1} \\
&= \left(a * (b * b^{-1})\right) * a^{-1} \\
&= (a * e) * a^{-1} \\
&= a * a^{-1} \\
&= e.
\end{aligned}
$$

Similarly, $(b^{-1} * a^{-1}) * (a * b) = e$. Hence, $b^{-1} * a^{-1}$ is an inverse of $a * b$. Since the inverse of an element is unique in a group and since $(a * b)^{-1}$ denotes the inverse of $a * b$, it follows that $(a * b)^{-1} = b^{-1} * a^{-1}$.

(iii)   Let $a, b, c \in G$. Suppose $a * c = b * c$. Now $(a * c) * c^{-1} = (b * c) * c^{-1}$ implies that $a * (c * c^{-1}) = b * (c * c^{-1})$. Hence, $a * e = b * e$ or $a = b$. Similarly, if $c * a = c * b$, then $a = b$.

(iv)   Let $a, b \subset G$. First we consider the equation $a * x = b$. Now $a^{-1} * b \in G$. Substituting $a^{-1} * b$ for x in the left hand side of the equation $a * x = b$, we see that,

$$
a * (a^{-1} * b) = (a * a^{-1}) * b = e * b = b.
$$

Thus, $a^{-1} * b$ is a solution of the equation $a * x = b$. Next we show the uniqueness of the solution. Suppose c is any solution of $a * x = b$. Then, $a * c = b$. Hence,

$$
\begin{aligned}
c &= e * c \\
&= (a^{-1} * a) * c \quad \text{(since } a^{-1} * a = e) \\
&= a^{-1} * (a * c) \quad \text{(since } * \text{ is associative)} \\
&= a^{-1} * b \quad \text{(since } a * c = b).
\end{aligned}
$$

This yields the uniqueness of the solution. A similar argument holds for the equation $y * a = b$. $\square$

Corollary 3.1.15. *Let $(G, *)$ be a group and $a \in G$. If $a * a = a$, then $a = e$.*

Proof. Since $a = a * a$, we have $a * a = a * e$. By the cancellation law, $a = e$. $\square$

Note that, in a mathematical system, an element a, such that $a * a = a$ is called an ***idempotent element***. The above corollary actually tells that, *in a group, identity element is the only idempotent element.*

The following three theorems give necessary and sufficient conditions for a semi-group to be a group:

Theorem 3.1.16. *A semigroup $(S,*)$ is a group if and only if*

(i)   *there exsists $e \in S$ such that $e * a = a$ for all $a \in S$ and*

(ii) *for all $a \in S$, there exists $b \in S$ such that $b * a = e$.*

Proof. Suppose $(S,*)$ is a semigroup that satisfies (i) and (ii). Let a be any element of S. Then there exists $b \in S$ such that $b * a = e$ by (ii). For $b \in S$, there exists $c \in S$ such that $c * b = e$ by (ii). Now,

$$a = e * a = (c * b) * a = c * (b * a) = c * e$$

and

$$a * b = (c * e) * b = c * (e * b) = c * b = e.$$

Hence, $a * b = e = b * a$. Also,

$$a * e = a * (b * a) = (a * b) * a = e * a = a.$$

Thus, $a * e = a = e * a$. This shows that e is the identity element of S. Now since $a * b = e = b * a$, we have $b = a^{-1}$. Therefore, $(S,*)$ is a group. The converse follows from the definition of a group. $\square$

Note that the above theorem tells that, in a semigroup if there exists a ***left identity*** and every element of the semigroup has a ***left inverse*** with respect to that left identity, then the semigroup becomes a group. However, it is important to note that, if in a semigroup with left identity, every element has a right inverse with respect to the left identity, then the semigroup may not be a group. A suitable counter example may be found in the Worked-out Exercise 3.1.9.

Theorem 3.1.17. *A semigroup $(S,*)$ is a group if and only if for all $a,b \in S$, the equations $a * x = b$ and $y * a = b$ have solutions in S for x and y.*

Proof. Suppose the given equations have solutions in S. Let $a \in S$. Consider the equation $y * a = a$. By our assumption, $y * a = a$ has a solution, say, $u \in S$. Then $u * a = a$. Let b be any element of S. Consider the equation $a * x = b$. Again by our assumption, $a * x = b$ has a solution in S. Let $c \in S$ be the solution in S. Then $a * c = b$. Now

$$\begin{aligned} u * b &= u * (a * c) &&\text{(since } b = a * c) \\ &= (u * a) * c &&\text{(since } * \text{ is assocative)} \\ &= a * c &&\text{(since } u * a = a) \\ &= b. \end{aligned}$$

Since b was an arbitrary element of S, we find that $u * b = b$ for all $b \in S$. Thus $(S, *)$ satisfies (i) of Theorem 3.1.16. Consider the equation $y * a = u$. Let $d \in S$ be a solution of $y * a = u$. This shows that $(S, *)$ satisfies (ii) of Theorem 3.1.16. Hence $(S, *)$ is a group by Theorem 3.1.16.

The converse part follows from part (iv) of Theorem 3.1.14. $\square$

Theorem 3.1.18. *A finite semigroup $(S, *)$ is a group if and only if $(S, *)$ satisfies the cancellation laws (i.e., $a * c = b * c$ implies $a = b$ and $c * a = c * b$ implies $a = b$ for all $a, b, c \in S$).*

Proof. Let $(S, *)$ be a finite semigroup satisfying cancellation laws. Let $a, b \in S$ and consider the equation $a * x = b$. We now show that this equation has a solution in S. Let us write $S = \{a_1, a_2, \ldots, a_n\}$, where a_i's are all distinct elements of S. Since S is a semigroup, $a * a_i \in S$ for all $i = 1, 2, \ldots, n$. Thus, $\{a * a_1, a * a_2, \ldots, a * a_n\} \subseteq S$. Suppose $a * a_i = a * a_j$ for some $i \neq j$. Then by the cancellation law, we have $a_i = a_j$, which is a contradiction, since $a_i \neq a_j$. Hence all the elements $\{a * a_1, a * a_2, \ldots, a * a_n\}$ are distinct. Thus $S = \{a * a_1, a * a_2, \ldots, a * a_n\}$. Let $b \in S$. Then $b = a * a_k$ for some $a_k \in S$. Therefore the equation $a * x = b$ has a solution a_k in S. Similarly, we can show that the equation $y * a = b$ has a solution in S. Hence, by Theorem 3.1.17, $(S, *)$ is a group.

The converse follows from the definition of a group and Theorem 3.1.14(iii). $\square$

Let $(G, *)$ be a group, $a \in G$ and $n \in \mathbb{Z}$. We now define the **integral power** a^n of a as follows:

$$\begin{aligned} a^0 &= e \\ a^n &= a * a^{n-1} \text{ if } n > 0 \\ a^n &= (a^{-1})^{-n} \text{ if } n < 0. \end{aligned}$$

Note that $a^n = (a^{-n})^{-1}$, if $n < 0$. In a group $(G, *)$, we can prove the following;

Theorem 3.1.19. *Let $(G, *)$ be a group, $a, b \in G$ and $m, n \in \mathbb{Z}$. Then*
(i) $a^n * a^m = a^{n+m} = a^m * a^n$,
(ii) $(a^n)^m = a^{nm}$,
(iii) $a^{-n} = (a^n)^{-1}$ *and*
(iv) $(a * b)^n = a^n * b^n$, *if $(G, *)$ is commutative.*

The proofs of these are left as simple exercises.

Remark 3.1.20. Although we have defined the integral power a^n of an element a in a group, it is not difficult to see that a similar definition may be given in case of the elements of a semigroup as well[4], of course with the restriction that $n \geq 0$, as elements of a semigroup do not have inverse. Naturally in that case, all the parts of Theorem 3.1.19 except (iii) will hold good.

Definition 3.1.21. Let $(G, *)$ be a group and $a \in G$. If there exists a positive integer n such that $a^n = e$, then the smallest such positive integer is called the **order** of a. If no such n exists, then we say that a is of **infinite order**.

We denote the order of an element a of a group $(G, *)$ by o(a). The concept of the *order of an element* is very important in group theory.[5]

Example 3.1.22. Consider the group $(\mathbb{Z}_6, +)$, where $+$ is the addition among classes as defined in Example 3.1.5. $\mathbb{Z}_6$ has order 6. The elements $[0], [1], [2], [3], [4], [5]$ have orders $1, 6, 3, 2, 3, 6$ respectively. For example, $2[3] = [3] + [3] = [6] = [0]$ and 2 is the smallest positive integer such that $2[3] = [0]$.

Example 3.1.23. Consider the group $\left(\mathcal{P}(X), \triangle\right)$ discussed in the Example 3.1.9 where $\mathcal{P}(X)$ is the power set of an *infinite* set X. Since every element of $\mathcal{P}(X)$ is its own inverse, so every element of this group is of order 2. *This is an infinite group where every element is of finite order.*[6]

Let G be a group and $a \in G$. If o(a) is infinite, then by the definition of the order of an element, it follows that o(a^k) is also infinite, for all $k \geq 1$, i.e., the order of every positive power of a is also infinite. If o(a) is finite, then the following theorem tells us how to compute the order of various powers of a.

Theorem 3.1.24. *Let* $(G, *)$ *be a group and* a *be an element of* G *such that* o(a) $= n$.

(i)   If $a^m = e$ *for some positive integer* m, *then* n *divides* m.

(ii)   For every positive integer t,

$$o(a^t) = \frac{n}{gcd\,(t, n)}.$$

---

[4]This definition will come in handy when such a concept will be introduced in a Ring for its multiplicative reduct in the relevant chapter.

[5]Recall that the term 'order' was also used in a different context to denote the number of elements of a finite group. This distinction should be noted carefully. However, for a finite group these two concepts are beautifully interrelated as we shall see later.

[6]Here the order of each element of the infinite group turns out to be the same. A more general example of an infinite group with elements having finite but different order is given in Problem 29 of Exercise 5.4. A group with every element of finite order is often called a **torsion group**, while the group with every non-identity element of infinite order is called a **torsion-free group**. Note that the group $(\mathbb{R}^*, \cdot)$ is neither a torsion group nor torsion-free.

Proof. (i) By division algorithm, there exist $q, r \in \mathbb{Z}$ such that $m = nq + r$, where $0 \le r < n$. Now

$$a^r = a^{m-nq} = a^m * a^{-nq} = a^m * (a^n)^{-q} = e * (e)^{-q} = e.$$

Since n is the smallest positive integer such that $a^n = e$ and $a^r = e$ though $r < n$, it follows that $r = 0$. Thus $m = nq$. This implies that n divides m.

(ii) Let $o(a^t) = k$. Then $a^{kt} = e$. By (i), n divides kt. Thus there exists $r \in \mathbb{Z}$ such that $kt = nr$. Let $\gcd(t, n) = d$. Then there exist integers u and v such that $t = du$ and $n = dv$ and $\gcd(u, v) = 1$. Now $kt = nr$ implies that $kdu = dvr$. Hence $ku = rv$. Thus v divides ku. Since $\gcd(u, v) = 1$, v divides k. Thus $\frac{n}{d}$ divides k. Now,

$$(a^t)^{\frac{n}{d}} = a^{\frac{nt}{d}} = a^{\frac{ndu}{d}} = a^{nu} = (a^n)^u = e^u = e.$$

Since $o(a^t) = k$, k divides $\frac{n}{d}$. Since k and $\frac{n}{d}$ are positive integers, $k = \frac{n}{d}$. Hence, $o(a^t) = k = \frac{n}{d} = \frac{n}{\gcd(t,n)}$. $\qquad\square$

Worked-out Exercises

$\Diamond$ **Exercise 3.1.1.** Which of the following groupoids are semigroups? Which are groups?

(i) $(\mathbb{N}, *)$ where $a * b = ab$ for all $a, b \in \mathbb{N}$.

(ii) $(\mathbb{N}, *)$ where $a * b = b$ for all $a, b \in \mathbb{N}$.

(iii) $(\mathbb{Z}, *)$ where $a * b = a + b + 2$ for all $a, b \in \mathbb{Z}$.

(iv) $(\mathbb{Z}, *)$ where $a * b = a - b$ for all $a, b \in \mathbb{Z}$.

(v) $(\mathbb{Z}, *)$ where $a * b = a + b + ab$ for all $a, b \in \mathbb{Z}$.

(vi) $(\mathbb{R}, *)$ where $a * b = a|b|$ for all $a, b \in \mathbb{R}$.

(vii) $(\mathbb{R}, *)$ where $a * b = 2^a b$ for all $a, b \in \mathbb{R}$.

(viii) $(\mathbb{R} \smallsetminus \{-1\}, *)$ where $a * b = a + b + ab$ for all $a, b \in \mathbb{R} \smallsetminus \{-1\}$.

Solution. (i) For any three natural numbers a, b, c we know that $a(bc) = (ab)c$. Hence $(\mathbb{N}, *)$ is a semigroup. Now, $1 \in \mathbb{N}$ and $1a = a1 = a$ for all $a \in \mathbb{N}$. So, we find that 1 is the identity element. In this semigroup, for the integer 2, there does not exist any natural number x such that $x2 = 2x = 1$. This implies that the inverse of 2 does not exist in $\mathbb{N}$. Hence $(\mathbb{N}, *)$ is not a group.

(ii) It is easy to see that this mathematical system is a semigroup. Indeed, for any three natural numbers $a, b, c \in \mathbb{N}$ we have $a * (b * c) = a * c = c$ and also $(a * b) * c = b * c = c$ whence $a * (b * c) = (a * b) * c$, which proves our claim. However, this is not a group as there does not exist an identity element in $(\mathbb{N}, *)$. In fact, the very nature of the operation shows that whatever element a may be chosen from $\mathbb{N}$, we cannot find a unique element e (say) from $\mathbb{N}$, such that $a * e = a$ holds for every choice of a.

(iii)   It is routine to check that this groupoid is a semigroup. We only show that this mathematical system is actually a group. Indeed, we see that $-2 \in \mathbb{Z}$, so that $a * (-2) = a + (-2) + 2 = a = (-2) + a + 2 = (-2) * a$, proving thereby that -2 is the identity element of $(\mathbb{Z}, *)$.

Again for any $a \in \mathbb{Z}$, we see that $-a + (-4) \in \mathbb{Z}$, so that $a * \left(-a + (-4)\right) = a + (-a) + (-4) + 2 = -2 = \left(-a + (-4)\right) + a + 2 = \left(-a + (-4)\right) * a$, whence we conclude that $-a + (-4)$ is the inverse of a in $(\mathbb{Z}, *)$. Hence $(\mathbb{Z}, *)$ is a group.

(iv)   This groupoid is not a semigroup. For $1, 2, 3 \in \mathbb{Z}$ we see that $1 * (2 * 3) = 1 * (2 - 3) = 1 * (-1) = 1 + 1 = 2$ but $(1 * 2) * 3 = (1 - 2) * 3 = (-1) * 3 = (-1) - 3 = -4$, whence the operation is clearly non-associative.

(v)   This groupoid is a semigroup.
Indeed, for all $a, b, c \in \mathbb{Z}$, $a * (b * c) = a * (b + c + bc) = a + (b + c + bc) + a(b + c + bc) = a + b + c + ab + bc + ac + abc$ and $(a * b) * c = (a + b + ab) * c = a + b + ab + c + (a + b + ab)c = a + b + c + ab + bc + ac + abc$.

However, this is not a group, as $-1 \in \mathbb{Z}$ and $-1 * x = -1$ for any $x \in \mathbb{Z}$.

(vi)   This groupoid is a semigroup. In fact, for all $a, b, c \in \mathbb{R}$, we have $a * (b * c) = a * (b|c|) = a\left|b|c|\right| = a|b||c| = (a|b|) * c = (a * b) * c$.

This mathematical system fails to be a group. In fact, we know that in a group there can be only one idempotent element, which is its identity element. Observe that here, both 1 and -1 are idempotents of this mathematical system $(\mathbb{R}, *)$. Indeed, $1 * 1 = 1|1| = 1$ as well as $(-1) * (-1) = (-1)|-1| = (-1)1 = -1$ proves our claim.

(vii)   This groupoid is not a semigroup. In fact, for $2, 1, 3 \in \mathbb{R}$, we see that $2 * (1 * 3) = 2 * (2^1.3) = 2 * 6 = 2^2.6 = 24$ whereas $(2 * 1) * 3 = (2^2.1) * 3 = 4 * 3 = 2^4.3 = 48$.

(viii)   At the outset, observe that, if $a, b \in \mathbb{R} \smallsetminus \{-1\}$, i.e., if $a, b \in \mathbb{R}$ but $a \neq -1$ and $b \neq -1$, then $a + b + ab \in \mathbb{R}$ but $a + b + ab \neq -1$; as otherwise, $a + b + ab = -1$ would lead to $(a + 1)(b + 1) = 0$, whence either $a = -1$ or $b = -1$, which would have been contradictory to the choice of a and b. Hence $a + b + ab \in \mathbb{R} \smallsetminus \{-1\}$.

That this groupoid is a semigroup follows from the arguments similar to the one presented in (v) above.

Note that $0 \in \mathbb{R} \smallsetminus \{-1\}$, so that $0 * a = 0 + a + 0.a = a$ for all $a \in \mathbb{R} \smallsetminus \{-1\}$, whence 0 is the left identity element of $(\mathbb{R} \smallsetminus \{-1\}, *)$.

Again, for any $a \in \mathbb{R} \smallsetminus \{-1\}$, we have $-\frac{a}{1+a} \in \mathbb{R} \smallsetminus \{-1\}$ (note that $a \neq -1$ and also $-\frac{a}{1+a} \neq -1$, as otherwise $a = 1 + a$ -a contradiction) so that $\left(-\frac{a}{1+a}\right) * a = -\frac{a}{1+a} + a - \frac{a^2}{1+a} = \frac{-a+a+a^2-a^2}{1+a} = 0$, whence we see that every element of $\mathbb{R} \smallsetminus \{-1\}$ has a left inverse in it with respect to the left identity 0. Consequently, $(\mathbb{R} \smallsetminus \{-1\}, *)$ is a group by Theorem 3.1.16.

◊ **Exercise 3.1.2.** Write all complex roots of $x^6 = 1$. Show that they form a group under the usual complex multiplication.

Solution. All complex roots of $x^6 = 1$ are given by $\cos \frac{2k\pi}{6} + i \sin \frac{2k\pi}{6}$, where $k = 0, 1, 2, 3, 4, 5$. Let T be the set of all roots of $x^6 = 1$. If $\alpha, \beta \in T$, then $\alpha^6 = 1, \beta^6 = 1$ and hence $(\alpha\beta)^6 = \alpha^6 \beta^6 = 1.1 = 1$. Hence the set T is a groupoid under usual multiplication of complex numbers. Usual multiplication of complex numbers is known to be associative and also $1 = \cos 0 + i \sin 0$, for $k = 0$, is a member of T, which plays the role of identity. Let $\alpha \in T$. Certainly, $\alpha \neq 0$. Then $\alpha^6 = 1$. Now $\left(\frac{1}{\alpha}\right)^6 = \frac{1}{\alpha^6} = \frac{1}{1} = 1$. Hence for each $\alpha \in T$, the inverse of α exists in T. Hence T is a group under the usual multiplication of complex numbers.

Remark. The above problem can easily be extended to all the complex roots of $x^n = 1$ with a similar result, for any $n \in \mathbb{N}$.

◊ **Exercise 3.1.3.** Let $G = \{a \in \mathbb{R} : -1 < a < 1\}$. Define $*$ on G by $a * b = \frac{a+b}{1+ab}$ for all $a, b \in G$. Show that $*$ is a binary operation on G. Hence prove that $(G, *)$ is a group.

Solution. Observe that $-1 < x < 1$ if and only if $x^2 < 1$ for all $x \in \mathbb{R}$. Let $a, b \in G$. First let us show that $a * b \in G$. Now, $a^2 < 1$ and $b^2 < 1$. Thus, $(1 - a^2)(1 - b^2) > 0$. This indicates that $1 - a^2 - b^2 + a^2b^2 > 0$. Now $(1 + ab)^2 - (a + b)^2 = 1 + a^2b^2 + 2ab - a^2 - b^2 - 2ab = 1 - a^2 - b^2 + a^2b^2 > 0$ and so $\left(\frac{a+b}{1+ab}\right)^2 < 1$. Therefore, $a * b \in G$. Hence G is closed under $*$. Associativity of $*$ i.e., $(a * b) * c = a * (b * c)$ for all $a, b.c \in G$ can be routinely verified. Therefore, $(G, *)$ is a semigroup.

Note that $0 \in G$ so that

$$0 * a = \frac{0 + a}{1 + 0a} = a \quad \text{for all } a \in G.$$

This shows that the semigroup $(G, *)$ has a left identity. Let $a \in G$. Then $-a \in G$ and

$$(-a) * a = \frac{-a + a}{1 + (-a)a} = 0.$$

Thus in $(G, *)$ for each $a \in G$, there exists a left inverse. So we conclude that $(G, *)$ is a group.

◊ **Exercise 3.1.4.** Write down the Cayley table for the group operation of the group $\mathbb{Z}_5$.

Solution. The Cayley table for the group operation of $\mathbb{Z}_5$ is given by

+	[0]	[1]	[2]	[3]	[4]
[0]	[0]	[1]	[2]	[3]	[4]
[1]	[1]	[2]	[3]	[4]	[0]
[2]	[2]	[3]	[4]	[0]	[1]
[3]	[3]	[4]	[0]	[1]	[2]
[4]	[4]	[0]	[1]	[2]	[3]

◊ **Exercise 3.1.5.** Consider the group $\mathbb{Z}_{30}$. Find the smallest positive integer n such that $n[5] = [0]$ in $\mathbb{Z}_{30}$.

Solution. $n[5] = [0]$ implies that $[5n] = [0]$, in $\mathbb{Z}_{30}$, i.e., 30 divides $5n$. So we find that 6 is the smallest positive integer such that $6[5] = [30] = [0]$.

◊ **Exercise 3.1.6.** Write down all elements of the group U_{10}. Write the Cayley table for this group.

Solution. We note that $U_{10} = \left\{ [a] \in \mathbb{Z}_{10} \mid 0 < a < 10 \text{ and } \gcd(a, 10) = 1 \right\}$. Hence $U_{10} = \left\{ [1], [3], [7], [9] \right\}$. Now U_{10} is a group under the binary operation $*$ defined by $[a] * [b] = [ab]$. For example, $[3] * [7] = [21] = [1]$ in $\mathbb{Z}_{10}$. The Cayley table for this group is given by

*	[1]	[3]	[7]	[9]
[1]	[1]	[3]	[7]	[9]
[3]	[3]	[9]	[1]	[7]
[7]	[7]	[1]	[9]	[3]
[9]	[9]	[7]	[3]	[1]

◊ **Exercise 3.1.7.** Let $(G, *)$ be a group such that $(a * b)^{-1} = a^{-1} * b^{-1}$ for all $a, b \in G$, then show that G is a commutative group.

Solution. For all $a, b \in G$, $a^{-1} * b^{-1} = (a * b)^{-1} = b^{-1} * a^{-1}$. Hence $(a^{-1} * b^{-1})^{-1} = (b^{-1} * a^{-1})^{-1}$, i.e., $(b^{-1})^{-1} * (a^{-1})^{-1} = (a^{-1})^{-1} * (b^{-1})^{-1}$ i.e., $b * a = a * b$. So it follows that the group $(G, *)$ is a commutative group.

◊ **Exercise 3.1.8.** Let $G = \left\{ \begin{bmatrix} x & x \\ x & x \end{bmatrix} \mid x \in \mathbb{R}^* \right\}$. Show that G is a commutative group under usual matrix multiplication.

Solution. Clearly

$$\begin{bmatrix} x & x \\ x & x \end{bmatrix} \begin{bmatrix} y & y \\ y & y \end{bmatrix} = \begin{bmatrix} 2xy & 2xy \\ 2xy & 2xy \end{bmatrix} \in G$$

since $2xy \in \mathbb{R}^*$. Also commutativity of these matrices under multiplication is easily seen. Again

$$\begin{bmatrix} \frac{1}{2} & \frac{1}{2} \\ \frac{1}{2} & \frac{1}{2} \end{bmatrix} \begin{bmatrix} x & x \\ x & x \end{bmatrix} = \begin{bmatrix} \frac{x}{2} + \frac{x}{2} & \frac{x}{2} + \frac{x}{2} \\ \frac{x}{2} + \frac{x}{2} & \frac{x}{2} + \frac{x}{2} \end{bmatrix} = \begin{bmatrix} x & x \\ x & x \end{bmatrix}$$

shows that $\begin{bmatrix} \frac{1}{2} & \frac{1}{2} \\ \frac{1}{2} & \frac{1}{2} \end{bmatrix}$ is the identity here and

$$\begin{bmatrix} \frac{1}{4x} & \frac{1}{4x} \\ \frac{1}{4x} & \frac{1}{4x} \end{bmatrix} \begin{bmatrix} x & x \\ x & x \end{bmatrix} = \begin{bmatrix} \frac{x}{4x} + \frac{x}{4x} & \frac{x}{4x} + \frac{x}{4x} \\ \frac{x}{4x} + \frac{x}{4x} & \frac{x}{4x} + \frac{x}{4x} \end{bmatrix} = \begin{bmatrix} \frac{1}{2} & \frac{1}{2} \\ \frac{1}{2} & \frac{1}{2} \end{bmatrix}$$

shows that $\begin{bmatrix} \frac{1}{4x} & \frac{1}{4x} \\ \frac{1}{4x} & \frac{1}{4x} \end{bmatrix}$ is the inverse of $\begin{bmatrix} x & x \\ x & x \end{bmatrix}$. Hence, G is a commutative group under matrix multiplication.

Note: Since the matrices in the above Example are *singular*, they are clearly not 'invertible' in matrix theoretic sense. However, they do have group theoretic inverse as has been shown. Also their group theoretic 'identity element' is different from the usual 'identity matrix', which is not even a member of the set concerned. The matrix theoretic significance of the group theoretic inverse is highly non trivial. It involves the concept of generalized inverse of a matrix and is out of scope of discussion here.

◊ **Exercise 3.1.9.** Give a counter example to justify that in a semigroup with left identity, if every element has a right inverse with respect to the left identity, it need not be a group.

Solution. Consider the set $\mathbb{Z} \times \mathbb{Z}$ endowed with the operation $(a, b) * (c, d) = (c, b+d)$ for all $(a, b), (c, d) \in \mathbb{Z} \times \mathbb{Z}$. It is a routine exercise to verify that $(\mathbb{Z} \times \mathbb{Z}, *)$ is a semigroup. Observe that, $(0, 0) * (a, b) = (a, 0+b) = (a, b)$ for all $(a, b) \in \mathbb{Z} \times \mathbb{Z}$, whence $(0, 0) \in \mathbb{Z} \times \mathbb{Z}$ is a left identity of $(\mathbb{Z} \times \mathbb{Z}, *)$. Note that, for $(a, b) \in \mathbb{Z} \times \mathbb{Z}$, we have $(0, -b) \in \mathbb{Z} \times \mathbb{Z}$ such that $(a, b) * (0, -b) = \left(0, b + (-b)\right) = (0, 0)$, whence $(0, -b)$ is a right $(0, 0)$-inverse of (a, b) in $(\mathbb{Z} \times \mathbb{Z}, *)$. However, observe that $(\mathbb{Z} \times \mathbb{Z}, *)$ does not admit an identity and hence $(\mathbb{Z} \times \mathbb{Z}, *)$ is not a group.

Note: Another counter example of similar nature can be constructed with the set $\mathbb{R}^*$ endowed with the operation $a \cdot b = |a|b$ where -1 plays the role of left identity. We leave it to the reader to verify this example in details.

◇ **Exercise 3.1.10.** Find the order of $[6]$ in the group $\mathbb{Z}_{14}$ and the order of $[3]$ in the group U_{14}.

Solution. Let n be the order of $[6]$ in $\mathbb{Z}_{14}$. Then n is the smallest positive integer such that $n[6] = [0]$. Now $n[6] = [0]$ if and only if $[6n] = [0]$, i.e., 14 divides $6n$. Hence $n = 7$, i.e., the order of $[6]$ in $\mathbb{Z}_{14}$ is 7.

Let n be the order of $[3]$ in U_{14}. This means that n is the smallest positive integer such that $[3]^n = [1]$. Now $[3]^n = [1]$ if and only if $[3^n] = [1]$, i.e., if and only if 14 divides $3^n - 1$. For $n = 6$, $3^6 - 1 = 728$ is divisible by 14 and for $0 < n < 6$, $3^n - 1$ is not divisible by 14. Hence the order of $[3]$ in U_{14} is 6.

◇ **Exercise 3.1.11.** Prove that in a group $(G, *)$ of even order, there must exist at least one nonidentity element $a \in G$ such that $a^2 = e$.

Solution. Let $A = \{g \in G \mid g \neq g^{-1}\} \subseteq G$. Then $e \notin A$. If $g \in A$, then $g^{-1} \in A$, i.e., elements of A occur in pairs. Therefore, the number of elelments in A is even. This implies that the number of elements in $\{e\} \cup A$ is odd. Since the number of elements in G is even and $\{e\} \cup A \subseteq G$ there exists $a \in G$, such that $a \notin \{e\} \cup A$. But then $a \neq e$ and $a \notin A$. Hence there exists $a \in G$ such that $a \neq e$ and $a = a^{-1}$ i.e., $a^2 = e$.

◇ **Exercise 3.1.12.** Let $(G, *)$ be a group and $a, b \in G$. Suppose that $a^2 = e$ and $a * b * a = b^7$. Prove that $b^{48} = e$.

Solution. Here $a * b * a = b^7$. Then $a * (a * b * a) * a = a * b^7 * a$, i.e., $a^2 * b * a^2 = a * b^7 * a$. Hence, $b = (a * b * a)^7$ (since $a^2 = e$ and $(a * b * a)(a * b * a) * \ldots * (a * b * a) = a * b * a^2 * b * a^2 * \ldots * a^2 * b * a = a * b^7 * a$). This implies that $b = (b^7)^7$, i.e., $b = b^{49}$. Hence $b^{48} = e$.

◇ **Exercise 3.1.13.** In a finite monoid $(S, *)$, if the identity element is the only idempotent element, then prove that each element of the monoid is invertible.

Solution. Let $(S, *)$ be a finite monoid and e be its identity. Let a be any element of S. Since S is finite, we must have $a^n = a^m$ for some $n, m \in \mathbb{N}$ with $n > m$. Let r be the smallest positive integer such that $a^{m+r} = a^m$. Now $m + 1, m + 2, \ldots, m + r$ are distinct r consecutive positive integers. Clearly there exists an integer k such that $m + k \equiv 1 \pmod{r}$. Then $m + k - 1 = rt$ for some nonnegative integer t. Now $(a^{m+k-1})(a^{m+k-1}) = a^{rt+m+k-1} = a^{rt+m}a^{k-1} = a^m a^{k-1}$ [as $a^m = a^{m+rt}$] $= a^{m+k-1}$. By the given condition $a^{m+k-1} = e$. This shows that $a * a^{m+k-2} = e = a^{m+k-2} * a$ (considering $a^0 = e$). Hence the result.

◇ **Exercise 3.1.14.** Let $(S, *)$ be a semigroup such that for all $a \in S$, there exists some $x \in S$ such that $a = a * x * a$. If such a semigroup S has a single idempotent, prove that it is a group.

Solution. Let the single idempotent of $(S, *)$ be denoted by e. Let a be an arbitrary element of S. Then there exists $x \in S$ such that $a = a * x * a$ so that $a * x = a * x * a * x$, whence $a * x$ is an idempotent in S, so that $a * x = e$. In a similar way we can show $x * a = x * a * x * a$ so that $x * a = e$ and consequently we have $x * a = e = a * x$ in S. This shows that $a = a * x * a = a * e$ and also $a = a * x * a = e * a$. Let $b \in S$. Then there exists $y \in S$ such that $b = b * y * b$. Hence $b * y$ and $y * b$ are idempotents. So $b * y = y * b = e$ and $e * b = b * e = b$. Hence $(S, *)$ is a group.

♦ **Exercise 3.1.15.** Prove that a group $(G, *)$ is commutative if $(a * b)^n = a^n * b^n$, for any three consecutive integers n and for all $a, b \in G$.

Solution. Suppose in the group $(G, *)$, $(a * b)^n = a^n * b^n$ for all $a, b \in G$ and for any three consecutive integers n. Then

$$(a * b)^n \quad = \quad a^n * b^n \qquad \ldots (1)$$
$$(a * b)^{n+1} \quad = \quad a^{n+1} * b^{n+1} \qquad \ldots (2)$$
$$\text{and} \quad (a * b)^{n+2} \quad = \quad a^{n+2} * b^{n+2} \qquad \ldots (3)$$

From (2),	$(a * b)^n * (a * b)$	$=$	$a^{n+1} * b^{n+1}$
By (1),	$(a^n * b^n) * (a * b)$	$=$	$a^{n+1} * b^{n+1}$
$\Rightarrow$	$a^n * \left(b^n * (a * b)\right)$	$=$	$a^{n+1} * b^{n+1}$
$\Rightarrow$	$b^n * (a * b)$	$=$	$a * b^{n+1}$ (by cancellation property)
$\Rightarrow$	$(b^n * a) * b$	$=$	$a * b^{n+1}$
$\Rightarrow$	$b^n * a$	$=$	$a * b^n$ (by cancellation property)

$$\ldots (4)$$

Again from (3),

	$(a * b)^{n+1} * (a * b)$	$=$	$a^{n+2} * b^{n+2}$
$\Rightarrow$	$(a^{n+1} * b^{n+1}) * (a * b)$	$=$	$a^{n+2} * b^{n+2}$
$\Rightarrow$	$a^{n+1} * \left(b^{n+1} * (a * b)\right)$	$=$	$a^{n+2} * b^{n+2}$
$\Rightarrow$	$b^{n+1} * (a * b)$	$=$	$a * b^{n+2}$
$\Rightarrow$	$b * (b^n * a) * b$	$=$	$a * b^{n+2}$
$\Rightarrow$	$b * (a * b^n) * b$	$=$	$a * b^{n+2}$ (by (4))

Hence $(b * a) * b^{n+1} = a * b^{n+2}$. Then by cancellation,

$$b * a = a * b.$$

Hence $(G, *)$ is a commutative group.

◇ **Exercise 3.1.16.** Let $\mathbb{Z}$ be the set of all integers. Consider the group $(\mathbb{Z}, \oplus)$ where $\oplus : \mathbb{Z} \times \mathbb{Z} \longrightarrow \mathbb{Z}$ is defined by $a \oplus b = a + b - 5$ for all $a, b \in \mathbb{Z}$ ['+' denotes the usual addition of integers]. Then the identity element of this group is
(i) 0   (ii) 5   (iii) −5   (iv) 25.

Solution. Let $c \in \mathbb{Z}$ be the identity element in the group $(\mathbb{Z}, \oplus)$. Then $a \oplus c = a$ implies $a + c - 5 = a$, i.e., $c = 5$. Therefore, option (ii) is correct.

◇ **Exercise 3.1.17.** Let a and b be two elements of finite order in a group G. Pick the correct statement from below.
   (i) $o(ab) = o(a)o(b)$.
   (ii) $o(ab) = \text{lcm}\,(o(a), o(b))$.
   (iii) $o(ab)$ may be infinite.
   (iv) $o(ab) = \gcd(o(a), o(b))$.

Solution. In the group $GL_2(\mathbb{R})$, the group of all 2×2 non-singular matrices with respect to usual multiplication of matrices, consider two elements $A = \begin{pmatrix} 0 & 1 \\ -1 & 0 \end{pmatrix}$ and $B = \begin{pmatrix} 0 & -1 \\ 1 & -1 \end{pmatrix}$. In this case $AB = \begin{pmatrix} 1 & -1 \\ 0 & 1 \end{pmatrix}$, whence $(AB)^n = \begin{pmatrix} 1 & -n \\ 0 & 1 \end{pmatrix}$. Here $o(A) = 4$ and $o(B) = 3$ but $o(AB)$ is infinite. Therefore, option (iii) is correct. Indeed this fact itself is a counter example to other three cases.

◇ **Exercise 3.1.18.** Find out which of following is not a group.
   (i) $(\mathbb{R} \setminus \{1\}, \cdot)$, where '$\cdot$' is usual multiplication on $\mathbb{R}$.
   (ii) $(\mathbb{R} \setminus \{0\}, \cdot)$, where '$\cdot$' is usual multiplication on $\mathbb{R}$.
   (iii) $(\mathbb{R}^+, \cdot)$, where '$\cdot$' is usual multiplication on $\mathbb{R}$.
   (iv) $(\mathbb{R}^-, *)$; where '$*$' is defined by $a * b = |a|\, b$, for all $a, b \in \mathbb{R}^-$.

Solution. One can easily check that $(\mathbb{R} \setminus \{0\}, \cdot)$ and $(\mathbb{R}^+, \cdot)$ are two groups. Also it is easy to verify that $(\mathbb{R}^-, *)$ is a group with identity element -1 and inverse of any element $x \in \mathbb{R}^-$ is $\frac{1}{x}$. Finally, in $(\mathbb{R} \setminus \{1\}, \cdot)$, the element $0 \in \mathbb{R} \setminus \{1\}$ has no inverse. Hence $(\mathbb{R} \setminus \{1\}, \cdot)$ is not a group. Therefore, option (i) is correct.

Exercises

1. Which of the following groupoids are semigroups? Which are groups?

   (a) $(\mathbb{N}, *)$, where $a * b = a + b$ for all $a, b \in \mathbb{N}$.

   (b) $(\mathbb{N}, *)$, where $a * b = a$ for all $a, b \in \mathbb{N}$.

   (c) $(\mathbb{Z}, *)$, where $a * b = a + b + 1$ for all $a, b \in \mathbb{Z}$.

   (d) $(\mathbb{Z}, *)$, where $a * b = a + b - 1$ for all $a, b \in \mathbb{Z}$.

   (e) $(\mathbb{Z}, *)$, where $a * b = a + 2b$ for all $a, b \in \mathbb{Z}$.

   (f) $(\mathbb{Z}, *)$, where $a * b = a + b - ab$ for all $a, b \in \mathbb{Z}$.

   (g) $(\mathbb{R}, *)$, where $a * b = |a|b$ for all $a, b \in \mathbb{R}$.

   (h) $(\mathbb{R}, *)$, where $a * b = a^2 b^2$ for all $a, b \in \mathbb{R}$.

   (i) $(\mathbb{R}, *)$, where $a * b = a + b + ab$ for all $a, b \in \mathbb{R}$.

   (j) $(\mathbb{Q}^+, *)$, where $a * b = ab$ for all $a, b \in \mathbb{Q}^+$.

   (k) $(\mathbb{Q} \smallsetminus \{0\}, *)$, where $a * b = ab$ for all $a, b \in \mathbb{Q} \smallsetminus \{0\}$.

2. Let $\mathbb{R}^-$ denote the set of all negative real numbers. Can you define a binary operation $*$ on $\mathbb{R}^-$ so that the system $(\mathbb{R}^-, *)$ becomes a group?

3. Write all complex roots of $x^n = 1$ where $n \in \mathbb{N}$. Show that they form a group under the usual complex multiplication.

4. Show that the set of all complex numbers $z = a + ib$ such that $|z|^2 = a^2 + b^2 = 1$ is a group under the usual multiplication of complex numbers[7].

   [This group is called the **circle group**, as its elements lie on the circle of radius 1 centred at origin in the Argand plane.]

5. In each of the following problems show that the given set of matrices forms a group under usual matrix multiplication.

   (a) $G = \left\{ \begin{bmatrix} a & 0 \\ b & 1 \end{bmatrix} : a, b \in \mathbb{R}, a \neq 0 \right\}$.

   (b) $G = \left\{ \begin{bmatrix} 1 & n \\ 0 & 1 \end{bmatrix} \mid n \in \mathbb{Z} \right\}$.

   (c) $SL(2, \mathbb{R}) = \left\{ \begin{bmatrix} a & b \\ c & d \end{bmatrix} \mid a, b, c, d \in \mathbb{R}, ad - bc = 1 \right\}$.

   (d) $SL(2, \mathbb{Z}) = \left\{ \begin{bmatrix} a & b \\ c & d \end{bmatrix} \mid a, b, c, d \in \mathbb{Z}, ad - bc = 1 \right\}$.

   (e) $G = \left\{ \begin{bmatrix} a & b \\ -b & a \end{bmatrix} : a, b \in \mathbb{R}, a \text{ and } b \text{ not both zero} \right\}$. Show further that the group G is commutative.

   (f) $D = \{ diag(d_1, d_2, d_3) \mid d_i \in \mathbb{R}^* \}$, i.e., the set of 3×3 **diagonal matrices** with non zero diagonal entries.

---

[7]Note that a complex number $a + ib$ may also be looked upon as an ordered pair of reals $(a, b) = (a, 0) + (0, b) = (a, 0) + (0, 1)(b, 0)$. Now, since the complex multiplication is commutative, we have $(0, 1)(b, 0) = (b, 0)(0, 1)$, whence a complex number may also be written as $a + bi$.

(g) $L = \left\{ \begin{bmatrix} p & 0 & 0 \\ a & q & 0 \\ b & c & r \end{bmatrix} \Big| p, q, r \neq 0 \right\}$ over $\mathbb{R}$ i.e., the set of 3×3 **lower triangular matrices** with non zero diagonal entries.

Further show that if $p = q = r = 1$, still it is a group under the same operation.

(h) $H_3(\mathbb{R}) = \left\{ \begin{bmatrix} 1 & a & b \\ 0 & 1 & c \\ 0 & 0 & 1 \end{bmatrix} \Big| a, b, c \in \mathbb{R} \right\}.$

[This group of upper triangular matrices with each diagonal entry 1 is known as the 3-dimensional **Heisenberg group**.]

6. (a) Consider the matrices over $\mathbb{C}$ given by

$$\mathbf{1} = \begin{bmatrix} 1 & 0 \\ 0 & 1 \end{bmatrix}, \ \mathbf{i} = \begin{bmatrix} 0 & -1 \\ 1 & 0 \end{bmatrix}, \ \mathbf{j} = \begin{bmatrix} 0 & -i \\ -i & 0 \end{bmatrix}, \ \mathbf{k} = \begin{bmatrix} i & 0 \\ 0 & -i \end{bmatrix}.$$

Show that the set $\mathcal{Q}_8 = \{\pm\mathbf{1}, \pm\mathbf{i}, \pm\mathbf{j}, \pm\mathbf{k}\}$ is a non commutative group under matrix multiplication by writing down the corresponding Cayley table. Verify from Cayley table that $\mathbf{i}^2 = \mathbf{j}^2 = \mathbf{k}^2 = \mathbf{ijk} = -\mathbf{1}$. Show further that $o(\mathbf{i}) = 4$ and $\mathbf{ji} = \mathbf{i}^3\mathbf{j}$. [It is known as the **Quaternion group**. Further discussion on this group is given in Definition 5.1.15.]

(b) Consider the matrices over $\mathbb{R}$ given by

$$\mathbf{1} = \begin{bmatrix} 1 & 0 \\ 0 & 1 \end{bmatrix}, \ \mathbf{r} = \begin{bmatrix} 0 & -1 \\ 1 & 0 \end{bmatrix}, \ \mathbf{s} = \begin{bmatrix} 0 & -1 \\ -1 & 0 \end{bmatrix}, \ \mathbf{t} = \begin{bmatrix} 1 & 0 \\ 0 & -1 \end{bmatrix}.$$

Show that the set $\mathcal{D}_8 = \{\pm\mathbf{1}, \pm\mathbf{r}, \pm\mathbf{s}, \pm\mathbf{t}\}$ is a non commutative group under matrix multiplication by writing down the corresponding Cayley table. Show further that $o(\mathbf{r}) = 4$, $o(\mathbf{s}) = 2$ and $\mathbf{sr} = \mathbf{r}^3\mathbf{s}$. [It is known as the *fourth* **Dihedral group**. Further discussion on this group may be found in Definition 5.1.9 and Example 5.1.21.]

(c) A **linear motion** of $\mathbb{R}^2$ is a bijective mapping of the form $T_A : \mathbb{R}^2 \to \mathbb{R}^2$ given by $T_A(x) = A\underline{x}$ for $x \in \mathbb{R}^2$ and $A \in GL(2, \mathbb{R})$ where $A\underline{x}$ is given by the left multiplication of the matrix A with the column matrix $\underline{x}$. Show that the set of linear motions is a group under composition of mapping.

(d)† An **affine motion** of $\mathbb{R}^2$ is a bijective mapping of the form $T_{A,v} : \mathbb{R}^2 \to \mathbb{R}^2$ given by $T_{A,v}(x) = A\underline{x} + \underline{v}$ for $x, v \in \mathbb{R}^2$ and $A \in GL(2, \mathbb{R})$ where $A\underline{x}$ is as above. Show that the set of affine motions is a group under composition of mapping.

7. Let $G = \left\{ \begin{bmatrix} 1 & a \\ 0 & 0 \end{bmatrix} \Big| a \in \mathbb{R} \right\}$. Show that under usual matrix multiplication G is *not* a group, though G has a *left identity* and *right inverse* for every element with respect to that left identity.

8. Let $G = \{a, b, c, d\}$ be a group. Complete the following Cayley table for this group.

$*$	d	a	b	c
d	d			
a		c	d	
b				
c				

9. Find the smallest positive integer n such that
   (a) $n[5] = [0]$ in the group $\mathbb{Z}_{15}$.
   (b) $n[5] = [0]$ in the group $\mathbb{Z}_{20}$.

10. Suppose $G = \{f : \mathbb{R} \to \mathbb{R}\}$ be the set of all real valued functions on $\mathbb{R}$. Define $(f + g)(x) = f(x) + g(x)$ and $(f \cdot g)(x) = f(x)g(x)$ for all $f, g \in G$. Show that $(G, +)$ is a commutative group while $(G, \cdot)$ is not necessarily a group.

11. Let $G = \{(a, b) : a \neq 0, a, b \in \mathbb{R}\}$ and $\cdot$ be a binary operation on G given by $(a, b)\cdot(c, d) = (ac, bc + d)$. Show that $(G, \cdot)$ is a non commutative group.

12. Find the smallest positive integer n such that $[7]^n = [1]$ in U_{10} and in U_{12}.

13. (a) Find the order of $[6]$ in the group $\mathbb{Z}_{10}$ and the order of $[3]$ in U_{10}.
    (b) Suppose a group contains elements a, b such that $o(a) = 4, o(b) = 2$ and $a^3b = ba$. Find $o(ab)$.

14. Let $(G, *)$ be a group and $a, b, c \in G$. Show that there exists a unique element x in G such that $a * x * b = c$.

15. Let $(G, *)$ be a finite Abelian group and $G = \{a_1, a_2, \ldots, a_n\}$. Let $a_1 a_2 \ldots a_n = x$. Prove that $x * x = e$.

16. †Let $(G, *)$ be a group and $a, b \in G$. Suppose that $a * b^3 * a^{-1} = b^2$ and $b^{-1} * a^2 * b = a^3$. Show that $a = b = e$.

17. Let $(G, *)$ be a group and $a, b \in G$. Show that $(a * b * a^{-1})^n = a * b^n * a^{-1}$ for all positive integers n.

18. In a group G, if $a^5 = e$ and $a * b * a^{-1} = b^m$ for some positive integer m, and some $a, b \in G$, then prove that $b^{m^5-1} = e$.

19. (a) Let $(G, *)$ be a group and $a, b \in G$. Suppose that $a^2 = e$ and $a * b^4 * a = b^7$. Prove that $b^{33} = e$.
    (b) Let G be a finite group and $a, b \in G$ be such that $b \neq e$, $a^3 = e$ and $aba^{-1} = b^2$. Show that, $o(b) = 7$.
    (c) Let G be a group and $x, y \in G$. If $x^4 = e$ then show that $x^2y = yx$ implies $x = e$.

20. In $GL(2, \mathbb{R})$, show that $A = \begin{bmatrix} 1 & -1 \\ 0 & -1 \end{bmatrix}$ and $B = \begin{bmatrix} 1 & 1 \\ 0 & -1 \end{bmatrix}$ are elements of finite order, whereas AB is of infinite order.

21. (a) Prove that a group $(G, *)$ is commutative if and only if $(a * b)^2 = a^2 * b^2$, for all elements a, b of G.
    (b) Let $(G, *)$ be a group. If for $a, b \in G$, $(a * b)^3 = a^3 * b^3$ and $(a * b)^5 = a^5 * b^5$, then prove that $a * b = b * a$.
    (c) Show that a group $(G, *)$ is commutative if and only if $(a*b)^5 - a^5*b^5, (a*b)^6 = a^6*b^6$ and $(a * b)^7 = a^7 * b^7$ for all $a, b \in G$.

22. Let G be a group such that $a^2 = e$ for all $a \in G$. Show that G is a commutative group.

23. Let $(G, *)$ be a group. If for all elements a, b, c of G, $a * b = c * a$ implies that $b = c$, then show that G is a commutative group.

24. (a) Let G be a group. If $a^{-1}b^2(bab)^{-1}ba^2 = b$ for all $a, b \in G$, then prove that G is commutative.
    (b) In a group G, if for any two elements $a, b \in G$, $a^{-1}(ab)^{-1}a^2b^2 = b$, then show that G is an Abelian group.

25. Let S be a semigroup. If for any $x, y \in S$, $x^2 y = y = y x^2$, then prove that S is an Abelian group.

26. In the group $\mathbb{Z}_{15}$, find the order of the following elements: $[5], [8]$, and $[10]$.

27. Let G be a group and $a \in G$. If $o(a) = 24$, then find $o(a^4)$, $o(a^7)$ and $o(a^{10})$.

28. Let G be a group and $a, b \in G$, such that $ab = ba$ and $o(a)$ and $o(b)$ are relatively prime. Then prove that $o(ab) = o(a)o(b)$.

Find the correct answer(s) in the following exercises:

29. The number of elements of order 5 in $\mathbb{Z}_{20}$ is
    (i) 1 (ii) 2 (iii) 4 (iv) 5.

30. The number of elements of order 10 in $\mathbb{Z}_{10}$ is
    (i) 4 (ii) 10 (iii) 5 (iv) 0.

31. Let G be a group and $a \in G$. If $o(a) = 20$, then $o(a^4)$ is
    (i) 15 (ii) 5 (iii) 12 (iv) 20.

32. let G be a group and $a \in G$. If $o(a) = 17$, then $o(a^8)$ is
    (i) 17 (ii) 16 (iii) 8 (iv) 5.

33. Suppose a group G contains elements a and b such that $o(a) = 4$, $o(b) = 2, a^3 b = ba$. Then $o(ab)$ is
    (i) 2 (ii) 5 (iii) infinite (iv) 6.

34. In a group G, the number of elements $a \in G$ such that $a^2 = a$ is
    (i) 0 (ii) 1 (iii) 2 (iv) none of these.

35. Let G be a non-Abelian group. Let $a \in G$ have order 4 and let $b \in G$ have order 3. Then the order of the element ab in G is
    (i) 6   (ii) 12   (iii) of the form $12k$ for $k \geq 2$ (iv) need not be finite.

36. Let G be a group with identity 1. If x, y and z are elements of G such that $xyz = 1$, then
    (i) $yzx = 1$ (ii) $yxz = 1$ (iii) $zxy = 1$ (iv) $zyx = 1$.

37. Write the proof if the following statements are true, otherwise, give a counter example.
    (a) For every positive integer n there may not exist a group of order n.
    (b) For every positive integer n there exists a commutative group of order n.
    (c) If a, b, c are elements of a group $(G, *)$ such that $a * b * c = e$, then $b * c * a = e$.
    (d) In a finite group every element is of finite order.
    (e) A semigroup with right identity is a group, if every element of it has a right inverse in it with respect to that right identity.
    (f) In a group G, $ab = e$ implies $a^n b^n = e$ for all $n \in \mathbb{N}$.

Chapter 4

Permutation Groups

Almost without hyperbole, one can say that no branch of modern mathematics is now presented in the way as it was actually generated and group theory is no exception. Indeed, the genesis of group theory actually began with the permutation group, as it is called nowadays, towards analyzing and describing the relations between the roots of a polynomial equation. It was Cauchy (1815) who first made the systematic study of permutation group, irrespective of its reference to some polynomial equations. Actually it was the genius of Galois, who first (1829) understood them[1] to be a special case of a more general phenomenon and stressed upon the necessity of studying the underlying abstract structure and thus the theory of (finite) groups came into being.

4.1 Permutation group

Right from our school days we know that a *permutation* of n different elements is nothing but an arrangement of those elements in any order. For example, if we consider three elements x_1, x_2, x_3, then we can arrange them in any of the following six manners only.

$$x_1\, x_2\, x_3 \quad x_2\, x_1\, x_3 \quad x_3\, x_1\, x_2 \quad x_1\, x_3\, x_2 \quad x_2\, x_3\, x_1 \quad x_3\, x_2\, x_1$$

Each of these arrangements of x_1, x_2, x_3 is called a permutation. Note that each of these arrangements can be described as a bijective mapping from the set $S = \{x_1, x_2, x_3\}$ onto itself as shown on the next page:

---

[1]It is a pity that his epoch-making works came to light only in 1846, almost 14 years after his death. Galois failed twice at the entrance examination of the École Polytechnique. Twice he tried to communicate his works personally, once through Cauchy and then through Fourier, both of whom showed no interest; he then formally submitted it for publication to the Académie, which Poisson rejected as incomprehensible!

$$\begin{array}{c|c|c|c|c|c}
x_1 \to x_1 & x_1 \to x_2 & x_1 \to x_3 & x_1 \to x_1 & x_1 \to x_2 & x_1 \to x_3 \\
x_2 \to x_2 & x_2 \to x_1 & x_2 \to x_1 & x_2 \to x_3 & x_2 \to x_3 & x_2 \to x_2 \\
x_3 \to x_3 & x_3 \to x_3 & x_3 \to x_2 & x_3 \to x_2 & x_3 \to x_1 & x_3 \to x_1
\end{array}$$

We now extend this idea over an arbitrary set of elements.

Definition 4.1.1. Let A be a nonempty set. A **permutation** of A is a bijective mapping (function) of A onto itself.

Definition 4.1.2. A group $(G, *)$ is called a **permutation group** on a nonempty set A if the elements of G are some permutations of A and the operation $*$ is the composition of two mappings.

Example 4.1.3. Let X be a nonempty set and let S_X be the set of all bijective functions of X onto itself. Then $(S_X, \circ)$ is a group as we have shown in Example 3.1.10, where $\circ$ is the composition of functions. Hence $(S_X, \circ)$ is a permutation group.

Let us now consider permutation of a finite set. Suppose for any positive integer n, I_n denotes the finite set $\{1, 2, 3, \ldots, n\}$. For example, $I_3 = \{1, 2, 3\}$. Now any permutation on I_n is a bijective function on $\{1, 2, 3, \ldots, n\}$. The set of all permutations on I_n forms a group under the binary operation 'composition of two functions'. This group is called the **symmetric group** on n elements and is denoted by S_n. It is easy to see that $|S_n| = n!$. Let $\alpha \in S_n$. Generally we demonstrate α in the following way:

$$\begin{aligned}
& 1 \longrightarrow \alpha(1) \\
& 2 \longrightarrow \alpha(2) \\
\alpha \quad : \quad & 3 \longrightarrow \alpha(3) \\
& \quad \vdots \\
& n \longrightarrow \alpha(n)
\end{aligned}$$

where $\alpha(i)$ denotes the image of i under α, for all $i = 1, 2, \ldots, n$. But it is sometimes convenient to describe this permutation by means of the following notational device:

$$\alpha = \begin{pmatrix} 1 & 2 & 3 & \cdots & n \\ \alpha(1) & \alpha(2) & \alpha(3) & \cdots & \alpha(n) \end{pmatrix}.$$

This notation is due to Cauchy and is called the **two-row notation**. In the upper row, we list all the elements of I_n and in the lower row under each element $i \in I_n$, we write the image of the element, i.e., $\alpha(i)$. For example, if $n = 3$ and α is a permutation on I_3 defined by $\alpha(1) = 2, \alpha(2) = 3, \alpha(3) = 1$, then using the two-row notation we can write

$$\alpha = \begin{pmatrix} 1 & 2 & 3 \\ 2 & 3 & 1 \end{pmatrix}.$$

The two-row notation of permutations is quite convenient while doing computations, such as determining the composition of permutations. Let

$$\alpha = \begin{pmatrix} 1 & 2 & \dots & n \\ \alpha(1) & \alpha(2) & \dots & \alpha(n) \end{pmatrix} \text{ and } \beta = \begin{pmatrix} 1 & 2 & \dots & n \\ \beta(1) & \beta(2) & \dots & \beta(n) \end{pmatrix}.$$

Now the composition $\alpha \circ \beta$ (equivalently denoted by juxtaposition $\alpha\beta$) is also a permutation on I_n defined by $(\alpha \circ \beta)(i) = \alpha(\beta(i))$ for all $i \in I_n$. Then,

$$\alpha \circ \beta = \begin{pmatrix} 1 & 2 & \dots & n \\ \alpha(1) & \alpha(2) & \dots & \alpha(n) \end{pmatrix} \circ \begin{pmatrix} 1 & 2 & \dots & n \\ \beta(1) & \beta(2) & \dots & \beta(n) \end{pmatrix}$$

$$= \begin{pmatrix} 1 & 2 & \dots & n \\ \alpha\big(\beta(1)\big) & \alpha\big(\beta(2)\big) & \dots & \alpha\big(\beta(n)\big) \end{pmatrix}.$$

Let us consider the example with $n = 6$. Let α and β be two permutations on I_6 defined by

$$\alpha = \begin{pmatrix} 1 & 2 & 3 & 4 & 5 & 6 \\ 1 & 3 & 4 & 6 & 2 & 5 \end{pmatrix}$$

and

$$\beta = \begin{pmatrix} 1 & 2 & 3 & 4 & 5 & 6 \\ 6 & 5 & 3 & 1 & 2 & 4 \end{pmatrix}.$$

Let us compute $\alpha \circ \beta$ where $\alpha \circ \beta : I_6 \to I_6$ defined by $(\alpha \circ \beta)(i) = \alpha(\beta(i))$ for all $i \in I_6$. Thus,

$$(\alpha \circ \beta)(1) = \alpha(\beta(1)) = \alpha(6) = 5$$
$$(\alpha \circ \beta)(2) = \alpha(\beta(2)) = \alpha(5) = 2$$

and so on. From the above, it is clear that, when determining $(\alpha \circ \beta)(1)$(say), we start with β and finish with α, and read as follows : 1 goes to 6 (under β), 6 goes to 5 (under α) and so 1 goes to 5 (under $\alpha \circ \beta$). We can exhibit this in the following form:

$$1 \xrightarrow{\beta} 6 \xrightarrow{\alpha} 5 \qquad 1 \xrightarrow{\alpha \circ \beta} 5$$
$$2 \xrightarrow{\beta} 5 \xrightarrow{\alpha} 2 \qquad 2 \xrightarrow{\alpha \circ \beta} 2$$
$$3 \xrightarrow{\beta} 3 \xrightarrow{\alpha} 4 \qquad 3 \xrightarrow{\alpha \circ \beta} 4$$
$$4 \xrightarrow{\beta} 1 \xrightarrow{\alpha} 1 \qquad 4 \xrightarrow{\alpha \circ \beta} 1$$
$$5 \xrightarrow{\beta} 2 \xrightarrow{\alpha} 3 \qquad 5 \xrightarrow{\alpha \circ \beta} 3$$
$$6 \xrightarrow{\beta} 4 \xrightarrow{\alpha} 6 \qquad 6 \xrightarrow{\alpha \circ \beta} 6$$

Thus,

$$\alpha \circ \beta = \begin{pmatrix} 1 & 2 & 3 & 4 & 5 & 6 \\ 5 & 2 & 4 & 1 & 3 & 6 \end{pmatrix}.$$

Example 4.1.4. Consider the **symmetric[2] group** S_3, the elements of this group being all the permutations on $I_3 = \{1, 2, 3\}$. As the number of bijective functions of I_3 onto itself is $3! = 6$, we have $|S_3| = 6$. We now enlist below the permutations on $I_3 = \{1, 2, 3\}$.

$$e = \begin{pmatrix} 1 & 2 & 3 \\ 1 & 2 & 3 \end{pmatrix} \qquad \alpha = \begin{pmatrix} 1 & 2 & 3 \\ 2 & 3 & 1 \end{pmatrix} \qquad \beta = \begin{pmatrix} 1 & 2 & 3 \\ 3 & 1 & 2 \end{pmatrix}$$

$$\gamma = \begin{pmatrix} 1 & 2 & 3 \\ 1 & 3 & 2 \end{pmatrix} \qquad \delta = \begin{pmatrix} 1 & 2 & 3 \\ 2 & 1 & 3 \end{pmatrix} \qquad \sigma = \begin{pmatrix} 1 & 2 & 3 \\ 3 & 2 & 1 \end{pmatrix}.$$

We now show some computations regarding the composition or product of elements of S_3.

$$\gamma \circ \delta = \begin{pmatrix} 1 & 2 & 3 \\ 1 & 3 & 2 \end{pmatrix} \circ \begin{pmatrix} 1 & 2 & 3 \\ 2 & 1 & 3 \end{pmatrix} = \begin{pmatrix} 1 & 2 & 3 \\ 3 & 1 & 2 \end{pmatrix} = \beta.$$

As a composition of mappings γ and δ, we may write:

$$(\gamma \circ \delta)(1) = \gamma\big(\delta(1)\big) = \gamma(2) = 3$$
$$(\gamma \circ \delta)(2) = \gamma\big(\delta(2)\big) = \gamma(1) = 1$$
$$(\gamma \circ \delta)(3) = \gamma\big(\delta(3)\big) = \gamma(3) = 2$$

Following calculation of $\delta \circ \gamma$ reveals an important fact.

$$\delta \circ \gamma = \begin{pmatrix} 1 & 2 & 3 \\ 2 & 1 & 3 \end{pmatrix} \circ \begin{pmatrix} 1 & 2 & 3 \\ 1 & 3 & 2 \end{pmatrix} = \begin{pmatrix} 1 & 2 & 3 \\ 2 & 3 & 1 \end{pmatrix} = \alpha.$$

We find that $\gamma \circ \delta \neq \delta \circ \gamma$. Following is the incomplete Cayley table of this group. We leave it for the reader to fill it up.

---

[2] As the word *symmetry* unfailingly refers to a pictorial essence, an inquisitive mind may ponder about any possible geometric significance of this nomenclature. Indeed, this group can be beautifully described as the group of 'symmetries' of an equilateral triangle. Refer to Example 8.3.6 for relevant discussions and further details about this and some other similar examples.

∘	e	α	β	γ	δ	σ
e	e	α	β	γ	δ	σ
α	α	β	e			
β	β	e	α			
γ	γ			e	β	
δ	δ			α	e	
σ	σ					e

The group S_3 is a *noncommutative* group of order 6.

In the following theorem, we prove this for any symmetric group $S_n, n \geq 3$.

Theorem 4.1.5. *If n is a positive integer such that $n \geq 3$, then the symmetric group S_n is a noncommutative group.*

Proof. Let $n \geq 3$. Let $\alpha, \beta \in S_n$ be defined by

$$\alpha(1) = 2, \alpha(2) = 1, \text{ and } \alpha(x) = x \text{ for all } x \neq 1, 2;$$
$$\beta(1) = 3, \beta(3) = 1, \text{ and } \beta(x) = x \text{ for all } x \neq 1, 3.$$

Then,

$$\alpha = \begin{pmatrix} 1 & 2 & 3 & 4 & \cdots & n \\ 2 & 1 & 3 & 4 & \cdots & n \end{pmatrix} \text{ and } \beta = \begin{pmatrix} 1 & 2 & 3 & 4 & \cdots & n \\ 3 & 2 & 1 & 4 & \cdots & n \end{pmatrix}$$

Now,

$$\alpha \circ \beta = \begin{pmatrix} 1 & 2 & 3 & 4 & \cdots & n \\ 3 & 1 & 2 & 4 & \cdots & n \end{pmatrix}$$

and

$$\beta \circ \alpha = \begin{pmatrix} 1 & 2 & 3 & 4 & \cdots & n \\ 2 & 3 & 1 & 4 & \cdots & n \end{pmatrix}.$$

Thus $(\alpha \circ \beta)(1) = 3 \neq 2 = (\beta \circ \alpha)(1)$. Hence $\alpha \circ \beta \neq \beta \circ \alpha$ and so S_n is noncommutative, for $n \geq 3$. □

Let us now introduce a convention towards simplifying the two-row notation of a permutation. Consider the permutation

$$\alpha = \begin{pmatrix} 1 & 2 & 3 & \cdots & n \\ \alpha(1) & \alpha(2) & \alpha(3) & \cdots & \alpha(n) \end{pmatrix}.$$

If $\alpha(i) = i$, then we drop the column $\begin{matrix} i \\ \alpha(i) \end{matrix}$. For example, let $\alpha = \begin{pmatrix} 1 & 2 & 3 & 4 \\ 1 & 4 & 3 & 2 \end{pmatrix}$.

Here $\alpha(1) = 1$ and $\alpha(3) = 3$. So we denote α by $\begin{pmatrix} 2 & 4 \\ 4 & 2 \end{pmatrix}$. Hence if we write $\alpha = \begin{pmatrix} 1 & 3 & 4 \\ 4 & 1 & 3 \end{pmatrix} \in S_5$, then we mean the permutation $\alpha = \begin{pmatrix} 1 & 2 & 3 & 4 & 5 \\ 4 & 2 & 1 & 3 & 5 \end{pmatrix}$.

Definition 4.1.6. A permutation σ on $I_n = \{1, 2, \ldots, n\}$ is called a **k-cycle** or cycle of length k if there exist distinct elements $i_1, i_2, \ldots, i_k$ in I_n such that

$$\sigma(i_1) = i_2, \sigma(i_2) = i_3, \sigma(i_3) = i_4, \ldots, \sigma(i_{k-1}) = i_k,$$
$$\sigma(i_k) = i_1 \text{ and } \sigma(x) = x \text{ for all } x \in I_n \smallsetminus \{i_1, i_2, \ldots, i_k\}.$$

A k-cycle with $k = 2$ is called a **transposition**.

If a permutation σ on I_n is a k-cycle, we shall denote it by $(i_1\ i_2\ \ldots\ i_k)$. We shall refer to this new notation as *cycle notation*. For example,

$$\sigma = \begin{pmatrix} 1 & 2 & 3 & 4 & 5 & 6 \\ 3 & 5 & 2 & 4 & 1 & 6 \end{pmatrix}$$

is a permutation on $I_6 = \{1, 2, 3, 4, 5, 6\}$ such that:

$$\sigma(1) = 3, \ \sigma(3) = 2, \ \sigma(2) = 5, \ \sigma(5) = 1, \ \sigma(4) = 4, \ \sigma(6) = 6.$$

Hence, σ is a 4-cycle and we denote σ by $(1\,3\,2\,5)$. Observe that:

$$(1\,3\,2\,5) = (3\,2\,5\,1) = (2\,5\,1\,3) = (5\,1\,3\,2).$$

The term *cycle* regarding the cyclic notation may be understood in the light of the following diagram (Fig. 10). We show the diagram for the above permutation σ.

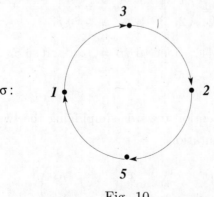

Fig. 10

$$\text{or,} \qquad \sigma : 1 \rightarrow 3 \rightarrow 2 \rightarrow 5 \rightarrow 1$$

Consider the permutation $\alpha = \begin{pmatrix} 1 & 2 & 3 & 4 \\ 3 & 4 & 1 & 2 \end{pmatrix}$. Observe that, for this permutation $\alpha(1) = 3, \alpha(3) = 1$ whereas $\alpha(2) = 4, \alpha(4) = 2$. Hence α is not a k-cycle.

Since k-cycles are nothing but special type of permutations, they can be composed, i.e., multiplied just like any two permutations. Consider the cycles $\sigma = (2\,4\,3)$ and $\delta = (1\,2\,6\,5)$. Then

$$\sigma : 2 \rightarrow 4 \rightarrow 3 \rightarrow 2 \text{ and } \sigma(x) = x \text{ when } x \neq 2, 4, 3 \text{ and,}$$

$$\delta : 1 \rightarrow 2 \rightarrow 6 \rightarrow 5 \rightarrow 1 \text{ and } \delta(x) = x \text{ when } x \neq 1, 2, 5, 6.$$

In other words, we can look upon σ and δ as mappings in the following manner:

$$
\sigma : \quad
\begin{aligned}
2 &\rightarrow 4 \\
4 &\rightarrow 3 \\
3 &\rightarrow 2 \\
x &\rightarrow x \\
\text{when } & x \neq 2, 4, 3
\end{aligned}
\qquad
\delta : \quad
\begin{aligned}
1 &\rightarrow 2 \\
2 &\rightarrow 6 \\
6 &\rightarrow 5 \\
5 &\rightarrow 1 \\
x &\rightarrow x \\
\text{when } & x \neq 1, 2, 5, 6
\end{aligned}
$$

Again viewed as permutations in a two-row notation, σ and δ are as follows:

$$\sigma = \begin{pmatrix} 1 & 2 & 3 & 4 & 5 & 6 \\ 1 & 4 & 2 & 3 & 5 & 6 \end{pmatrix} \text{ and } \delta = \begin{pmatrix} 1 & 2 & 3 & 4 & 5 & 6 \\ 2 & 6 & 3 & 4 & 1 & 5 \end{pmatrix}.$$

Now

$$\sigma\delta = \sigma \circ \delta = \begin{pmatrix} 1 & 2 & 3 & 4 & 5 & 6 \\ 4 & 6 & 2 & 3 & 1 & 5 \end{pmatrix}.$$

It is worth noticing that *while calculating $\sigma\delta$, we first consider the image of δ on the elements of I_6 and then on that image set, we further consider the image of σ.* Hence $\sigma \circ \delta : 1 \xrightarrow{\delta} 2 \xrightarrow{\sigma} 4$. Notice that under $\sigma\delta$,

$$1 \rightarrow 4 \rightarrow 3 \rightarrow 2 \rightarrow 6 \rightarrow 5 \rightarrow 1$$

Hence in this case $\sigma\delta$ is a 6-cycle.

But in general, *product of two cycles may not be a cycle.* To show this we consider the product of $\sigma = (5\,6)$ and $\delta = (3\,2\,4)$ from S_6. Then

$$\sigma\delta = \sigma \circ \delta = \begin{pmatrix} 1 & 2 & 3 & 4 & 5 & 6 \\ 1 & 4 & 2 & 3 & 6 & 5 \end{pmatrix}$$

is not a cycle.

Example 4.1.7. Using the cycle notation we now rewrite the elements of S_3 from Example 4.1.4 as follows:

$$e = \begin{pmatrix} 1 & 2 & 3 \\ 1 & 2 & 3 \end{pmatrix} = (1) \qquad \alpha = \begin{pmatrix} 1 & 2 & 3 \\ 2 & 3 & 1 \end{pmatrix} = (1\,2\,3)$$

$$\beta = \begin{pmatrix} 1 & 2 & 3 \\ 3 & 1 & 2 \end{pmatrix} = (1\,3\,2) \qquad \gamma = \begin{pmatrix} 1 & 2 & 3 \\ 1 & 3 & 2 \end{pmatrix} = (2\,3)$$

$$\delta = \begin{pmatrix} 1 & 2 & 3 \\ 2 & 1 & 3 \end{pmatrix} = (1\,2) \qquad \sigma = \begin{pmatrix} 1 & 2 & 3 \\ 3 & 2 & 1 \end{pmatrix} = (1\,3)$$

Hence,

$$S_3 = \{e, (1\,2), (1\,3), (2\,3), (1\,2\,3), (1\,3\,2)\}$$

which consists of one 1-cycle, three 2-cycles and two 3-cycles.

Remark 4.1.8. Note that *the identity permutation e in the above example could have been represented as* (2) *or* (3) *also.*

Definition 4.1.9. Two cycles $(i_1\, i_2 \ldots i_t)$ and $(j_1\, j_2 \ldots j_k)$ of S_n are said to be **disjoint** if $\{i_1, i_2, \ldots, i_t\} \cap \{j_1, j_2, \ldots, j_k\} = \emptyset$.

Example 4.1.10. The cycles $(2\,4\,3\,5)$ and $(1\,6\,8)$ are disjoint cycles, whereas the cycles $(4\,5\,3\,2)$ and $(1\,3\,8)$ are not disjoint.

In the Example 4.1.10 above, we have considered two disjoint cycles $\alpha = (2\,4\,3\,5)$ and $\beta = (1\,6\,8)$. Now let us work out their compositions.

$$\alpha\beta = (2\,4\,3\,5)(1\,6\,8) = \begin{pmatrix} 1 & 2 & 3 & 4 & 5 & 6 & 7 & 8 \\ 6 & 4 & 5 & 3 & 2 & 8 & 7 & 1 \end{pmatrix};$$

$$\beta\alpha = (1\,6\,8)(2\,4\,3\,5) = \begin{pmatrix} 1 & 2 & 3 & 4 & 5 & 6 & 7 & 8 \\ 6 & 4 & 5 & 3 & 2 & 8 & 7 & 1 \end{pmatrix}.$$

Hence $\alpha\beta = \beta\alpha$. Indeed, we have the following general result in the form of a theorem.

Theorem 4.1.11. *Let α and β be any two disjoint cycles in S_n. Then, $\alpha\beta = \beta\alpha$.*

Proof. Let $\alpha = (i_1\, i_2 \ldots i_t)$ and $\beta = (j_1\, j_2 \ldots j_k)$ be two disjoint cycles. We show that $(\alpha\beta)(x) = (\beta\alpha)(x)$ for all $x \in I_n$. Now,

$$
\begin{array}{cc}
\begin{aligned}
i_1 &\to i_2 \\
i_2 &\to i_3 \\
&\vdots \\
i_{t-1} &\to i_t \\
i_t &\to i_1 \\
y &\to y
\end{aligned}
&
\begin{aligned}
j_1 &\to j_2 \\
j_2 &\to j_3 \\
&\vdots \\
j_{k-1} &\to j_k \\
j_k &\to j_1 \\
y &\to y
\end{aligned}
\end{array}
$$

$$\alpha : \qquad\qquad\qquad\qquad \beta :$$

when $y \notin \{i_1, i_2, \ldots, i_t\}$ $\qquad$ when $y \notin \{j_1, j_2, \ldots, j_k\}$

Suppose x is neither $i_1, i_2, \ldots, i_t$ nor $j_1, j_2, \ldots, j_k$. Then $\alpha(x) = x$ and $\beta(x) = x$. Hence

$$(\alpha\beta)(x) = \alpha\Big(\beta(x)\Big) = \alpha(x) = x \text{ and } (\beta\alpha)(x) = \beta\Big(\alpha(x)\Big) = \beta(x) = x.$$

Suppose now x is one of $i_1, i_2, \ldots, i_t$. Hence, $x \notin \{j_1, j_2, \ldots, j_k\}$. Then $\beta(x) = x$ and $\alpha(x)$ is one of $i_1, i_2, \ldots, i_t$. Hence $(\alpha\beta)(x) = \alpha\Big(\beta(x)\Big) = \alpha(x)$ and $(\beta\alpha)(x) = \beta\Big(\alpha(x)\Big) = \alpha(x)$ (since $\alpha(x) \notin \{j_1, j_2, \ldots, j_k\}$). Similarly, if x is one of $j_1, j_2, \ldots, j_k$, then $x \notin \{i_1, i_2, \ldots, i_t\}$ and as above we can show that $(\alpha\beta)(x) = \beta(x) = (\beta\alpha)(x)$. So we find that $(\alpha\beta)(x) = (\beta\alpha)(x)$ for all $x \in I_n$. Consequently, $\alpha\beta = \beta\alpha$. $\square$

Next, we consider the following permutation from S_9.

$$\alpha = \begin{pmatrix} 1 & 2 & 3 & 4 & 5 & 6 & 7 & 8 & 9 \\ 5 & 8 & 2 & 1 & 4 & 3 & 6 & 7 & 9 \end{pmatrix}$$

Under this permutation

$$\alpha(1) = 5$$
$$\alpha^2(1) = \alpha(\alpha(1)) = \alpha(5) = 4$$
$$\alpha^3(1) = \alpha(\alpha^2(1)) = \alpha(4) = 1.$$

So we find that 3 is the smallest positive integer such that $\alpha^3(1) = 1$. Now we define $\alpha_1 : I_9 = \{1, 2, 3 \ldots, 9\} \to I_9$ by

$$\alpha_1(1) = \alpha(1) = 5$$
$$\alpha_1(5) = \alpha^2(1) = 4$$
$$\alpha_1(4) = \alpha^3(1) = 1$$
$$\text{and } \alpha_1(x) = x \text{ for all } x \in I_9 \smallsetminus \{1, 4, 5\}.$$

Hence $\alpha_1 \in S_9$ and α_1 is a cycle given by $1 \to 5 \to 4 \to 1$. So we find that $\alpha_1 = (1\,5\,4)$ and $\alpha_1 \in S_9$.

Now, $2 \notin \{\alpha(1), \alpha^2(1), \alpha^3(1)\} = \{1, 5, 4\}$. Starting with 2, we find that

$$\alpha(2) = 8$$
$$\alpha^2(2) = \alpha(\alpha(2)) = \alpha(8) = 7$$
$$\alpha^3(2) = \alpha(\alpha^2(2)) = \alpha(7) = 6$$
$$\alpha^4(2) = \alpha(\alpha^3(2)) = \alpha(6) = 3$$
$$\alpha^5(2) = \alpha(\alpha^4(2)) = \alpha(3) = 2.$$

Hence, 5 is the smallest positive integer such that $\alpha^5(2) = 2$.

Now we define $\alpha_2 : I_9 = \{1, 2, 3 \ldots, 9\} \to I_9$ by

$$\alpha_2(2) = \alpha(2) = 8$$
$$\alpha_2(8) = \alpha^2(2) = 7$$
$$\alpha_2(7) = \alpha^3(2) = 6$$
$$\alpha_2(6) = \alpha^4(2) = 3$$
$$\alpha_2(3) = \alpha^5(2) = 2$$

and $\alpha_2(x) = x$ for all $x \in I_9 \smallsetminus \{2, 8, 7, 6, 3\}$.

Clearly, $\alpha_2 \in S_9$ and under α_2

$$2 \to 8 \to 7 \to 6 \to 3 \to 2$$

and $x \to x$ for all $x \in I_9 \smallsetminus \{2, 8, 7, 6, 3\}$. Hence α_2 defines a cycle $(2\,8\,7\,6\,3)$.

Note that $\alpha_1 = (1\,5\,4)$ and $\alpha_2 = (2\,8\,7\,6\,3)$ are disjoint and hence $\alpha_1\alpha_2 = \alpha_2\alpha_1$. Now $9 \notin \{1, 5, 4\} \cup \{2, 8, 7, 6, 3\}$. Starting with 9 we obtain $\alpha(9) = 9$. Hence 1 is the smallest positive integer such that $\alpha^1(9) = 9$. Now define $\alpha_3 : I_9 \to I_9$ by

$$\alpha_3(9) = \alpha(9) = 9$$
and $\alpha_3(x) = x$ for all $x \in I_9 \smallsetminus \{9\}$.

Note that $\alpha_3 \in S_9$ and under α_3,

$$9 \to 9$$

and $x \to x$ for all $x \in I_9 \smallsetminus \{9\}$. Consequently, α_3 is the identity permutation. Now it is easy to see that

$$\alpha = \alpha_1\alpha_2\alpha_3 = \alpha_1\alpha_2 = (1\,5\,4)(2\,8\,7\,6\,3)(9) = (1\,5\,4)(2\,8\,7\,6\,3).$$

Hence, α is a product of disjoint cycles.

We can apply the above process for any permutation α on I_n for any integer $n \geq 2$ and show that α can be expressed as a product of disjoint cycles.

Theorem 4.1.12. *Any nonidentity permutation $\alpha \in S_n$ ($n \geq 2$) can be expressed as a product of disjoint cycles, where each cycle is of length ≥ 2.*

Proof. Let α be a permutation on S_n, $n \geq 2$. We begin by considering $1, \alpha(1), \alpha^2(1), \ldots$ until we find the smallest positive integer r such that $\alpha^r(1) = 1$. This gives us a r-cycle, say α_1, so that

$$\alpha_1 = (1\ \alpha(1)\ \alpha^2(1)\ \ldots \alpha^{r-1}(1)).$$

Let i be the smallest integer in I_n, that does not appear in α_1. Then we consider $\alpha(i), \alpha^2(i), \ldots$ so on, until we come across the smallest positive integer s such that $\alpha^s(i) = i$. Evidently, this gives us an s-cycle, say α_2, so that:

$$\alpha_2 = (i\ \alpha(i)\ \alpha^2(i)\ \ldots \alpha^{s-1}(i)).$$

Before proceeding further, observe that α_1 and α_2, as we have constructed them, must be disjoint cycles, i.e.,

$$\left\{1,\, \alpha(1),\, \alpha^2(1),\, \ldots,\, \alpha^{r-1}(1)\right\} \cap \left\{i,\, \alpha(i),\, \alpha^2(i),\, \ldots,\, \alpha^{s-1}(i)\right\} = \emptyset.$$

Indeed, otherwise, if $\alpha^p(i) = \alpha^k(1)$ for some p, k ($1 \leq p \leq s-1$ and $1 \leq k \leq r-1$), then we must have $\alpha^{p+1}(i) = \alpha(\alpha^p(i)) = \alpha(\alpha^k(1)) = \alpha^{k+1}(1)$ and so on, which in turn implies that $\alpha^{p+t}(i) = \alpha^{k+t}(1)$ for $t = 1, 2, \ldots$ Now there exists some t such that $p + t = s$. Hence for this t, $i = \alpha^s(i) = \alpha^{p+t}(i) = \alpha^{k+t}(1)$. This implies that i appears in α_1, a contradiction to the choice of i. Now if

$$\left\{1,\, \alpha(1),\, \alpha^2(1),\, \ldots,\, \alpha^{r-1}(1)\right\} \cup \left\{i,\, \alpha(i),\, \alpha^2(i),\, \ldots,\, \alpha^{s-1}(i)\right\} \neq I_n,$$

then we consider the smallest member of I_n not appearing in the left hand side union above and continue the same process as before to construct cycle α_3. Since I_n is finite, the aforesaid process must terminate after a finite number of steps, with some cycle, say, α_m. From the definition of the cycles $\alpha_1, \alpha_2, \ldots, \alpha_m$, it now follows that $\alpha = \alpha_1 \circ \alpha_2 \circ \ldots \circ \alpha_m$. □

Next, we consider a cycle $\alpha = (2\,4\,3\,5)$ on S_6. Under this permutation, we have

$$\alpha : 2 \to 4 \to 3 \to 5 \to 2$$

and $x \to x$ whenever $x \in I_6 \setminus \{2, 4, 3, 5\}$. Now consider the 2-cycles $(2\,5), (2\,3), (2\,4)$. Let $\alpha_1 = (2\,5)$, $\alpha_2 = (2\,3)$ and $\alpha_3 = (2\,4)$. Consider the product

$$\alpha_1 \alpha_2 \alpha_3 = (2\,5)(2\,3)(2\,4).$$

Under this product,

$$2 \xrightarrow{\alpha_3} 4 \xrightarrow{\alpha_2} 4 \xrightarrow{\alpha_1} 4$$
$$4 \xrightarrow{\alpha_3} 2 \xrightarrow{\alpha_2} 3 \xrightarrow{\alpha_1} 3$$
$$3 \xrightarrow{\alpha_3} 3 \xrightarrow{\alpha_2} 2 \xrightarrow{\alpha_1} 5$$
$$5 \xrightarrow{\alpha_3} 5 \xrightarrow{\alpha_2} 5 \xrightarrow{\alpha_1} 2$$
$$x \xrightarrow{\alpha_3} x \xrightarrow{\alpha_2} x \xrightarrow{\alpha_1} x$$

$$\text{when } x \neq 2, 3, 4, 5.$$

Then,

$$\alpha_1 \alpha_2 \alpha_3 : 2 \to 4 \to 3 \to 5 \,, \to 2 \text{ and } x \to x \text{ for the rest.}$$

Consequently, $\alpha_1 \alpha_2 \alpha_3 = (2\,4\,3\,5)$.

In this way we can show that *any cycle* $(i_1\, i_2\, \ldots\, i_k)$, $k \geq 3$ *can be expressed as* $(i_1\, i_k)(i_1\, i_{k-1}) \ldots (i_1\, i_2)$. Indeed, we may have the following theorem.

Theorem 4.1.13. *Any cycle of length ≥ 2 is either a transposition (i.e., 2-cycle) or can be expressed as a product of transpositions.*

Combining the last two theorems we state the following:

Theorem 4.1.14. *Any nonidentity permutation of S_n $(n \geq 2)$ is either a transposition or can be expressed as a product of transpositions.*

Definition 4.1.15. Two permutations $\alpha, \beta \in S_n$ are called **conjugate** to each other if there exists $\gamma \in S_n$ such that $\gamma \alpha \gamma^{-1} = \beta$.

Example 4.1.16. Let

$$\pi = \begin{pmatrix} 1 & 2 & 3 & 4 & 5 & 6 & 7 \\ 6 & 3 & 5 & 2 & 4 & 7 & 1 \end{pmatrix} \in S_7.$$

Consider

$$\alpha = \begin{pmatrix} 1 & 2 & 3 & 4 & 5 & 6 & 7 \\ 3 & 2 & 4 & 7 & 5 & 6 & 1 \end{pmatrix} \in S_7$$

so that

$$\alpha^{-1} = \begin{pmatrix} 1 & 2 & 3 & 4 & 5 & 6 & 7 \\ 7 & 2 & 1 & 3 & 5 & 6 & 4 \end{pmatrix}.$$

Then a conjugate of π in S_7 is $\alpha \pi \alpha^{-1} = \eta$ (say), given by

$$\eta = \begin{pmatrix} 1 & 2 & 3 & 4 & 5 & 6 & 7 \\ 3 & 4 & 6 & 5 & 7 & 1 & 2 \end{pmatrix}$$

as can be easily verified.

However, if the permutation under consideration is a cycle, then we have a smarter way of calculating its conjugates. We merely state the following theorem which is a useful computational aid towards this objective.

Theorem 4.1.17. *Let $\pi = (i_1 \ i_2 \ \ldots i_r) \in S_n$ be a cycle. Then for all $\alpha \in S_n$*

$$\alpha \pi \alpha^{-1} = (\alpha(i_1) \ \alpha(i_2) \ \ldots \alpha(i_r)).$$

Let $\alpha, \beta \in S_n$ such that $\alpha = \alpha_1 \circ \alpha_2 \circ \ldots \circ \alpha_k$ and $\beta = \beta_1 \circ \beta_2 \circ \ldots \circ \beta_s$ are products of disjoint cycles. Let $\text{length}(\alpha_i) = d_i$ and $\text{length}(\beta_j) = m_j$ for all $i = 1, 2, \ldots, k$ and $j = 1, 2, \ldots, s$ with $d_1 \leq d_2 \leq \ldots \leq d_k$ and $m_1 \leq m_2 \leq \ldots \leq m_s$. We say that α and β have the same **cyclic structure** if $k = s$ and $d_i = m_i$ for all $i = 1, 2, \ldots k$. Observe that the conjugate permutations π and η in Example 4.1.16 have same cyclic structure. Indeed, expressing π and η as products of disjoint cycles, we see that $\pi = (1\ 6\ 7)(2\ 3\ 5\ 4)$ and $\eta = (1\ 3\ 6)(2\ 4\ 5\ 7)$, which establishes our claim. Turning the matter around, let us consider two permutations, say $\beta = (1\ 4\ 7)(2\ 3\ 5\ 6)$ and $\gamma = (2\ 5\ 6)(1\ 3\ 4\ 7)$ in S_7, both having the same cyclic structure as is evident from their representations as product of disjoint cycles. Now construct σ mechanically, by putting γ below β as follows

$$\sigma = \begin{pmatrix} 1 & 4 & 7 & | & 2 & 3 & 5 & 6 \\ 2 & 5 & 6 & | & 1 & 3 & 4 & 7 \end{pmatrix} = \begin{pmatrix} 1 & 2 & 3 & 4 & 5 & 6 & 7 \\ 2 & 1 & 3 & 5 & 4 & 7 & 6 \end{pmatrix}.$$

Clearly

$$\sigma^{-1} = \begin{pmatrix} 1 & 2 & 3 & 4 & 5 & 6 & 7 \\ 2 & 1 & 3 & 5 & 4 & 7 & 6 \end{pmatrix}$$

and

$$\gamma = (2\ 5\ 6)(1\ 3\ 4\ 7) = \begin{pmatrix} 1 & 2 & 3 & 4 & 5 & 6 & 7 \\ 3 & 5 & 4 & 7 & 6 & 2 & 1 \end{pmatrix}.$$

It is interesting to note that

$$\sigma^{-1}\gamma\sigma = \begin{pmatrix} 1 & 2 & 3 & 4 & 5 & 6 & 7 \\ 4 & 3 & 5 & 7 & 6 & 2 & 1 \end{pmatrix} = (1\ 4\ 7)(2\ 3\ 5\ 6) = \beta,$$

showing thereby that β and γ are conjugates of each other. Indeed, what we have experienced through this discussion is merely an example of a general truth, which we now present in the next theorem without proof.

Theorem 4.1.18. *Two permutations α and $\beta \in S_n$ have the same cyclic structure if and only if α and β are conjugate.*

Definition 4.1.19. A permutation $\alpha \in S_n$ is called an **even permutation** if α can be expressed as a product of an even number of 2-cycles and a permutation $\alpha \in S_n$ is called an **odd permutation** if α is either a 2-cycle or can be expressed as a product of an odd number of 2-cycles. The set of all even permutations in S_n forms a group. This group is called the **alternating group** and is denoted by A_n.

Note that according to the above definition the identity permutation is an even permutation. (why?) We now merely state the following theorem, which is a very important property of a permutation.

Theorem 4.1.20. *Any permutation in S_n is either an odd permutation or an even permutation, but never both.*

Example 4.1.21. Let

$$\alpha = \begin{pmatrix} 1 & 2 & 3 & 4 & 5 & 6 & 7 & 8 \\ 8 & 5 & 6 & 3 & 7 & 4 & 2 & 1 \end{pmatrix} \in S_8.$$

Here $\alpha(1) = 8, \alpha^2(1) = \alpha(8) = 1$. Hence $1 \rightarrow 8 \rightarrow 1$ defines a 2-cycle, viz., $(1\,8)$.
Now $2 \notin \{1, 8\}$ and

$$\alpha(2) = 5, \alpha^2(2) = \alpha(5) = 7, \alpha^3(2) = \alpha(7) = 2$$

imply that $2 \rightarrow 5 \rightarrow 7 \rightarrow 2$ forms a 3-cycle $(2\,5\,7)$.
Now $3 \notin \{1, 8\} \cup \{2, 5, 7\}$ and

$$\alpha(3) = 6, \alpha^2(3) = \alpha(6) = 4, \alpha^3(3) = \alpha(4) = 3,$$

whence $3 \rightarrow 6 \rightarrow 4 \rightarrow 3$ forms a 3-cycle $(3\,6\,4)$. Hence $\alpha = (1\,8)(2\,5\,7)(3\,6\,4)$. Now $(2\,5\,7) = (2\,7)(2\,5)$ and $(3\,6\,4) = (3\,4)(3\,6)$. Hence

$$\alpha = (1\,8)(3\,4)(3\,6)(2\,7)(2\,5)$$

is a product of *five* 2-cycles and so α is an odd permutation.

We have defined earlier, the notion of the *order of an element* in a group. Based on this definition, let us examine the order of various elements of the permutation group S_n. *Since this group is finite, the order of any element of this group must also be finite.* Let $\alpha \in S_n$. To find the order of α, we need to compute $\alpha, \alpha^2, \alpha^3, \ldots$, until we find the first positive integer n, such that α^n becomes the identity permutation e. The following example is instructive in this regard.

Example 4.1.22. Let us consider the group from Example 4.1.7 once again. We know,

$$S_3 = \{e, (1\,2), (1\,3), (2\,3), (1\,2\,3), (1\,3\,2)\}.$$

Note that $(1\,2\,3) \circ (1\,2\,3) = (1\,3\,2) \neq e$ and $(1\,2\,3) \circ (1\,2\,3) \circ (1\,2\,3) = e$, whence order of $(1\,2\,3)$ is 3. In a similar manner, we may show that the order of $(1\,3\,2)$ is also 3.

Let us now consider $(1\,2) \in S_3$. Observe that, $(1\,2) \circ (1\,2) = e$ whence order of $(1\,2)$ is 2. Similarly, order of $(1\,3)$ as well as of $(2\,3)$ is 2. So we see that the order of 2-cycles in S_3 is 2, and the order of 3-cycles in S_3 is 3.

Indeed, we have the following general result.

Theorem 4.1.23. *Let $n \geq 2$ and $\sigma \in S_n$ be a cycle. Then σ is a k-cycle if and only if order of σ is k.*

Proof. Let σ be a k-cycle in S_n, $n \geq 2$. Let $\sigma = (a_1 \, a_2 \, \ldots a_k)$. Then $\sigma(a) = a$ for all $a \notin \{a_1, a_2, \ldots, a_k\}$. Now $\sigma^i(a_1) = a_{i+1}$ for all $1 \leq i < k$ and $\sigma^k(a_1) = a_1$. Consider a_i, $1 \leq i \leq k$. Now $\sigma^{k-i}(a_i) = a_k$, $\sigma^{k-i+1}(a_i) = a_1$. This implies that $\sigma^{k+l-i}(a_i) = a_l$ for all $1 \leq l < k$ and so $\sigma^k(a_i) = a_i$. Thus, $\sigma^k(a) = a$ for all a and so $\sigma^k = e$, whence $o(\sigma) \mid k$. Suppose $o(\sigma) = t$ and $t < k$. Then $a_1 = \sigma^t(a_1) = a_{t+1}$ is a contradiction, since $a_{t+1} \neq a_1$. Hence $t = k$, i.e., $o(\sigma) = k$.

Conversely, suppose that $o(\sigma) = k$. Suppose σ is a t-cycle. Then as before we can show that $o(\sigma) = t$. This implies that $k = t$, i.e., σ is a k-cycle. $\square$

Observe that, for a permutation $\alpha \in S_n$, which is not a cycle itself, a direct process to find the smallest positive integer n, for which $\alpha^n = e$, may be a very tedious task. However, we can decompose α into disjoint cycles, and then compute the order of each of them, which is nothing but the length of the respective cycles (by Theorem 4.1.23), and then use them to find the order of α. The next result will throw some light in this regard.

Theorem 4.1.24. *Let $\sigma \in S_r$, $r \geq 2$ and $\sigma = \sigma_1 \circ \sigma_2 \circ \ldots \circ \sigma_k$ be a product of disjoint cycles. Suppose $o(\sigma_i) = n_i$, $i = 1, 2, \ldots, k$. Then $o(\sigma) = lcm(n_1, n_2, \ldots, n_k)$.*

Proof. Let $o(\sigma) = t$ and $m = lcm(n_1, n_2, \ldots, n_k)$. Now $m = n_i r_i$ for some $r_i \in \mathbb{N}$, for each $i = 1, 2, \ldots, k$. Since disjoint cycles commute,

$$\sigma^m = \sigma_1^m \circ \sigma_2^m \circ \ldots \circ \sigma_k^m = \sigma_1^{n_1 r_1} \circ \sigma_2^{n_2 r_2} \circ \ldots \circ \sigma_k^{n_k r_k} = e$$

since $o(\sigma_i) = n_i$ for each i. Thus, $t \mid m$. In order to show that $m \mid t$, it suffices to show that $n_i \mid t$, i.e., $\sigma_i^t = e$, for each $i = 1, 2, \ldots, k$. Since disjoint cycles commute, $\sigma = \sigma_i \circ \sigma_1 \circ \sigma_2 \circ \cdots \circ \sigma_{i-1} \circ \sigma_{i+1} \circ \cdots \circ \sigma_k$. Let $a \in I_r$. If $\sigma_i(a) = a$, then $\sigma_i^t(a) = a$. Suppose σ_i moves a. Then as σ_i's are disjoint, $\sigma_j(a) = a$ for all $j \neq i$. Hence $\sigma_j^t(a) = a$ for all $j, j \neq i$. Thus,

$$a = \sigma^t(a) = (\sigma_i^t \circ \sigma_1^t \circ \sigma_2^t \circ \cdots \circ \sigma_{i-1}^t \circ \sigma_{i+1}^t \circ \cdots \circ \sigma_k^t)(a) = \sigma_i^t(a).$$

Hence $\sigma_i^t = e$. As this is true for each $i = 1, 2, \ldots, k$, the theorem follows. $\square$

Before we end this section and plunge into exercises, let us discuss in brief a mind-boggling problem that comes under the purview of the so-called **recreational mathematics**. Known as the *Fifteen Puzzle*, this interesting game was conceived by Sam

Loyd in 1878, and soon it became very popular. Even today one may find this game, which consists of fifteen square blocks, numbered from 1 to 15, contained within a square frame, with the sixteenth place empty (usually at the right-hand bottom corner). The blocks can be slided only horizontally and vertically via the empty slot. One may shuffle the blocks arbitrarily, and the game is to rearrange them back to the initial regular position.

1	2	3	4
5	6	7	8
9	10	11	12
13	14	15	

Now suppose we get hold of one such toy which is set at the initial regular position. We deliberately erase the numbers 14 and 15 from the respective blocks and then imprint there 15 and 14 respectively.

1	2	3	4
5	6	7	8
9	10	11	12
13	15	14	

Can you rearrange it back to the initial regular position by the admissible movements of the blocks? It is amazing how your knowledge of *permutation* may refrain you from such a futile exercise! Indeed, observe that in the language of permutation, as we have discussed earlier in this chapter, the initial regular position refers to the *identity permutation e* (which is an even permutation), whereas the deliberately changed position refers to the permutation (14 15) (which is odd) and the problem is to solve (if possible) the equation $\sigma \circ (14\ 15) = e$, for some admissible movement σ where $\sigma \in S_{15}$. Clearly then, such a σ has to be an odd permutation. However, it is not very difficult to see that any sequence of admissible movements (*so as to keep the right-hand bottom corner empty at the end of the sequence*) gives rise to an even permutation. For example, the sequence of admissible movements given by $14 \to 11 \to 12 \to 14$ represents the 3-cycle $(14\,11\,12)$, which is obviously an even permutation. Hence the unsolvability of the problem follows.

Worked-out Exercises

◊ **Exercise 4.1.1.** Consider the following permutations in S_6.

$$\alpha = \begin{pmatrix} 1 & 2 & 3 & 4 & 5 & 6 \\ 2 & 1 & 4 & 5 & 6 & 3 \end{pmatrix}, \beta = \begin{pmatrix} 1 & 2 & 3 & 4 & 5 & 6 \\ 3 & 2 & 4 & 1 & 6 & 5 \end{pmatrix} \text{ and } \gamma = \begin{pmatrix} 1 & 2 & 3 & 4 & 5 & 6 \\ 4 & 3 & 2 & 5 & 1 & 6 \end{pmatrix}.$$

Then compute each of the following:

(i) $\alpha\beta$ (ii) $\beta\alpha$ (iii) $\alpha\gamma^2$ (iv) γ^{-1} and (v) $\gamma\alpha\gamma^{-1}$, where $(\alpha\beta)(x) = \alpha(\beta(x))$ for all $x \in I_6$.

Solution. (i) Note that to compute $\alpha\beta$ we have to apply β first and then α. This gives,

$$
\begin{array}{ll}
1 \xrightarrow{\beta} 3 \xrightarrow{\alpha} 4 & \quad 1 \xrightarrow{\alpha\circ\beta} 4 \\
2 \xrightarrow{\beta} 2 \xrightarrow{\alpha} 1 & \quad 2 \xrightarrow{\alpha\circ\beta} 1 \\
3 \xrightarrow{\beta} 4 \xrightarrow{\alpha} 5 & \quad 3 \xrightarrow{\alpha\circ\beta} 5 \\
4 \xrightarrow{\beta} 1 \xrightarrow{\alpha} 2 & \quad 4 \xrightarrow{\alpha\circ\beta} 2 \\
5 \xrightarrow{\beta} 6 \xrightarrow{\alpha} 3 & \quad 5 \xrightarrow{\alpha\circ\beta} 3 \\
6 \xrightarrow{\beta} 5 \xrightarrow{\alpha} 6 & \quad 6 \xrightarrow{\alpha\circ\beta} 6
\end{array}
$$

Hence,

$$\alpha \circ \beta = \begin{pmatrix} 1 & 2 & 3 & 4 & 5 & 6 \\ 4 & 1 & 5 & 2 & 3 & 6 \end{pmatrix}.$$

(ii) If we compute $\beta\alpha$ in an essentially similar manner we get,

$$\beta \circ \alpha = \begin{pmatrix} 1 & 2 & 3 & 4 & 5 & 6 \\ 2 & 3 & 1 & 6 & 5 & 4 \end{pmatrix}.$$

(iii) To compute $\alpha\gamma^2$, we first compute γ^2. Now, as $\gamma = \begin{pmatrix} 1 & 2 & 3 & 4 & 5 & 6 \\ 4 & 3 & 2 & 5 & 1 & 6 \end{pmatrix}$,

$$\gamma^2 = \gamma \circ \gamma = \begin{pmatrix} 1 & 2 & 3 & 4 & 5 & 6 \\ 5 & 2 & 3 & 1 & 4 & 6 \end{pmatrix}.$$

Now,

$$\alpha\gamma^2 = \begin{pmatrix} 1 & 2 & 3 & 4 & 5 & 6 \\ 2 & 1 & 4 & 5 & 6 & 3 \end{pmatrix} \circ \begin{pmatrix} 1 & 2 & 3 & 4 & 5 & 6 \\ 5 & 2 & 3 & 1 & 4 & 6 \end{pmatrix} = \begin{pmatrix} 1 & 2 & 3 & 4 & 5 & 6 \\ 6 & 1 & 4 & 2 & 5 & 3 \end{pmatrix}.$$

(iv) As

$$\gamma = \begin{pmatrix} 1 & 2 & 3 & 4 & 5 & 6 \\ 4 & 3 & 2 & 5 & 1 & 6 \end{pmatrix} \in S_6,$$

we have

$$\gamma : \begin{array}{c} 1 \longrightarrow 4 \\ 2 \longrightarrow 3 \\ 3 \longrightarrow 2 \\ 4 \longrightarrow 5 \\ 5 \longrightarrow 1 \\ 6 \longrightarrow 6 \end{array} \quad \text{and} \quad \gamma^{-1} : \begin{array}{c} 1 \longrightarrow 5 \\ 2 \longrightarrow 3 \\ 3 \longrightarrow 2 \\ 4 \longrightarrow 1 \\ 5 \longrightarrow 4 \\ 6 \longrightarrow 6 \end{array}$$

and so

$$\gamma^{-1} = \begin{pmatrix} 1 & 2 & 3 & 4 & 5 & 6 \\ 5 & 3 & 2 & 1 & 4 & 6 \end{pmatrix}.$$

(v) Using γ^{-1} from above, we compute $\gamma\alpha\gamma^{-1}$ as follows:

$$\gamma \circ \alpha \circ \gamma^{-1} = \begin{pmatrix} 1 & 2 & 3 & 4 & 5 & 6 \\ 4 & 3 & 2 & 5 & 1 & 6 \end{pmatrix} \circ \begin{pmatrix} 1 & 2 & 3 & 4 & 5 & 6 \\ 2 & 1 & 4 & 5 & 6 & 3 \end{pmatrix} \circ \begin{pmatrix} 1 & 2 & 3 & 4 & 5 & 6 \\ 5 & 3 & 2 & 1 & 4 & 6 \end{pmatrix}$$

$$= \begin{pmatrix} 1 & 2 & 3 & 4 & 5 & 6 \\ 6 & 5 & 4 & 3 & 1 & 2 \end{pmatrix}.$$

◊ **Exercise 4.1.2.** Let $\alpha = \begin{pmatrix} 1 & 2 & 3 & 4 & 5 & 6 & 7 \\ 6 & 4 & 7 & 5 & 2 & 3 & 1 \end{pmatrix}, \beta = \begin{pmatrix} 1 & 2 & 3 & 4 & 5 & 6 & 7 \\ 1 & 4 & 6 & 7 & 3 & 5 & 2 \end{pmatrix}$ be elements of S_7.

(i) Write α as a product of disjoint cycles.

(ii) Write β as a product of 2-cycles.

(iii) Is β an even permutation?

(iv) Is α^{-1} an even permutation?

Solution. (i) First let us show the working in details. Here α is such that,

$$\alpha(1) = 6; \ \alpha(6) = 3; \ \alpha(3) = 7; \ \alpha(7) = 1;$$

Now, we define $\alpha_1 : I_7 \to I_7$ by

$$\alpha_1 : \begin{array}{c} 1 \to 6 \\ 6 \to 3 \\ 3 \to 7 \\ 7 \to 1 \\ x \to x \end{array}$$

when $x \neq 1, 6, 3, 7$.

Hence, we have a cycle $\alpha_1 = (1\,6\,3\,7)$. Now, $2 \notin \{1, 6, 3, 7\}$ and we see that

$$\alpha(2) = 4; \ \alpha(4) = 5; \ \alpha(5) = 2;$$

So we define, $\alpha_2 : I_7 \to I_7$ by

$$
\alpha_2 \quad : \quad
\begin{aligned}
2 &\to 4 \\
4 &\to 5 \\
5 &\to 2 \\
x &\to x
\end{aligned}
$$

$$\text{when } x \neq 2, 4, 5.$$

Hence, we have a cycle $\alpha_2 = (2\,4\,5)$. As we see that $\{1, 6, 3, 7\} \cup \{2, 4, 5\} = I_7$, we conclude that

$$\alpha = \alpha_1 \alpha_2 = (1\,6\,3\,7)(2\,4\,5).$$

However, in a shortcut method one can proceed as follows:

The given permutation α can be described as

$$
\alpha \quad : \quad
\begin{aligned}
1 &\to 6 \\
6 &\to 3 \\
3 &\to 7 \\
7 &\to 1 \\
2 &\to 4 \\
4 &\to 5 \\
5 &\to 2.
\end{aligned}
$$

Hence $\alpha = (1\,6\,3\,7)(2\,4\,5)$.

(ii) We see that the permutation β can be written as:

$$
\beta \quad : \quad
\begin{aligned}
1 &\to 1 \\
2 &\to 4 \\
4 &\to 7 \\
7 &\to 2 \\
3 &\to 6 \\
6 &\to 5 \\
5 &\to 3.
\end{aligned}
$$

Hence $\beta = (1)(2\,4\,7)(3\,6\,5) = (2\,4\,7)(3\,6\,5) = (2\,7)(2\,4)(3\,5)(3\,6)$.

(iii) Since β is a product of an even number of 2-cycles, β is an even permutation.

(iv)   From the given permutation α, we may calculate α^{-1} side by side as follows:

$$
\begin{array}{cccc}
 & 1 \to 6 & & 1 \to 7 \\
 & 2 \to 4 & & 2 \to 5 \\
 & 3 \to 7 & & 3 \to 6 \\
\alpha \quad : & 4 \to 5 \quad \text{so that,} \quad \alpha^{-1} \quad : & & 4 \to 2 \\
 & 5 \to 2 & & 5 \to 4 \\
 & 6 \to 3 & & 6 \to 1 \\
 & 7 \to 1 & & 7 \to 3.
\end{array}
$$

Hence $\alpha^{-1} = (1\,7\,3\,6)(2\,5\,4) = (1\,6)(1\,3)(1\,7)(2\,4)(2\,5)$. As α^{-1} is a product of an odd number of 2-cycles, we conclude that α^{-1} is not an even permutation.

$\Diamond$ **Exercise 4.1.3.** Let $\alpha = \begin{pmatrix} 1 & 2 & 3 & 4 \\ 3 & 1 & 2 & 4 \end{pmatrix}$. Find the smallest positive integer k such that $\alpha^k = e$ in S_4.

Solution. Observe that $\alpha^1 \neq e$. Now,

$$
\alpha^2 = \begin{pmatrix} 1 & 2 & 3 & 4 \\ 3 & 1 & 2 & 4 \end{pmatrix} \begin{pmatrix} 1 & 2 & 3 & 4 \\ 3 & 1 & 2 & 4 \end{pmatrix} = \begin{pmatrix} 1 & 2 & 3 & 4 \\ 2 & 3 & 1 & 4 \end{pmatrix}.
$$

Again,

$$
\alpha^3 = \alpha^2 \alpha = \begin{pmatrix} 1 & 2 & 3 & 4 \\ 2 & 3 & 1 & 4 \end{pmatrix} \begin{pmatrix} 1 & 2 & 3 & 4 \\ 3 & 1 & 2 & 4 \end{pmatrix} = \begin{pmatrix} 1 & 2 & 3 & 4 \\ 1 & 2 & 3 & 4 \end{pmatrix} = e.
$$

Hence 3 is the smallest positive integer such that $\alpha^3 = e$.

$\Diamond$ **Exercise 4.1.4.** Compute each of the following and express it in two-row notation in S_7.

   (i) $(1\,3\,4\,7)(5\,4\,2)$ (ii) $(1\,2\,5\,4)^2(1\,2\,3)(2\,5)$.

Solution. Let $\alpha = (1\,3\,4\,7)$ and $\beta = (5\,4\,2)$. Then,

$$
\begin{array}{cccc}
 & 1 \to 3 & & 5 \to 4 \\
 & 3 \to 4 & & 4 \to 2 \\
\alpha \quad : & 4 \to 7 \qquad \beta \quad : & & 2 \to 5 \\
 & 7 \to 1 & & x \to x \\
 & x \to x & & \text{when } x \neq 5, 4, 2. \\
 & \text{when } x \neq 1, 3, 4, 7. & &
\end{array}
$$

Hence

$$
\alpha \circ \beta = \begin{pmatrix} 1 & 2 & 3 & 4 & 5 & 6 & 7 \\ 3 & 5 & 4 & 2 & 7 & 6 & 1 \end{pmatrix}.
$$

(ii) Let $\alpha = (1\,2\,5\,4)$, $\beta = (1\,2\,3)$ and $\gamma = (2\,5)$. Then, α^2 is given by the following:

$$
\begin{array}{ll}
1 \xrightarrow{\alpha} 2 \xrightarrow{\alpha} 5 & 1 \xrightarrow{\alpha^2} 5 \\
2 \xrightarrow{\alpha} 5 \xrightarrow{\alpha} 4 & 2 \xrightarrow{\alpha^2} 4 \\
3 \xrightarrow{\alpha} 3 \xrightarrow{\alpha} 3 & 3 \xrightarrow{\alpha^2} 3 \\
4 \xrightarrow{\alpha} 1 \xrightarrow{\alpha} 2 & 4 \xrightarrow{\alpha^2} 2 \\
5 \xrightarrow{\alpha} 4 \xrightarrow{\alpha} 1 & 5 \xrightarrow{\alpha^2} 1 \\
6 \xrightarrow{\alpha} 6 \xrightarrow{\alpha} 6 & 6 \xrightarrow{\alpha^2} 6 \\
7 \xrightarrow{\alpha} 7 \xrightarrow{\alpha} 7 & 7 \xrightarrow{\alpha^2} 7.
\end{array}
$$

Hence $\alpha^2\beta\gamma$ can be realized as follows:

$$
\begin{array}{l}
1 \xrightarrow{\gamma} 1 \xrightarrow{\beta} 2 \xrightarrow{\alpha^2} 4 \\
2 \xrightarrow{\gamma} 5 \xrightarrow{\beta} 5 \xrightarrow{\alpha^2} 1 \\
3 \xrightarrow{\gamma} 3 \xrightarrow{\beta} 1 \xrightarrow{\alpha^2} 5 \\
4 \xrightarrow{\gamma} 4 \xrightarrow{\beta} 4 \xrightarrow{\alpha^2} 2 \\
5 \xrightarrow{\gamma} 2 \xrightarrow{\beta} 3 \xrightarrow{\alpha^2} 3 \\
6 \xrightarrow{\gamma} 6 \xrightarrow{\beta} 6 \xrightarrow{\alpha^2} 6 \\
7 \xrightarrow{\gamma} 7 \xrightarrow{\beta} 7 \xrightarrow{\alpha^2} 7
\end{array}
$$

and so

$$
\alpha^2\beta\gamma = \begin{pmatrix} 1 & 2 & 3 & 4 & 5 & 6 & 7 \\ 4 & 1 & 5 & 2 & 3 & 6 & 7 \end{pmatrix}.
$$

◊ **Exercise 4.1.5.** Compute each of the following:

(i) $(1\,4\,2\,3)(3\,4)(1\,3\,2\,4)$ in S_4; (ii) $(1\,2\,5\,4)(2\,4\,3)(1\,2)$ in S_5

Solution. (i) Let $\alpha = (1\,4\,2\,3)$, $\beta = (3\,4)$ and $\delta = (1\,3\,2\,4)$. Then $\alpha\beta\delta$ can be obtained as follows:

$$
\begin{array}{l}
1 \xrightarrow{\delta} 3 \xrightarrow{\beta} 4 \xrightarrow{\alpha} 2 \\
2 \xrightarrow{\delta} 4 \xrightarrow{\beta} 3 \xrightarrow{\alpha} 1 \\
3 \xrightarrow{\delta} 2 \xrightarrow{\beta} 2 \xrightarrow{\alpha} 3 \\
4 \xrightarrow{\delta} 1 \xrightarrow{\beta} 1 \xrightarrow{\alpha} 4
\end{array}
$$

and so

$$
\alpha\beta\delta = \begin{pmatrix} 1 & 2 & 3 & 4 \\ 2 & 1 & 3 & 4 \end{pmatrix} = (1\,2).
$$

(ii)   Let $\alpha = (1\,2\,5\,4)$, $\beta = (2\,4\,3)$ and $\gamma = (1\,2)$. Then $\alpha\beta\gamma$ can be obtained as follows:

$$1 \xrightarrow{\gamma} 2 \xrightarrow{\beta} 4 \xrightarrow{\alpha} 1$$
$$2 \xrightarrow{\gamma} 1 \xrightarrow{\beta} 1 \xrightarrow{\alpha} 2$$
$$3 \xrightarrow{\gamma} 3 \xrightarrow{\beta} 2 \xrightarrow{\alpha} 5$$
$$4 \xrightarrow{\gamma} 4 \xrightarrow{\beta} 3 \xrightarrow{\alpha} 3$$
$$5 \xrightarrow{\gamma} 5 \xrightarrow{\beta} 5 \xrightarrow{\alpha} 4$$

and so

$$\alpha\beta\gamma = \begin{pmatrix} 1 & 2 & 3 & 4 & 5 \\ 1 & 2 & 5 & 3 & 4 \end{pmatrix} = (3\,5\,4).$$

◊ **Exercise 4.1.6** List all elements of S_4 in cycle notation.

Solution. S_4 has $4! = 24$ elements and they are:

$$e, (1\,2), (1\,3), (1\,4), (2\,3), (2\,4), (3\,4), (1\,2\,3), (1\,3\,2), (1\,2\,4), (1\,4\,2), (1\,3\,4)$$
$$(1\,4\,3), (2\,3\,4), (2\,4\,3), (1\,2\,3\,4), (1\,4\,3\,2), (1\,3\,2\,4), (1\,4\,2\,3), (1\,2\,4\,3),$$
$$(1\,3\,4\,2), (1\,2)(3\,4), (1\,3)(2\,4), (1\,4)(2\,3).$$

◊ **Exercise 4.1.7.** Show that the number of even permutations in S_n, $(n \geq 2)$ is the same as that of the odd permutations.

Solution. Let A be the set of all even permutations and B be the set of all odd permutations in S_n. Since $n \geq 2$, there exist $i, j \in I_n = \{1, 2, \ldots, n\}$, such that $i \neq j$. Hence, $(i\,j)$ is a 2-cycle and $(i\,j) \in B$. Again $(i\,j)(i\,j) \in A$. So $A \neq \emptyset, B \neq \emptyset$. Let α be an even permutation. Then α can be expressed as a product of an even number of 2-cycles. Hence, there exists 2-cycles $\alpha_1, \alpha_2, \ldots, \alpha_k$ where k is even, such that $\alpha = \alpha_1 \alpha_2 \ldots \alpha_k$. Consider a 2-cycle $(i\,j)$. Then $\beta = \alpha(i\,j) \in S_n$ and the number of 2-cycles in it is $k + 1$, which is odd. Hence β is an odd permutation. Now suppose $\gamma \in B$. Then we can express $\gamma = \gamma_1 \gamma_2 \ldots \gamma_t$, where $\gamma_1, \gamma_2, \ldots, \gamma_t$ are 2-cycles and t is odd. Then $\delta = \gamma_1 \gamma_2 \ldots \gamma_t (i\,j)$ is an even permutation. Hence defining $f : A \to B$ by $f(\sigma) = \sigma(i\,j)$, one can see that f is a one-one mapping from the set A onto the set B (verify!) and hence $|A| = |B|$.

◊ **Exercise 4.1.8.** Let σ be an element of the permutation group S_5. Then the maximum possible order of σ is

(i) 5   (ii) 6   (iii) 10   (iv) 15.

Solution. We know every permutation can be expressed as product of disjoint cycles. Now $\sigma \in S_5$ is either a 5-cycle or a 4-cycle or product of two disjoint cycles one of them is a 3-cycle and another is 2-cycle or product of two disjoint 2-cycles or a 3-cycle or a two cycle. If σ is a k-cycle, then its order is k $(k = 2, 3, 4, 5)$. If σ is a product of two disjoint cycles one of them is a 3-cycle and another is 2-cycle, then its order is 6. If σ is a product of two disjoint 2-cycles, then its order is 2. Therefore, option (ii) is correct.

$\diamondsuit$ **Exercise 4.1.9.** In the permutation group S_8 consider two elements $\alpha = (1\ 4\ 7\ 6)$ and $\beta = (2\ 5\ 6\ 7)$. Then $o(\alpha\beta)$ is

(i) 3   (ii) 4   (iii) 5   (iv) 6.

Solution. Here $\alpha\beta = (1\ 4\ 7\ 2\ 5)$, which is a 5-cycle and hence $o(\alpha\beta) = 5$. Hence, option (iii) is correct.

Exercises

1. Let $\alpha = \begin{pmatrix} 1 & 2 & 3 & 4 \\ 4 & 3 & 1 & 2 \end{pmatrix}$, $\beta = \begin{pmatrix} 1 & 2 & 3 & 4 \\ 1 & 4 & 3 & 2 \end{pmatrix}$ and $\gamma = \begin{pmatrix} 1 & 2 & 3 & 4 \\ 3 & 4 & 1 & 2 \end{pmatrix}$ in S_4.

   Compute each of the following, where $(\alpha\beta)(x) = \alpha(\beta(x))$ for all $x \in I_4$.
   (i) $\alpha\beta$ (ii) $\beta\alpha$ (iii) γ^{-1} (iv) $\alpha\beta\gamma^{-1}$ and (v) $\alpha^2\beta$

2. Let $\alpha = \begin{pmatrix} 1 & 2 & 3 & 4 \\ 4 & 3 & 1 & 2 \end{pmatrix} \in S_4$. Find the smallest positive integer k such that $\alpha^k = e$.

3. Let $\alpha = \begin{pmatrix} 1 & 2 & 3 & 4 & 5 \\ 3 & 2 & 1 & 5 & 4 \end{pmatrix}$ and $\beta = \begin{pmatrix} 1 & 2 & 3 & 4 & 5 \\ 2 & 4 & 3 & 5 & 1 \end{pmatrix}$ in S_5. Find a permutation γ in S_5 such that $\alpha\gamma = \beta$.

4. Express each of the following permutations as a product of disjoint cycles:
   (a) $\begin{pmatrix} 1 & 2 & 3 & 4 & 5 & 6 & 7 & 8 \\ 5 & 7 & 8 & 6 & 4 & 1 & 2 & 3 \end{pmatrix}$; (b) $\begin{pmatrix} 1 & 2 & 3 & 4 & 5 & 6 & 7 & 8 \\ 3 & 2 & 1 & 6 & 8 & 7 & 4 & 5 \end{pmatrix}$.

5. Compute the following:
   (a) $(2\,3\,4)(1\,4\,3\,2)(2\,4)$ in S_4 (b) $(3\,5)(1\,2\,4\,5)(2\,3\,1\,5)$ in S_5.

6. Express the following permutations as a product of 2-cycles:
   (a) $(4\,2\,5\,3)(1\,5\,2\,4)$, (b) $(3\,1)(5\,2\,3)^{-1}(1\,2\,3\,4)$; (c) $\left((1\,4\,2)(3\,2\,4\,5)\right)^{-1}$.

7. Determine whether the following permutations are even or odd.
   (a) $(1\,2\,3\,4)$; (b) $(2\,3\,4)$; (c) $(1\,2\,3\,8)(3\,5\,8)(1\,3)$; (d) $(1\,2\,3\,4)(1\,2\,5\,3)$;
   (e) $\begin{pmatrix} 1 & 2 & 3 & 4 & 5 & 6 & 7 & 8 \\ 2 & 1 & 3 & 5 & 4 & 7 & 6 & 8 \end{pmatrix}$.

8. List all even permutations of S_3.

9. List all even permutations of S_4.

10. If $\beta \in S_7$ and $\beta^4 = (2\,1\,4\,3\,5\,6\,7)$ then find β.

11. If $\beta = (1\,2\,3)(1\,4\,5)$, write β^{99} in cycle notation.

12. Let $\beta = (1\,3\,5\,7\,9\,8\,6)(2\,4\,1\,0)$ in S_{10}. What is the smallest positive integer n for which $\beta^n = \beta^{-5}$?

13. Let f, g be two given permutations on a finite set S. Show that there is a unique permutation p on S, such that $fp = g$ and there is a unique permutation q on S, such that $qf = g$. Determine p, q where $S = \{1, 2, 3\}$, $f = (1\,2\,3)$ and $g = (1\,3\,2)$.

14. In S_6, let $\rho = (1\,2\,3)$ and $\sigma = (4\,5\,6)$. Find a permutation x in S_6 such that $x\rho x^{-1} = \sigma$.

Find out the correct option(s) in each of the the following statements:

15. The order of the permutation $(1\,2\,3\,4)(5\,6) \in S_6$ is
    (i) 6 (ii) 2 (iii) 3 (iv) 4.

16. The number of elements of order 3 in A_4 is
    (i) 1 (ii) 2 (iii) 7 (iv) 8.

17. The number of elements of order 6 in S_4 is
    (i) 1 (ii) 2 (iii) 6 (iv) 0.

18. The number of elements of order 2 in A_4 is
    (i) 1 (ii) 2 (iii) 3 (iv) 6.

19. In the permutation group S_{15} consider the two elements $\alpha = (1\ 3\ 6\ 15\ 10\ 13)$ and $\beta = (2\ 7\ 1\ 5\ 13\ 15\ 6)$. Then $\alpha \circ \beta$ is
    (i) $(1\ 5)(2\ 7\ 11\ 6)(10\ 13)(3\ 8)$ (ii) $(1\ 5)(2\ 9\ 3\ 6)(10\ 13)(4\ 8)$
    (iii) $(1\ 5)(2\ 7\ 8\ 6)(10\ 13)(14\ 15)$ (iv) $(1\ 5)(2\ 7\ 3\ 6)(10\ 13)$.

20. Let $\sigma : \{1, 2, 3, 4, 5\} \longrightarrow \{1, 2, 3, 4, 5\}$ be a permutation such that $\sigma^{-1}(j) \leq \sigma(j)$ for all $1 \leq j \leq 5$. Then
    (i) $\sigma \circ \sigma^{-1}(j) = j$ for all j, $1 \leq j \leq 5$.
    (ii) $\sigma^{-1}(j) = \sigma(j)$ for all j, $1 \leq j \leq 5$.
    (iii) The set $\{k : \sigma(k) = k\}$ has an odd number of elements.
    (iv) The set $\{k : \sigma(k) \neq k\}$ has an even number of elements.

Chapter 5

Subgroups

It took more than a century for the abstract concept of a group to evolve. The formal inception took place in a way essentially similar to that of the most of the other theories in abstract mathematics; it began with a steady influx of discrete examples having striking similarity, followed by the recognition of their common features; next there was a search for more and more particular cases with an attempt to classify them in several categories; then emerged the object independent set up, based on general principles and finally abstract postulates were laid down to define a new system.

What are the subsets of a group that are of natural importance? Presumably, a subset which inherits the group structure. Well, does a subset of a group automatically inherit the group structure? Any number of counter examples can be cited to answer this in the negative. On the other hand, in a previous chapter, we have seen that for the groups $(\mathbb{Z}, +)$ and $(\mathbb{Q}, +)$, $\mathbb{Z}$ is a subset of $\mathbb{Q}$. There are many examples where the underlying set of one group is a subset of the underlying set of another group. All these lead us to the concept of a subgroup.

5.1 Subgroups

Let $(G, *)$ be a group and H be a nonempty subset of G. Then H is said to be ***closed*** under the binary operation $*$ if $a * b \in H$ for all $a, b \in H$.

Suppose H is closed under the binary operation $*$. Then the restriction of $*$ to $H \times H$ is a mapping from $H \times H$ into H. Thus the binary operation $*$, defined on G induces a binary operation on H. Let us denote this induced binary operation on H, also by $*$ (to avoid notational complication). Thus $(H, *)$ is a groupoid. If $(H, *)$ is a group, then we call H a subgroup of G. More formally, we have the following definition.

Definition 5.1.1. Let $(G, *)$ be a group and H be a nonempty subset of G. Then H is called a ***subgroup*** of $(G, *)$, if H is closed under the binary operation $*$ and $(H, *)$ is a group. Note that every group G has at least two subgroups, viz., $\{e\}$ and G itself. These two are called ***trivial*** subgroups. If H is a subgroup of a group G such that $H \neq \{e\}$ and $H \neq G$, then H is called a ***nontrivial*** subgroup of G.

Example 5.1.2. Let E be the set of all even integers. Then E is a subset of $\mathbb{Z}$, where $\mathbb{Z}$ is a set of all integers. Now $(\mathbb{Z}, +)$ is a group, where the binary operation $+$ is the usual addition of two integers. Notice that E is a subset of $\mathbb{Z}$. Since the sum of two even integers is again an even integer, it follows that E is closed under the operation $+$. It can be shown easily that $(E, +)$ is a group. Hence E is a subgroup of $(\mathbb{Z}, +)$. Now consider the set T of all odd integers. Since the sum of two odd integers is an even integer, T is not closed under addition. Hence T is not a subgroup of $(\mathbb{Z}, +)$. Again consider the set $\mathbb{N}_0$ of all nonnegative integers. Since the sum of two nonnegative integers is again a nonnegative integer, $\mathbb{N}_0$ is closed under the binary operation of addition. Note that $(\mathbb{N}_0, +)$ is not a group. Hence $\mathbb{N}_0$ is not a subgroup of $(\mathbb{Z}, +)$.

The following is an important property of a subgroup of a group:

Theorem 5.1.3. *All subgroups of a group $(G, *)$ have the same identity element.*

Proof. Let e_G denote the identity element of the group $(G, *)$. Suppose H is a subgroup of G and we denote the identity element of this subgroup by e_H. Then we have $e_H * e_H = e_H = e_H * e_G$. Now by the cancellation property of the group $(G, *)$, it follows that $e_H = e_G$. Hence the theorem. $\qquad\square$

Example 5.1.4. Consider the following list of groups.

$$(\{1\}, \cdot), (\mathbb{Q} \smallsetminus \{0\}, \cdot), (\mathbb{R} \smallsetminus \{0\}, \cdot), (\mathbb{C} \smallsetminus \{0\}, \cdot);$$

where $\cdot$ is the usual multiplication of complex numbers. Now $(\{1\}, \cdot)$ is a subgroup of $(\mathbb{Q} \smallsetminus \{0\}, \cdot)$, $(\mathbb{Q} \smallsetminus \{0\}, \cdot)$ is a subgroup of $(\mathbb{R} \smallsetminus \{0\}, \cdot)$ and $(\mathbb{R} \smallsetminus \{0\}, \cdot)$ is a subgroup of $(\mathbb{C} \smallsetminus \{0\}, \cdot)$.

In the remainder of the text, we shall generally use the notation G instead of $(G, *)$ for a group. Furthermore, we shall take recourse to the so called multiplicative notation and refer to $a * b$ as the product of a and b and shall henceforth denote it by ab.

Next we present a very useful result to test whether a subset of a group is actually a subgroup.

Theorem 5.1.5. *Let G be a group and H be a nonempty subset of G. Then H is a subgroup of G if and only if for all $a, b \in H, ab^{-1} \in H$.*

Proof. Suppose H is a subgroup of G. Let $h \in H$. Let h' denote the inverse of h in H and h^{-1} denote that of h in G. Then $h' = h'e = h'(hh^{-1}) = (h'h)h^{-1} = eh^{-1} = h^{-1}$. So the inverse of h in H and the inverse of h in G are one and the same. Let $a, b \in H$. Then $b^{-1} \in H$. Since H is closed under the binary operation, it follows that for all $a, b \in H$ we have $a, b^{-1} \in H$ and hence $ab^{-1} \in H$.

Conversely, suppose H is a nonempty subset of G that satisfies the property: for all $a, b \in H, ab^{-1} \in H$. Since $H \neq \emptyset$, there exists $a \in H$ and so $e = aa^{-1} \in H$, i.e., H contains the identity. Now, for all $b \in H, b^{-1} = eb^{-1} \in H$, i.e., every element of H has an inverse in H. Thus for all $a, b \in H, a, b^{-1} \in H$ and so $ab = a(b^{-1})^{-1} \in H$, i.e., H is closed under the binary operation. Since $H \subseteq G$, the associativity of H follows from the associativity of G[1]. Hence H is a group and so we see that H is a subgroup of G. $\qquad\square$

With the help of the above theorem, we can check in a very simple way whether a given subset H is a subgroup of a given group G or not. For example, in the group $\mathbb{Q} \setminus \{0\}$ of all nonzero rational numbers under multiplication, the subset $\mathbb{Z}^+$ of all positive integers is not a subgroup, because for $2, 3 \in \mathbb{Z}^+, 2 \cdot 3^{-1} = \frac{2}{3} \notin \mathbb{Z}^+$.

The above theorem also comes in very handy to show that a given set H is a group under some binary operation, by showing that it is a subgroup of a known group. For example, the set $\mathbb{Q}(\sqrt{2}) = \{a + b\sqrt{2} \mid a, b \in \mathbb{Q}\}$ is a group under usual addition, because we can show that $\mathbb{Q}(\sqrt{2})$ is a subgroup of the group of all real numbers under addition.

In order to see whether a finite nonempty subset of a given group is a subgroup or not, we have the following useful result.

Corollary 5.1.6. *Let G be a group and H a nonempty finite subset of G. Then H is a subgroup if and only if, for all $a, b \in H, ab \in H$.*

Proof. Let H be a subgroup of a group G. Since H is closed, we find that for all $a, b \in H, ab \in H$.

Conversely, suppose that for all $a, b \in H, ab \in H$. Let $h \in H$. Then each of $h, h^2, \ldots, h^n, \ldots$ is in H. Since H is finite, all the elements $h, h^2, \ldots, h^n, \ldots$ cannot be distinct. Thus there exist integers r and s such that $0 \leq r < s$ and $h^r = h^s$. Hence $e = h^{s-r} \in H$. Now $s - r \geq 1$. Thus $e = hh^{s-r-1}$ implies that $h^{-1} = h^{s-r-1} \in H$. Let

---

[1]Associativity is a *hereditary* property. A property is called hereditary, if the validity of the property in a mathematical system implies its validity in any of the subsets of that system. Note that *closure* property is *not* hereditary.

$a, b \in H$. Then $a, b^{-1} \in H$. Hence by the hypothesis $ab^{-1} \in H$, whence by Theorem 5.1.5, H is a subgroup. $\qquad\square$

Example 5.1.7. Let $T = \{1, -1, i, -i\}$. Then T is a subset of the set $\mathbb{C}^*$ of all nonzero complex numbers. Since the product of any two elements of T is also an element of T, it follows from the above Corollary 5.1.6 that T is a subgroup of the multiplicative group of all nonzero complex numbers.

It is important to note that the finiteness of the nonempty subset H in the above Corollary 5.1.6 is indispensable. Indeed, if we consider the *infinite subset* $\mathbb{N}$ of all natural numbers, in the additive group $\mathbb{Z}$ of all integers, we see that though $\mathbb{N}$ is closed under addition, it fails to be a group.

Rest of this section is devoted to show how new subgroups arise from the existing subgroups of a group.

Theorem 5.1.8. *The intersection of any collection of subgroups of a group G is a subgroup of G.*

Proof. Let $T = \{H_\alpha \mid \alpha \in I\}$ be any collection of subgroups H_α of G. Since each H_α is a subgroup, $e \in H_\alpha$ for all $\alpha \in I$. Hence $e \in \bigcap_{\alpha \in I} H_\alpha$ and so $\bigcap_{\alpha \in I} H_\alpha \neq \emptyset$. Now if $a, b \in \bigcap_{\alpha \in I} H_\alpha$, then $a, b \in H_\alpha$ for each $\alpha \in I$, whence $ab^{-1} \in H_\alpha$ for all $\alpha \in I$, since each H_α is a subgroup. Consequently, $ab^{-1} \in \bigcap_{\alpha \in I} H_\alpha$, and so by Theorem 5.1.5, $\bigcap_{\alpha \in I} H_\alpha$ is a subgroup of G. $\qquad\square$

Suppose now that G is a group and S is a subset of the set G. Consider the collection T of all those subgroups of G that contain S. This collection is nonempty, since G is a member of this collection. By Theorem 5.1.8, the intersection of all the subgroups of this collection is also a subgroup of G and it contains S. We denote this subgroup by $\langle S \rangle$. The subgroup $\langle S \rangle$ of G is called the ***subgroup generated*** by S. If $G = \langle S \rangle$, then S is called a set of ***generators*** for G. In particular, if the generator set S is finite, then G is called ***finitely generated***. If either $S = \emptyset$ or $S = \{e\}$, then $\langle S \rangle = \{e\}$. Also, $\langle G \rangle = G$.

Some well known groups may be abstractly described as finitely generated groups as follows.

Definition 5.1.9. Consider $G = \langle \{a, b\} \rangle$, such that

$$o(a) = 4, o(b) = 2, \text{ and } ba = a^3 b.$$

This is the abstract formulation of *the **dihedral group*** of degree 4, or the fourth dihedral group $\mathcal{D}_4$, a noncommutative group with 8 elements.

Example 5.1.10. Let G be the subgroup of $GL(2, \mathbb{R})$ generated by the matrices

$$R = \begin{bmatrix} 0 & -1 \\ 1 & 0 \end{bmatrix}, \; S = \begin{bmatrix} 0 & -1 \\ -1 & 0 \end{bmatrix}.$$

Then it is routine to check that $o(R) = 4$, $o(S) = 2$ and $SR = R^3S$. Hence G is an example of *dihedral group of degree* 4.

Example 5.1.11. Consider the symmetric group S_4. Let $G = \langle \{a, b\} \rangle$ be a subgroup of S_4 generated by the permutations $a = (1\ 2\ 3\ 4)$ and $b = (2\ 4)$. Clearly, $o(a) = 4, o(b) = 2$ and we invite the reader to verify that $ba = a^3b$, whence G is another example of *dihedral group of degree* 4.

Remark 5.1.12. Consider symmetric group S_3 as described in Example 4.1.22. In the light of present discussion, we see that it is generated by two permutations $a = (1\ 2\ 3)$ and $b = (1\ 2)$. Clearly $o(a) = 3, o(b) = 2$ and in this case one can verify that $ba = a^2b$, which is the abstract description of $\mathcal{D}_3$, the *dihedral group of degree* 3 with six elements.[2]

Definition 5.1.13. Consider $G = \langle \{a, b\} \rangle$, such that

$$o(a) = 2, o(b) = 2, \text{ and } ba = ab.$$

This is the abstract formulation of *the **Klein's four-group** $\mathcal{K}_4$*, a commutative group with 4 elements. We shall refer to this interesting group again in Example 5.2.5 with a greater details.

Example 5.1.14. Let G be the subgroup of $GL(2, \mathbb{R})$ generated by the matrices

$$r = \begin{bmatrix} -1 & 0 \\ 0 & -1 \end{bmatrix}, \; s = \begin{bmatrix} 1 & 0 \\ 0 & -1 \end{bmatrix}.$$

Then it is routine to check that $o(r) = 2$, $o(s) = 2$ and $sr = rs$. Hence G is an example of Klein's four-group.

Definition 5.1.15. Consider $G = \langle \{a, b\} \rangle$, such that

$$o(a) = 4, a^2 = b^2, \text{ and } ba = a^3b.$$

This is the abstract formulation of *the **quaternion group** $\mathcal{Q}_8$*, a noncommutative group with 8 elements.

---

[2]In view of its pictorial presentation in Example 8.3.6, as the group of symmetries of an equilateral triangle, it can easily be seen that S_3 is the same as $\mathcal{D}_3$.

Example 5.1.16. Let G be the subgroup of $GL(2, \mathbb{C})$ generated by the matrices

$$A = \begin{bmatrix} 0 & -1 \\ 1 & 0 \end{bmatrix}, \; B = \begin{bmatrix} 0 & -i \\ -i & 0 \end{bmatrix}.$$

Then it is routine to check that $o(A) = 4$, $A^2 = B^2$ and $BA = A^3 B$. Hence G is an example of *quaternion group*.

Remark 5.1.17. Though both $\mathcal{D}_4$ and $\mathcal{Q}_8$ are noncommutative groups of order 8, they are distinct groups, as they differ in certain group theoretic properties. It can be shown that, while $\mathcal{Q}_8$ contains six elements of order 4, such elements of $\mathcal{D}_4$ are only two. In as much as S_3 is same as $\mathcal{D}_3$, it is also interesting to note that $\mathcal{K}_4$ is same as $\mathcal{D}_2$. Sure enough, this observations indicates a general abstract formulation of the nth dihedral group $\mathcal{D}_n$, which we will take up in due course of time.

Let $\mathcal{S} = \{H \,|\, H$ be a subgroup of G and $S \subseteq H\}$. Then $(\mathcal{S}, \leq)$ is a partially ordered set, where $\leq$ denotes the set inclusion relation. In this poset, $\langle S \rangle$ is the least element. Hence, $\langle S \rangle$ is the smallest subgroup of G to contain S. Since $\langle S \rangle$ is a subgroup of G, we must have for $S \neq \emptyset$ and for any $s_1, s_2, \ldots, s_n \in S$, the product $s_1^{e_1} \ldots s_n^{e_n} \in \langle S \rangle$ where $e_i = \pm 1$ for $i = 1, 2, \ldots, n$. Thus, if A denotes the set $\{s_1^{e_1} \ldots s_n^{e_n} \,|\, s_i \in S, e_i = \pm 1, i = 1, 2, \ldots, n; n \in \mathbb{N}\}$, then $A \subseteq \langle S \rangle$. In the following theorem, we show that $A = \langle S \rangle$. Thus, S does *generate* $\langle S \rangle$ in the sense of multiplying elements of S or their inverses together to build up the smallest subgroup containing S. For a nonempty subset S of a group G, we now describe the subgroup $\langle S \rangle$ in the following theorem.

Theorem 5.1.18. *Let S be a nonempty subset of a group G. Then*

$$\langle S \rangle = \{s_1^{e_1} \ldots s_n^{e_n} \,|\, s_i \in S, e_i = \pm 1, i = 1, 2, \ldots, n; \, n \in \mathbb{N}\}.$$

Proof. Let

$$H = \{s_1^{e_1} \ldots s_n^{e_n} \,|\, s_i \in S, e_i = \pm 1, i = 1, 2, \ldots, n; \, n \in \mathbb{N}\}.$$

Since $\langle S \rangle$ is a subgroup, we find that for any $s_1, s_2, \ldots s_n \in S$, the product $s_1^{e_1} s_2^{e_2} \ldots s_n^{e_n} \in \langle S \rangle$. Hence $H \subseteq \langle S \rangle$. We now show that $\langle S \rangle \subseteq H$, by showing that H is a subgroup of G containing S. (Recall that $\langle S \rangle$ is the smallest subgroup of G containing S.) Let $s \in S$. Then $s = s^1 \in H$ and so $S \subseteq H$. If $x, y \in H$, say $x = s_1^{f_1} \ldots s_m^{f_m}$ and $y = t_1^{g_1} \ldots t_q^{g_q}$, then

$$\left(s_1^{f_1} \ldots s_m^{f_m}\right)\left(t_1^{g_1} \ldots t_q^{g_q}\right)^{-1} = s_1^{f_1} \ldots s_m^{f_m} t_q^{-g_q} \ldots t_1^{-g_1} \in H$$

and so H is a subgroup of G, by Theorem 5.1.5. Hence $\langle S \rangle \subseteq H$. $\square$

However, for $a \in G$, we shall use the notation $\langle a \rangle$ rather than $\langle \{a\} \rangle$ to denote the subgroup of G generated by $\{a\}$.

Corollary 5.1.19. *Let G be a group and $a \in G$. Then $\langle a \rangle = \{a^n \mid n \in \mathbb{Z}\}$.*

Proof. By Theorem 5.1.18, we have $\langle a \rangle = \{a^{e_1} \ldots a^{e_m} \mid e_i = \pm 1, i = 1, 2, \ldots, m; m \in \mathbb{N}\} = \{a^{e_1 + \cdots + e_m} \mid e_i = \pm 1, i = 1, 2, \ldots, m; m \in \mathbb{N}\} = \{a^n \mid n \in \mathbb{Z}\}$. $\square$

In the group $(\mathbb{Z}, +)$, for any $a \in \mathbb{Z}$, note that, $\langle a \rangle = \{na \mid n \in \mathbb{Z}\}$.

In the light of Theorem 5.1.18, we now directly compute the Cayley table of Klein's four-group $\mathcal{K}_4$ discussed in Definition 5.1.13.

Example 5.1.20. We know that, $\mathcal{K}_4 = \langle \{a, b\} \rangle$, such that $o(a) = 2, o(b) = 2$, and $ba = ab$. Note that $o(ba) = 2$ as well, since $baba = b(ab)a = b(ba)a = b^2 a^2 = e$, where e is the identity as usual. So $e, a, b, ab \in \mathcal{K}_4$. That $\mathcal{K}_4 = \{e, a, b, ab\}$ may be seen from the following Cayley table, where $c = ab = ba$.

$*$	e	a	b	c
e	e	a	b	c
a	a	e	c	b
b	b	c	e	a
c	c	b	a	e

We now state the *general rule* for computing the Cayley table for nth *dihedral group*.

Example 5.1.21. The abstract description of the nth dihedral group $\mathcal{D}_n$ is

$$\mathcal{D}_n = \langle \{r, s\} \rangle, \text{ where } o(r) = n, o(s) = 2 \text{ and } sr = r^{n-1}s.$$

If the $2n$ elements[3] of $\mathcal{D}_n = \{r^0, r^1, r^2, \ldots r^{n-1}, s, rs, r^2s \ldots r^{n-1}s\}$ are denoted respectively by $\rho_0, \rho_1, \ldots \rho_{n-1}, \sigma_0, \sigma_1, \ldots \sigma_{n-1}$, then the multiplication table[4] may be computed by the mechanical rule given by,

$$\rho_i \rho_j = \rho_{i+j}, \quad \rho_i \sigma_j = \sigma_{i+j}, \quad \sigma_i \rho_j = \sigma_{i-j}, \quad \sigma_i \sigma_j = \rho_{i-j},$$

where both the addition and subtraction in the subscripts are to be calculated *modulo* n.

---

[3] That every element of $\mathcal{D}_n$ is of the form $r^i s^j$ for $0 \leq i < n, 0 \leq j < 2$ can be proved using the conditions on the generators r and s of the group.

[4] Check that in the light of pictorial presentation given in Remark 8.3.12, all the ρ_i stand for rotational symmetries and σ_j stand for reflection symmetries of a regular n-gon. Regular polygons $(n > 2)$ in space were looked upon as degenerate solid objects with two faces, called *dihedron* in ancient Greece. Hence the name *dihedral*.

We now construct the Cayley table of $\mathcal{D}_2$ using the above rule and show that it is exactly same as that of the Klein's four-group in Example 5.1.20. Clearly $\mathcal{D}_2 = \{e, a, b, ab\} = \{a^0, a^1, b, ab\} = \{\rho_0, \rho_1, \sigma_0, \sigma_1\}$ (say), where

$$\rho_0 = e, \rho_1 = a, \sigma_0 = b, \sigma_1 = ab.$$

Keeping in mind the arithmetic of modulo 2 in this case, we see that,

*	ρ_0	ρ_1	σ_0	σ_1
ρ_0	$\rho_0 = e$	$\rho_1 = a$	$\sigma_0 = b$	$\sigma_1 = ab$
ρ_1	$\rho_1 = a$	$\rho_2 = \rho_0 = e$	$\sigma_1 = ab$	$\sigma_2 = \sigma_0 = b$
σ_0	$\sigma_0 = b$	$\sigma_{-1} = \sigma_1 = ab$	$\rho_0 = e$	$\rho_{-1} = \rho_1 = a$
σ_1	$\sigma_1 = ab$	$\sigma_0 = b$	$\rho_1 = a$	$\rho_0 = e$

Remark 5.1.22. We point out that, in an essentially similar manner, the Cayley tables for the groups $\mathcal{D}_3 = \{r^0, r^1, r^2, s, rs, r^2 s\}$ and $\mathcal{D}_4 = \{r^0, r^1, r^2, r^3, s, rs, r^2 s, r^3 s\}$ may also be calculated, from which it can be easily seen that the Cayley table for $\mathcal{D}_3$ is exactly same as that of S_3. However, it must be noted that, though the quaternion group $\mathcal{Q}_8$ in Example 5.1.15 is also given by $\mathcal{Q}_8 = \{r^0, r^1, r^2, r^3, s, rs, r^2 s, r^3 s\}$, its Cayley table will be different from that of $\mathcal{D}_4$, as the governing conditions on the generators r and s are different in two cases.

In the following theorem, we present an important characterization of the alternating group $A_n, n \geq 3$.

Theorem 5.1.23. *Let $n \geq 3$. Then A_n is generated by the set of all 3-cycles.*

Proof. First note that any 3-cycle is an even permutation. Hence A_n contains all 3-cycles. Let $\alpha \in A_n$. Hence α is an even permutation. So there exist an even number of 2-cycles $\alpha_1, \alpha_2, \ldots \alpha_m$ such that $\alpha = \alpha_1 \alpha_2 \ldots \alpha_m$. Let α_i be the 2-cycle $(a_i\, b_i)$. Now $(a_i\, b_i) = (1\, a_i)(1\, b_i)(1\, a_i)$. Hence α can be expressed as $\alpha = \tau_1 \tau_2 \ldots \tau_r$, where r is even and each τ_i is of the form $(1\, x)$. Now for any two 2-cycles $(1\, x), (1\, y)$, we have $(1\, x)(1\, y) = (1\, y\, x)$. Hence it follows that α is a product of 3-cycles. $\square$

We now turn our attention to the product of subgroups.

Definition 5.1.24. Let H and K be two nonempty subsets of a group G. The product of H and K is defined to be the set

$$HK = \{hk \,|\, h \in H \text{ and } k \in K\}.$$

Example 5.1.25. Consider the symmetric group S_3. In this group, $H = \{e, (1\,2)\}$ and $K = \{e, (1\,3)\}$ are two subgroups. Now $HK = \{e, (1\,3), (1\,2), (1\,3\,2)\}$.

The above example shows that in general *the product of subgroups may not be a subgroup*. Indeed, observe that $(1\,3)(1\,2) = (1\,2\,3) \notin HK$. However, we have the following theorem.

Theorem 5.1.26. *Let H and K be two subgroups of a group G. Then the following are equivalent:*

   (i) HK is a subgroup of G.

   (ii) $HK = KH$.

   (iii) KH is a subgroup of G.

Proof. $(i) \Rightarrow (ii)$ Suppose HK is a subgroup of G. Let $kh \in KH$ where $k \in K$ and $h \in H$. Now $h = he \in HK$ and $k = ek \in HK$. Since HK is a subgroup, it follows that $kh \in HK$. Hence $KH \subseteq HK$. Again, let $hk \in HK$. Then $(hk)^{-1} \in HK$ and so $(hk)^{-1} = h_1 k_1$ for some $h_1 \in H$ and $k_1 \in K$, and $hk = (h_1 k_1)^{-1} = k_1^{-1} h_1^{-1} \in KH$. Thus $HK \subseteq KH$. Hence, $HK = KH$.

$(ii) \Rightarrow (i)$ Suppose $HK = KH$. Let $h_1 k_1, h_2 k_2 \in HK$. Then

$$(h_1 k_1)(h_2 k_2)^{-1} = h_1 k_1 k_2^{-1} h_2^{-1} \tag{5.1.1}$$

Now, $k_1 k_2^{-1} \in K$ as K is a subgroup of G. Let $k_3 = k_1 k_2^{-1}$. Hence $k_3 h_2^{-1} \in KH = HK$. So, there exist $h_3 \in H$ and $k_4 \in K$ such that $k_3 h_2^{-1} = h_3 k_4$. Then from (5.1.1),

$$(h_1 k_1)(h_2 k_2)^{-1} = h_1 k_3 h_2^{-1} = h_1 h_3 k_4 \in HK. \tag{5.1.2}$$

Hence HK is a subgroup of G by Theorem 5.1.5

$(ii) \iff (iii)$ Similar to $(i) \iff (ii)$.   □

Corollary 5.1.27. *If H and K are two subgroups of a commutative group G, then HK is a subgroup of G.*

Proof. Since G is commutative, $HK = KH$. The result now follows directly from the Theorem 5.1.26   □

Definition 5.1.28. Let G be a group and let $a \in G$ be a fixed element of G. Then

$$C(a) = \{g \in G \mid ga = ag\}$$

is called the **centralizer** of a in G.

Theorem 5.1.29. *Let G be a group. The centralizer $C(a)$ of an element $a \in G$ is a subgroup of G.*

Proof. Since $e \in C(a)$, we have $C(a) \neq \emptyset$. Note that, $y \in C(a)$ implies $ya = ay$, whence $y^{-1}(ya)y^{-1} = y^{-1}(ay)y^{-1}$ gives $(y^{-1}y)ay^{-1} = y^{-1}a(yy^{-1})$, i.e., $ay^{-1} = y^{-1}a$. So, for any $x, y \in C(a)$ we have,

$$(xy^{-1})a = x(y^{-1}a) = x(ay^{-1}) = (xa)y^{-1} = (ax)y^{-1} = a(xy^{-1})$$

showing that $xy^{-1} \in C(a)$, which proves our claim. $\square$

Generalizing the notion of the aforesaid definition, it can be shown that [vide Exercise 5.1.6] for any subset S of a group G, the set

$$Z(S) = \{g \in G \,|\, gs = sg \text{ for all } s \in S\}$$

is a subgroup of G as well. If in particular we take G for S, we have the following definition.

Definition 5.1.30. In a group G, define

$$Z(G) = \{x \in G \,|\, gx = xg, \text{ for all } g \in G\}.$$

Then $Z(G)$ is called the **centre** of the group G. Clearly, $Z(G) \subseteq C(a)$ for any $a \in G$. Further note that, if G is a commutative group, then $G = Z(G)$ and vice versa.

Theorem 5.1.31. *Let G be a group. Then $Z(G)$ is a subgroup of G.*

Proof. The proof is essentially similar to the proof of Theorem 5.1.29 and hence is omitted. $\square$

Worked-out Exercises

$\Diamond$ **Exercise 5.1.1.** In each of the following cases determine whether H is a subgroup of the group G.

(i) $H = \{2n \,|\, n \in \mathbb{Z}\}$, $G = \mathbb{Z}$, the additive group of all integers.

(ii) $H = \{1, -1\}$, $G = \mathbb{Z}$, the additive group of all integers.

(iii) $H = \{1, -1\}$, $G = \mathbb{Q}^*$, the group of all nonzero rational numbers under multiplication.

(iv) $H = \mathbb{Z}^+$, the set of all positive integers, $G = \mathbb{Q}^*$, the group of all nonzero rational numbers under multiplication.

(v) $H = \left\{ \frac{1+3n}{1+3m} \,|\, n, m \in \mathbb{Z} \right\}$, $G = \mathbb{Q}^*$, the group of all nonzero rational numbers under multiplication.

(vi) $H = \{[0], [4]\}$, $G = \mathbb{Z}_8$, the additive group of integers modulo 8.

Solution. (i) Clearly, $H \neq \emptyset$. Let $a = 2n$ and $b = 2m$ be two elements of H. Then $a - b = 2n - 2m = 2(n - m) \in H$. Hence H is a subgroup of $\mathbb{Z}$.

(ii) Since $1 + (-1) = 0 \notin H$, we find that H is not a subgroup of $\mathbb{Z}$.

(iii) H is a nonempty finite set. Since the product of any two elements of H is also an element of H, it follows that H is a subgroup of $\mathbb{Q}^*$.

(iv) $2, 3 \in \mathbb{Z}^+$. But $2 \cdot 3^{-1} = \frac{2}{3} \notin \mathbb{Z}^+$. Hence $\mathbb{Z}^+$ is not a subgroup of Q^*.

(v) Note that $H \neq \emptyset$. Let $a = \frac{1+3k}{1+3n}$ and $b = \frac{1+3t}{1+3r}$ be two elements of H. Since t is an integer $1 + 3t \neq 0$. Hence $b^{-1} = \frac{1+3r}{1+3t} \in H$. Now,

$$ab^{-1} = \frac{1+3k}{1+3n} \, \frac{1+3r}{1+3t} = \frac{1+3r+3k+9kr}{1+3n+3t+9nt} = \frac{1+3(r+k+3rk)}{1+3(n+t+3nt)} \in H.$$

Hence H is a subgroup of $\mathbb{Q}^*$.

(vi) Here H is a nonempty finite set. Since the sum of any two elements of A is also an element of H, e.g., $[4] + [4] = [8] = [0]$, we find that H is closed under the group operation of $\mathbb{Z}_8$. Hence H is a subgroup of $\mathbb{Z}_8$.

◊ **Exercise 5.1.2.** Let H be a subgroup of a group G. Show that for any $g \in G$, $K = gHg^{-1} = \{ghg^{-1} \,|\, h \in H\}$ is a subgroup of G and $|K| = |H|$.

Solution. Let $a = ghg^{-1}$ and $b = gh_1g^{-1}$ be two elements of K. Then

$$
\begin{aligned}
ab^{-1} &= ghg^{-1}\left(gh_1g^{-1}\right)^{-1} \\
&= ghg^{-1}\left((g^{-1})^{-1}h_1^{-1}g^{-1}\right) \\
&= ghg^{-1}gh_1^{-1}g^{-1} \\
&= ghh_1^{-1}g^{-1} \qquad \ldots (*)
\end{aligned}
$$

Now, $h, h_1 \in H$ and H is a subgroup of G. Hence $hh_1^{-1} \in H$. Then from $(*)$ above,

$$ab^{-1} = g(hh_1^{-1})g^{-1} \in gHg^{-1}.$$

Hence K is a subgroup of G.

To show that $|K| = |H|$, we prove that there exists a bijective function from H onto gHg^{-1}. Define $f : H \to gHg^{-1}$ by $f(h) = ghg^{-1}$ for all $h \in H$. Let h_1 and

$h_2 \in H$, such that $f(h_1) = f(h_2)$. Then $gh_1g^{-1} = gh_2g^{-1}$. By cancellation, we obtain $h_1 = h_2$. Hence f is injective. Let $a \in gHg^{-1}$. Then $a = ghg^{-1}$ for some $h \in H$ and $f(h) = ghg^{-1} = a$. This implies f is surjective and so $|H| = |K|$.

$\Diamond$ **Exercise 5.1.3.** Let $GL(2, \mathbb{R})$ be the group of all nonsingular 2×2 matrices over $\mathbb{R}$. Show that each of the following sets is a subgroup of $GL(2, \mathbb{R})$.

(i) $H = \left\{ \begin{bmatrix} a & 0 \\ c & d \end{bmatrix} \in GL(2, \mathbb{R}) \mid ad \neq 0 \right\}.$

(ii) $H = \left\{ \begin{bmatrix} a & b \\ -b & a \end{bmatrix} \in GL(2, \mathbb{R}) \mid \text{either } a \text{ or } b \neq 0 \right\}.$

Solution. (i) $\begin{bmatrix} 1 & 0 \\ 0 & 1 \end{bmatrix} \in H$. Hence $H \neq \emptyset$. Let $A = \begin{bmatrix} a & 0 \\ c & d \end{bmatrix} \in H$ and $B = \begin{bmatrix} a_1 & 0 \\ c_1 & d_1 \end{bmatrix} \in$ H. Since $B \in H, a_1 d_1 \neq 0$. Hence

$$B^{-1} = \begin{bmatrix} \frac{d_1}{a_1 d_1} & 0 \\ -\frac{c_1}{a_1 d_1} & \frac{a_1}{a_1 d_1} \end{bmatrix} = \begin{bmatrix} \frac{1}{a_1} & 0 \\ -\frac{c_1}{a_1 d_1} & \frac{1}{d_1} \end{bmatrix}.$$

Then,

$$AB^{-1} = \begin{bmatrix} a & 0 \\ c & d \end{bmatrix} \begin{bmatrix} \frac{1}{a_1} & 0 \\ \frac{c_1}{a_1 d_1} & \frac{1}{d_1} \end{bmatrix} = \begin{bmatrix} \frac{a}{a_1} & 0 \\ \frac{c}{a_1} - \frac{dc_1}{a_1 d_1} & \frac{d}{d_1} \end{bmatrix}.$$

Since $ad \neq 0, a_1 d_1 \neq 0$, we find that $\frac{a}{a_1} \frac{d}{d_1} = \frac{ad}{a_1 d_1} \neq 0$. Hence $AB^{-1} \in H$. Consequently, H is a subgroup of G.

(ii) $\begin{bmatrix} 1 & 0 \\ 0 & 1 \end{bmatrix} \in H$. Hence $H \neq \emptyset$. Let $A = \begin{bmatrix} a & b \\ -b & a \end{bmatrix}$ and $B = \begin{bmatrix} c & d \\ -d & c \end{bmatrix}$ be two elements of H. Since a and b cannot be both zero, we find that $a^2 + b^2 \neq 0$. Similarly, $c^2 + d^2 \neq 0$. Now,

$$B^{-1} = \begin{bmatrix} \frac{c}{c^2+d^2} & -\frac{d}{c^2+d^2} \\ \frac{d}{c^2+d^2} & \frac{c}{c^2+d^2} \end{bmatrix}.$$

Hence,

$$AB^{-1} = \begin{bmatrix} a & b \\ -b & a \end{bmatrix} \begin{bmatrix} \frac{c}{c^2+d^2} & -\frac{d}{c^2+d^2} \\ \frac{d}{c^2+d^2} & \frac{c}{c^2+d^2} \end{bmatrix} = \begin{bmatrix} \frac{ac+bd}{c^2+d^2} & \frac{-ad+bc}{c^2+d^2} \\ \frac{-bc+ad}{c^2+d^2} & \frac{bd+ac}{c^2+d^2} \end{bmatrix} = \begin{bmatrix} x & y \\ -y & x \end{bmatrix},$$

where $x = \frac{ac+bd}{c^2+d^2}$ and $y = \frac{-ad+bc}{c^2+d^2}$. Now,

$$x^2 + y^2 = \frac{(ac+bd)^2 + (-ad+bc)^2}{(c^2+d^2)^2}$$
$$= \frac{a^2c^2 + b^2d^2 + a^2d^2 + b^2c^2}{(c^2+d^2)^2}$$
$$= \frac{(a^2+b^2)(c^2+d^2)}{(c^2+d^2)^2}$$
$$= \frac{(a^2+b^2)}{(c^2+d^2)} \neq 0.$$

Hence, either $x \neq 0$ or $y \neq 0$. So, we find that $AB^{-1} \in H$. Hence H is a subgroup of $GL(2, \mathbb{R})$.

◊ **Exercise 5.1.4.** Find all subgroups of the group $\mathbb{Z}$ of all integers under usual addition.

Solution. Let n be a nonnegative integer. Let $T_n = \{rn \,|\, r \in \mathbb{Z}\}$. Certainly, $T_n \neq \emptyset$. Let $a = rn$ and $b = tn$ be two elements of T_n. Now $a - b = rn - tn = (r - t)n \in T_n$. Hence T_n is a subgroup of $\mathbb{Z}$.

Let H be a subgroup of $\mathbb{Z}$. We now show that $H = T_n$ for some nonnegative integer n. If $H = \{0\}$, then $H = T_0$.

Suppose, $H \neq \{0\}$. Let $0 \neq a \in H$. Since H is a subgroup, $-a \in H$. Hence H contains both a and $-a$. This implies that H contains positive integers. By the well-ordering principle, H contains a positive integer, which is the smallest among its members. Let n be the smallest positive integer in H. We show that $H = T_n$. Since $n \in H$ and H is a subgroup, we find that $T_n = \{rn \,|\, r \in \mathbb{Z}\} \subseteq H$. Let $a \in H$. Then dividing a by n, by virtue of division algorithm, there exist integers b and d such that $a = bn + d$ where $0 \le d < n$. Now $d = a - bn$. Since $n \in H$ and H is a subgroup, $bn \in H$, whence we find that a and bn are both in H. Hence $d = a - bn \in H$. If $d \neq 0$, then H contains a positive integer d such that $d < n$. This contradicts the fact that n is the smallest positive integer in H. Hence $d = 0$, which shows that $a = bn \in T_n$. So we find that $H \subseteq T_n$ and consequently $H = T_n$. Thus it follows that all the subgroups of $\mathbb{Z}$ are $T_n, n \in \mathbb{N}_0$.

◊ **Exercise 5.1.5.** In the group $(\mathbb{Z}, +)$, if H is the smallest subgroup containing 4 and 6, then which one of the following is true?
(i) $H = 24\mathbb{Z}$ (ii) $H = 12\mathbb{Z}$ (iii) $H = 2\mathbb{Z}$ (iv) $H = \mathbb{Z}$.

Solution. Here $4, 6 \in H$ implies $2 = 6 - 4 \in H$. So $2\mathbb{Z} \subseteq H$. Again, if $x \in H$, then $x = 4p + 6q$ for some $p, q \in \mathbb{Z}$. This imples $x = 2(2p + 3q) \in 2\mathbb{Z}$. Hence $H \subseteq 2\mathbb{Z}$ and consequently, $H = 2\mathbb{Z}$. Therefore, option (iii) is correct.

◇ **Exercise 5.1.6.** Consider the group of all 2×2 invertible matrices with entries from $\mathbb{R}$ under usual multiplication of matrices. Then which of the following is a subgroup of G?

(i) $H_1 = \left\{ \begin{pmatrix} a & b \\ c & d \end{pmatrix} : ad - bc = 0 \right\}$ (ii) $H_2 = \left\{ \begin{pmatrix} a & b \\ c & d \end{pmatrix} : ad - bc = 1 \right\}$

(iii) $H_3 = \left\{ \begin{pmatrix} a & b \\ c & d \end{pmatrix} : ad - bc = -1 \right\}$ (iv) $H_4 = \left\{ \begin{pmatrix} a & b \\ c & d \end{pmatrix} : ad - bc = \pm 1 \right\}$.

Solution. One can easily check that H_2 and H_4 are subgroups of G. Since singular matrix has no inverse, it follows that H_1 is not a group. Moreover, H_3 is not closed under multiplication. Therefore, options (ii) and (iv) are correct.

Exercises

1. In each case, determine whether H is a subgroup of the group G under usual operation.
   (a) $H = \{3n \mid n \in \mathbb{Z}\}, G = \mathbb{Z}$.
   (b) $H = \{n \mid n \in \mathbb{Z} \text{ and } n \geq 0\}, G = \mathbb{Z}$.
   (c) $H = \{n \mid n \in \mathbb{Z} \text{ and } |n| \geq 1\}, G = \mathbb{Z}$.
   (d) $H = \{(m, n) \mid m, n \in \mathbb{Z} \text{ and } m + n \text{ is even}\}, G = \mathbb{Z} \times \mathbb{Z}$.
   (e) $H = \{1, -1, 0\}, G = \mathbb{Z}$.
   (f) $H = \{[0], [2], [4], [6]\}, G = \mathbb{Z}_8$.

2. In each case, determine whether H is a subgroup of the group $\mathbb{R}^* = (\mathbb{R} \setminus \{0\}, \cdot)$.
   (a) $H = \{1, -1\}$.
   (b) $H =$ the set of all positive real numbers.
   (c) $H =$ the set of all positive integers.
   (d) $H = \{a + b\sqrt{3} \in \mathbb{R}^* \mid a, b \in \mathbb{Q}\}$.

3. Let $GL(2, \mathbb{R})$ denote the group of all nonsingular 2×2 matrices with real entries. In each case, determine whether S is a subgroup of the group $GL(2, \mathbb{R})$.

   (a) $S = \left\{ \begin{bmatrix} a & b \\ c & d \end{bmatrix} \in GL(2, \mathbb{R}) \mid ad - bc = 1 \right\}$.[5]

   (b) $S = \left\{ \begin{bmatrix} 1 & n \\ 0 & 1 \end{bmatrix} \in GL(2, \mathbb{R}) \mid n \in \mathbb{Z} \right\}$.

   (c) $S = \left\{ \begin{bmatrix} 0 & b \\ -b & 0 \end{bmatrix} \in GL(2, \mathbb{R}) \mid b \text{ is nonzero} \right\}$.

   (d) $S = \left\{ \begin{bmatrix} a & b \\ 0 & d \end{bmatrix} \in GL(2, \mathbb{R}) \mid ad > 0 \right\}$.

   (e) $S = \left\{ \begin{bmatrix} a & b \\ b & a \end{bmatrix} \in GL(2, \mathbb{R}) \right\}$.

---

[5]This subgroup is called the special linear group of degree 2 and is denoted by $SL(2, \mathbb{R})$.

(f) $\quad S = \left\{ \begin{bmatrix} a & 0 \\ b & 1 \end{bmatrix} \in GL(2, \mathbb{R}) \,|\, a \neq 0 \right\}.$

4. Show that the set $H = \{a + ib \in \mathbb{C}^* \,|\, a^2 + b^2 = 1\}$ is a subgroup of $(\mathbb{C}^*, \cdot)$, where $\cdot$ is the usual multiplication of complex numbers.

5. Let G be a group. Prove that a nonempty subset H is a subgroup of G if and only if for $a, b \in H$, ab in H and a^{-1} in H.

6. Let G be a group and $S \subseteq G$. Show that $Z(S) = \{g \in G \,|\, gs = sg \text{ for all } s \in S\}$ is a subgroup of G containing the centre of G.

7. If G is a commutative group, then prove that $H = \{a^2 \,|\, a \in G\}$ is a subgroup of G.

8. If G is a commutative group, then prove that $H = \{a \in G \,|\, a^2 = e\}$ is a subgroup of G.

9. Let K be a subgroup of a group G and H be a subgroup of K. Is it true that H is a subgroup of G? Justify.

10. Let G be a group and $a \in G$. Show that $H = \{a^{2n} : n \in \mathbb{Z}\}$ is a subgroup of G.

11. Let $G = \{(a, b) : a, b \in \mathbb{R} \text{ and } b \neq 0\}$. Show that $(G, *)$ is a noncommutative group under the binary operation $(a, b) * (c, d) = (a + bc, bd)$ for all $(a, b), (c, d) \in G$.
    (a) Show that $H = \{(a, b) \in G \,|\, a = 0\}$ is a subgroup of G.
    (b) Show that $K = \{(a, b) \in G \,|\, b > 0\}$ is a subgroup of G.
    (c) Show that $T = \{(a, b) \in G \,|\, b = 1\}$ is a subgroup of G.
    (d) Does G contain a finite subgroup of order 2?

12. Let G be a commutative group. Prove that the set H of all elements of finite order in G is a subgroup of G.

13. Let G be a commutative group. Prove that the subset $H = \{a \in G \,|\, o(a) \text{ divides } 10\}$ is a subgroup of G.

14. In the group S_3, show that the subset $H = \{a \in S_3 \,|\, o(a) \text{ divides } 2\}$ is not a subgroup.

15. In the symmetric group S_3, show that $H = \{e, (2\,3)\}$ and $K = \{e, (1\,2)\}$ are subgroups but $H \cup K$ is not a subgroup of S_3.

16. If H and K are subgroups of a group G, then prove that $H \cup K$ is a subgroup of G if and only if $H \subseteq K$ or $K \subseteq H$.

17. Let H, K, N be subgroups of a group G such that $H \subseteq N$. Then prove that $(HK) \cap N = H(K \cap N)$.

18. Find the subgroup $\langle \{6, 8\} \rangle$ in $(\mathbb{Z}, +)$.

19. In $\mathbb{Z}$, find the subgroup generated by $\{2, 3\}$.

20. Let G be a group and H be a nonempty subset of G.
    (a) Show that if H is a subgroup of G, then $HH = H$.
    (b) If H is finite and $HH \subseteq H$, then prove that H is a subgroup of G.
    (c) Give an example of a group G and a nonempty subset H such that $HH \subseteq H$, but H is not a subgroup of G.

21. Let H be a subgroup of a group G. Prove that $\langle H \rangle = H$.

22. Show that $(\mathbb{Q}, +)$ is not finitely generated.

23. Show that every subgroup (except $\{0\}$) of $(\mathbb{Z}, +)$ contains infinitely many subgroups.

24. Find whether the following statements are true or false. Give a proof in case it is true or else give a counter example.

   (a)   The group $(\mathbb{R}^*, \cdot)$ has no finite subgroups other than $\{1\}$.

   (b) $T = \{a + b\sqrt{2} \mid a, b \in \mathbb{Q}$ and a, b not both zero$\}$ is a subgroup of $\mathbb{R}^*$.

   (c)   Let G be a group and H be a nonempty subset of G such that $a^{-1} \in H$ for all $a \in H$. Then H is a subgroup.

   (d)   There does not exist a proper subgroup H of $(\mathbb{Z}, +)$ such that H contains both $5\mathbb{Z}$ and $7\mathbb{Z}$.

25. In the permutation group $S_n (n \geq 5)$, if H is the smallest subgroup containing all the 3-cycles, then which one of the following is true?

   (i) $H = S_n$ (ii) $H = A_n$ (iii) H is Abelian   (iv) $|H| = 2$.

5.2   Cyclic Groups

In the previous section, we have seen that in a group G, for any $a \in G$, $\{a^n \mid n \in \mathbb{Z}\}$ is a subgroup of G. If in addition, $G = \{a^n \mid n \in \mathbb{Z}\}$ for some $a \in G$, then G is said to be generated by that single element a, and we write $G = \langle a \rangle$. Groups that are generated by a single element, called cyclic groups, are of special importance. These groups play an important role, much like building blocks, in studying the structure of a commutative group. Cyclic groups have special properties, some of which we will discuss in this section.

Definition 5.2.1. A group G is called a ***cyclic group*** if there exists an element $a \in G$ such that $G = \langle a \rangle = \{a^n \mid n \in \mathbb{Z}\}$. Such an element $a \in G$ is called a ***generator*** of the cyclic group G.

Example 5.2.2. The group $G = \{1, -1, i, -i\}$, consisting of all roots of $x^4 = 1$ is a cyclic group. In fact, $i^0 = 1, i^1 = i, i^2 = -1, i^3 = -i$ show that $G = \langle i \rangle$. Hence i is a generator of this group. Again $(-i)^0 = 1, (-i)^1 = -i, (-i)^2 = -1$, and $(-i)^3 = i$ show that $G = \langle -i \rangle$. Hence $-i$ is also a generator of G.

Example 5.2.3. (i) $(\mathbb{Z}, +)$ is a cyclic group since $\mathbb{Z} = \langle 1 \rangle$.

   (ii) $(\{2n \mid n \in \mathbb{Z}\}, +)$ is a cyclic group since it is generated by 2.

   (iii) $(\mathbb{Z}_n, +)$ is a cyclic group since $\mathbb{Z}_n = \langle [1] \rangle$.

Theorem 5.2.4. *Every cyclic group is a commutative group.*

Proof. Let $G = \langle a \rangle$ be a cyclic group and $b, c \in G$. Then $b = a^n$ and $c = a^m$ for some $n, m \in \mathbb{Z}$. Now $bc = a^n a^m = a^{n+m} = a^{m+n} = a^m a^n = cb$. This shows that G is commutative. $\qquad \square$

The following example shows that the converse of the above theorem is not true.

Example 5.2.5. A classic counter example that a finite commutative group need not be cyclic is given by **Klein's four-group**[6], usually denoted by $\mathcal{K}_4$. See Example 5.1.20 for its multiplication table, which clearly shows that it is a commutative group with four elements. Observe that $\mathcal{K}_4 = \{e, a, b, ab\}$, such that $o(a) = 2, o(b) = 2$, and $ba = ab$. It is not a cyclic group since

$$\langle e \rangle = \{e\}, \langle a \rangle = \{e, a\}, \langle b \rangle = \{e, b\}, \text{ and } \langle c \rangle = \{e, c\}$$

and each of these subgroups is a proper subgroup of G.

Theorem 5.2.6. *A finite group G is a cyclic group if and only if there exists an element $a \in G$ such that $o(a) = |G|$.*

Proof. Let G be a finite cyclic group of order n. Hence, there exists an element $a \in G$ such that $G = \langle a \rangle = \{a^i \mid i \in \mathbb{Z}\}$. Since G is finite, there exist $i, j \in \mathbb{Z} (i < j)$ such that $a^i = a^j$. Thus $a^{j-i} = e$ and $j - i$ is positive. Let m be the smallest positive integer such that $a^m = e$. Then $o(a) = m$ and for all integers i, j such that $0 \leq i < j < m, a^i \neq a^j$ or else $a^{j-i} = e$, which contradicts the minimality of m. Hence, the elements of the set $S = \{e, a, a^2, \ldots, a^{m-1}\}$ are distinct. Clearly, $S \subseteq \langle a \rangle$. Let $a^k \in \langle a \rangle$. Then there exist integers q, r such that $k = qm + r, 0 \leq r < m$. Thus, $a^k = a^{qm+r} = (a^m)^q a^r = ea^r = a^r \in S$. Hence $\langle a \rangle \subseteq S$ and so $S = \langle a \rangle$. Since elements of S are distinct and $\langle a \rangle$ has order n, it must be the case that $m = n$. Hence $o(a) = n$.

Conversely, assume that G is a finite group of order n and G has an element a such that $o(a) = n$. Since $o(a) = n$, $a^0, a^1, a^2, \ldots, a^{n-1}$ are distinct elements in G and hence $G = \{a^0, a^1, a^2, \ldots, a^{n-1}\} = \langle a \rangle$. So we find that G is a cyclic group. $\square$

Corollary 5.2.7. *Let $\langle a \rangle$ be a finite cyclic group. Then $o(a) = |\langle a \rangle|$.*

We now consider the group $(\mathbb{Z}_8, +)$. The elements of $\mathbb{Z}_8$ are $[0], [1], \ldots, [7]$. In this group $o([1]) = o([3]) = o([5]) = o([7]) = 8$. $o([0]) = 1$, $o([2]) = 4$, $o([4]) = 2$ and $o([6]) = 4$. So we find that there are four elements in $\mathbb{Z}_8$ of order 8. Hence, the group $\mathbb{Z}_8$ is a cyclic group and there are four generators of this cyclic group.

Now consider the group U_8, where $U_8 = \{[a] \in \mathbb{Z}_8 \mid gcd(a, 8) = 1\}$. Hence $U_8 = \{[1], [3], [5], [7]\}$ is a group under the operation defined by $[a][b] = [ab]$. In this group, $[1]$ is the identity element. Now $[3]^2 = [9] = [1]$, $[5]^2 = [25] = [1]$, $[7]^2 = [49] = [1]$. Hence U_8 has no element of order 4. Consequently U_8 is not a cyclic group.

---

[6]See Example 8.3.5 for a beautiful geometric perspective of this group from the point of view of symmetry.

Theorem 5.2.8. *Let $G = \langle a \rangle$ be a cyclic group of order n. Then for any integer k where $1 \leq k < n$, a^k is a generator of G if and only if $gcd(n, k) = 1$.*

Proof. Suppose a^k is a generator of G. Then by Theorem 5.2.6, $o(a^k) = |G| = n$. Since $G = \langle a \rangle$, we also find that $o(a) = n$. Now we know that,

$$o(a^k) = \frac{o(a)}{gcd(n, k)} = \frac{n}{gcd(n, k)}.$$

Hence $n = \frac{n}{gcd(n,k)}$. This implies that $gcd(n, k) = 1$.

Conversely, assume that $gcd(n, k) = 1$. Then

$$o(a^k) = \frac{o(a)}{gcd(n, k)} = o(a) = n = |G|.$$

Hence G has an element a^k such that $o(a^k) = |G|$. Consequently, we find that $G = \langle a^k \rangle$.   □

With the help of the above theorem, let us determine all generators of the cyclic group $G = \{1, -1, i, -i\}$. We first note that $G = \langle i \rangle = \{i^0, i^1, i^2, i^3\}$. Now $|G| = 4$ and observe that 1 and 3 are the only positive integers less than 4 such that $gcd(1, 4) = gcd(3, 4) = 1$. Hence i and $i^3 = -i$ are the only generators of this group.

It is true that the subgroups of a commutative group are commutative. In the following theorem, we prove that subgroups of a cyclic group are also cyclic.

Theorem 5.2.9. *Every subgroup of a cyclic group is cyclic.*

Proof. Let H be a subgroup of a cyclic group $G = \langle a \rangle$. If $H = \{e\}$, then $H = \langle e \rangle$ is cyclic. Suppose $H \neq \{e\}$. Then there exists $b \in H$ such that $b \neq e$. Now $b = a^m$ for some integer m. Then $m \neq 0$ since $b \neq e$. Since H is a subgroup, $a^{-m} = b^{-1} \in H$. Now either m or $-m$ is positive. Hence, there exists a positive integer i such that $a^i \in H$. Let n be the smallest positive integer such that $a^n \in H$. We show in the following that, every element of H is a power of a^n. Let $h \in H$. Then $h \in G = \langle a \rangle$ and hence $h = a^k$ for some integer k. By the division algorithm, there exist integers q, r such that $k = nq + r, 0 \leq r < n$. Since a^n and $a^k \in H$, we have $a^r = a^{k-nq} = a^k (a^n)^{-q} \in H$. However, if $r > 0$, it contradicts the minimality of n. Thus $r = 0$ so that $a^k = (a^n)^q$. Hence $H \subseteq \langle a^n \rangle$. Since $\langle a^n \rangle \subseteq H$ follows from the fact that $a^n \in H$, we deduce that $H = \langle a^n \rangle$. Therefore H is cyclic.   □

In the Worked-out Exercise 5.1.4, we have given a complete description of all subgroups of the additive group $\mathbb{Z}$ of all integers. We know that for every positive integer

n, $(\mathbb{Z}_n, +)$ is a finite cyclic group. Can we describe all subgroups of this group? The following theorem gives a complete description of all subgroups of a finite cyclic group.

Theorem 5.2.10. *Let $G = \langle a \rangle$ be a cyclic group of order n.*

(i)   If H is a subgroup of G, then $|H|$ divides $|G|$.

(ii)   If m is a positive integer such that m divides n, then there exists a unique subgroup of G of order m.

Proof. (i)   If $H = \{e\}$, then $|H| = 1$ and hence $|H|$ divides $|G|$. So suppose $H \neq \{e\}$. Since H is a subgroup of a finite cyclic group, H is also a cyclic group of finite order. Let $|H| = k$. Then there exists an element b in H such that $H = \langle b \rangle$ and then $o(b) = |H|$. Now $b \in G = \langle a \rangle$. Hence $b = a^m$ for some integer m such that $0 < m \leq n$. Now $|H| = k = o(b) = o(a^m) = \frac{o(a)}{gcd(n,m)}$, where $o(a) = |G| = n$. Hence $|H| \cdot gcd(n, m) = n$. This implies that $|H|$ divides $|G|$.

(ii)   There exists a positive integer k such that $n = mk$. Now $G = \langle a \rangle$. Hence $a^k \in G$ and $o(a^k) = \frac{o(a)}{gcd(k,n)} = \frac{n}{k}$ (since k divides n) $= m$ .... (i)

Let H be the subgroup of G generated by a^k. Then the subgroup $H = \langle a^k \rangle$ is of order $o(a^k) = m$.

Now suppose that K is a subgroup of $G = \langle a \rangle$ of order m. Since K is a cyclic subgroup of G, $K = \langle a^t \rangle$ for some $t \in \mathbb{Z}$. Then $o(a^t) = |K| = m$. Hence $a^{mt} = e$. But $o(a) = n$. Hence n divides mt, which implies that $mt = nr$ for some $r \in \mathbb{Z}$. Now from (i) $n = km$. Hence $mt = kmr$, so $t = kr$. This implies $a^t = a^{kr} = (a^k)^r \in \langle a^k \rangle = H$. Hence $K = \langle a^t \rangle \subseteq \langle a^k \rangle = H$. Both these subgroups have order m. Hence $K = H$. $\square$

By Theorem 5.2.10, if G is a finite cyclic group and H is a subgroup of G, then $|H|$ divides $|G|$. This is a special case of a more general result, called Lagrange's theorem, which we shall discuss in a later section.

Worked-out Exercises

◇ **Exercise 5.2.1.** Show that the 8th roots of unity form a cyclic group. Find all generators of this group.

Solution. The 8th roots of unity are

$$\alpha_k = \cos \frac{2k\pi}{8} + i \sin \frac{2k\pi}{8}, \quad k = 0, 1, 2, \ldots, 7$$

Let $G = \{\alpha_0, \alpha_1, \ldots, \alpha_7\}$. Similarly, as in the Worked-out Exercise 3.1.2 we may show that G is a group of order 8. Now

$$\alpha_k = \cos \frac{2k\pi}{8} + i \sin \frac{2k\pi}{8} = \left(\cos \frac{2\pi}{8} + i \sin \frac{2\pi}{8} \right)^k = \alpha_1^k \text{ for } k = 0, 1, 2, \ldots, 7.$$

Hence we find that $G = \langle \alpha_1 \rangle$ and so, G is a cyclic group of order 8. Now for any integer $1 \leq t < 8$, α_1^t is a generator of G if and only if $gcd(t, 8) = 1$. Hence $\alpha_1^1, \alpha_1^3, \alpha_1^5$ and α_1^7 are generators of this cyclic group.

$\Diamond$ **Exercise 5.2.2.** Show that $\mathbb{Z}_{10}$, the additive group of all integers modulo 10 is a cyclic group. Find all generators of $\mathbb{Z}_{10}$.

Solution. The group $\mathbb{Z}_{10}$ consists of the following 10 distinct elements, viz., $[0], [1], [2]$, ..., $[9]$. Since $[m] = m[1]$ for $m = 0, 1, \ldots 9$, it follows that $\mathbb{Z}_{10}$ is generated by $[1]$. Hence $\mathbb{Z}_{10}$ is a cyclic group. Now an element $m[1]$, $(m = 1, 2, \ldots 9)$ is a generator of $\mathbb{Z}_{10}$ if and only if $gcd(m, 10) = 1$. Hence $1[1], 3[1], 7[1]$, and $9[1]$ are the generators of $\mathbb{Z}_{10}$, i.e., $[1], [3], [7]$ and $[9]$ are the generators of $\mathbb{Z}_{10}$.

$\Diamond$ **Exercise 5.2.3.** The group $(\mathbb{Q}, +)$ is not cyclic.

Solution. Suppose $(\mathbb{Q}, +)$ is cyclic. Then $\mathbb{Q} = \langle x \rangle$ for some $x \in \mathbb{Q}$. Clearly $x \neq 0$. Hence $x = \frac{p}{q}$, where p and q are integers prime to each other and $q \neq 0$. Since $\frac{p}{2q} \in \mathbb{Q}$, there exists $n \in \mathbb{Z}$, $n \neq 0$ such that $\frac{p}{2q} = n\frac{p}{q}$. This implies that $\frac{1}{2} = n \in \mathbb{Z}$, which is a contradiction. Hence $(\mathbb{Q}, +)$ is not cyclic.

$\Diamond$ **Exercise 5.2.4.** $(\mathbb{R}, +)$ is not a cyclic group.

Solution. Suppose $(\mathbb{R}, +)$ is a cyclic group. Now $\mathbb{Q}$ is a subgroup of this group. Hence by Theorem 5.2.9, $(\mathbb{Q}, +)$ must be a cyclic group. But in the Worked-out Exercise 5.2.3, we have shown that $(\mathbb{Q}, +)$ is not cyclic. Hence $(\mathbb{R}, +)$ is not a cyclic group.

$\Diamond$ **Exercise 5.2.5.** Prove that any finitely generated subgroup of $(\mathbb{Q}, +)$ is cyclic.

Solution. Let H be any finitely generated subgroup of $(\mathbb{Q}, +)$ and suppose $H = \left\langle \left\{ \frac{p_1}{q_1}, \frac{p_2}{q_2}, \ldots, \frac{p_n}{q_n} \right\} \right\rangle$. Let $x \in H$. Then $x = k_1\frac{p_1}{q_1} + k_2\frac{p_2}{q_2} + \ldots + k_n\frac{p_n}{q_n}$ for some $k_1, k_2, \ldots, k_n \in \mathbb{Z}$. Now,

$$x = \frac{\displaystyle\sum_{i=1}^{n} k_i p_i \overline{q_i}}{q_1 q_2 \cdots q_n} \qquad \text{where } \overline{q_i} = \prod_{\substack{j=1 \\ j \neq i}}^{n} q_j.$$

Then it is easy to see that $x \in \left\langle \frac{1}{q_1 q_2 \cdots q_n} \right\rangle$ since $\displaystyle\sum_{i=1}^{n} k_i p_i \overline{q_i} \in \mathbb{Z}$. Thus $H \subseteq \left\langle \frac{1}{q_1 q_2 \cdots q_n} \right\rangle$, whence H becomes a subgroup of a cyclic group $\left\langle \frac{1}{q_1 q_2 \cdots q_n} \right\rangle$ and consequently H is cyclic. Hence the result.

◊ **Exercise 5.2.6.** Let G be a group of order 28. Show that G has a nontrivial subgroup.

Solution. First suppose that G is cyclic. Then by Theorem 5.2.10, for every positive divisor m of $|G|$, G has a subgroup of order m. Now 4 is a divisor of 28. So G has a subgroup of order 4. Hence there is a nontrivial subgroup of G. Now suppose that G is not cyclic. Let $e \neq a \in G$ and let H be the subgroup $\langle a \rangle$ generated by a. Then $H \neq \{e\}$. Also $G \neq H = \langle a \rangle$, as otherwise G becomes cyclic. Hence H is a proper subgroup of G.

◊ **Exercise 5.2.7.** If $G = \langle a \rangle$ is an infinite cyclic group, then show that any subgroup $H \neq \{e\}$ of G is also an infinite cyclic group.

Solution. Let $H \neq \langle e \rangle$ be a subgroup of G. Now by Theorem 5.2.9, H is also a cyclic group. Let $e \neq b \in H$. Then $b \in G = \langle a \rangle$. Hence $b = a^t$ for some $t \in \mathbb{Z}$. Suppose $o(b)$ is finite and let $o(b) = m$. Then $a^{tm} = b^m = e$. This implies that $o(a)$ is finite and hence $G = \langle a \rangle$ is finite. This contradicts our assumption. Then $o(b)$ is infinite and so $\langle b \rangle$ is an infinite cyclic group. But $\langle b \rangle \subseteq H$. Hence H is also an infinite cyclic group.

◊ **Exercise 5.2.8.** If $G = \langle a \rangle$ is a cyclic group of order 30, then find all distinct elements of the subgroups (i) $\langle a^5 \rangle$ (ii) $\langle a^6 \rangle$.

Solution. (i) Here $\langle a^5 \rangle = \left\{ (a^5)^n \mid n \in \mathbb{Z} \right\}$. Now $o(a) = |\langle a \rangle| = |G| = 30$. Hence $a^{30} = e$. Then $(a^5)^6 = e$ implies that $o(a^5) = 6$. Observe that the divisors of 6 are $1, 2, 3$ and 6. Since $(a^5)^1 \neq e, (a^5)^2 \neq e, (a^5)^3 \neq e$ it follows that $o(a^5) = 6$. Hence,

$$\langle a^5 \rangle = \left\{ (a^5)^0, (a^5)^1, (a^5)^2, (a^5)^3, (a^5)^4, (a^5)^5 \right\} = \{e, a^5, a^{10}, a^{15}, a^{20}, a^{25}\}.$$

(ii) The order of a^6 is 5. Hence,

$$\langle a^6 \rangle = \left\{ (a^6)^0, (a^6)^1, (a^6)^2, (a^6)^3, (a^6)^4 \right\} = \{e, a^6, a^{12}, a^{18}, a^{24}\}.$$

◊ **Exercise 5.2.9.** Let $G = \langle a \rangle$ be an infinite cyclic group. Show that

  (i) $a^r = a^t$ if and only if $r = t$ where $r, t \in \mathbb{Z}$.

  (ii) G has only two generators.

Solution. Suppose $a^r = a^t$ and $r \neq t$. Let $r > t$. Then $a^{r-t} = e$. Hence there exists a positive integer i such that $a^i = e$. Let n be the smallest positive integer such that $a^n = e$. This n is of the order of a. Now $G = \langle a \rangle = \{a^k \mid k \in \mathbb{Z}\}$. Let $b \in G$. Then $b = a^m$ for some $m \in \mathbb{Z}$. Dividing m by n, we get by division algorithm that $m = nt + r$

for some $t, r \in \mathbb{Z}$, where $0 \le r < n$. Then $a^r = a^{m-nt} = a^m a^{-nt} = a^m (a^n)^{-t} = a^m \left((e)^{-1} \right)^t = a^m e = a^m = b$. Hence, b is one of $a^0, a^1, a^2, \ldots, a^{n-1}$. Consequently, $G = \{e, a, a^2, \ldots, a^{n-1}\}$, which is a contradiction since G is an infinite group. The converse is obvious.

(ii)   Let $G = \langle b \rangle$ for some $b \in G$. Since $a \in G = \langle b \rangle$ and $b \in G = \langle a \rangle$, $a = b^r$ and $b = a^t$ for some $r, t \in \mathbb{Z}$. Thus $a = b^r = (a^t)^r = a^{rt}$. Hence by (i), $rt = 1$. This implies that either $r = 1 = t$ or $r = -1 = t$. Thus, either $b = a$ or $b = a^{-1}$. Now from (i), $a \ne a^{-1}$. Hence G has only two generators.

$\Diamond$ **Exercise 5.2.10.** The number of generators of the additive group $\mathbb{Z}_{36}$ is equal to
(i) 6   (ii) 12   (iii) 18   (iv) 36.

Solution. Now $\mathbb{Z}_{36}$ is a cyclic group of order 36 and we know the number of generators in a cyclic group of order 36 is $\phi(36) = 12$. Therefore, option (ii) is correct.

$\Diamond$ **Exercise 5.2.11.** Consider the multiplicative group G of all the (complex) 2^n-th roots of unity where $n = 0, 1, 2, \ldots$. Pick the correct statement(s).
(i) Every proper subgroup of G is finite.   (ii) G has a finite set of generators.
(iii) G is cyclic.   (iv) Every finite subgroup of G is cyclic.

Solution. Let $G_n = \{x \in \mathbb{C} : x^{2^n} = 1\}$, for $n = 0, 1, 2, \ldots$. Then $G = \bigcup_{n=0}^{\infty} G_n$. Let H be a finite subgroup of G. Let $k = \max\{n \in \mathbb{N}_0 (= \mathbb{N} \cup \{0\}) : x \in G_n \text{ for some } x \in H\}$. Then $H \subseteq G_k$. Since G_n is cyclic for all $n \in \mathbb{N}$, it follows that H is also cyclic.

Next let K be a proper subgroup of G. Then $G \setminus K \ne \emptyset$ and hence there exists an element $y \in G$ such that $y \notin K$. This implies $y \in G_r \setminus K$ for some $r \in \mathbb{N}$. Consider the set $T = \{n \in \mathbb{N}_0 : x \in G_n \text{ for some } x \in G \setminus K\}$. Then $r \in T$ and thus T is a non-empty subset of $\mathbb{N}_0$. Hence by well-ordering principle, T has a least element. Let m be the least element in T. Then one can prove that $K \subseteq \bigcup_{i=0}^{m-1} G_i \subseteq G_{m-1}$. Since G_{m-1} is finite, it follows that K is also finite.

Now, if possible, let G be generated by finite number of elements $\alpha_1, \alpha_2, \ldots, \alpha_p \in G$, for some $p \in \mathbb{N}$. Let $\alpha_i \in G_{n_i}$ for $i = 1, 2, \ldots, p$; and let $q = \max\{n_1, n_2, \ldots, n_p\}$. Then $\alpha_i \in G_q$ for all $i = 1, 2, \ldots, p$. Hence $G = \langle \alpha_1, \alpha_2, \ldots, \alpha_p \rangle \subseteq G_q \subset G$, a contradiction. Hence G is not finitely generated and thus G is not cyclic. Therefore, only options (i) and (iv) are correct.

Exercises

1. Show that the 7th roots of unity form a cyclic group. Find all generators of this group.

2. Show that the cyclic group $(\mathbb{Z}, +)$ has only two generators.

3. Is the group $(\mathbb{Z}_{10}, +)$ a cyclic group? If so, find all generators of this group and also find all its subgroups.

4. Show that for every positive integer n, the nth roots of unity form a cyclic group.

5. Show that $(\mathbb{Q}^+, \cdot), (\mathbb{Q}^*, \cdot), (\mathbb{R}^+, \cdot), (\mathbb{R}^*, \cdot), (\mathbb{C}^*, \cdot)$ are not cyclic groups.

6. If a group G has only two subgroups, then prove that G is a cyclic group.

7. Let $G = \langle a \rangle$ be a cyclic group of order 20. Find all distinct elements of the subgroups (i) $\langle a^4 \rangle$ (ii) $\langle a^7 \rangle$.

8. Let G be a cyclic group of order 42. Find the number of elements of order 6 and the number of elements of order 7 in G.

9. Prove that every noncommutative group has a nontrivial cyclic subgroup.

10. Let $G = \{a, b, c, d, e\}$ be a group. Complete the following Cayley table for this group:

$*$	e	a	b	c	d
e	e	a	b	c	d
a	a				
b	b		c	d	
c	c				
d	d				

11. Find whether the following statements are true or false. Justify your answer.

    (a) $\{a + b\sqrt{2} \in \mathbb{R} \mid a, b \in \mathbb{Q}\}$ is a cyclic group under usual addition of real numbers.

    (b) $G = \{(1, 1), (1, -1), (-1, 1), (-1, -1)\}$ is a group under the operation $(a, b)(c, d) = (ac, bd)$ but not a cyclic group.

    (c) The number of elements of the subgroup $\langle a^{10} \rangle$ in the cyclic group $\langle a \rangle$ of order 30 is 10.

    (d) The symmetric group S_n contains a cyclic group of order n.

    Find out the correct answer to the following:

12. Suppose G is a cyclic group such that G has exactly three subgroups viz. G, $\{e\}$ and a subgroup of order 5. Then the order of G is

    (i) 5 (ii) 10 (iii) 25 (iv) 125.

13. The number of elements of order 5 in $\mathbb{Z}_{1000}$ is

    (i) 1 (ii) 4 (iii) 5 (iv) none of these.

14. Let G be a cyclic group of infinite order. Then the number of elements of finite order in G is

    (i) 1 (ii) 2 (iii) 5 (iv) 0.

15. The number of generators of an infinite cyclic group is

    (i) 1 (ii) 2 (iii) 0 (iv) infinite.

16. The number of elements of order 5 in the cyclic group of order 25 is

    (i) 1 (ii) 2 (iii) 5 (iv) none of these.

5.3   Cosets and Lagrange's Theorem

It is amazing to know that Lagrange's theorem, a distinct milestone in abstract algebra, a result which is of paramount importance in the theory of finite groups, was proved as early as in 1770, much before the formal inception of the concept of a group! Indeed, this was a period when eminent mathematicians all over Europe were busy trying to find a possible general *formula* (aptly known as solution by *radicals*) for the roots of a general polynomial equation (of degree n, say), explicitly in terms of its coefficients. After Sridharacharya's ancient solution for quadratic in 750 AD, the stage was set by H. Cardano (1501-1576) with such a solution for a cubic equation and then by L. Ferrari (1526-1565), one of his students, who successfully did it for a biquadratic. How nice it would be to have a general *formula*[7] for the roots of an nth degree polynomial, which might perhaps reduce to these particular cases on putting the respective values of $n = 2, 3, 4$ etc.! In this atmosphere, J.L. Lagrange (1736-1813) investigated the effects of permutations of the roots of a polynomial equation. Though he did not know it, his works[8] (1770) paved the path towards the concept of *permutation groups* in mathematics, the path that was appreciated only after almost 60 years by the genius of Galois, who in 1829 defined a finite group as a group of permutations. In this section, we shall discuss Lagrange's theorem and relevant results.

Definition 5.3.1. Let H be a subgroup of a group G. If $a \in G$, the subset $aH = \{ah \,|\, h \in H\}$ is called a **left coset** of H in G. Similarly, $Ha = \{ha \,|\, h \in H\}$ is called a **right coset** of H in G.

Observe that $eH = H = He$. Hence H is a left and right coset of itself in G.

Example 5.3.2. Let $G = \{1, a, b, ab\}$ be the Klein's four-group. Then $o(a) = o(b) = 2$, $ab = ba$. In this group, $H = \{1, a\}$ is a subgroup and $1H = \{1, a\}, aH = \{a, a^2\} = \{a, 1\} = \{1, a\}$, $bH = \{b, ba\} = \{b, ab\}$, $abH = \{ab, aba\} = \{ab, a^2b\} = \{ab, b\}$ are the left cosets of H in G.

Example 5.3.3. Consider the group $(\mathbb{Z}, +)$. Let $H = 5\mathbb{Z} = \{5n \,|\, n \in \mathbb{Z}\}$. H is a

---

[7]However, a result to the effect that such a dream is not to be fulfilled for equations of degree 5 is credited to Neils Heinrich Abel(1802-1829) of Norway. The corresponding general theory for equations of a higher degree is due to Galois.

[8]The famous Lagrange's theorem, in his contemporary terminology was as follows: *the number of distinct polynomials obtained from a polynomial in n variables by applying all possible permutations of the variables is a factor of n!* In modern day terminology of group theory it says : *the order of a subgroup of a finite group divides the order of that group*, which was actually formulated by Jordan in 1870.

subgroup of the group $(\mathbb{Z}, +)$. Now the left cosets of H in $\mathbb{Z}$ are given by $n + H$ for all $n \in \mathbb{Z}$, i.e., $n + 5\mathbb{Z}$ for $n = 0, \pm 1, \pm 2, \ldots$

Any integer n is of the form $5m + r$, where $r = 0, 1, 2, 3$ or 4. Hence $n + 5\mathbb{Z} = 5m + r + 5\mathbb{Z} = r + 5m + 5\mathbb{Z} = r + 5\mathbb{Z}$. Hence the left cosets of $H = 5\mathbb{Z}$ in $\mathbb{Z}$ are $0 + 5\mathbb{Z}, 1 + 5\mathbb{Z}, 2 + 5\mathbb{Z}, 3 + 5\mathbb{Z}, 4 + 5\mathbb{Z}$.

Example 5.3.4. Consider the symmetric group $S_3 = \{e, (1\,2), (1\,3), (2\,3), (1\,2\,3), (1\,3\,2)\}$. In this group, $H = \{e, (1\,2)\}$ is a subgroup. The left cosets of H in S_3 are

$$
\begin{aligned}
eH &= H \\
(1\,2)H &= \{(1\,2), (1\,2)(1\,2)\} = \{(1\,2), e\} \\
(2\,3)H &= \{(2\,3), (2\,3)(1\,2)\} = \{(2\,3), (1\,3\,2)\} \\
(1\,3)H &= \{(1\,3), (1\,3)(1\,2)\} = \{(1\,3), (1\,2\,3)\} \\
(1\,2\,3)H &= \{(1\,2\,3), (1\,2\,3)(1\,2)\} = \{(1\,2\,3), (1\,3)\} \\
(1\,3\,2)H &= \{(1\,3\,2), (1\,3\,2)(1\,2)\} = \{(1\,3\,2), (2\,3)\}.
\end{aligned}
$$

Notice that any two left cosets of H in S_3 are either disjoint, e.g., $(2\,3)H$ and $(1\,3)H$ or, two left cosets are equal, e.g., $(2\,3)H$ and $(1\,3\,2)H$. Now all the distinct left cosets of H in S_3 are as follows:

$$H = \{e, (1\,2)\}; (2\,3)H = \{(2\,3), (1\,3\,2)\}; (1\,3)H = \{(1\,3), (1\,2\,3)\}.$$

Notice that $S_3 = H \cup (2\,3)H \cup (1\,3)H$ and $|H| = |(2\,3)H| = |(1\,3)H|$.

Next, we compute all the right cosets of H in S_3. The right cosets of H in S_3 are Ha for all $a \in S_3$.

$$
\begin{aligned}
He &= H \\
H(1\,2) &= \{(1\,2), (1\,2)(1\,2)\} = \{(1\,2), e\} \\
H(2\,3) &= \{(2\,3), (1\,2)(2\,3)\} = \{(2\,3), (1\,2\,3)\} \\
H(1\,3) &= \{(1\,3), (1\,2)(1\,3)\} = \{(1\,3), (1\,3\,2)\} \\
H(1\,2\,3) &= \{(1\,2\,3), (1\,2)(1\,2\,3)\} = \{(1\,2\,3), (2\,3)\} \\
H(1\,3\,2) &= \{(1\,3\,2), (1\,2)(1\,3\,2)\} = \{(1\,3\,2), (1\,3)\}.
\end{aligned}
$$

For right cosets also, we find that, any two right cosets are either equal or disjoint. All the distinct right cosets of H in S_3 are as follows:

$$H = \{e, (1\,2)\}; H(1\,3) = \{(1\,3), (1\,3\,2)\}; H(2\,3) = \{(2\,3), (1\,2\,3)\}.$$

Here also $S_3 = H \cup H(1\,3) \cup H(2\,3)$ and $|H| = |H(1\,3)| = |H(2\,3)|$. But we note that a left coset aH may not be equal to the corresponding right coset Ha, e.g., $(2\,3)H \neq H(2\,3)$.

In the above example, we see that all left cosets and right cosets of H in S_3 have the same number of elements, viz., 2. Also there are the same number of distinct left cosets of H in S_3, as of distinct right cosets, viz., 3. We now prove in the following theorem that these results hold in general for left and right cosets in any group.

Theorem 5.3.5. *Let H be a subgroup of a group G and let $a, b \in G$.*

  (i)   *$aH = H$ if and only if $a \in H$.*

  (ii) *$Ha = H$ if and only if $a \in H$.*

  (iii) *$aH = bH$ if and only if $a^{-1}b \in H$.*

  (iv) *$Ha = Hb$ if and only if $ba^{-1} \in H$.*

  (v)   *Either $aH \cap bH = \emptyset$ or $aH = bH$.*

  (vi) *Either $Ha \cap Hb = \emptyset$ or $Ha = Hb$.*

Proof. (i)   Suppose $aH = H$. Then $a = ae \in aH = H$. Conversely, suppose $a \in H$. Then for any $h \in H$, $h = eh = aa^{-1}h \in aH$ implies that $H \subseteq aH$. Since H is a subgroup and $a \in H$, we find that $aH = \{ah \mid h \in H\} \subseteq H$. Hence $H = aH$.

  (ii)   Proof is similar to (i).

  (iii)   Suppose $aH = bH$. Since $b = be \in bH = aH$, there exists $h \in H$ such that $b = ah$. Then $a^{-1}b = h \in H$. Conversely, suppose $a^{-1}b \in H$. Hence $bH = aa^{-1}bH = a(a^{-1}bH) = aH$, since by (i), $a^{-1}b \in H$ implies $a^{-1}bH = H$.

  (iv)   Proof is similar to (iii).

  (v)   If $aH \cap bH \neq \emptyset$, there exists $x \in aH \cap bH$. Let $x = ah_1 = bh_2$ where $h_1, h_2 \in H$. Then $a^{-1}b = h_1 h_2^{-1} \in H$, so $aH = bH$ by (iii).

  (vi)   Proof is similar to (v). $\square$

Corollary 5.3.6. *Let H be a subgroup of a group G. Then $\{aH \mid a \in G\}$ forms a partition of G.*

Proof. Let $\mathcal{P} = \{aH \mid a \in G\}$, i.e., $\mathcal{P}$ is the set of all left cosets of H in G. By Theorem 5.3.5, for all $aH, bH \in \mathcal{P}$, either $aH \cap bH = \emptyset$ or $aH = bH$. Now for all $a \in G, aH \subseteq G$ and so $\bigcup_{a \in G} aH \subseteq G$. Again, if $a \in G$, then $a \in aH$ and hence $G \subseteq \bigcup_{a \in G} aH$. So we find that $G = \bigcup_{a \in G} aH$. Consequently, $\mathcal{P}$ is a partition of G. $\square$

Theorem 5.3.7. *Let H be a subgroup of a group G. If $a \in G$, then $|aH| = |H| = |Ha|$.*

Proof. To show that $|H| = |aH|$, we show that there exists a bijective mapping of H onto aH. Define $f : H \to aH$ by $f(h) = ah$ for all $h \in H$. Let $h, h_1 \in H$. Suppose $f(h) = f(h_1)$. Then $ah = ah_1$ which implies that $h = h_1$ (by cancellation property) and so f is one-one. To show f is onto, let $ah \in aH$. Then $ah = f(h)$ and hence f

maps H onto aH. Similarly, we can show that there exists a bijective mapping of H onto Ha. $\qquad\square$

Theorem 5.3.8. *Let H be a subgroup of a group G. Then $|\mathcal{L}| = |\mathcal{R}|$, where $\mathcal{L}$ (resp.$\mathcal{R}$) denotes the set of all left (resp. right) cosets of H in G.*

Proof. To establish this, we need to show the existence of a bijective function from $\mathcal{L}$ onto $\mathcal{R}$. Define $f : \mathcal{L} \to \mathcal{R}$ by $f(aH) = Ha^{-1}$ for all $aH \in \mathcal{L}$. Observe that Ha^{-1} is a right coset of H in G and hence $Ha^{-1} \in \mathcal{R}$. Now, we show that $aH = bH$ if and only if $Ha^{-1} = Hb^{-1}$. Suppose $aH = bH$. Then $a^{-1}b \in H$. Hence $b^{-1}(a^{-1})^{-1} \in H$ and so by Theorem 5.3.5(iv), we have $Ha^{-1} = Hb^{-1}$.

Conversely, assume that $Ha^{-1} = Hb^{-1}$. Then by Theorem 5.3.5(iv), $b^{-1}(a^{-1})^{-1} \in H$, i.e., $b^{-1}a \in H$ and so $a^{-1}b = (b^{-1}a)^{-1} \in H$. Then by Theorem 5.3.5(iii), $aH = bH$. Thus we find that f is well-defined and one-one. Since for all $Ha \in \mathcal{R}$, $Ha = H(a^{-1})^{-1} = f(a^{-1}H)$ and $a^{-1}H \in \mathcal{L}$, f is onto. Thus f is a one-one and onto mapping. $\qquad\square$

Definition 5.3.9. Let H be a subgroup of a group G. Then the number of distinct left (or right) cosets of H in G, written $[G : H]$, is called the ***index*** of H in G.

By Theorem 5.3.8, the number of distinct left cosets and the number of distinct right cosets of a subgroup H of a group G are the same. Thus, $[G : H]$ is well-defined.

Theorem 5.3.10. (Lagrange) *Let H be a subgroup of a finite group. Then the order of H divides the order of G. In particular,*

$$|G| = [G : H]|H|.$$

Proof. Since G is a finite group, $[G : H]$ is finite. Let $[G : H] = r$. This implies that there exist r distinct left cosets $a_1 H, a_2 H, \ldots, a_r H$ of H in G. Since distinct left cosets are mutually disjoint, we have

$$|G| = \left| \bigcup_{i=1}^{r} a_i H \right| = |a_1 H| + |a_2 H| + \ldots + |a_r H|$$

$$= \underbrace{|H| + |H| + \ldots + |H|}_{r \text{ copies}} \quad \text{(by Theorem 5.3.7, } |a_i H| = |H|)$$

$$= r|H| = [G : H]\,|H|.$$

Hence the theorem. $\qquad\square$

Note that by virtue of Lagrange's theorem, we have a useful formula to calculate the index of a subgroup H in a finite group G. Indeed,

$$[G : H] = \frac{|G|}{|H|}.$$

Lagrange's theorem is a very useful theorem in finite groups. In the study of finite groups, we need this theorem most of the times. Let us now show some applications of this theorem.

Corollary 5.3.11. *Every group of prime order is cyclic.*

Proof. Let G be a group of prime order, say p. Since $p > 1$, G has an element $a \neq e$. Let H be the subgroup $\langle a \rangle = \{a^n \mid n \in \mathbb{Z}\}$. By Lagrange's theorem, $|\langle a \rangle|$ divides p. Hence $|\langle a \rangle| = 1$ or p. Since $a \neq e$, $|\langle a \rangle| \neq 1$ and so $|\langle a \rangle| = p$. Now $\langle a \rangle \subseteq G$ and $|\langle a \rangle| = |G| = p$. Hence, $G = \langle a \rangle$. This shows that G is a cyclic group. □

Since every cyclic group is commutative, the above corollary also tells us that *every group of prime order is commutative.*

Corollary 5.3.12. *Let G be a group of finite order n and $a \in G$. Then $o(a)$ divides n and $a^n = e$.*

Proof. Let $H = \langle a \rangle$. Then H is a cyclic subgroup of G and $|H| = o(a)$. By Lagrange's theorem, $|H|$ divides $|G|$. Hence $o(a)$ divides n. Let $o(a) = m$. Then $n = mk$ for some integer k. Now $a^m = e$ and hence $a^n = a^{mk} = (a^m)^k = e$. □

Our next result, known as **Fermat's little theorem**, has already been discussed without proof in Theorem 2.6.12. We now show that this result can be proved elegantly by Largange's theorem.

Theorem 5.3.13. (Fermat) *Let p be a prime integer and a be an integer such that p does not divide a. Then $a^{p-1} \equiv 1 (mod \, p)$.*

Proof. For the prime integer p, $U_p = \{[a] \in \mathbb{Z}_p \mid gcd(a, p) = 1\}$. Then $U_p = \mathbb{Z}_p \setminus \{[0]\}$ is a group of order $p - 1$. Let a be an integer such that p does not divide a. Then $[a]$ is a nonzero element of $\mathbb{Z}_p$ and so $[a] \in U_p$. Thus by Corollary 5.3.12, $[a]^{p-1} = [1]$, i.e., $[a^{p-1}] = [1]$. Hence $a^{p-1} \equiv 1 (\, mod \, p)$. □

In Theorem 2.6.15 we have already seen the **Euler's generalization of Fermat's Little Theorem**. It is now time to give a formal proof of the theorem.

Theorem 5.3.14. (Euler) *Let a and n be integers such that $n > 0$ and $\gcd(a, n) = 1$. Then*

$$a^{\phi(n)} \equiv 1(\text{mod } n).$$

Proof. Consider the group $U_n = \{[a] \in \mathbb{Z}_n \smallsetminus \{[0]\} \mid \gcd(a, n) = 1\}$ (see Example 3.1.6). It follows from Definition 2.5.11 that $|U_n| = \phi(n)$. Since $\gcd(a, n) = 1$, we have $[a] \in U_n$. Thus by Corollary 5.3.12, $[a]^{\phi(n)} = [1]$ which implies $a^{\phi(n)} \equiv 1(\text{mod } n)$, as required. $\square$

Let H and K be two subgroups of a group G. If H and K are both finite, then $|HK|$ is finite but HK *need not* be a subgroup of G and so $|HK|$ need not divide $|G|$. However, with the help of Lagrange's theorem we can determine $|HK|$. This is a very useful result and we will use it very effectively in the sequel. In the next theorem, we determine $|HK|$ when H and K are both finite.

Theorem 5.3.15. *Let H and K be finite subgroups of a group G. Then*

$$|HK| = \frac{|H||K|}{|H \cap K|}.$$

Proof. Let $A = H \cap K$. Since H and K are subgroups of G, A is a subgroup of G and so A is also a subgroup of H. By Lagrange's theorem, $|A|$ divides $|H|$. Let $n = \frac{|H|}{|A|}$. Then $[H : A] = n$ and so A has n distinct left cosets in H. Let $\{x_1 A, x_2 A, \ldots, x_n A\}$ be the set of all distinct left cosets of A in H. Then $H = \bigcup_{i=1}^{n} x_i A$. Since $A \subseteq K$, it follows that

$$HK = \left(\bigcup_{i=1}^{n} x_i A \right) K = \bigcup_{i=1}^{n} x_i K.$$

We now show that $x_i K \cap x_j K = \emptyset$ if $i \neq j$. Suppose $x_i K \cap x_j K \neq \emptyset$ for some $i \neq j$. Then $x_i K = x_j K$. Thus, $x_i^{-1} x_j \in K$. Since $x_i^{-1} x_j \in H$, we have $x_i^{-1} x_j \in A$ and so $x_i A = x_j A$. This contradicts the assumption that $x_1 A, \ldots, x_n A$ are all distinct left cosets. Hence $x_1 K, \ldots, x_n K$ are distinct left cosets of K. Also, $|K| = |x_i K|$ by Theorem 5.3.7, for all $i = 1, 2, \ldots, n$. Hence,

$$|HK| = |x_1 K| + \ldots + |x_n K| = n|K| = \frac{|H||K|}{|A|} = \frac{|H||K|}{|H \cap K|}.$$

$\square$

We conclude this section by showing that the *converse of Lagrange's theorem is not true in general*. However, in a finite cyclic group of order n, we have shown that, for each divisor d of n, there exists a subgroup of order d. Hence the converse of Lagrange's theorem holds in a finite cyclic group in particular. Now, we show that there are groups in which the converse of Lagrange's theorem does *not* hold.

Example 5.3.16. Consider the symmetric group S_4 of all the 24 permutations on $I_4 = \{1, 2, 3, 4\}$. In this group, the alternating subgroup A_4 of all *even permutations* is known to be of order 12. We now show that A_4 has no subgroup of order 6.

Suppose on the contrary that A_4 has a subgroup H of order 6. Now $(1\,2\,3), (1\,3\,2)$, $(1\,2\,4), (1\,4\,2), (2\,3\,4), (2\,4\,3), (1\,3\,4)$, and $(1\,4\,3)$ are all even permutations and hence these are all members of A_4. Since $|H|$ is 6, H cannot contain all these 3-cycles. Let $\alpha = (a\,b\,c)$ be a 3-cycle such that $\alpha \notin H$. Now $o(\alpha) = 3$. Hence, $K = \{e, \alpha, \alpha^2\}$ is a subgroup of A_4. Note that $\alpha^2 = \alpha^{-1}$. Hence $H \cap K = \{e\}$. Then, by Theorem 5.3.15

$$|HK| = \frac{|H|\,|K|}{|H \cap K|} = \frac{6 \cdot 3}{1} = 18.$$

But as $HK \subseteq A_4$, this contradicts the fact that $|A_4| = 12$. Consequently, A_4 has no subgroup of order 6. So we find that the *converse of Lagrange's theorem does not hold in A_4*.

Worked-out Exercises

◊ **Exercise 5.3.1.** Find all the distinct left cosets of $H = 6\mathbb{Z}$ in the $(\mathbb{Z}, +)$.

Solution. All the left cosets of H in $(\mathbb{Z}, +)$ are $n + 6\mathbb{Z}$ for all $n \in \mathbb{Z}$. Now, any integer n is of the form $n = 6k + r$, $r = 0, 1, 2, 3, 4, 5$. Hence, for any $n \in \mathbb{Z}, n + 6\mathbb{Z} = r + 6k + 6\mathbb{Z} = r + 6\mathbb{Z}$. So, there are six distinct left cosets of $6\mathbb{Z}$ in $\mathbb{Z}$ and these are:

$$6\mathbb{Z},\ 1 + 6\mathbb{Z},\ 2 + 6\mathbb{Z},\ 3 + 6\mathbb{Z},\ 4 + 6\mathbb{Z},\ 5 + 6\mathbb{Z}.$$

◊ **Exercise 5.3.2.** Find all the distinct left cosets of the subgroup $H = \{e, (1\,2\,3),$ $(1\,3\,2)\}$ in the group S_3.

Solution. The elements of S_3 are

$$e,\ (1\,2),\ (1\,3),\ (2\,3),\ (1\,2\,3)\ \text{ and }\ (1\,3\,2).$$

Now,

$$
\begin{aligned}
eH &= H \\
(1\,2)H &= \{(1\,2), (1\,2)(1\,2\,3), (1\,2)(1\,3\,2)\} = \{(1\,2), (2\,3), (1\,3)\} \\
(1\,3)H &= \{(1\,3), (1\,3)(1\,2\,3), (1\,3)(1\,3\,2)\} = \{(1\,3), (1\,2), (2\,3)\} \\
(2\,3)H &= \{(2\,3), (2\,3)(1\,2\,3), (2\,3)(1\,3\,2)\} = \{(2\,3), (1\,3), (1\,2)\} \\
(1\,2\,3)H &= \{(1\,2\,3), (1\,2\,3)(1\,2\,3), (1\,2\,3)(1\,3\,2)\} = \{(1\,2\,3), e, (1\,3\,2)\} \\
(1\,3\,2)H &= \{(1\,3\,2), (1\,3\,2)(1\,2\,3), (1\,3\,2)(1\,3\,2)\} = \{(1\,3\,2), (1\,2\,3), e\}
\end{aligned}
$$

We find that there are two distinct left cosets of H in S_3 and these are eH and $(1\,3)H$.

◇ **Exercise 5.3.3.** In the group $\mathbb{C}^* = \mathbb{C} \setminus \{0\}$, find all cosets of the subgroup $H = \{z \in \mathbb{C}^* : |z| = 1\}$. Describe them geometrically.

Solution. Any nonzero complex number z is of the form $z = re^{i\theta}$ where r is a nonzero real number and $e^{i\theta} = \cos\theta + i\sin\theta$. Now any left coset of H in $\mathbb{C}^*$ is as follows:

$$zH = re^{i\theta}H = \{re^{i\theta}w \in \mathbb{C}^* : |w| = 1\} = \{z \in \mathbb{C}^* : |z| = r\}.$$

Hence zH is a circle of radius $r > 0$, so we find that all the cosets of H in $\mathbb{C}^*$ are the concentric circles with centre $(0,0)$. The following diagram (Fig. 11) represents it geometrically:

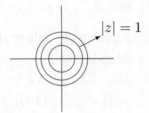

$|z| = 1$

Fig. 11

◇ **Exercise 5.3.4.** Consider the group $\mathbb{R} \times \mathbb{R} = \{(a,b) \mid a, b \in \mathbb{R}\}$ under componentwise addition of real numbers. Let $H = \{(x, 3x) \in \mathbb{R} \times \mathbb{R}\}$. Show that H is a subgroup of $\mathbb{R} \times \mathbb{R}$ and that H represents geometrically all points on the line $y = 3x$. Show that the coset $(3,7) + H$ is a straight line parallel to $y = 3x$.

Solution. Certainly $H \neq \emptyset$ as, $(1,3) \in H$. Let (a,b) and (c,d) be two elements of H. Then $b = 3a$ and $d = 3c$. Now $(a,b) - (c,d) = (a - c, b - d) = (a - c, 3a - 3c) = (a - c, 3(a - c)) \in H$. Hence H is a subgroup of G. The coset

$$(3,7) + H = \{(3,7) + (a, 3a) : a \in \mathbb{R}\} = \{(3 + a, 7 + 3a) : a \in \mathbb{R}\}.$$

Then any point $(3+a, 7+3a)$ satisfies $y = 7+3a$ and $x = 3+a$. Hence $y = 7+3(x-3) = 3x - 2$. So we find that all the points of $(3,7) + H$ are on the straight line $y = 3x - 2$.

Conversely, suppose (a,b) be a point on the line $y = 3x - 2$. Hence $b = 3a - 2 = 7 + 3(a - 3)$ shows that

$$(a,b) = (3,7) + \big((a - 3), 3(a - 3)\big) \in (3,7) + H.$$

So, we find that the coset $(3,7) + H$ is straight line $y = 3x - 2$, which is parallel to $y = 3x$ (Fig.12).

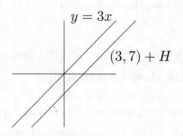

Fig. 12

$\Diamond$ **Exercise 5.3.5.** Considering the above exercise, show that any straight line parallel to $y = 3x$ is a coset of H.

Solution. Any straight line parallel to $y = 3x$ is of the form $y = 3x + c$. Then $(0, c)$ is a point on $y = 3x + c$. Let us show that the coset $(0, c) + H$ and $A = \{(a, b) \in \mathbb{R} \times \mathbb{R} : (a, b)$ is on $y = 3x + c\}$ are the same set. Now $(0, c) + H = \{(0, c) + (x, 3x) : x \in \mathbb{R}\} = \{(x, 3x + c) : x \in \mathbb{R}\} = \{(x, y) \in \mathbb{R} \times \mathbb{R} : y = 3x + c\}$. Hence the result follows.

$\Diamond$ **Exercise 5.3.6.** Find all subgroups of S_3. Show that union of any two nontrivial distinct subgroups of S_3 is not a subgroup of S_3.

Solution. $S_3 = \{e, (1\,2), (1\,3), (2\,3), (1\,2\,3), (1\,3\,2)\}$, $o(1\,2) = o(1\,3) = o(2\,3) = 2$, $o(1\,2\,3) = o(1\,3\,2) = 3$. Now $\{e\}, \{e, (1\,2)\}, \{e, (1\,3)\}, \{e, (2\,3)\}, \{e, (1\,2\,3), (1\,3\,2)\}$ and S_3 itself are the subgroups of S_3. Let H be a subgroup of S_3. Now, $|H|$ divides $|G|$. Thus, $|H| = 1, 2, 3$ or 6. If $|H| = 1$, then $H = \{e\}$. If $|H| = 6$, then $H = S_3$. If $|H| = 2$, then H is a cyclic group of order 2. Hence H is one of $\{e, (1\,2)\}, \{e, (1\,3)\}, \{e, (2\,3)\}$. Suppose $|H| = 3$. Then by Lagrange's theorem, H has no subgroup of order 2. Thus, $(1\,2), (1\,3), (2\,3) \notin H$. Hence $e, (1\,2\,3), (1\,3\,2) \in H$. Also $\{e, (1\,2\,3), (1\,3\,2)\}$ is a subgroup and so $H = \{e, (1\,2\,3), (1\,3\,2)\}$. Hence $H_0 = \{e\}, H_1 = \{e, (1\,2)\}, H_2 = \{e, (1\,3)\}, H_3 = \{e, (2\,3)\}, H_4 = \{e, (1\,2\,3), (1\,3\,2)\}$ and S_3 itself are the only subgroups of S_3.

Let H and K be two nontrivial distinct subgroups of S_3. Then $|H| = 2$ or 3 and $|K| = 2$ or 3. Also we note that $H \cap K = \{e\}$. Now $|H \cup K| = 3$ or 4, as there exists only one subgroup of order 3 in S_3. Again, a subgroup of order 3 cannot contain any subgroup of order 2. Also 4 does not divide $|S_3|$, whence we find that $H \cup K$ is not a subgroup of S_3.

$\Diamond$ **Exercise 5.3.7.** Prove that any finite subgroup of the group of nonzero complex numbers is a cyclic group.

Solution. Let H be a finite subgroup of $C^* = \mathbb{C} \setminus \{0\}$. Let $|H| = n$ and $a \in H$. Then by Corollary 5.3.12, $a^n = 1$. Hence any element of H is a root of $x^n = 1$. On the other hand, $x^n = 1$ has only n distinct roots. So it follows that $H = \{w \in \mathbb{C}^* : w$ is a root of $x^n = 1\}$. We know that the set of nth roots of unity forms a cyclic group. Hence H is a cyclic subgroup of $\mathbb{C}^*$.

◊ **Exercise 5.3.8.** Let G be a group such that $|G| > 1$. Prove that G has only trivial subgroups if and only if $|G|$ is prime.

Solution. Let $|G| = p$, for some prime number p. Let H be a subgroup of G. Then $|H|$ divides $|G|$. This implies that $|H| = 1$ or p. Thus, $H = \{e\}$ or $H = G$. Conversely, suppose that G has only the trivial subgroups. Let $a \in G$ be such that $a \neq e$. Now $\langle a \rangle = \{a^n \mid n \in \mathbb{Z}\}$ is a cyclic subgroup of G and $\langle a \rangle \neq \{e\}$. Thus, $G = \langle a \rangle$. If G is infinite, then $a^r \neq a^s$ for all $r, s \in \mathbb{Z}, r \neq s$. Hence $\{a^{2n} \mid n \in \mathbb{Z}\}$ is a nontrivial subgroup of G, which is a contradiction. Consequently, G is a finite cyclic group of order say, $m > 1$. Suppose m is not prime. Then $m = rs$ for some $r, s \in \mathbb{Z}, 1 < r, s < m$. Since r divides $|G|$ and G is cyclic, G has a cyclic subgroup H of order r. This contradicts the assumption. Hence $|G|$ is prime.

◊ **Exercise 5.3.9.** Let $G \neq \{e\}$ be a group of order p^n, p a prime. Show that G contains an element of order p.

Solution. Let $a \in G, a \neq e$. Then $H = \langle a \rangle$ is a cyclic subgroup of G. Now $|H|$ divides $|G| = p^n$ and so $|H| = p^m$ for some $m \in \mathbb{Z}, 0 < m \leq n$. Now in a cyclic group of order p^m, for every divisor d of p^m, there exists a subgroup of order d. Since p divides $|\langle a \rangle|$, there exists a subgroup T of H such that $|T| = p$. Let $T = \langle b \rangle$. Then $o(b) = p$. Hence the result.

◊ **Exercise 5.3.10.** Let H be a subgroup of a group G. Denote by L_H, the relation on G defined by

$$L_H = \Big\{(a,b) \in G \times G : a^{-1}b \in H\Big\}.$$

Prove that

(i) L_H is an equivalence relation.

(ii) Every equivalence class is a left coset of H in G.

(iii) Every left coset of H is an equivalence class of the relation L_H.

Solution. (i) Let $a \in G$. Since $a^{-1}a = e \in H$, we find that $(a,a) \in L_H$ for all $a \in G$. Let $a, b \in G$ such that $(a, b) \in L_H$. Then $a^{-1}b \in H$ and so $b^{-1}a = (a^{-1}b)^{-1} \in H$. Hence $(b, a) \in L_H$. Suppose now $(a, b) \in L_H$ and $(b, c) \in L_H$. Hence $a^{-1}b \in H$ and $b^{-1}c \in H$. Then $a^{-1}c = (a^{-1}b)(b^{-1}c) \in H$. Consequently, $(a, c) \in L_H$. So it follows that L_H is an equivalence relation.

(ii)   Let $[a]$ be an equivalence class of the relation L_H. Now,

$$[a] = \{x \in G \,|\, (a,x) \in L_H\} = \{x \in G \,|\, a^{-1}x \in H\} = \{x \in G \,|\, x \in aH\} \subseteq aH.$$

Again for any $ah \in aH$, $a^{-1}(ah) = h \in H$ implies that $(a, ah) \in L_H$. Hence $ah \in [a]$ and then $aH \subseteq [a]$. Consequently, $[a] = aH$.

(iii)   Let aH be a left coset. Proceeding as in (ii), show that $[a] = aH$.

$\diamond$ **Exercise 5.3.11.** Let S_n be the group of all permutations on the set $\{1, 2, \ldots, n\}$ under the compositions of mappings. For $n > 2$, if H is the smallest subgroup of S_n containing the transposition $(1\ 2)$ and the cycle $(1\ 2\ 3\ \ldots\ n)$, then
(i) $H = S_n$ (ii) H is Abelian   (iii) $[S_n : H] = 2$ (iv) H is cyclic.

Solution. Let $\sigma = (1\ 2\ 3\ \ldots\ n)$ and $\tau = (1\ 2)$. We first show that using σ and τ, we can generate all transpositions of the form $(k\ \ k+1)$. In fact it is easy to show that $(k\ \ k+1) = \sigma^{k-1}\tau\sigma^{1-k}$. Similarly we can generate $(k+1\ \ k+2)$ as $(k+1\ \ k+2) = \sigma(k\ \ k+1)\sigma^{-1}$. We now show that all transpositions of the form $(1\ k)$ $(k = 2, 3, \ldots, n)$ can also be generated by σ and τ. We show this by the method of mathematical induction. For $k = 2$, the transposition $(1\ 2)$ is generated by σ and τ, since the transposition $(1\ 2)$ is just equal to τ. Now suppose that we can generate $(1\ k)$ for some $k < n$. Now $(1\ \ k+1) = (1\ k)(k\ \ k+1)(1\ k)$ and since σ and τ generates $(1\ k)$ and $(k\ \ k+1)$, it follows that σ and τ also generates $(1\ \ k+1)$. Finally, we now show that σ and τ generate arbitrary transpositions. For this let $(m\ k)$ be any transposition. Then $(m\ k) = (1\ m)(1\ k)(1\ m)$. Thus the subgroup generated by σ and τ includes all transpositions. Since we know that every element in S_n can be expressed as product of transpositions, we see that σ and τ must in fact generate all of S_n. Therefore, option (i) is correct.

Exercises

1. Find all distinct left cosets of the subgroup H in the group G.
     (a) $H = \{1, -1\}, G = (\mathbb{R} \smallsetminus \{0\}, \cdot)$.
     (b) $H = 7\mathbb{Z}, G = \mathbb{Z}$.
     (c) $H = \{e, (2\,3)\}, G = S_3$.
     (d) $H = \{e, (1\,2\,3), (1\,3\,2)\}, G = S_3$.

2. In the multiplicative group $\mathbb{C}^*$, describe geometrically the coset $(2+3i)H$ of the subgroup $H = \{z \in \mathbb{C}^* : |z| = 1\}$.

3. Let $G = \mathbb{R} \times \mathbb{R}$ be the group under binary operation $*$ defined by $(a, b) * (c, d) = (a+c, b+d)$. Let $H = \{(a, 5a) : a \in \mathbb{R}\}$. Show that H is a subgroup of G. Describe the left cosets of H in G. Describe this subgroup and its cosets geometrically.

4. Show that the set $\mathcal{L}$ of all left cosets of $\mathbb{Z}$ in the additive group $(\mathbb{R}, +)$ of all real numbers is given by $\mathcal{L} = \{x + \mathbb{Z} \mid 0 \leq x < 1\}$.

5. Show that the set of all left cosets of the subgroup $8\mathbb{Z}$ in the group $(\mathbb{Z}, +)$ is given by $\mathcal{L} = \{x + 8\mathbb{Z} \mid x = 0, 1, 2, \ldots, 7\}$.

6. Let H be a subgroup of G and suppose that $g_1, g_2 \in G$. Prove that the following conditions are equivalent:

    (a) $g_1 H = g_2 H$
    (b) $H g_1^{-1} = H g_2^{-1}$
    (c) $g_2 \in g_1 H$
    (d) $g_1^{-1} g_2 \in H$.

7. Determine whether or not the following cosets of the subgroup $H = 5\mathbb{Z}$ in the group $(\mathbb{Z}, +)$ are equal:

    (i) $-1 + H$ and $5 + H$
    (ii) $3 + H$ and $2 + H$.

8. Let G be a group and H and K be subgroups of G. Show that $(H \cap K)x = Hx \cap Kx$ for all $x \in G$.

9. Let G be a group and H and K be subgroups of G. Let $a, b \in G$. Show that either $Ha \cap Kb = \emptyset$ or $Ha \cap Kb = (H \cap K)c$ for some $c \in G$.

10. † (**Poincaré**) Let G be a group and H and K be subgroups of G of finite indices. Show that $H \cap K$ is of finite index.

11. Give an example of a group G and a subgroup H of G, such that $aH = bH$ but $Ha \neq Hb$ for some $a, b \in G$.

12. Let G be a group of order pq where p and q are prime integers. Show that every subgroup $H \neq G$ is a cyclic subgroup.

13. Find all subgroups of Klein's four-group.

14. Prove that every proper subgroup of S_3 is cyclic.

15. Prove that every group of order 4 is a commutative group.

16. Prove that every group of order 49 contains a subgroup of order 7.

17. Let H be a subgroup of the group G. Define a relation R_H on G by $a\, R_H\, b$, if and only if $ab^{-1} \in H$. Show that R_H is an equivalence relation on G and the equivalence classes of R_H are precisely the right cosets $Ha, a \in G$.

18. Let H and K be subgroups of a finite group G such that $|H| > \sqrt{|G|}$ and $|K| > \sqrt{|G|}$. Show that $|H \cap K| > 1$.

19. Let G be a group. If a subset A is a left coset of some subgroup of G, then show that A is a right coset of some subgroup of G.

20. Let G be a group such that $|G| < 320$. Suppose G has subgroups of order 35 and 45. Find the order of G.

21. Let G be a group of order 15 and A and B subgroups of G of order 5 and 3, respectively. Show that $G = AB$.

22. Let A and B be two subgroups of a group G. If $|A| = p$, a prime integer, then show that either $A \cap B = \{e\}$ or $A \subseteq B$.

23. Prove that a non Abelian group G of order 10 must have a subgroup of order 5.

24. If a cyclic group G has exactly three subgroups, G itself, $\{e\}$ and a subgroup of order 7, find $|G|$.

25. If the following statement is true, then write a proof of it, otherwise justify your answer and give a counter example, whenever necessary.

   (a) Every left coset of a subgroup of a group is also a right coset of that subgroup.

   (b) There may exist a subgroup of order sixteen in a group of order fifty.

   (c) Let $G = \langle a \rangle$ be a cyclic group of order 35. Then the index $[G : \langle a^7 \rangle] = 5$.

   (d) A group of order 28 contains at most one subgroup of order seven.

   (e) The set of left cosets of $\mathbb{Z}$ in the additive group of real numbers is infinite.

   (f) The set of left cosets of $\mathbb{Z}$ in the group $(\mathbb{Q}, +)$ of all rational numbers is finite.

   (g) A_n is of index 2 in S_n, $n \geq 2$.

   (h) Every proper subgroup of a group of order 25 is cyclic.

Find the correct answer to the following:

26. Let H and K be two subgroups of a group G such that H has 7 elements and K has 13 elements. Then the number of elements of $H \cap K$ is

   (i) 1 (ii) 6 (iii) 0 (iv) 2.

27. Let H and K be two subgroups of a group G such that H has 7 elements and K has 13 elements. Then the number of elements of HK is

   (i) 1 (ii) 6 (iii) 0 (iv) 91.

28. Suppose G has subgroups of order 45 and 75. If $|G| < 400$, then $|G|$ is

   (i) 90 (ii) 150 (iii) 225 (iv) none of this.

29. The number of right cosets of the subgroup $H = \{e, (1\,2)(3\,4), (1\,4)(2\,3), (1\,3)(2\,4)\}$ in S_4 is

   (i) 2 (ii) 4 (iii) 6 (iv) 3.

5.4   Normal Subgroups and Quotient Groups

In the theory of groups, it was a great leap forward to understand and appreciate that those subgroups for which the left and right cosets coincide, were of immensely greater significance than the ordinary subgroups. Again it was the French prodigy Galois, who recognized this fact clearly[9]. We have seen that a subgroup of a group induces two decompositions of the group, in terms of its left and right cosets. Galois called such a

---

[9]The last two lines of his letter written to a friend on the eve of the fateful duel goes as, "Please ask Jacobi or Gauss to give their opinion publicly, not about the truth, but about the importance of these theorems. After that, I hope there will be some people who will take profit from deciphering all this mess".

decomposition *proper*, if the two decompositions coincided. He then showed how the solvability of a polynomial equation by means of radicals is related to the concept of this special class of subgroups of the group of permutations of the roots. This special class of subgroups are now referred to as the *normal* subgroups, which play a very crucial role in attaining structural results in the theory of groups.

Though the concept of a normal subgroup was tacitly there in the works of Galois (1831), it was C. Jordan who first formally defined this concept in our present-day terminology.

Definition 5.4.1. Let G be a group. A subgroup H of G is said to be a ***normal*** subgroup of G if $aH = Ha$ for all $a \in G$.

For any group G, G and $\{e\}$ are normal subgroups. Also, it follows directly from the above definition that *every subgroup of a commutative group is a normal subgroup*. However, the converse of this statement fails to hold. We merely state that every subgroup of the quaternion group $\mathcal{Q}_8$ [vide Definition 5.1.15] can be shown to be normal, while the group itself is non-commutative.

Note that, even if H is a normal subgroup of G, this does not always mean that $ah = ha$ for all $h \in H$ and for all $a \in G$, as is shown in the following example:

Example 5.4.2. Consider the group S_3. Let $H = \{e, (1\,2\,3), (1\,3\,2)\}$. Then H is a subgroup of S_3. Since $e, (1\,2\,3)$ and $(1\,3\,2)$ are elements of H, it follows that $eH = He, (1\,2\,3)H = H(1\,2\,3)$ and $(1\,3\,2)H = H(1\,3\,2)$. Now,

$$(1\,2)H = \{(1\,2), (1\,2)(1\,2\,3), (1\,2)(1\,3\,2)\} = \{(1\,2), (2\,3), (1\,3)\}$$
$$H(1\,2) = \{(1\,2), (1\,2\,3)(1\,2), (1\,3\,2)(1\,2)\} = \{(1\,2), (1\,3), (2\,3)\}.$$

Hence, $(1\,2)H = H(1\,2)$. Again,

$$(2\,3)H = \{(2\,3), (2\,3)(1\,2\,3), (2\,3)(1\,3\,2)\} = \{(2\,3), (1\,3), (1\,2)\}$$
$$H(2\,3) = \{(2\,3), (1\,2\,3)(2\,3), (1\,3\,2)(2\,3)\} = \{(2\,3), (1\,2), (1\,3)\}.$$

Hence, $(2\,3)H = H(2\,3)$. Also, we can show that $(1\,3)H = H(1\,3)$. Consequently, H is a normal subgroup. However, we point out that for $(1\,2\,3) \in H$ and $(2\,3) \in G$,

$$(2\,3)(1\,2\,3) = (1\,3) \neq (1\,2) = (1\,2\,3)(2\,3).$$

Now consider the subgroup $H = \{e, (1\,2)\}$ in S_3. For this subgroup,

$$(1\,3)H = \{(1\,3), (1\,3)(1\,2)\} = \{(1\,3), (1\,2\,3)\}$$
$$H(1\,3) = \{(1\,3), (1\,2)(1\,3)\} = \{(1\,3), (1\,3\,2)\}.$$

Hence, $(1\,3)H \neq H(1\,3)$ and so, $H = \{e, (1\,2)\}$ is not a normal subgroup of S_3.

The following theorem gives some equivalent conditions for a subgroup to be a normal subgroup.

Theorem 5.4.3. *Let H be a subgroup of a group G. The following conditions are equivalent:*

(i) *H is a normal subgroup.*

(ii) *$gHg^{-1} \subseteq H$ for all $g \in G$.*

(iii) *$gHg^{-1} = H$ for all $g \in G$.*

Proof. **(i) $\Rightarrow$ (ii)**   Let $g \in G$. Since H is a normal subgroup of G, $gH = Hg$. Hence for any $h \in H, gh \in gH = Hg$ and so $gh = h'g$ for some $h' \in H$. Thus, $ghg^{-1} = h' \in H$. Hence $gHg^{-1} \subseteq H$.

(ii) $\Rightarrow$ (iii)   Let $h \in H$. Then $g^{-1}h(g^{-1})^{-1} \in g^{-1}H(g^{-1})^{-1} \subseteq H$. Hence $g(g^{-1}hg)g^{-1} \in gHg^{-1}$ and so $h \in gHg^{-1}$. Thus we find that $H \subseteq gHg^{-1} \subseteq H$. Hence $gHg^{-1} = H$.

(iii) $\Rightarrow$ (i)   Since $gHg^{-1} = H$ for all $g \in G$, we find that $gH = Hg$ for all $g \in G$. Hence H is a normal subgroup. $\square$

Definition 5.4.4. Let H and K be subgroups of a group G. The set $N_K(H)$, given by

$$N_K(H) = \{k \in K \mid kHk^{-1} = H\},$$

is called the ***normalizer of H in K***.

It can be easily seen that $N_K(H)$ is a subgroup of K [vide Exercise 5.4.26] and $N_K(H) = N_G(H) \cap K$. In particular, for $K = G$ we write $N(H)$ instead of $N_G(H)$ and the subgroup

$$N(H) = \{a \in G \mid aHa^{-1} = H\}$$

is referred to simply as the ***normalizer*** of H. It can be shown that [vide Exercise 5.4.27(c)], $N(H)$ is the largest subgroup of G in which H is normal. Clearly, when H is normal in G, we have $N(H) = G$.

The following theorem describes some important properties of the normal subgroups of a group.

Theorem 5.4.5. *Let H and K be two subgroups of a group G. Then*

(i)   *if H is a normal subgroup of G, then $HK = KH$ is a subgroup of G;*

(ii)   *if H and K are both normal subgroups, then $HK = KH$ is a normal subgroup of G;*

(iii)   *if H and K are both normal subgroups, then $H \cap K$ is a normal subgroup.*

Proof. (i) Let $b \in K$. Then $Hb = bH$ implies $Hb \subseteq KH$. This is true for any $b \in K$. Hence $HK \subseteq KH$. Similarly, we can show that $KH \subseteq HK$. Hence $HK = KH$. Now from Theorem 5.1.26, it follows that HK is a subgroup of G.

(ii) Suppose that H and K are both normal subgroups of the group G. Now from (i), $HK = KH$ is a subgroup of G. Let $g \in G$. Then $gHKg^{-1} = gHg^{-1}gKg^{-1} = (gHg^{-1})(gKg^{-1}) \subseteq HK$. Hence HK is a normal subgroup of G.

(iii) Since H and K are subgroups, $H \cap K$ is also a subgroup. Let $g \in G$ and $a \in H \cap K$. Then $gag^{-1} \in gHg^{-1} \subseteq H$ and $gag^{-1} \in gKg^{-1} \subseteq K$. Since $gag^{-1} \in H \cap K$ for all $a \in H \cap K$, we find that $g(H \cap K)g^{-1} \subseteq H \cap K$ for all $g \in G$. Hence $H \cap K$ is a normal subgroup of G. □

The idea of a normal subgroup is a very important concept in the group theory. Now we shall show that with the help of a normal subgroup of a group, we can construct a new group from the given group. In fact, we are going to show that, given a normal subgroup H, we can define a binary operation on the set of left cosets of that normal subgroup H, so that we may get a new group from the given group. Since for a normal subgroup H, every left coset is also a right coset and vice versa, so henceforth we may refer to a coset of H instead of a right or left coset.

Theorem 5.4.6. *Let H be a normal subgroup of a group G. Denote the set of all cosets $\{aH \mid a \in G\}$ by G/H and define $*$ on G/H by,*

$$\text{for all } aH, bH \in G/H, (aH) * (bH) = abH.$$

Then $(G/H, *)$ is a group.

Proof. Our first and foremost task is to show that the operation $*$ is a well-defined binary operation on G/H. In other words, we must show that if $aH = a_1H$ and $bH = b_1H$, then $(ab)H = (a_1b_1)H$, because this will show that $aH * bH = (ab)H = (a_1b_1)H = a_1H * b_1H$. Now $aH = a_1H$ and $bH = b_1H$ imply that $a = a_1h_1$ and $b = b_1h_2$ where $h_1, h_2 \in H$. Then

$$(a_1b_1)^{-1}ab = b_1^{-1}a_1^{-1}ab = b_1^{-1}a_1^{-1}a_1h_1b_1h_2 = b_1^{-1}h_1b_1h_2 \tag{5.4.1}$$

Since H is a normal subgroup, $Hb_1 = b_1H$ and hence $h_1b_1 = b_1h_3$ for some $h_3 \in H$. Hence from (5.4.1), $(a_1b_1)^{-1}ab = b_1^{-1}b_1h_3h_2 = h_3h_2 \in H$. This implies that $(a_1b_1)H = (ab)H$. Hence $aH * bH = abH = a_1b_1H = a_1H * b_1H$ and so $*$ is a well-defined binary operation on G/H.

Next we show that $*$ is associative. Let $aH, bH, cH \in G/H$. Now $aH * (bH * cH) = aH * bcH = a(bc)H = (ab)cH = abH * cH = (aH * bH) * cH$. Hence $*$ is associative. Now $eH \in G/H$ and

$$aH * eH = aeH = aH = eaH = eH * aH$$

for all $aH \in G/H$. Hence eH is the identity of $(G/H, *)$. Also, for all $aH \in G/H, a^{-1}H \in G/H$ and

$$aH * a^{-1}H = aa^{-1}H = eH = a^{-1}aH = a^{-1}H * aH.$$

Hence for all $aH \in G/H, a^{-1}H$ is the inverse of aH. Thus, $(G/H, *)$ is a group.   □

Definition 5.4.7. Let G be a group and H be a normal subgroup of G. Then the group G/H of all cosets of H in G under the binary operation $aH * bH = abH$ is called the **quotient group** or **factor group** of G by H.

From now on, we shall omit the notation $*$ of group operation in the group $(G/H, *)$ and use the same notation as that of the group G.

Example 5.4.8. Consider the group S_3 and let $H = \{e, (1\,2\,3), (1\,3\,2)\}$. Now H is a normal subgroup of G and $[G : H] = \frac{|G|}{|H|} = 2$. Hence, there are two distinct cosets of H in G. Then $G/H = \{eH, (1\,2)H\}$. The Cayley table for the group operation of the factor group G/H is as follows:

$*$	eH	$(1\,2)H$
eH	eH	$(1\,2)H$
$(1\,2)H$	$(1\,2)H$	eH

Example 5.4.9. Consider the subgroup $4\mathbb{Z}$ of the group $(\mathbb{Z}, +)$. Since $\mathbb{Z}$ is commutative, $4\mathbb{Z}$ is a normal subgroup of $\mathbb{Z}$. Let $m \in \mathbb{Z}$. By the division algorithm, there exist $q, r \in \mathbb{Z}$ such that $m = 4q + r$, $0 \le r < 4$. Thus, $m + 4\mathbb{Z} = (4q + r) + 4\mathbb{Z} = r + 4q + 4\mathbb{Z} = r + 4\mathbb{Z}$. Hence $\mathbb{Z}/4\mathbb{Z} = \{0 + 4\mathbb{Z}, 1 + 4\mathbb{Z}, 2 + 4\mathbb{Z}, 3 + 4\mathbb{Z}\}$. The Cayley table for the group operation $*$ of the factor group $\mathbb{Z}/4\mathbb{Z}$ is given by

$*$	$0 + 4\mathbb{Z}$	$1 + 4\mathbb{Z}$	$2 + 4\mathbb{Z}$	$3 + 4\mathbb{Z}$
$0 + 4\mathbb{Z}$	$0 + 4\mathbb{Z}$	$1 + 4\mathbb{Z}$	$2 + 4\mathbb{Z}$	$3 + 4\mathbb{Z}$
$1 + 4\mathbb{Z}$	$1 + 4\mathbb{Z}$	$2 + 4\mathbb{Z}$	$3 + 4\mathbb{Z}$	$0 + 4\mathbb{Z}$
$2 + 4\mathbb{Z}$	$2 + 4\mathbb{Z}$	$3 + 4\mathbb{Z}$	$0 + 4\mathbb{Z}$	$1 + 4\mathbb{Z}$
$3 + 4\mathbb{Z}$	$3 + 4\mathbb{Z}$	$0 + 4\mathbb{Z}$	$1 + 4\mathbb{Z}$	$2 + 4\mathbb{Z}$

Example 5.4.10. Consider the group $(\mathbb{Z}_{10}, +)$ and let $H = \{[0], [5]\}$. Then H is a normal subgroup of $\mathbb{Z}_{10}$. Now $|H| = 2$ and $|\mathbb{Z}_{10}| = 10$. Thus $|\mathbb{Z}_{10}/H| = \frac{|\mathbb{Z}_{10}|}{|H|} = 5$. Hence $\mathbb{Z}_{10}/H$ has five elements. Now,

$$[0] + H = H = [5] + H$$
$$[1] + H = \{[1], [6]\} = [6] + H$$
$$[2] + H = \{[2], [7]\} = [7] + H$$
$$[3] + H = \{[3], [8]\} = [8] + H$$
$$[4] + H = \{[4], [9]\} = [9] + H$$

Hence $\mathbb{Z}_{10}/H = \Big\{[0] + H, [1] + H, [2] + H, [3] + H, [4] + H\Big\}$.

We put an end to this section with an interesting interrelation between the *normal subgroups* of a group G and the *congruence relations*[10] that can be defined on G as follows.

Definition 5.4.11. Let G be a group. An equivalance relation ρ on G is called a ***congruence relation on the group*** G if $a \, \rho \, b$ implies $ca \, \rho \, cb$ and $ac \, \rho \, bc$ for all $a, b, c \in G$.

Theorem 5.4.12. *Let G be a group.*

(i) If N is a normal subgroup of G, then the relation ρ_N on G defined by $a\rho_N b$ if and only if $a^{-1}b \in N$, for all $a, b \in G$, is a congruence relation on G. For each $g \in G$, the ρ_N class of g is the coset gN.

(ii) If ρ is a congruence on G then $N = \rho(e)$ is a normal subgroup of G, where $\rho(e)$ denotes the ρ congruence class containing the identity e of G and $\rho = \rho_N$.

Proof. (i) It can be shown easily that ρ_N is an equivalance relation on G. Let $a, b \in G$ such that $a\rho_N b$. Then $a^{-1}b \in N$. Let $c \in G$. Now $(ca)^{-1}cb = a^{-1}c^{-1}cb = a^{-1}b \in N$ and $(ac)^{-1}bc = c^{-1}a^{-1}bc = c^{-1}(a^{-1}b)c \in N$, as N is a normal subgroup. Thus $a\rho_N b$ implies $ca \, \rho_N \, cb$ and $ac \, \rho_N \, bc$ for all $a, b, c \in G$. Hence the relation ρ_N is a congruence relation on the group G and ρ_N class of g is $\{a \in G \mid g \, \rho_N \, a\} = \{a \in G \mid g^{-1}a \in N\} = \{a \in G \mid a \subset gN\} = gN$.

(ii) Let ρ be a congruence on G. Suppose $a, b \in \rho(e)$. Then $a\rho e$ and $b\rho e$. Now $ab^{-1} \rho \, b^{-1}$ and $b^{-1} \rho \, e$. Thus $ab^{-1} \rho \, e$. Hence $ab^{-1} \in \rho(e)$. It follows that $\rho(e)$ is a subgroup. Next we show that $\rho(e)$ is a normal subgroup. Let $a \in \rho(e)$. Then $a \, \rho \, e$. Now for any $g \in G$, $gag^{-1} \rho \, geg^{-1} = e$. Hence $gag^{-1} \in \rho(e)$. It follows that $\rho(e)$ is a normal subgroup.

---

[10]Such a relation defined on a mathematical system is basically an *equivalence relation compatible with the operation(s) of the system.*

Finally we show that the congruence relation ρ_N defined by the normal subgroup $N = \rho(e)$ is identical with ρ. Let $a\rho_N b$ for $a, b \in G$. Then $a^{-1}b \in N = \rho(e)$. Hence $a^{-1}b \rho e$. This implies $a(a^{-1}b) \rho ae$, i.e., $b\rho a$, i.e., $a\rho b$. Hence $\rho_N \subseteq \rho$. Suppose now $a\rho b$. Then $e\rho a^{-1}b$. Hence $a^{-1}b \in \rho(e) = N$. This shows that $a\,\rho_N\,b$. Consequently $\rho \subseteq \rho_N$. Therefore $\rho_N = \rho$. $\square$

Remark 5.4.13. From the above theorem it follows that there exists a one-to-one correspondence between the set of all normal subgroups of the group G and the set of all congruences on G.

Worked-out Exercises

$\Diamond$ **Exercise 5.4.1.** Let H be a subgroup of a group G such that $[G : H] = 2$. Then prove that H is a normal subgroup of G.

Solution. Since $[G : H] = 2$, the group has only two distinct left cosets and only two distinct right cosets. Now H itself is a left coset as well as a right coset of H in G. Let $a \in G$. If $a \in H$, then $aH = H = Ha$. Suppose $a \notin H$. Then $aH \neq H$. Hence $G = H \cup aH$ and $H \cap aH = \emptyset$. Then $aH = G \smallsetminus H$. Again, since $a \notin H$ and H has only two right cosets, we find that $G = H \cup Ha$ where $H \cap Ha = \emptyset$. Thus $Ha = G \smallsetminus H$.

Hence $aH = Ha$. Thus we find that $aH = Ha$ for all $a \in G$ and so H is a normal subgroup of G.

$\Diamond$ **Exercise 5.4.2.** Show that the centre of a group G, given by $Z(G) = \{a \in G : ag = ga$ for all $g \in G\}$, is a normal subgroup of G.

Solution. We have already proved (cf. Theorem 5.1.31) that $Z(G)$ is a subgroup of G. Now for any $g \in G$ and any $a \in Z(G)$, $gag^{-1} = agg^{-1} = a \in Z(G)$ and hence, $gZ(G)g^{-1} \subseteq Z(G)$. Consequently, $Z(G)$ is a normal subgroup of G.

$\Diamond$ **Exercise 5.4.3.** Let H be a subgroup of a group G. Then $W = \bigcap\limits_{g \in G} gHg^{-1}$ is a normal subgroup of G.

Solution. In the Worked-out Exercise 5.1.2, we have shown that gHg^{-1} is a subgroup of G for all $g \in G$. Since the intersection of subgroups is a subgroup, W is a subgroup of G. Let $x \in G$, $w \in W$. Then $w \in gHg^{-1}$ for all $g \in G$. We have to show that $xwx^{-1} \in gHg^{-1}$ for all $g \in G$, which in turn will yield that $xwx^{-1} \in W$.

Let $g \in G$ and let us suppose that $xwx^{-1} \in gHg^{-1}$. Then $xwx^{-1} = ghg^{-1}$ for some $h \in H$. Thus $g^{-1}xwx^{-1}g = h \in H$. This implies that $(g^{-1}x)w(g^{-1}x)^{-1} \in H$.

Put $y = x^{-1}g$. Then $g = xy$. Hence in order to show that $xwx^{-1} \in gHg^{-1}$ for a given $g \in G$, first we need to find $y \in G$ such that $g = xy$. Since $g = x(x^{-1}g)$, we can choose $y = x^{-1}g$.

So there exists $y \in G$ such that $g = xy$. Since $y \in G$, we have $w \in yHy^{-1}$ and $w = yhy^{-1}$ for some $h \in H$. Hence $xwx^{-1} = x(yhy^{-1})x^{-1} = xyhy^{-1}x^{-1} = (xy)h(xy)^{-1} = ghg^{-1} \in gHg^{-1}$. Since $g \in G$ was arbitrary, $xwx^{-1} \in gHg^{-1}$ for all $g \in G$. Thus, W is a normal subgroup of G.

$\Diamond$ **Exercise 5.4.4.** Let H be a subgroup of a group G. If $x^2 \in H$ for all $x \in G$, then prove that H is a normal subgroup of G and G/H is commutative.

Solution. Let $g \in G$ and $h \in H$. Consider ghg^{-1} and note that

$$ghg^{-1} = ghghh^{-1}g^{-2} = (gh)^2h^{-1}g^{-2}.$$

Now $h^{-1} \in H$ and by our hypothesis $(gh)^2, g^{-2} \in H$. This implies that $ghg^{-1} \in H$ which in turn shows that $gHg^{-1} \subseteq H$. Hence H is a normal subgroup of G. To show G/H is commutative, let $xH, yH \in G/H$. We show that $xHyH = yHxH$ or $xyH = yxH$ or $(yx)^{-1}(xy) \in H$. Now,

$$(yx)^{-1}(xy) = (x^{-1}y^{-1})(xy) = (x^{-1}y^{-1})^2(yxy^{-1})^2y^2.$$

Since $a^2 \in H$ for all $a \in G$, it follows $(x^{-1}y^{-1})^2(yxy^{-1})^2y^2 \in H$ and so $(yx)^{-1}(xy) \in H$. Hence G/H is commutative.

$\Diamond$ **Exercise 5.4.5.** Let G be a group such that every cyclic subgroup of G is a normal subgroup of G. Prove that every subgroup of G is a normal subgroup of G.

Solution. Let H be a subgroup of G. Let $g \in G$ and $a \in H$. Then, $gag^{-1} \in \langle a \rangle \subseteq H$. Hence H is normal in G.

$\Diamond$ **Exercise 5.4.6.** Let H be a proper subgroup of a group G such that for all $x, y \in G \smallsetminus H$, $xy \in H$. Prove that H is a normal subgroup of G.

Solution. Let $x \in G \smallsetminus H$. Then $x^{-1} \in G \smallsetminus H$. Let $y \in H$. Then $xy \in G \smallsetminus H$, (for otherwise, $x = xyy^{-1} \in H$). Thus $xy, x^{-1} \in G \smallsetminus H$. Hence $xyx^{-1} \in H$. Also for any $x \in H$, we have $xyx^{-1} \in H$. Thus H is a normal subgroup of G.

$\Diamond$ **Exercise 5.4.7.** Let H be a subgroup of a group G. Suppose that the product of two left cosets of H in G is again a left coset of H in G. Prove that H is a normal subgroup of G.

Solution. Let $g \in G$. Then $gHg^{-1}H = tH$ for some $t \in G$. Thus $e = geg^{-1}e \in tH$. Hence $e = th$ for some $h \in H$. Thus $t = h^{-1} \in H$ so that $tH = H$. Now $gHg^{-1} \subseteq gHg^{-1}H = H$. Hence H is a normal subgroup of G.

◊ **Exercise 5.4.8.** If H is the only subgroup of order n in a group G, then prove that H is a normal subgroup.

Solution. Let $g \in G$. Then by Worked-out Exercise 5.1.2, gHg^{-1} is a subgroup of G and $|H| = |gHg^{-1}|$. Hence $|gHg^{-1}| = n$ and so by the given condition $gHg^{-1} = H$. This is true for all $g \in G$. Thus we find that H is a normal subgroup of G.

◊ **Exercise 5.4.9.** Show that $K = \{e, (1\,2)(3\,4), (1\,3)(2\,4), (1\,4)(2\,3)\}$ is a normal subgroup of A_4.

Solution. A_4 has 12 elements. These elements are $e, (1\,2\,3), (1\,3\,2), (1\,2\,4), (1\,4\,2), (1\,3\,4), (1\,4\,3), (2\,3\,4), (2\,4\,3), (1\,2)(3\,4), (1\,3)(2\,4), (1\,4)(2\,3)$. Hence A_4 has no element of order 4. The only elements of order 2 are $a = (1\,2)(3\,4)$, $b = (1\,3)(2\,4), c = (1\,4)(2\,3)$. Now $a^2 = b^2 = e$ and $ab = ba = c$. Hence $K = \{e, a, b, ab = c\}$ is a subgroup of order 4 and this is the only subgroup of order 4 in G. Therefore by Worked-out Exercise 5.4.8, we conclude that K is a normal subgroup of G.

◊ **Exercise 5.4.10.** Let H and K be two normal subgroups of G such that $H \cap K = \{e\}$. Prove that $hk = kh$ for all $h \in H$ and $k \in K$.

Solution. For all $h \in H, k \in K$, we see that

$$
\begin{aligned}
hkh^{-1}k^{-1} &\in (hKh^{-1})k^{-1} \\
&\subseteq Kk^{-1} \quad &&\text{(since } K \text{ is a normal subgroup)} \\
&= K \quad &&\text{(since } k^{-1} \in K)
\end{aligned}
$$

$$
\begin{aligned}
\text{and} \quad hkh^{-1}k^{-1} &= h(kh^{-1}k^{-1}) \\
&\in h(kHk^{-1}) \quad &&\text{(since } H \text{ is a subgroup)} \\
&\subseteq hH \quad &&\text{(since } H \text{ is a normal subgroup)} \\
&= H \quad &&\text{(since } h \in H).
\end{aligned}
$$

Hence $hkh^{-1}k^{-1} \in H \cap K = \{e\}$ and so $hkh^{-1}k^{-1} = e$. This proves that $hk = kh$, for all $h \in H$ and $k \in K$.

◊ **Exercise 5.4.11.** Let G be a group. Show that if $G/Z(G)$ is cyclic, then G is Abelian.

Solution. Write $Z = Z(G)$. Let $G/Z = \langle gZ \rangle$ for some $g \in G$. Let $a, b \in G$. Then $aZ, bZ \in G/Z$. Hence $aZ = g^n Z$ and $bZ = g^m Z$ for some $n, m \in \mathbb{Z}$. Then $a \in g^n Z$ and $b \in g^m Z$. Hence $a = g^n d$ and $b = g^m h$ for some $d, h \in Z$. Now,

$$
\begin{aligned}
ab &= g^n d g^m h \\
&= g^n g^m dh \quad (\text{since } d \in Z) \\
&= g^{n+m} hd \quad (\text{since } h \in Z) \\
&= g^m g^n hd \\
&= g^m h g^n d \quad (\text{since } h \in Z) \\
&= b\, a.
\end{aligned}
$$

Hence G is Abelian.

$\Diamond$ **Exercise 5.4.12.** M, N are finite normal subgroups of a group G such that $\gcd\left(|M|, |N|\right) = 1$. If G/M and G/N are cyclic, prove that G is Abelian.

Solution. Let $a, b \in G$. Consider $aM, bM \in G/M$. Then $abM, b\,aM \in G/M$ as well. Since G/M is cyclic and hence commutative, we have $abM = b\,aM$ in G/M, whence $(ab)(b\,a)^{-1} \in M$. Similarly, we have $(ab)(b\,a)^{-1} \in N$ as well, so that $(ab)(b\,a)^{-1} \in M \cap N$. Now since $\gcd(|M|, |N|) = 1$, we see that $M \cap N = \{e\}$, as $M \cap N$ has to be a subgroup of both M and N. This gives, $(ab)(b\,a)^{-1} \in M \cap N = \{e\}$, whence $(ab)(b\,a)^{-1} = e$, so taht $ab = b\,a$ for all $a, b \in G$. Hence G is Abelian.

$\Diamond$ **Exercise 5.4.13.** Let G denote the group of all invertible 2×2 matrices with entries from $\mathbb{R}$. Let $H_1 = \{A \in G : \det(A) = 1\}$ and $H_2 = \{A \in G : A \text{ is upper triangular}\}$. Consider the following statements:

$P : H_1$ is a normal subgroup of G. $\qquad$ $Q : H_2$ is a normal subgroup of G.

Then

(i) Both P and Q are true $\qquad$ (ii) P is true but Q is false

(iii) P is false but Q is true $\qquad$ (iv) Both P and Q are false.

Solution. It is easy to verify that H_1 is a subgroup of G. Let $A \in H_1$ and $B \in G$. Then $\det(BAB^{-1}) = \det(B)\det(A)\det(B^{-1}) = \det(B)\det(B^{-1}) = \det(BB^{-1}) = \det(I) = 1$. Hence $BAB^{-1} \in H_1$ and thus H_1 is a normal subgroup of G.

Again, $C = \begin{pmatrix} 2 & 1 \\ 1 & 1 \end{pmatrix} \in G$ with $C^{-1} = \begin{pmatrix} 1 & -1 \\ -1 & 2 \end{pmatrix}$ and $D = \begin{pmatrix} 2 & 1 \\ 0 & 2 \end{pmatrix} \in H_2$.

Now $CDC^{-1} = \begin{pmatrix} 0 & 4 \\ -1 & 4 \end{pmatrix} \notin H_2$. Thus H_2 is not normal in G. Therefore, option (ii) is correct.

◊ **Exercise 5.4.14.** Suppose N is a normal subgroup of a group G. Which one of the following is true?

(i) If G is an infinite group then G/N is an infinite group

(ii) If G is a non-Abelian group then G/N is a non-Abelian group

(iii) If G is a cyclic group then G/N is an Abelian group

(iv) If G is an Abelian group then G/N is a cyclic group.

Solution. If we consider the infinite group $(\mathbb{Z}, +)$ and its normal subgroup $2\mathbb{Z}$, then the quotient group $\mathbb{Z}/2\mathbb{Z}$ is finite. Hence statement (i) is false. Again, if we consider the non-Abelian group S_3 and its normal subgroup A_3, then the quotient group S_3/A_3 is commutative. Thus statement (ii) is false. Again, if we consider the Abelian group K_4 and its normal subgroup $\{e\}$, then the quotient group $K_4/\{e\}$ is non-cyclic. Thus statement (iv) is also false. Finally, is $G = \langle a \rangle$ is a cyclic group, then for any normal subgroup N of G we have $G/N = \langle aN \rangle$ is also cyclic and hence Abelian. Therefore, option (iii) is correct.

◊ **Exercise 5.4.15.** Let G be a finite group and $|G|$ denote its order. Then which of the following statement(s) is(are) true?

(i) G is Abelian if $|G| = pq$ where p and q are distinct primes.

(ii) G is Abelian if every non-identity element of G is of order 2.

(iii) G is Abelian if the quotient group $G/Z(G)$ is cyclic.

(iv) G is Abelian if $|G| = p^3$, where p is prime.

Solution. In a group G, if $x^2 = e$ for all $x \in G$, then G is Abelian. Now $|S_3| = 6 = 2 \cdot 3$, but S_3 is non-Abelian. By Worked-out Exercise 5.4.11, it follows that if $G/Z(G)$ is cyclic then G is Abelian. Finally, $|D_4| = 8 = 2^3$, where 2 is prime, but D_4 is not Abelian. Therefore, options (ii) and (iii) are correct.

Exercises

1. Let H be a normal subgroup of a group G such that H contains only two elements, then prove that $H \subseteq Z(G)$.

2. Let $GL(2, \mathbb{R})$ denote the set of all nonsingular 2×2 matrices with real entries. Show that

$$SL(2, \mathbb{R}) = \left\{ \begin{bmatrix} a & b \\ c & d \end{bmatrix} \in GL(2, \mathbb{R}) : ad - bc = 1 \right\}$$

is a normal subgroup of the group $GL(2, \mathbb{R})$.

3. Let T denote the group of all nonsingular upper triangular 2×2 matrices with real entries, i.e., the matrices of the form, $\begin{bmatrix} a & b \\ 0 & c \end{bmatrix}$ where $a, b, c \in \mathbb{R}$ and $ac \neq 0$. Show that

$H = \left\{ \begin{bmatrix} 1 & x \\ 0 & 1 \end{bmatrix} \in T \right\}$ is a normal subgroup of T.

4. Show that A_n is a normal subgroup of S_n.

5. In the symmetric group S_3, show that $H = \{e, (2\,3)\}$ is a subgroup but not a normal subgroup.

6. Show that $H = \{e, (1\,2)(3\,4)\}$ is not a normal subgroup of A_4.

7. In A_4, find subgroups H and K such that H is normal in K and K is normal in A_4, but H is not normal in A_4.

8. Let G be a group and H a subgroup of G. If for all $a, b \in G$, $ab \in H$ implies $ba \in H$, then prove that H is a normal subgroup of G.

9. Let H and K be subgroups of G such that H is a normal subgroup of G. Prove that $H \cap K$ is a normal subgroup of K.

10. Let H be a proper subgroup of a group G and $a \in G$, $a \notin H$. Suppose that for all $b \in G$, either $b \in H$, or $Ha = Hb$. Show that H is a normal subgroup of G.

11. Let H be a subgroup of a group G. If for each $a \in G$, there exists $b \in G$ such that $aH = Hb$, then prove that H is a normal subgroup of G.

12. Show that $12\mathbb{Z}$ is a normal subgroup of the group $(3\mathbb{Z}, +)$. Write the Cayley table for the factor group $3\mathbb{Z}/12\mathbb{Z}$.

13. Write down the Cayley table for the quotient group $\mathbb{Z}/5\mathbb{Z}$.

14. Let $G = \langle a \rangle$ be the cyclic group such that $o(a) = 12$. Let $H = \langle a^4 \rangle$. Find the order of $a^3 H$ in G/H.

15. Write down the Cayley table for the quotient group A_4/K, where $K = \{e, (1\,2)(3\,4), (1\,4)(3\,2), (1\,3)(2\,4)\}$. Is the group A_4/K a commutative group?

16. Let $\mathbb{R}^*$ be the group of all nonzero real numbers under usual multiplication. Show that the set $\mathbb{R}^+$ of all positive real numbers is a subgroup of R^*. What is the index of R^+ in R^*?

17. Let G be a group and $a \in Z(G)$. Prove that $H = \langle a \rangle$ is a normal subgroup.

18. Let $a, b \in \mathbb{R}$ and a mapping $T_{ab} : \mathbb{R} \to \mathbb{R}$ be defined by $T_{ab}(x) = ax + b$ for all $x \in \mathbb{R}$. Let $G = \{T_{ab} : a \neq 0\}$. Assume that $(G, \circ)$ is a group, where $\circ$ is the composition of mappings. If $H = \{T_{ab} : a = 1\}$, prove that $(H, \circ)$ is a normal subgroup of $(G, \circ)$.

19. Let H be a cyclic subgroup of a group G. If H is normal in G, prove that, every subgroup of H is normal in G.

20. Let G be a group and H be a subgroup of G such that $aba^{-1}b^{-1} \in H$, for all $a, b \in G$. Prove that H is normal in G.

21. Let G be a group in which $(ab)^3 = a^3b^3$ for all $a, b \in G$. Prove that $H = \{x^3 : x \in G\}$ is a normal subgroup of G.

22. Let H be a normal subgroup of a group G. Prove that
    (i) if G is commutative, then so is the quotient group G/H
    (ii) if G is cyclic, then so is G/H.

23. Let G be a group. Let H be a subgroup of G such that $H \subseteq Z(G)$. Show that if G/H is cyclic, then $G = Z(G)$, i.e., G is Abelian.

24. Let K be a normal subgroup of a group G such that $[G : K] = m$. If n is a positive integer such that $\gcd(m, n) = 1$, then show that $K \supseteq \{g \in G \,|\, o(g) = n\}$.

25. (a) Let K be a normal subgroup of a finite group G. If G/K has an element of order n, then show that G has an element of order n.
    (b) Let G be a group such that $|G| = 8$. Suppose $x \in G$ such that $o(x) = 4$. Show that $x^2 \in Z(G)$.

26. Prove that the normalizer $N_K(H)$ of a subgroup H in a subgroup K of a group G, is a subgroup of K.

27. Let H be a subset of a group G and let $N(H)$ be the **normalizer** of H. Prove that $N(H)$ is a subgroup of G. If in addition, H be a subgroup of G, then prove that
    (a) H is normal in $N(H)$.
    (b) H is normal in G if and only if $N(H) = G$.
    (c) if H is normal in a subgroup K of G, then $K \subseteq N(H)$.

28. Let ρ be a congruence relation on a group G. Show that there exists a normal subgroup H of G such that $\rho = \{(a, b) \in G \times G \,|\, a^{-1}b \in H\}$.

29. Prove that the quotient group $(\mathbb{Q}/\mathbb{Z}, +)$ is infinite but each of its elements is of finite order.

30. Consider the group $\mathbb{Q}/\mathbb{Z}$, where $\mathbb{Q}$ and $\mathbb{Z}$ are the group of rational numbers and integers respectively. Does there exist a cyclic subgroup of order n?
    (i) Not necessarily.
    (ii) Yes, a unique one.
    (iii) Yes, but not necessarily a unique one.
    (iv) Never.

Find the correct answer to the following:

31. If G be a group of order pq where p and q are prime integers then $|Z(G)|$ is
    (i) 1 or p (ii) 1 or q (iii) 1 or pq (iv) None of these.

32. The order of the quotient group $\mathbb{Z}/10\mathbb{Z}$ is
    (i) 10 (ii) 5 (iii) 1 (iv) 9.

33. The order of the quotient group $4\mathbb{Z}/12\mathbb{Z}$ is
    (i) 4 (ii) 3 (iii) 12 (iv) 1.

34. The number of normal subgroups of A_4 is
    (i) 3 (ii) 1 (iii) 6 (iv) 2.

35. The set $\mathbb{Q}^+$ of all positive rational numbers is a subgroup of index k of the multiplicative group $\mathbb{Q}^* \setminus \{0\}$ of all nonzero rational numbers. The value of k is
    (i) 2 (ii) 3 (iii) 6 (iv) 8.

36. The number of proper subgroups of $(\mathbb{R}^+, \cdot)$ having finite index is
    (i) 1 (ii) 2 (iii) 0 (iv) None of these.

37. Consider the quotient group $\mathbb{Q}/\mathbb{Z}$ of the additive group of rational numbers. The order of the element $\frac{2}{3} + \mathbb{Z}$ in $\mathbb{Q}/\mathbb{Z}$ is
    (i) 2   (ii) 3   (iii) 5   (iv) 6.

Chapter 6

Homomorphisms of Groups

Up till now, we were concerned only with a group and its substructure and had observed several important algebraic features of this fundamental structure. In this chapter, we are going to examine the interplay between algebraic properties of two groups by defining some suitable mappings between them. This idea will lead us towards the concept of *homomorphism*, which in a sense, establishes a structural compatibility between two algebraic structures. Gradually it enables us to develop the key concept of *isomorphism* among algebraic structures— in particular, groups. Two isomorphic algebraic structures can be regarded, for all practical purposes, to be algebraically similar, in the sense that they share precisely the same algebraic characters. That is why the concept of isomorphism plays the central role in classification of different algebraic structures.

6.1   Homomorphisms

Let us begin our discussion by considering the groups $(\mathbb{R}, +)$ and $(\mathbb{R}^+, \cdot)$, where the first one is the group of all real numbers under addition and the other one is the group of all positive real numbers under multiplication. Define a mapping $h : \mathbb{R} \to \mathbb{R}^+$ by $h(a) = e^a$ for all $a \in \mathbb{R}$. Observe that

$$h(a + b) = e^{a+b} = e^a \cdot e^b = h(a) \cdot h(b) \text{ for all } a, b \in \mathbb{R}.$$

So we see that the above mapping establishes an interesting relation between the operations of two groups under discussion. In this example, note that $a, b \in \mathbb{R}$, whence $a+b \in \mathbb{R}$. Now $h(a)$ and $h(b)$ are elements of $\mathbb{R}^+$ and so is $h(a) \cdot h(b)$. Now $h(a+b) \in \mathbb{R}^+$ and also satisfies $h(a + b) = h(a) \cdot h(b)$. Obviously, any arbitrary mapping between two groups do not necessarily enjoy this kind of property. In the sequel, mappings of this special type between two groups will establish a relation between two groups.

Definition 6.1.1. Let $(G, *)$ and $(G_1, *_1)$ be two groups and f be a mapping (function) from G into G_1. Then f is called a **homomorphism** of G into G_1 if for all $a, b \in G$,

$$f(a * b) = f(a) *_1 f(b).$$

Observe that the above defined mapping $h : \mathbb{R} \to \mathbb{R}^+$ is an example of a homomorphism from the group $(\mathbb{R}, +)$ to the group $(\mathbb{R}^+, \cdot)$.

We now consider some examples to explain the notion of homomorphism of groups.

Example 6.1.2. Consider the groups $(\mathbb{Z}, +)$, the group of all integers under addition and the multiplicative group $(\{1, -1\}, \cdot)$. Define $f : \mathbb{Z} \to \{1, -1\}$ by

$$f(n) = 1, \text{ if } n \text{ is an even integer};$$

$$= -1, \text{ if } n \text{ is an odd integer}.$$

Let $n, m \in \mathbb{Z}$. If n, m are both even, then $n + m$ is even and hence $f(n + m) = 1 = 1 \cdot 1 = f(n) \cdot f(m)$. Suppose n is even and m is odd, then $n + m$ is odd. Then $f(n) = 1, f(m) = -1$ and $f(n + m) = -1 = 1 \cdot (-1) = f(n) \cdot f(m)$. Similar is the situation, when m is even and n is odd. Now, when both n and m are odd, we see that $n + m$ is even, whence $f(n + m) = 1 = (-1) \cdot (-1) = f(n) \cdot f(m)$. Combining all these cases, we find that for any two integers n, m, $f(n + m) = f(n) \cdot f(m)$. Hence f is a homomorphism from the group $(\mathbb{Z}, +)$ to the group $(\{1, -1\}, \cdot)$.

Example 6.1.3. Let $(G, *)$ and $(G_1, *_1)$ be two groups. Let the identity element of the group $(G_1, *_1)$ be e_1. Define $f : G \to G_1$ by $f(a) = e_1$ for all $a \in G$. Since $f(a * b) = e_1 = e_1 *_1 e_1 = f(a) *_1 f(b)$ for all $a, b \in G$, we find that f is a homomorphism.

This example shows that between any two groups there always exists a homomorphism. This homomorphism is called the **trivial homomorphism**.

Example 6.1.4. Consider the group $GL(2, \mathbb{R})$ of all 2×2 nonsingular matrices under matrix multiplication and the group R^* of all nonzero real numbers under usual multiplication. Define $f : GL(2, \mathbb{R}) \to \mathbb{R}^*$ by $f(A) = det\, A$ for all $A \in GL(2, \mathbb{R})$, where $det\, A$ means the determinant value of the nonsingular square matrix A. Let $A, B \in GL(2, \mathbb{R})$. Hence $det\, A, det\, B \in R^*$. Now $AB \in GL(2, \mathbb{R})$ and we know that $det\, AB = det\, A\, det\, B$. Hence,

$$f(AB) = det\,(AB) = det\, A\, det\, B = f(A)f(B).$$

So it follows that f is a homomorphism.

Example 6.1.5. Consider the group $(\mathbb{Z}, +)$. Define $f : \mathbb{Z} \to \mathbb{Z}$ by $f(n) = n + 1$. This is a mapping from $\mathbb{Z}$ to $\mathbb{Z}$. But for this mapping,

$$f(2+5) = f(7) = 7 + 1 = 8 \neq 9 = (2+1) + (5+1) = f(2) + f(5).$$

Hence this mapping f is *not a homomorphism* from the group $(\mathbb{Z}, +)$ to itself.

Suppose on the same group, f is defined by $f(n) = 3n$ for all $n \in \mathbb{Z}$. Let $n, m \in \mathbb{Z}$, then $n + m \in \mathbb{Z}$ and we have

$$f(n+m) = 3(n+m) = 3n + 3m = f(n) + f(m).$$

Hence the mapping f is a homomorphism.

The reader will shortly realize that one of the most useful tools in group theory is the idea of homomorphism of groups. Indeed, the fact that there exists a homomorphism of groups $f : G \to G_1$ helps us to draw some conclusion about the nature of G_1 from the nature of G.

From the definition of homomorphism f of groups, we have seen that f preserves group operations. In the following theorem, we show that f also preserves identities and inverses.

Theorem 6.1.6. *If f is a homomorphism from a group G into a group G_1 and e, e_1 are the identity elements of G and G_1 respectively, then*

(i) $f(e) = e_1$.

(ii) $f(a^{-1}) = f(a)^{-1}$ *for all $a \in G$.*

(iii) $f(a^n) = f(a)^n$ *for all $a \in G$ and for all $n \in \mathbb{Z}$.* [We denote $\left(f(a)\right)^n$ by $f(a)^n$].

Proof. (i) By the definition of homomorphism, $f(e) = f(ee) = f(e)f(e)$. Since $f(e) \in G_1, f(e) = f(e)e_1$. Hence $f(e)e_1 = f(e)f(e)$. By the cancellation property, we find that $f(e) = e_1$.

(ii) Let $a \in G$. Then $f(a)f(a^{-1}) = f(aa^{-1}) = f(e) = e_1$ (by (i)). Similarly, $f(a^{-1})f(a) = f(a^{-1}a) = f(e) = e_1$. Hence $f(a^{-1})$ is an inverse of $f(a)$ in G_1, and as inverse of an element in a group is unique, we have $f(a^{-1}) = f(a)^{-1}$.

(iii) We first prove that $f(a^n) = f(a)^n$ for all $n \geq 0$. For $n = 0$, the result follows from (i). If $n = 1$, then $f(a) = f(a)$. Suppose $f(a^k) = f(a)^k$ for some positive integer k. Now,

$$
\begin{aligned}
f(a^{k+1}) &= f(a^k a) \\
&= f(a^k)f(a) \quad \text{(since } f \text{ is a homomorphism)} \\
&= f(a)^k f(a) \quad \text{(by induction hypothesis)} \\
&= f(a)^{k+1}.
\end{aligned}
$$

Hence by induction, $f(a^n) = f(a)^n$ for $n \geq 1$.

Now suppose that $n = -m$, where for $m > 0$. Then,

$$
\begin{aligned}
f(a^n) &= f(a^{-m}) \\
&= f\left((a^{-1})^m\right) \\
&= f(a^{-1})^m \quad \text{(since } m > 0) \\
&= \left(f(a)^{-1}\right)^m \quad \text{(by (ii))} \\
&= f(a)^{-m} \\
&= f(a)^n.
\end{aligned}
$$

$\square$

Observe that the mapping $f : \mathbb{Z} \to \mathbb{Z}$ defined by $f(n) = n+1$ in the Example 6.1.5 above, is not a homomorphism, follows from the last theorem also, since $f(0) = 0+1 = 1$, which is not the identity element of $(\mathbb{Z}, +)$.

We now prove some other basic properties of homomorphism.

Theorem 6.1.7. *Let f be a homomorphism of a group G into a group G_1. Then the following results hold:*

  (i) *if H is a subgroup of G, then $f(H) = \{f(h) \mid h \in H\}$ is a subgroup of G_1;*

  (ii) *if H_1 is a subgroup of G_1, then $f^{-1}(H_1) = \{g \in G \mid f(g) \in H_1\}$ is a subgroup of G and if H_1 is a normal subgroup, then $f^{-1}(H_1)$ is a normal subgroup of G;*

  (iii) *if $a \in G$ is such that $o(a) = n$, then $o\left(f(a)\right)$ divides n.*

Proof. (i)   Let H be a subgroup of G. Then $e \in H$ and by Theorem 6.1.6(i), $f(e) = e_1$, where e_1 is the identity of G_1. Thus, $e_1 = f(e) \in f(H)$ and so $f(H) \neq \emptyset$. Let $x, y \in f(H)$. Then there exist a, b in H such that $f(a) = x, f(b) = y$. Since H is a subgroup, $ab^{-1} \in H$ and so $xy^{-1} = f(a)f(b)^{-1} = f(a)f(b^{-1}) = f(ab^{-1}) \in f(H)$. Hence, by Theorem 5.1.5, $f(H)$ is a subgroup of G_1.

(ii)   Since $e_1 \in H_1$ and $f(e) = e_1$, we find that $e \in f^{-1}(H_1)$ and so $f^{-1}(H_1) \neq \emptyset$. Let $a, b \in f^{-1}(H_1)$. Then $f(a), f(b) \in H_1$. Hence, $f(ab^{-1}) = f(a)f(b^{-1}) = f(a)f(b)^{-1} \in H_1$ and so $ab^{-1} \in f^{-1}(H_1)$. Then by Theorem 5.1.5, $f^{-1}(H_1)$ is a subgroup of G. Suppose now, that H_1 is a normal subgroup of G_1. Let $g \in G$. We now show that $gf^{-1}(H_1)g^{-1} \subseteq f^{-1}(H_1)$. Let $a \in gf^{-1}(H_1)g^{-1}$. Then $a = gbg^{-1}$ for some $b \in f^{-1}(H_1)$. Now $f(a) = f(gbg^{-1}) = f(g)f(b)f(g^{-1}) = f(g)f(b)f(g)^{-1} \in H_1$, since $f(g) \in G_1$, $f(b) \in H_1$ and H_1 is a normal subgroup in G_1. Hence $a \in f^{-1}(H_1)$ and this shows that $gf^{-1}(H_1)g^{-1} \subseteq f^{-1}(H_1)$. Thus, $f^{-1}(H_1)$ is a normal subgroup of G.

(iii)   Since $f(a)^n = f(a^n) = f(e) = e_1$, we have $o\left(f(a)\right)$ divides n, by Theorem 3.1.24(i).

$\square$

Before proceeding further, we consider another example of homomorphism of groups.

Example 6.1.8. Let $\mathbb{R}^+$ denote the group of all positive real numbers under multiplication and $\mathbb{C}^*$ denote the group of all nonzero complex numbers under usual multiplication. Define a mapping $f : \mathbb{C}^* \to \mathbb{R}^+$ by $f(a + ib) = |a + ib|^2 = a^2 + b^2$. Since $a + ib \neq 0$, both a and b cannot be zero simultaneously. Hence $a^2 + b^2 \neq 0$, whence $a^2 + b^2 \in \mathbb{R}^+$. Let $u = a + ib$ and $v = c + id$ be two elements of $\mathbb{C}^*$. Then $a^2 + b^2 \neq 0$ and $c^2 + d^2 \neq 0$. Now,

$$
\begin{aligned}
f(uv) &= f\Big((a + ib)(c + id)\Big) \\
&= f\Big((ac - bd) + i(ad + bc)\Big) \\
&= (ac - bd)^2 + (ad + bc)^2 \\
&= a^2c^2 + b^2d^2 + a^2d^2 + b^2c^2 \\
&= (a^2 + b^2)(c^2 + d^2) \\
&= f(u)f(v)
\end{aligned}
$$

Hence f is a homomorphism. Now $H_1 = \{1\}$ is a subgroup of $\mathbb{R}^+$. Then,

$$
\begin{aligned}
f^{-1}(H_1) &= \{z \in \mathbb{C}^* \,|\, f(z) \in H_1\} \\
&= \{z \in \mathbb{C}^* \,|\, f(z) = 1\} \\
&= \{z = a + ib \in \mathbb{C}^* \,|\, a^2 + b^2 = 1\},
\end{aligned}
$$

which is known to be a subgroup of $\mathbb{C}^*$.

Let $f : G \to G_1$ be a homomorphism of groups. Then one may associate, in a natural way, two subsets with f. One of these is the ***image*** of f, viz.,

$$
Im\, f = \{f(x) \in G_1 \,|\, x \in G\}
$$

and the other is the ***kernel*** of f, i.e., the set

$$
ker\, f = \{x \in G \,|\, f(x) = e_{G_1}, \text{ the identity element of } G_1\}.
$$

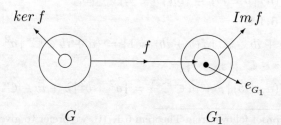

$$G \qquad\qquad\qquad G_1$$

Theorem 6.1.9. *Let G and G_1 be two groups and $f : G \to G_1$ be a group homomorphism. Then,*

(i)   *$Im f$ is a subgroup of G_1;*

(ii)   *$ker f$ is a normal subgroup of G.*

Proof. [1] (i) Clearly $Im f \neq \emptyset$. Let $a, b \in Im f$. There exist $x, y \in G$ such that $f(x) = a$ and $f(y) = b$. Now $x^{-1}y \in G$ and $f(x^{-1}y) \in Im f$. But $f(x^{-1}y) = f(x^{-1})f(y) = f(x)^{-1}f(y) = a^{-1}b$. Hence $a^{-1}b \in Im f$ and so $Im f$ is a subgroup of G.

(ii)   Let e_1 be the identity element of the group G_1. Then $ker f = \{x \in G \mid f(x) = e_1\}$. Since $f(e) = e_1$, it follows that $e \in kerf$. Hence $ker f \neq \emptyset$. Let $a, b \in ker f$. Then $f(a) = e_1, f(b) = e_1$ and hence $f(ab^{-1}) = f(a)f(b)^{-1} = e_1 e_1^{-1} = e_1 e_1 = e_1$. This implies that $ab^{-1} \in ker f$, whence $ker f$ is a subgroup of G. To show that $ker f$ is a normal subgroup, let $a \in ker f$ and $g \in G$; then $f(gag^{-1}) = f(g)f(a)f(g^{-1}) = f(g)e_1 f(g^{-1}) = f(g)f(g)^{-1} = e_1$ and hence $gag^{-1} \in ker f$. Consequently, $ker f$ is a normal subgroup of G.   □

Let us now find the kernels of some of the homomorphisms already discussed in the various examples of this section.

In Example 6.1.2,

$ker f = \{a \in \mathbb{Z} \mid f(a) = 1\} = \{2n \mid n \in \mathbb{Z}\}$,

$Im f = \{f(a) \mid a \in \mathbb{Z}\} = \{1, -1\}$.

In Example 6.1.3,

$ker f = \{a \in G \mid f(a) = e_1\} = G$,

$Im f = \{f(a) \mid a \in G\} = \{e_1\}$.

In Example 6.1.4,

$ker f = \{A \in GL(2, \mathbb{R}) \mid f(A) = 1\} = \{A \in GL(2, \mathbb{R}) \mid det\, A = 1\}$

$\quad = SL(2, \mathbb{R})$,

$Im f = \{f(A) \mid A \in GL(2, \mathbb{R})\} = \{det\, A \mid A \in GL(2, \mathbb{R})\} = \mathbb{R}^*$.

In Example 6.1.5,   (Second part)

$ker f = \{n \in \mathbb{Z} \mid f(n) = 0\} = \{n \in \mathbb{Z} \mid 3n = 0\} = \{0\}$,

$Im f = \{f(n) \mid n \in \mathbb{Z}\} = \{3n \mid n \in \mathbb{Z}\} = 3\mathbb{Z}$.

In Example 6.1.8,

$ker f = \{a + ib \in \mathbb{C}^* \mid f(a + ib) = 1\} = \{a + ib \in \mathbb{C}^* \mid a^2 + b^2 = 1\}$

$\quad = \{z \in \mathbb{C}^* \mid |z| = 1\}$,

$Im f = \{f(a + ib) \mid a + ib \in \mathbb{C}^*\} = \{a^2 + b^2 \mid a + ib \in C^*\} = \mathbb{R}^+$.

---

[1]Though the proof follows from Theorem 6.1.7(i), we prefer to give a detailed proof here.

Definition 6.1.10. Let G and G_1 be two groups and $f : G \to G_1$ be a homomorphism of groups.

    (i) f is called a **monomorphism**, if f is an injective mapping.

    (ii) f is called an **epimorphism**, if f is a surjective mapping.

The homomorphism of Example 6.1.2 is not a monomorphism, since $f(2) = 1 = f(4)$ implies that f is not injective. However for this homomorphism $Im\, f = \{1, -1\}$, whence f is surjective and so f is an epimorphism.

Now consider the homomorphism of Example 6.1.5. Here f is an injective mapping. Hence f is a monomorphism. For this f, $Im\, f = 3\mathbb{Z} \neq \mathbb{Z}$ implies that f is not surjective and hence f is not an epimorphism.

Theorem 6.1.11. *A homomorphism $f : G \to G_1$ of groups is a monomorphism if and only if $\ker f = \{e\}$.*

Proof. Suppose f is a monomorphism. Then f is injective. Let $a \in \ker f$. Now $f(a) = e_1 = f(e)$, where e_1 is the identity element of G_1 and e is the identity element of G. Since f is injective, $a = e$. Hence $\ker f = \{e\}$.

Conversely, suppose that $\ker f = \{e\}$. Let $x, y \in G$ such that $f(x) = f(y)$. Then $f(x)f(y)^{-1} = e_1$, i.e., $f(x)f(y^{-1}) = e_1$, i.e., $f(xy^{-1}) = e_1$. Hence $xy^{-1} \in \ker f = \{e\}$ and so $xy^{-1} = e$. Consequently, $x = y$. Therefore f is injective and so f is a monomorphism. $\qquad\qquad\qquad\qquad\qquad\qquad\qquad\qquad\qquad\qquad\qquad\square$

We shall frequently use this theorem to test whether a homomorphism f is a monomorphism or not, i.e., whether or not f is injective. For example, by virtue of this theorem also, we can say that the homomorphism f of Example 6.1.5 is a monomorphism.

Definition 6.1.12. A group G_1 is called a **homomorphic image** of a group G if there exists an epimorphism f from the group G onto the group G_1.

Consider the homomorphisms discussed in Example 6.1.2 and Example 6.1.4. These homomorphisms are epimorphisms. Hence the group $\{1, -1\}$ is a homomorphic image of the group $\mathbb{Z}$ and the group $\mathbb{R}^*$ is a homomorphic image of $GL(2, \mathbb{R})$. It is interesting to note that the homomorphic image of an infinite group may be a finite group.

Let us now establish the following important results.

Theorem 6.1.13. *Let G and G_1 be two groups such that G_1 is a homomorphic image of G.*

    (i) *If G is a commutative group, then so is G_1.*

    (ii) *If G is a cyclic group, then so is G_1.*

Proof. Since G_1 is a homomorphic image of G, there exists a homomorphism $f : G \to$ G_1 of groups, such that $Im\, f = G_1$, i.e., $f(G) = \{f(x) \mid x \in G\} = G_1$.

(i)   Suppose G is commutative. Let $a, b \in G_1 = f(G)$. Then there exist $x, y \in G$ such that $f(x) = a$ and $f(y) = b$. Now $ab = f(x)f(y) = f(xy) = f(yx) = f(y)f(x) =$ ba. Hence G_1 is a commutative group.

(ii)   Suppose G is cyclic. Let $G = \langle a \rangle$. Then $f(a) \in G_1$. Let $b = f(a)$. We show that $G_1 = \langle b \rangle$. Let $u \in G_1 = f(G)$. There exists $y \in G$ such that $f(y) = u$. Now $y \in \langle a \rangle$. Hence $y = a^n$ for some $n \in \mathbb{Z}$. Then $u = f(y) = f(a^n) = f(a)^n = b^n \in \langle b \rangle$. Consequently, $G_1 = \langle b \rangle$. $\qquad\qquad\square$

Finding all homomorphic images of a given group is an interesting problem. We will now discuss this problem in brief.

Definition 6.1.14. A homomorphism f from a group G to a group G_1 is called an *isomorphism* if the mapping $f : G \to G_1$ is a bijective mapping. A group G_1 is said to be isomorphic to a group G, if there exists an isomorphism from G onto G_1. In this case we write $G \simeq G_1$.

Example 6.1.15. Let $(\mathbb{R}, +)$ be the group of real numbers under addition and $(\mathbb{R}^+, \cdot)$ be the group of positive real numbers under multiplication. Define $f : \mathbb{R} \to \mathbb{R}^+$ by $f(a) = e^a$ for all $a \in \mathbb{R}$. Clearly f is well-defined. We have already seen at the beginning of this section that $f(a + b) = f(a)f(b)$, whence f is a homomorphism. Suppose $f(a) = f(b)$. Then $e^a = e^b$. This implies that $a = b$, whence f is one-one. Let $b \in \mathbb{R}^+$. Then $\log_e b \in \mathbb{R}$ and $f(\log_e b) = e^{\log_e b} = b$. Thus f is onto $\mathbb{R}^+$. Consequently, f is an isomorphism of $(\mathbb{R}, +)$ onto $(\mathbb{R}^+, \cdot)$.

In the following theorem, we enlist some basic properties of isomorphisms, which shall be used to test whether a given group is isomorphic to another group or not.

Theorem 6.1.16. *Let f be an isomorphism of a group G onto a group G_1. Then,*

(i) $f^{-1} : G_1 \to G$ *is an isomorphism.*

(ii)   *G is commutative if and only if G_1 is commutative.*

(iii)   *G is cyclic if and only if G_1 is so.*

(iv)   *For all $a \in G, o(a) = o\Big(f(a)\Big)$.*

Proof. (i)   Since f is a bijective mapping, f^{-1} exists and is also a bijective mapping from G_1 onto G. Now we show that f^{-1} is a homomorphism. Let $x, y \in G_1$. Then there exist $a, b \in G$ such that $f(a) = x$ and $f(b) = y$. This implies that $a = f^{-1}(x), b = f^{-1}(y)$ and $xy = f(a)f(b) = f(ab)$. Thus, $f^{-1}(xy) = ab = f^{-1}(x)f^{-1}(y)$ and so f^{-1} is a homomorphism. Hence, f^{-1} is an isomorphism.

(ii) Since f and f^{-1} are both bijective homomorphisms, we find that G_1 is a homomorphic image of G and G is a homomorphic image of G_1. Hence (ii) follows from Theorem 6.1.13(i).

(iii) Since f^{-1} is also an isomorphism, this follows from Theorem 6.1.13(ii).

(iv) By Theorem 6.1.7(iii), $o\big(f(a)\big)$ divides $o(a)$. Again since f^{-1} is a homomorphism and $f^{-1}\big(f(a)\big) = a$, we have $o(a)$ divides $o\big(f(a)\big)$. Hence $o(a) = o\big(f(a)\big)$. $\qquad\square$

From Theorem 6.1.16(i) above, we find that if G_1 is isomorphic to G then G is also isomorphic to G_1. Henceforth, such groups will be called *isomorphic* to each other. Following are the consequences of the above theorem:

I. A finite group can never be isomorphic with an infinite group as there cannot exist a bijective mapping between two such groups.

II. Two groups G and G_1 may be of the same order, yet they may not be isomorphic. For example, consider the groups S_3 and $\mathbb{Z}_6$; they are both finite groups of order 6. Note that S_3 is a noncommutative group and $\mathbb{Z}_6$ is a commutative group. Hence by Theorem 6.1.16(ii), we conclude that these two groups are nonisomorphic.

III. There may be two groups G and G_1 such that both of them are commutative and finite, say, $|G| = |G_1| = n$; yet they may not be isomorphic. For example, $\mathbb{Z}_4$ and K_4 are both commutative groups of order 4. $\mathbb{Z}_4$ is a cyclic group and K_4 is a noncyclic group, hence $\mathbb{Z}_4$ and K_4 are nonisomorphic.

IV. Two groups G and G_1 may be infinite commutative groups, yet they may not be isomorphic to each other. For example, the groups $(\mathbb{Z}, +)$ and $(\mathbb{Q}, +)$ are both infinite commutative groups, yet they are nonisomorphic since $(\mathbb{Z}, +)$ is cyclic, whereas $(\mathbb{Q}, +)$ is noncyclic.

V. Two groups G and G_1 may be infinite noncyclic but commutative, yet they may not be isomorphic. For example, $(\mathbb{R}^*, \cdot)$ and $(\mathbb{C}^*, \cdot)$ are both infinite commutative groups which are not cyclic, yet they are not isomorphic because $\mathbb{C}^*$ has an element i of order 4 and $\mathbb{R}^*$ has no element of order 4. Hence by Theorem 6.1.16(iv), $\mathbb{R}^*$ and $\mathbb{C}^*$ are not isomorphic.

Regarding isomorphism of groups, we can easily prove the following properties:

I. If G is a group, then $G \simeq G$.

II. If G_1 and G_2 are any two groups such that $G_1 \simeq G_2$, then $G_2 \simeq G_1$.

III. If G_1, G_2, G_3 are any three groups such that $G_1 \simeq G_2$ and $G_2 \simeq G_3$, then
$G_1 \simeq G_3$.

Hence given a group G, by an ***isomorphic class of G***, we mean the collection of those groups which are isomorphic to G. So, if two groups belong to the *same isomorphic class*, we say that these two groups are *same upto isomorphism*. Loosely speaking, in group theory, two groups are said to be equal, if they are isomorphic groups.

We would like to draw the attention of the reader towards another very interesting feature. Observe that, on the same set G, one may define two different operations say, $*_1$ and $*_2$, in such a way that $(G, *_1)$ and $(G, *_2)$ may become two different groups. But if they are isomorphic, then we say that upto isomorphism they are equal. For example, consider the groups $(\mathbb{Z}, *_1)$ and $(\mathbb{Z}, *_2)$ on the set of all integers, where $a *_1 b = a + b$ and $a *_2 b = a + b + 1$. These are two different operations on the set $\mathbb{Z}$. For the first group, 0 is the identity element but for the second group -1 plays the role of the identity. One may easily show that the mapping $f : \mathbb{Z} \to \mathbb{Z}$ defined by $f(n) = n - 1$ is an isomorphism from the group $(\mathbb{Z}, *_1)$ onto the group $(\mathbb{Z}, *_2)$. Hence upto isomorphism, these two groups are regarded as same.

One important problem in the theory of groups is the *classification of groups*, where classification means the *description of isomorphic classes of groups*. In this section, we will classify all infinite cyclic groups.

Theorem 6.1.17. *Any infinite cyclic group is isomorphic to the additive group $\mathbb{Z}$ of all integers.*

Proof. Let $G = \langle a \rangle$ be an infinite cyclic group. Then $o(a)$ is not finite and this implies that $a^n = e$ if and only if $n = 0$. Define $f : \mathbb{Z} \to G$ by $f(n) = a^n$ for all $n \in \mathbb{Z}$. Clearly, f is a surjective mapping and $f(n + m) = a^{n+m} = a^n a^m = f(n)f(m)$ for all $n, m \in \mathbb{Z}$. Now $ker\, f = \{n \in \mathbb{Z} \mid f(n) = e\} = \{n \in \mathbb{Z} \mid a^n = e\} = \{0\}$. This implies that f is injective. Hence f is a bijective homomorphism and so f is an isomorphism. Consequently, $\mathbb{Z} \simeq G$. $\qquad\square$

From the above theorem, it follows that all infinite cyclic groups belong to the same isomorphic class of the group $(\mathbb{Z}, +)$. Hence we can say that, *upto isomorphism there exists one and only one infinite cyclic group, which is* $(\mathbb{Z}, +)$.

We conclude this section by proving the following theorem due to Cayley:

Theorem 6.1.18. [Cayley] *Every group is isomorphic to some subgroup of the group $A(S)$ of all permutations of some set S.*

Proof. Let G be a group. We take $S = G$ and consider the group $A(G)$ of all permutations on the set G. Let $a \in G$. Define $\tau_a : G \to G$ by $\tau_a(g) = ag$ for all $g \in G$.

It is easy to verify that τ_a is a bijective mapping and hence $\tau_a \in A(G)$. Indeed, for $g_1, g_2 \in G$, $\tau_a(g_1) = \tau_a(g_2)$ implies $ag_1 = ag_2$, whence by cancellation law $g_1 = g_2$. Again, for any $g \in G$ $\tau_a(a^{-1}g) = aa^{-1}g = g$. Now for any two elements a, b of G and for any $x \in G$,

$$(\tau_a \tau_b)(x) = \tau_a\Big((\tau_b)(x)\Big) = \tau_a(bx) = a(bx) = (ab)x = \tau_{ab}(x)$$

implies that $\tau_a \tau_b = \tau_{ab}$.

Now define $\psi : G \to A(G)$ by $\psi(a) = \tau_a$ for all $a \in G$. Since for any two elements $a, b \in G$, $\tau_a \tau_b = \tau_{ab}$, ψ is a homomorphism. Now, if $a \neq b$, then $\tau_a(e) = a \neq b = \tau_b(e)$. So it follows that ψ is a monomorphism. Since $Im\psi = \psi(G)$ is a subgroup of $A(G)$, therefore G is isomorphic to the subgroup $\psi(G)$ of $A(G)$. □

Corollary 6.1.19. *Let G be a group of order n. G is isomorphic to a subgroup of the symmetric group S_n.*

Proof. The permutation group $A(G)$ on elements of G is isomorphic to the group S_n. Hence the corollary follows from the theorem above. □

Worked-out Exercises

◇ **Exercise 6.1.1.** Which of the following mappings $f : G \to G_1$ are homomorphisms of groups? Of the homomorphisms, which are epimorphisms; which are monomorphisms and which are isomorphisms?

(a) $G = (\mathbb{Z}, +)$; $G_1 = (\mathbb{Z}, +)$; $f(x) = 4x$

(b) $G = (\mathbb{Z}, +)$; $G_1 = (\mathbb{Z}, +)$; $f(x) = -x$

(c) $G = GL(2, \mathbb{R})$, $G_1 = (\mathbb{R}, +)$, $f\left(\begin{bmatrix} a & b \\ c & d \end{bmatrix}\right) = a + b + c + d$

(d) $G = S_3$; $G_1 = \{1, -1\}$; $f(\sigma) = 1$ if σ is even and $f(\sigma) = -1$ if σ is odd.

Solution.   (a) Let $a, b \in \mathbb{Z}$, $f(a + b) = 4(a + b) = 4a + 4b = f(a) + f(b)$. Hence f is a homomorphism. Now $3 \in \mathbb{Z}$, but there is no integer $n \in \mathbb{Z}$ such that $4n = 3$. Hence $f(n) \neq 3$ for any $n \in \mathbb{Z}$, whence f is not an epimorphism.

Let $a, b \in \mathbb{Z}$ such that $a \neq b$. Then $4a \neq 4b$. Hence $f(a) \neq f(b)$. Consequently, f is a monomorphism. Thus we see that f is a monomorphism but not an epimorphism and hence not an isomorphism.

(b) Let $a, b \in \mathbb{Z}$. Now $f(a + b) = -(a + b) = (-a) + (-b) = f(a) + f(b)$, whence f is a homomorphism. Let $b \in \mathbb{Z}$. Then $-b \in \mathbb{Z}$ and $f(-b) = -(-b) = b$, which shows that

f is an epimorphism. Also $a \neq b$ implies that $-a \neq -b$ and so $f(a) \neq f(b)$, whence f is a monomorphism. Combining all these, we find that f is an isomorphism.

(c)   Let us consider $A = \begin{bmatrix} 2 & 3 \\ 4 & 5 \end{bmatrix}$ and $B = \begin{bmatrix} 1 & -1 \\ 0 & 1 \end{bmatrix}$. Now $A, B \in GL(2, \mathbb{R})$ and

$AB = \begin{bmatrix} 2 & 1 \\ 4 & 1 \end{bmatrix}$.

Then $f(AB) = 2+1+4+1 = 8$ but $f(A)+f(B) = (2+3+4+5)+(1+(-1)+0+1) = 14 + 1 = 15$. Hence $f(AB) \neq f(A) + f(B)$ and so f is not a homomorphism.

(d)   Let $\sigma, \delta \in S_3$. If σ and δ are both even, then $\sigma\delta$ is even and hence $f(\sigma\delta) = 1 = 1 \cdot 1 = f(\sigma)f(\delta)$.

Suppose that σ is even and δ is odd. Then $\sigma\delta$ is odd and $f(\sigma\delta) = -1 = 1 \cdot (-1) = f(\sigma)f(\delta)$. Again if σ is odd and δ is even, then $\sigma\delta$ is odd and as above, we have $f(\sigma\delta) = f(\sigma)f(\delta)$.

Now suppose that both σ and δ are odd. Then $\sigma\delta$ is even and $f(\sigma\delta) = 1 = (-1) \cdot (-1) = f(\sigma)f(\delta)$. Hence f is a homomorphism.

Now $(1\,2\,3)$ is an even permutation and $(1\,2)$ is an odd permutation. Then, $1 = f\big((1\,2\,3)\big)$ and $-1 = f\big((1\,2)\big)$. Hence f is surjective and so f is an epimorphism. Now $(1\,2\,3)$ and $(1\,3\,2)$ are two distinct even permutations. But we find that $f\big((1\,2\,3)\big) = f\big((1\,3\,2)\big) = 1$, whence f is not injective and so f is not a monomorphism.

$\Diamond$ **Exercise 6.1.2.** If a mapping $f : G \to G_1$ of Worked-out Exercise 6.1.1 above is a homomorphism, then find its kernel.

Solution.   (a) Here f is a homomorphism.

$$\begin{aligned} ker\, f &= \{n \in \mathbb{Z} \,|\, f(n) = \text{ identity of the group } G_1\} \\ &= \{n \in \mathbb{Z} \,|\, f(n) = 0\} \\ &= \{n \in \mathbb{Z} \,|\, 4n = 0\} \\ &= \{0\}. \end{aligned}$$

(b) In this case also f is a homomorphism.

$$\begin{aligned} ker\, f &= \{n \in \mathbb{Z} \,|\, f(n) = \text{ identity of the group } G_1\} \\ &= \{n \in \mathbb{Z} \,|\, f(n) = 0\} \\ &= \{n \in \mathbb{Z} \,|\, -n = 0\} \\ &= \{0\}. \end{aligned}$$

(d) Again in this case f is a homomorphism.

$$ker f = \{\sigma \in S_3 \,|\, f(\sigma) = 1\}$$
$$= \{\sigma \in S_3 \,|\, \sigma \text{ is even}\}$$
$$= A_3.$$

◊ **Exercise 6.1.3.** Show that the group $(\mathbb{Z}_6, +)$ is a homomorphic image of the group $(\mathbb{Z}, +)$.

Solution. Define $f : \mathbb{Z} \to \mathbb{Z}_6$ by $f(n) = [n]$ for all $n \in \mathbb{Z}$. Let $n, m \in \mathbb{Z}$. Then $f(n + m) = [n + m] = [n] + [m] = f(n) + f(m)$. Hence f is a homomorphism. Let $[r] \in \mathbb{Z}_6$. Then $r \in \mathbb{Z}$ and hence $f(r) = [r]$. This shows that f is surjective and so f is an epimorphism. Consequently, $\mathbb{Z}_6$ is a homomorphic image of $\mathbb{Z}$.

◊ **Exercise 6.1.4.** Let $f : G \to G_1$ be an epimorphism of groups. If H is a normal subgroup of G, then show that $f(H)$ is a normal subgroup of G_1.

Solution. By Theorem 6.1.7(i), we know that $f(H)$ is a subgroup of G_1. Let $g_1 \in G_1$. Since $f(G) = G_1$, there exists $g \in G$ such that $f(g) = g_1$. Now for any $h \in H$, $g_1 f(h) g_1^{-1} = f(g) f(h) f(g)^{-1} = f(ghg^{-1})$. Since H is a normal subgroup of G, $ghg^{-1} \in H$, and so $g_1 f(h) g_1^{-1} \in f(H)$. Thus $g_1 f(H) g_1^{-1} \subseteq f(H)$. Hence $f(H)$ is a normal subgroup of G_1.

◊ **Exercise 6.1.5.** Find all homomorphisms of the group $(\mathbb{Z}, +)$ to itself.

Solution. Let n be an integer. Define $f : \mathbb{Z} \to \mathbb{Z}$ by $f(t) = nt$ for all $t \in \mathbb{Z}$. Let $r, s \in \mathbb{Z}$. Then $f(r+s) = n(r+s) = nr+ns = f(r)+f(s)$. Hence f is a homomorphism. We denote this homomorphism by f_n. We show that any homomorphism from $\mathbb{Z}$ to $\mathbb{Z}$ is one of these $f_n, n \in \mathbb{Z}$. To show this, let us consider an integer $m \in \mathbb{Z}$. Now if f is a homomorphism from $\mathbb{Z}$ to $\mathbb{Z}$, then $f(m) = f(m1) = mf(1)$ (by Theorem 6.1.6(iii)) $= f(1)m$. So we find that f is completely determined if we know $f(1)$. If $f(1) = n$, then $f(m) = nm = f_n(m)$. Hence, $f = f_n$ and all the homomorphisms of $\mathbb{Z}$ into $\mathbb{Z}$ are given by f_n, $n = 0, \pm 1, \pm 2, \ldots$.

◊ **Exercise 6.1.6.** Find all homomorphisms from $(\mathbb{Z}_8, +)$ into $(\mathbb{Z}_6, +)$.

Solution. We have $\mathbb{Z}_8 = \langle [1] \rangle$. Let $f : \mathbb{Z}_8 \to \mathbb{Z}_6$ be a homomorphism. For any $[a] \in \mathbb{Z}_8$, $f([a]) = af([1])$ shows that f is completely known if $f([1])$ is known. Now $o(f[1])$ divides $o([1])$ and $|\mathbb{Z}_6|$, i.e., $o(f[1])$ divides 8 and 6. Hence, $o(f[1]) = 1$ or 2. Thus, $f([1]) = [0]$ or $[3]$. If $f([1]) = [0]$ then f is the trivial homomorphism which maps every element to $[0]$. On the other hand, $f([1]) = [3]$ implies that $f([a]) = [3a]$ for all $[a] \in \mathbb{Z}_8$. Thus $f\big([a] + [b]\big) = f\big([a + b]\big) = [3(a + b)] = [3a + 3b] = [3a] + [3b] = f([a]) + f([b])$, proving that the mapping $f : \mathbb{Z}_8 \to \mathbb{Z}_6$ defined by $f([a]) = [3a]$ for all $[a] \in \mathbb{Z}_8$ is a homomorphism. Hence there are two homomorphisms from $\mathbb{Z}_8$ into $\mathbb{Z}_6$.

◇ **Exercise 6.1.7.** Show that there does not exist any isomorphism from the group $(\mathbb{R}, +)$ to the group $(\mathbb{R}^*, \cdot)$.

Solution.   Observe that 0 is the identity element of the group $(\mathbb{R}, +)$. Hence no nonzero element of $\mathbb{R}$ is of finite order. Now for the group $(\mathbb{R}^*, \cdot)$, 1 is the identity element and -1 is an element of order 2. So, if there exists an isomorphism $f : \mathbb{R} \to \mathbb{R}^*$, there should exist $a \in \mathbb{R}$ such that $o(a) = 2$. But this is not the case. Hence there is no isomorphism from the group $(\mathbb{R}, +)$ to the group $(\mathbb{R}^*, \cdot)$.

◇ **Exercise 6.1.8.** Show that $(\mathbb{Q}, +)$ is not isomorphic to $(\mathbb{Q}^+, \cdot)$.

Solution.   Suppose $f : \mathbb{Q} \to \mathbb{Q}^+$ is an isomorphism of groups. Now $2 \in \mathbb{Q}^+$. Hence there exists $x \in \mathbb{Q}$ such that $2 = f(x) = f\left(\frac{x}{2} + \frac{x}{2}\right) = f\left(\frac{x}{2}\right) f\left(\frac{x}{2}\right) = f\left(\frac{x}{2}\right)^2$. But there is no rational number y such that $2 = y^2$. So, there does not exist any isomorphism between $(\mathbb{Q}, +)$ and $(\mathbb{Q}^+, \cdot)$.

◇ **Exercise 6.1.9.** The number of group homomorphisms from the cyclic group $\mathbb{Z}_4$ to the cyclic group $\mathbb{Z}_7$ is

(i) 7   (ii) 3   (iii) 2   (iv) 1.

Solution. Let $f : \mathbb{Z}_4 \longrightarrow \mathbb{Z}_7$ be any group homomorphism. Now $\mathbb{Z}_4$ is a cyclic group and $[1]$ is a generator of $\mathbb{Z}_4$. Thus $o([1]) = 4$. Now $o\Big(f([1])\Big) \mid o([1]) = 4$. Again since $f([1]) \in \mathbb{Z}_7$, it follows that $o\Big(f([1])\Big) \mid 7$. Thus $o\Big(f([1])\Big) \mid \gcd(4, 7) = 1$ hence $f([1]) = [0]$. Consequently, $f([a]) = [0]$ for all $[a] \in \mathbb{Z}_4$. Therefore, option (iv) is correct.

Exercises

1. Which of the following mappings $f : G \to G_1$ are homomorphisms of groups? In the cases where f is a homomorphism, determine its kernel.

   (a) $G = (\mathbb{R}^+, \cdot)$; $G_1 = (\mathbb{R}^+, \cdot)$; $f(a) = a^4$ for all $a \in \mathbb{R}^+$.

   (b) $G = (\mathbb{R}, +)$; $G_1 = (\mathbb{R}^+, \cdot)$; $f(a) = 3^a$ for all $a \in \mathbb{R}$.

   (c) $G = (\mathbb{R}^*, \cdot)$; $G_1 = (\mathbb{R}^+, \cdot)$; $f(a) = |a|$ for all $a \in \mathbb{R}^*$.

   (d) $G = (\mathbb{Z}, +)$; $G_1 = (\mathbb{Z}, +)$; $f(a) = a + 5$ for all $a \in \mathbb{Z}$.

   (e) $G = (\mathbb{R}^*, \cdot)$; $G_1 = GL(2, \mathbb{R})$; $f(a) = \begin{bmatrix} 1 & 0 \\ 0 & a \end{bmatrix}$ for all $a \in \mathbb{R}^*$.

   (f) $G = GL(2, \mathbb{R})$; $G_1 = (\mathbb{R}, +)$; $f\left(\begin{bmatrix} a & b \\ c & d \end{bmatrix}\right) = a + d$ for all

   $\begin{bmatrix} a & b \\ c & d \end{bmatrix} \in GL(2, \mathbb{R})$.

   (g) $G = (\mathbb{R}^*, \cdot)$; $G_1 = \{1, -1\}$; $f(a) = 1$ if $a > 0$ and $f(a) = -1$ if $a < 0$.

2. Show that the group $(\mathbb{Z}_9, +)$ is a homomorphic image of the group $(\mathbb{Z}, +)$.

3. Show that there exists a homomorphism from the group $\mathbb{Z}$ onto the group $\mathbb{Z}/5\mathbb{Z}$.

4. Find all epimorphisms from $(\mathbb{Z}, +)$ onto $(\mathbb{Z}, +)$.

5. Find all homomorphisms from $(\mathbb{Z}, +)$ onto $(\mathbb{Z}_6, +)$.

6. Find all homomorphisms from $(\mathbb{Z}_6, +)$ into $(\mathbb{Z}_4, +)$.

7. Show that $(\mathbb{Z}, +)$ and $(\mathbb{R}, +)$ are not isomorphic groups.

8. Show that $\mathbb{Q}^*$, the group of all nonzero rational numbers under multiplication, is not isomorphic to $\mathbb{R}^*$, the group of all nonzero real numbers under multiplication.

9. Show that $(\mathbb{Q}, +)$ and $(\mathbb{Q}^*, \cdot)$ are not isomorphic groups.

10. Show that $(\mathbb{Q}, +)$ and $(\mathbb{R}, +)$ are not isomorphic groups.

11. Show that there exists an isomorphism from the group $(\mathbb{C}, +)$ onto the group $\mathbb{R} \times \mathbb{R}$.

12. Let G be a group. Prove that the mapping $f : G \to G$ defined by $f(a) = a^{-1}$ for all $a \in G$ is a homomorphism if and only if G is commutative.

13. Show that S_3 and $\mathbb{Z}_6$ are nonisomorphic groups and for every proper subgroup A of S_3 there exists a proper subgroup B of $\mathbb{Z}_6$ such that $A \simeq B$.

14. Let G, H and K be groups. Suppose that the mappings $f : G \to H$ and $g : H \to K$ are homomorphisms. Prove that $g \circ f : G \to K$ is also a homomorphism.

15. Let G, H and K be three groups. If $G \simeq H$ and $H \simeq K$, then prove that $G \simeq K$.

16. Let G and H be groups. Define a mapping $f : G \times H \to G$ by $f((a, b)) = a$ for all $(a, b) \in G \times H$. Prove that f is a homomorphism from $G \times H$ onto G. Determine $ker\, f$.

17. Show that every commutative group of order 6 is a cyclic group.

18. Prove that an infinite group G cannot have a finite number of subgroups.

19. Let f and g be two homomorphisms from $(\mathbb{Q}^*, \cdot)$ to $(\mathbb{R}^*, \cdot)$ such that $f(n) = g(n)$ for all $n \in \mathbb{Z}$. Prove that $f = g$.

20. Which of the following statements are true? Justify.

   (a) A noncommutative group may be a homomorphic image of a commutative group.
   (b) A cyclic group with more than one element may be a homomorphic image of a noncyclic group.
   (c) There does not exist a nontrivial homomorphism from a group G of order 5 into a group H of order 4.
   (d) The group $(2\mathbb{Z}, +)$ is isomorphic to the group $(3\mathbb{Z}, +)$.
   (e) The group $(\mathbb{Z}, +)$ is isomorphic to $(\mathbb{Q}, +)$.
   (f) There exists a monomorphism from a group of order 30 into a group of order 100.
   (g) There exists an epimorphism from $(\mathbb{Z}, +)$ onto $(\mathbb{R}, +)$.
   (h) There does not exist any epimorphism from $(\mathbb{Q}, +)$ onto $(\mathbb{Z}, +)$.
   (i) There does not exist any non zero homomorphism from $(\mathbb{Q}, +)$ onto $(\mathbb{Z}, +)$.
   (j) If f and g are two epimorphisms from a group G onto a group H such that $ker\, f = ker\, g$, then $f = g$.
   (k) There exists a permutation group of order n, for each $n \in \mathbb{N}$.

Pick the correct option(s) from the following:

21. The number of isomorphisms from the group $\mathbb{Z}$ onto the group $\mathbb{Z}$ is

    (*i*) 0   (*ii*) 1   (*iii*) 2   (*iv*) infinite.

22. The number of homomorphisms from the group $(\mathbb{Z}_6, +)$ into the group $(\mathbb{Z}_4, +)$ is

    (*i*) 6   (*ii*) 4   (*iii*) 1   (*iv*) 2.

6.2   Isomorphism Theorems

In this section, we shall prove some of the most classical theorems of group theory that have a trend-setting character for the line of investigation of almost all branches in abstract algebra. These theorems, in the context of group theory, reveal the interplay between homomorphisms and quotient groups.

Theorem 6.2.1. [First Isomorphism Theorem] : *Let* $f : G \to G_1$ *be a homomorphism of groups. Then the quotient group* $G/\ker f$ *is isomorphic to the subgroup* $Im\, f$ *of* G_1. *Moreover, if* f *is an epimorphism, then* $G/\ker f \simeq G_1$.

Proof. Let $H = \ker f$. We show that $G/H \simeq Im\, f$. Define a mapping $\psi : G/H \to Im\, f$ by $\psi(aH) = f(a)$, for all $aH \in G/H$. We first show that ψ is well-defined. [The diagram in Fig. 13 may be of help in appreciating the proof.] For this, let $aH = bH$ in G/H. Then $a^{-1}b \in H = \ker f$ and so $f(a^{-1}b) = e_1$, where e_1 is the identity of G_1. This implies that $e_1 = f(a^{-1})f(b) = f(a)^{-1}f(b)$ and hence $f(a) = f(b)$. Consequently, $\psi(aH) = f(a) = f(b) = \psi(bH)$ and so ψ is well-defined.

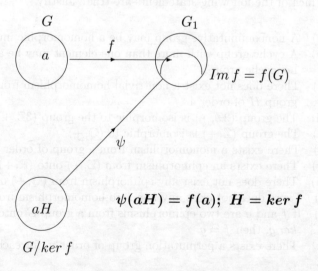

Fig. 13

Now for any $xH, yH \in G/H$, $\psi(xHyH) = \psi(xyH) = f(xy) = f(x)f(y) = \psi(xH)\psi(yH)$. Hence ψ is a homomorphism. Since $Im(f) = f(G)$, we find that, for any $a \in Im\, f$, there exists $u \in G$ such that $f(u) = a$ and then $uH \in G/H$, which shows that $\psi(uH) = f(u) = a$. So, ψ is surjective. Let $aH, bH \in G/H$, such that $\psi(aH) = \psi(bH)$. Then $f(a) = f(b)$. Hence $f(a^{-1}b) = f(a)^{-1}f(b) = f(b)^{-1}f(b) = e_1$ implies that $a^{-1}b \in ker\, f = H$. Thus it follows that $aH = bH$ and so ψ is injective. Hence ψ is an isomorphism. Now, if f is an epimorphism, f is surjective and hence $Im\, f = G_1$. Therefore $G/ker\, f \simeq G_1$. $\qquad\square$

Corollary 6.2.2. *For any group G, $G/\{e\} \simeq G$, where $\{e\}$ is the subgroup containing the identity element e of G.*

Proof. The identity mapping $I_G : G \to G$, defined by $I_g(x) = x$ for all $x \in G$, is an epimorphism such that $ker\, I_G = \{e\}$. Hence $G/\{e\} \simeq G$. $\qquad\square$

Theorem 6.2.3. *If G is a finite cyclic group of order n, $G \simeq \mathbb{Z}/n\mathbb{Z} \simeq \mathbb{Z}_n$.*

Proof. Let $G = \langle a \rangle$, where a is an element of order n in G. Define $f : \mathbb{Z} \to G$ by $f(m) = a^m$, for all $m \in \mathbb{Z}$. For any two integers m and r, $f(m+r) = a^{m+r} = a^m a^r = f(m)f(r)$. Hence f is a homomorphism. Let $x \in G$. Then $x = a^t$ for some $t \in \mathbb{Z}$. Then $f(t) = a^t = x$. Hence f is an epimorphism. Then by the First Isomorphism theorem, $\mathbb{Z}/ker\, f \simeq Im\, f = G$. Here,

$$
\begin{aligned}
ker\, f &= \{m \in \mathbb{Z}\,|\, f(m) = \text{ identity element of } G\} \\
&= \{m \in \mathbb{Z}\,|\, a^m = e\} \\
&= \{m \in \mathbb{Z}\,|\, n \text{ divides } m\} \quad [\text{as } o(a) = n] \ = n\mathbb{Z}.
\end{aligned}
$$

Hence $\mathbb{Z}/n\mathbb{Z} \simeq G$. Now define $g : \mathbb{Z} \to \mathbb{Z}_n$ by $g(t) = [t]$. It is easy to see that g is an epimorphism and $ker\, g = n\mathbb{Z}$. Hence $\mathbb{Z}/n\mathbb{Z} \simeq \mathbb{Z}_n$. So it follows that $G \simeq \mathbb{Z}_n$. $\qquad\square$

Corollary 6.2.4. *Any two finite cyclic groups of same order are isomorphic.*

From the above theorem, it follows that, up to isomorphism there exists one and only one cyclic group of order n, for every positive integer n. Thus we have found all finite cyclic groups. These are precisely $\mathbb{Z}_1, \mathbb{Z}_2, \mathbb{Z}_3, \ldots, \mathbb{Z}_n, \ldots\ldots$

Since every group of prime order is cyclic, we find from the above that *for each prime integer p, there exists one and only one group (upto isomorphism) of order p, which is $\mathbb{Z}_p$.*

This tells us that $\mathbb{Z}_2$ and $\mathbb{Z}_3$ are the only groups of order 2 and order 3 respectively. Now what are the groups of order 4? The next theorem will throw some light.

Theorem 6.2.5. *Upto isomorphism, there are only two groups of order four.*

Proof. The groups $\mathbb{Z}_4$ and $\mathcal{K}_4$ (Klein's four-group) are groups of order 4. Observe that $\mathbb{Z}_4$ is a cyclic group, whereas $\mathcal{K}_4$ is noncyclic. Hence these two groups are nonisomorphic. We assert that these two are the only groups (upto isomorphism) of order 4.

Towards the proof of our assertion, we show that any group of order 4 is isomorphic to either $\mathbb{Z}_4$ or $\mathcal{K}_4$. If G is a cyclic group of order 4, then by Theorem 6.2.3, $G \simeq \mathbb{Z}_4$. Suppose now that G is noncyclic. Then no element in G can be of order 4. As otherwise, if $a \in G$ be of order 4, then $\langle a \rangle = G$ shows that G is cyclic, which is a contradiction. Let $G = \{e, a, b, c\}$. Since the order of every element of G must divide the order of G, we see that the order of each of a, b, c must be 2. If $ab = a$, then $b = e$, which is not possible, whence we have $ab \neq a$. Similarly, $ab \neq b$. Suppose $ab = e$; then $a(ab) = ae$, whence $b = a$, (since $a^2 = e$) which is not possible either and this shows that we are left out with the only possibility that $ab = c$. Similarly, we may show $ba = c$. Hence $ab = ba$. Thus we find that $G = \langle a, b \rangle$ such that $o(a) = o(b) = 2$ and $ab = ba$. Hence G is the Klein's four-group $\mathcal{K}_4$ (see Definition 5.1.13). Hence the theorem. $\qquad\square$

Continuing our pursuit of distinct finite groups, we point out that $\mathbb{Z}_5$ is the only group of order 5. The next theorem shows that there are only two nonisomorphic groups of order 6.

Theorem 6.2.6. *There are only two (upto isomorphism) groups of order six.*

Proof. Evidently, $\mathbb{Z}_6$ is a cyclic group of order 6 and hence commutative, whereas S_3 is a noncommutative group of order 6. This clearly shows that these two groups are nonisomorphic. It will now be sufficient to show that any group of order 6 is either isomorphic to $\mathbb{Z}_6$ or to S_3.

Let G be a group of order 6. Since $|G|$ is even, there exists $a \in G$, $a \neq e$ such that $a^2 = e$. If $x^2 = e$ for all $x \in G$, then G is commutative and for any two distinct nonidentity elements a and b of G, $\{e, a, b, ab\}$ must be a subgroup of G. But since $|G| = 6$, it cannot have a subgroup of order 4. Hence, there exists $b \in G$ such that $b^2 \neq e$, i.e., $b \neq e$ and $o(b) \neq 2$. Since $o(b)$ must be a divisor of 6, we have $o(b) = 6$ or 3. If $o(b) = 6$, then $G = \langle b \rangle$ is a cyclic group of order 6 and $G \simeq \mathbb{Z}_6$.

Suppose G is not cyclic. Then $o(b) = 3$. Let $H = \{e, b, b^2\}$. Then H is a subgroup of G of index 2. Thus, H is a normal subgroup of G (by Worked-out Exercise 5.4.1). Clearly $a \notin H$. Now $G = H \cup aH$ and $H \cap aH = \emptyset$. Hence, $G = \{e, b, b^2, a, ab, ab^2\}$. Now $aba^{-1} \in H$, since H is normal and $b \in H$. This tells us that aba^{-1} is any one of the elements e, b, b^2. If $aba^{-1} = e$, then $b = e$, which is a contradiction. If however,

$aba^{-1} = b$, then $ab = ba$. Since $o(a)$ and $o(b)$ are relatively prime and $ab = ba$, we must have $o(ab) = o(a) \cdot o(b) = 2 \cdot 3 = 6$, whence in this case G becomes cyclic, again a contradiction. This leaves us with the option $aba^{-1} = b^2$. Thus $G = \langle a, b \rangle$, where $o(a) = 2$, $o(b) = 3$ and $ab = b^2 a$. It is now easy to see from Remark 5.1.12 that $G \simeq S_3$. $\square$

In the aforesaid discussions, we have tacitly justified another significant fact. Do you now realize that the *smallest noncommutative group* is of order 6 and it is precisely S_3 (upto isomorphism) ?

From the first isomorphism theorem we find that if a group G_1 is a homomorphic image of a group G, then the group G_1 is nothing but $G/ker\,f$. Now if H is any normal subgroup of a group G, then the mapping $f : G \rightarrow G/H$, defined by $f(a) = aH$ is an epimorphism with $ker\,f = H$, which is called the **natural homomorphism** or the **canonical homomorphism** of G onto G/H.

The following diagram (Fig. 14) depicts the natural homomorphism:

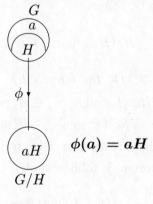

Fig. 14

Hence *all the homomorphic images of a group G are the groups G/H, where H is a normal subgroup of G*. Conversely, *every normal subgroup H of a group G is the kernel of some homomorphism*, viz., the natural homomorphism defined above. [cf. Worked-out Exercise 6.2.7].

In the light of the aforesaid discussions, we can now complete the diagram given with the first isomorphism theorem as below (Fig. 15):

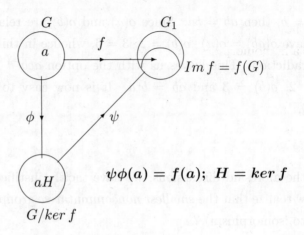

$$\psi\phi(a) = f(a); \quad H = ker \, f$$

Fig. 15

Example 6.2.7. Consider the group S_3. This group has only three normal subgroups, which are S_3, A_3, and $\{e\}$. Hence all the homomorphic images of S_3 are S_3/S_3, S_3/A_3, and $S_3/\{e\}$. Now S_3/S_3 is a group with only one element, whence $S_3/S_3 \simeq \{e\}$. Again, S_3/A_3 is a group of order $\dfrac{|S_3|}{|A_3|} = \dfrac{6}{3} = 2$. Hence $S_3/A_3 \simeq \mathbb{Z}_2$. Finally $S_3/\{e\} \simeq S_3$. So we find that $\{e\}, \mathbb{Z}_2$ and S_3 are the only homomorphic images of S_3.

Theorem 6.2.8. [Second Isomorphism Theorem] : *Let H and K be subgroups of a group G with K normal in G. Then,*

$$H/(H \cap K) \simeq (HK)/K.$$

Proof. Define $f : H \to (HK)/K$ by $f(h) = hK$ for all $h \in H$. Now $f(h_1 h_2) = h_1 h_2 K = h_1 K h_2 K = f(h_1)f(h_2)$ for all $h_1, h_2 \in H$, proving that f is a homomorphism. Let $xK \in (HK)/K$. Then $x = hk$ for some $h \in H$ and $k \in K$. Thus, $xK = (hk)K = (hK)(kK) = hK = f(h)$. This proves that f is onto and so $f(H) = (HK)/K$. Hence by the first isomorphism theorem, it follows that

$$H/ker \, f \simeq (HK)/K.$$

To complete the proof, we now show that $ker \, f = H \cap K$. Now,

$$
\begin{aligned}
ker \, f &= \{h \in H \,|\, f(h) = \text{ identity element of } HK/K\} \\
&= \{h \in H \,|\, hK = K\} \\
&= \{h \in H \,|\, h \in K\} \\
&= H \cap K.
\end{aligned}
$$

Consequently, $H/H \cap K \simeq (HK)/K.$ $\qquad\square$

We have seen that for any normal subgroup K of a group G, the quotient group G/K is a homomorphic image of G. Now what are the subgroups and normal subgroups of G/K?

Theorem 6.2.9. *Let K be a normal subgroup of a group G.*

(i)   If H is a subgroup of G such that $K \subseteq H$, then $H/K = \{aK \,|\, a \in H\}$ is a subgroup of G/K.

(ii)   If T is a subgroup of G/K, then there exists a subgroup H of G such that $K \subseteq H$ and $T = H/K$.

(iii)   The mapping ψ defined by $\psi(H) = H/K$ from the set of all subgroups of G that contain K and the set $\mathcal{B}$ of all subgroups of G/H is a bijective mapping.

(iv)   The mapping ψ as described in (iii) preserves inclusion relation, i.e., $K \subseteq H_1 \subseteq H$ if and only if $H_1/K \subseteq H/K$.

(v) H is a normal subgroup of G with $K \subseteq H$, if and only if H/K is a normal subgroup of G/K.

Proof. (i)   The mapping $f : G \to G/K$ defined by $f(a) = aK$ is an epimorphism. Now by Theorem 6.1.7(i), $f(H) = \{aK \,|\, a \in H\}$ is a subgroup of G/K. Hence H/K is a subgroup of G/K.

(ii)   Let T be a subgroup of G/K. Then by the Theorem 6.1.7(ii), $f^{-1}(T)$ is a subgroup of G. Now $f^{-1}(T) = \{a \in G \,|\, f(a) \in T\} = \{a \in G \,|\, aK \in T\}$. Let $H = \{a \in G \,|\, aK \in T\}$. Suppose $u \in K$. Then, $uK = K$ is the identity element of G/K and so $uK \in T$. Hence $u \in H$. This implies that $K \subseteq H$. Since $f(H) = \{aK \,|\, a \in H\} = \{aK \,|\, aK \in T\} = T$, it follows that $T = H/K$.

(iii)   Clearly, ψ is surjective. Now suppose that H_1 and H_2 be two subgroups of G such that $K \subseteq H_1$, $K \subseteq H_2$ and $f(H_1) = f(H_2)$. Then $H_1/K = H_2/K$. Let $a \in H_1$. Then $aK = bK$ for some $b \in H_2$. Hence $b^{-1}a \in K \subseteq H_2$ and so $a = b(b^{-1}a) \in H_2$. Thus we find that $H_1 \subseteq H_2$. Similarly, we can show that $H_2 \subseteq H_1$ and then $H_1 = H_2$ which implies that ψ is injective.

(iv)   If $H_1 \subseteq H$, then clearly, $H_1/K \subseteq H/K$. Conversely, assume that $H_1/K \subseteq H/K$. Let $a \in H_1$. Then $aK \in H_1/K \subseteq H/K$. Hence $aK = hK$ for some $h \in H$. Hence $h^{-1}a \in K \subseteq H$ and so, $a = h(h^{-1}a) \in H$. Thus we find that $H_1 \subseteq H$.

(v)   Since the natural homomorphism $f : G \to G/K$ is an epimorphism, it follows that if H is a normal subgroup of G, then $f(H) = H/K$ is also a normal subgroup of G/H. Conversely, assume that T is a normal subgroup of G/K. Then by (ii), $T = H/K$ where H is a subgroup of G such that $K \subseteq H$. Let $g \in G$. Then $gK(H/K)(gK)^{-1} \subseteq H/K$. Let $h \in H$. We find that $gKhK(gK)^{-1} \in H/K$, i.e., $(ghg^{-1})K \in H/K$. Hence $ghg^{-1} \in H$. This proves that H is a normal subgroup of G. $\square$

Now we can generalize this theorem and prove the following:

Theorem 6.2.10. [Correspondence Theorem] : *Let $f : G \to G_1$ be an epimorphism of groups. Let*

$$\mathcal{H} = \{H \mid H \text{ is a subgroup of } G \text{ that contains } ker\, f\}$$

and

$$\mathcal{K} = \{K \mid K \text{ is a subgroup of } G_1\}.$$

Then the mapping $f^* : \mathcal{H} \to \mathcal{K}$ defined by $f^*(H) = f(H)$ for all $H \in \mathcal{H}$ is an inclusion preserving bijective mapping and $f^*(H)$ is a normal subgroup of G_1 if and only if H is a normal subgroup of G.

Proof. Since f is an epimorphism, by the First Isomorphism theorem, $G_1 \simeq G/ker\, f$. So the proof is analogous to the Theorem 6.2.9 and we leave it to the reader. $\square$

Theorem 6.2.11. [Third Isomorphism Theorem] : *Suppose H_1 and H_2 be two normal subgroups of a group G such that $H_1 \subseteq H_2$. Then,*

$$(G/H_1)/(H_2/H_1) \simeq G/H_2.$$

Proof. Define $f : G/H_1 \to G/H_2$ by $f(aH_1) = aH_2$ for all $a \in G$. We leave it for the reader to verify that f is well-defined. Clearly, f is an epimorphism. By the First Isomorphism theorem,

$$(G/H_1)/ker\, f \simeq G/H_2.$$

Now,

$$
\begin{aligned}
ker\, f &= \{aH_1 \in G/H_1 \mid f(aH_1) = eH_2\} \\
&= \{aH_1 \in G/H_1 \mid aH_2 = eH_2\} \\
&= \{aH_1 \in G/H_1 \mid a \in H_2\} \\
&= H_2/H_1.
\end{aligned}
$$

This completes the proof. $\square$

Worked-out Exercises

$\Diamond$ **Exercise 6.2.1.** Show that $GL(2,\mathbb{R})\big/SL(2,\mathbb{R}) \simeq \mathbb{R}^*$.

Solution.   Define $f : GL(2,\mathbb{R}) \to \mathbb{R}^*$ by $f(A) = \det A$ for all $A \in GL(2,\mathbb{R})$. We have shown in Example 6.1.4 that f is a homomorphism. Let $a \in \mathbb{R}^*$. Then $A =$

$\begin{bmatrix} 1 & 0 \\ 0 & a \end{bmatrix} \in GL(2, \mathbb{R})$ and $f(A) = det\, A = a$. Hence f is an epimorphism and so by the First Isomorphism theorem,

$$GL(2, \mathbb{R}) \big/ ker\, f \simeq \mathbb{R}^*.$$

Now, $ker\, f = \{A \in GL(2, \mathbb{R}) \mid det\, A = 1\} = SL(2, \mathbb{R})$. Hence,

$$GL(2, \mathbb{R}) \big/ SL(2, \mathbb{R}) \simeq \mathbb{R}^*.$$

◊ **Exercise 6.2.2.** Prove that the group $4\mathbb{Z}/12\mathbb{Z} \simeq \mathbb{Z}_3$.

Solution. Define $f : 4\mathbb{Z} \to \mathbb{Z}_3$ by $f(4n) = [n]$ for all $n \in \mathbb{Z}$. Clearly, f is surjective and

$$f(4n + 4m) = f\Big(4(n + m)\Big) = [n + m] = [n] + [m] = f(4n) + f(4m).$$

Hence f is an epimorphism. So by the First Isomorphism theorem,

$$4\mathbb{Z}/ker\, f \simeq \mathbb{Z}_3.$$

Now,

$$
\begin{aligned}
ker\, f &= \{4n \in 4\mathbb{Z} \mid f(4n) = [0] \text{ in } \mathbb{Z}_3\} \\
&= \{4n \in 4\mathbb{Z} \mid [n] = [0] \text{ in } \mathbb{Z}_3\} \\
&= \{4n \in 4\mathbb{Z} \mid n \text{ is a multiple of 3}\} \\
&= \{4n \in 4\mathbb{Z} \mid n = 3k,\ k \in \mathbb{Z}\} \\
&= 12\mathbb{Z}
\end{aligned}
$$

Hence the result follows.

◊ **Exercise 6.2.3.** Find all homomorphic images of the additive group $\mathbb{Z}$.

Solution. The subgroups of $\mathbb{Z}$ are given by $n\mathbb{Z}$, $n \in \mathbb{N}_0$. Since $\mathbb{Z}$ is commutative, all these subgroups of $\mathbb{Z}$ are normal subgroups of $\mathbb{Z}$. Thus the homomorphic images of $\mathbb{Z}$ are the groups, $\mathbb{Z}/n\mathbb{Z} \simeq \mathbb{Z}_n$, $n = 0, 1, 2 \ldots$

◊ **Exercise 6.2.4.** Show that $\mathbb{Z}_9$ is not a homomorphic image of $\mathbb{Z}_{16}$.

Solution. Suppose there exists an epimorphism $f : \mathbb{Z}_{16} \to \mathbb{Z}_9$. Then by the First Isomorphism theorem, $\mathbb{Z}_{16}/ker\, f \simeq \mathbb{Z}_9$. Hence $\left| \mathbb{Z}_{16}/ker\, f \right| = |\mathbb{Z}_9| = 9$. This shows that

$$\frac{|\mathbb{Z}_{16}|}{|ker\, f|} = 9,$$

i.e., $9 \cdot |ker\, f| = 16$. This is absurd. Hence $\mathbb{Z}_9$ is not a homomorphic image of $\mathbb{Z}_{16}$.

◊ **Exercise 6.2.5.** Find all the subgroups of $\mathbb{Z}/21\mathbb{Z}$.

Solution. Let K be a subgroup of $\mathbb{Z}/21\mathbb{Z}$. Then $K = H/21\mathbb{Z}$ for some subgroup H of $\mathbb{Z}$ such that $21\mathbb{Z} \subseteq H$. Again, if H is a subgroup of $\mathbb{Z}$, such that $21\mathbb{Z} \subseteq H$, then $H/21\mathbb{Z}$ is a subgroup of $\mathbb{Z}/21\mathbb{Z}$. So we have to determine all subgroups of $\mathbb{Z}$ that contain $21\mathbb{Z}$. Now, $1, 3, 7, 21$ are the only positive divisors of 21. Hence $\mathbb{Z}, 3\mathbb{Z}, 7\mathbb{Z}$ and $21\mathbb{Z}$ are the only subgroups of $\mathbb{Z}$ that contain $21\mathbb{Z}$. Then $\mathbb{Z}/21\mathbb{Z}$, $3\mathbb{Z}/21\mathbb{Z}$, $7\mathbb{Z}/21\mathbb{Z}$ and $21\mathbb{Z}/21\mathbb{Z}$ are the only subgroups of $\mathbb{Z}/21\mathbb{Z}$.

◊ **Exercise 6.2.6.** If there exists an epimorphism from a finite group G onto the group $\mathbb{Z}_{15}$, then show that G has normal subgroups of indices 5 and 3.

Solution. Let $f : G \to \mathbb{Z}_{15}$ be an epimorphism of groups. Then by the First Isomorphism theorem, $G/\ker f \simeq \mathbb{Z}_{15}$. Hence $G/\ker f$ is a cyclic group of order 15. Now 5 divides 15. Hence $G/\ker f$ has a subgroup K of order 5. Since $G/\ker f$ is commutative, K is a normal subgroup. Then $K = H/\ker f$ for some normal subgroup H of G such that $\ker f \subseteq H \subseteq G$. Now,

$$15 = |\mathbb{Z}_{15}| = \left| G/\ker f \right| = \frac{|G|}{|H|} \cdot \frac{|H|}{|\ker f|} = [G : H] \cdot \left| H/\ker f \right| = [G : H] \cdot 5.$$

This shows that $[G : H] = 3$. Since 3 also divides 15, proceeding as above, we can show that G has a normal subgroup of index 5.

◊ **Exercise 6.2.7.** Let G be a group and H be a normal subgroup of G. Then show that there exists an epimorphism $f : G \to G/H$ such that $\ker f = H$.

Solution. Define the mapping $f : G \to G/H$ by $f(g) = gH$. Clearly, the mapping is well-defined. Let $g_1, g_2 \in G$. Then $f(g_1 g_2) = g_1 g_2 H = g_1 H \cdot g_2 H = f(g_1)f(g_2)$, whence it follows that f is a homomorphism. Let $x \in G/H$. Then $x = gH$ for some $g \in G$. This implies $x = gH = f(g)$ and hence f is onto, i.e., f is an epimorphism of G onto G/H. Now,

$$
\begin{aligned}
\ker f \;&=\; \{g \in G \,|\, f(g) = \text{ identity of } G/H\} \\
&=\; \{g \in G \,|\, f(g) = eH\} \\
&=\; \{g \in G \,|\, gH = eH = H\} \\
&=\; \{g \in G \,|\, g \in H\} \\
&=\; H.
\end{aligned}
$$

◊ **Exercise 6.2.8.** Let G be a group of order 17. Then the total number of nonisomorphic subgroups of G is

(i) 1   (ii) 2   (iii) 3   (iv) 17.

Solution. Here G is a group of order 17, which is a prime number. So the subgroups of G are $\{e\}$ and G itself. Thus there are exactly two nonisomorphic subgroups of G. Therefore, option (ii) is correct.

◇ **Exercise 6.2.9.** The number of group homomorphisms from the symmetric group S_3 to the additive group $\mathbb{Z}_6$ is

(i) 1   (ii) 2   (iii) 3   (iv) 0.

Solution. Now $S_3 = \{\langle a, b \rangle : o(a) = 3, o(b) = 2 \text{ and } ba = a^{-1}b\}$. Let $f : S_3 \longrightarrow \mathbb{Z}_6$ be a non-trivial group homomorphism. Then $f(a)$ and $f(b)$ are elements of $\mathbb{Z}_6$. Now $o(f(x)) \mid o(x)$ implies $o(f(a)) \mid 3$ and $o(f(b)) \mid 2$. Thus $o(f(a)) = 1$ or 3 and $o(f(b)) = 1$ or 2. This implies either $f(a) = [0]$ or $[2]$ or $[4]$ and $f(b) = [0]$ or $[3]$. Now $ba = a^{-1}b$ implies $f(ba) = f(a^{-1}b)$, i.e., $f(b) + f(a) = -f(a) + f(b)$ in $\mathbb{Z}_6$. This implies $2f(a) = [0]$. If $f(a) = [2]$ or $[4]$, then $2f(a) \neq [0]$. Hence $f(a) = [0]$. Since f is non-trivial, we must have $f(b) = [3]$. Thus there is exactly one non-trivial group homomorphism and thus there are exactly two group homomorphisms from S_3 to $\mathbb{Z}_6$. Therefore, option (ii) is correct.

◇ **Exercise 6.2.10.** Consider the following subsets of the group of 2×2 non-singular matrices over $\mathbb{R}$:

$$G = \left\{ \begin{bmatrix} a & b \\ 0 & d \end{bmatrix} : a, b, d \in \mathbb{R}, ad = 1 \right\} \text{ and } H = \left\{ \begin{bmatrix} 1 & b \\ 0 & 1 \end{bmatrix} : b \in \mathbb{R} \right\}.$$

Which of the following statements are correct?

(i) G forms a group under matrix multiplication.

(ii) H is a normal subgroup of G.

(iii) The quotient group G/H is well-defined and is Abelian.

(iv) The quotient group G/H is well defined and is isomorphic to the group of 2×2 diagonal matrices (over $\mathbb{R}$) with determinant 1.

Solution. One can easily check that G forms a group with respect to usual multiplication of matrices and H is a normal subgroup of G. Hence G/H is well defined. We now define a mapping $\varphi : G \longrightarrow G_1$ by $\varphi \left(\begin{bmatrix} a & b \\ 0 & d \end{bmatrix} \right) = \begin{bmatrix} a & 0 \\ 0 & d \end{bmatrix}$ for all $\begin{bmatrix} a & b \\ 0 & d \end{bmatrix} \in G$, where $G_1 = \left\{ \begin{bmatrix} a & 0 \\ 0 & d \end{bmatrix} : ad = 1, a, d \in \mathbb{R}, \right\}$ is the group of 2×2 diagonal matrices (over $\mathbb{R}$). It is easy to verify that φ is a group epimorphism with $\ker \varphi = H$. Hence by First Isomorphism theorem we have $G/H \simeq G_1$. Therefore, all the statements (i), (ii), (iii) and (iv) are correct.

Exercises

1. Let T be the group of all complex numbers z such that $|z| = 1$. Show that $C^*/T \simeq \mathbb{R}^+$.

2. Prove that $7\mathbb{Z}/56\mathbb{Z} \simeq \mathbb{Z}_8$.

3. Prove that $6\mathbb{Z}/30\mathbb{Z}$ is isomorphic to $\mathbb{Z}_5$.

4. If G is an infinite group such that G is a homomorphic image of $\mathbb{Z}$, then prove that $G \simeq \mathbb{Z}$.

5. Show that $\mathbb{Z}_{16}$ is not a homomorphic image of $\mathbb{Z}_4 \times \mathbb{Z}_4$.

6. Let T be the group of all complex numbers ω, such that $|\omega| = 1$. (This group is called **circle group**). Show that $\mathbb{R}/\mathbb{Z} \simeq T$, where $\mathbb{R}$ is the additive group of all real numbers.

7. Let H be a normal subgroup of G. If $f : G \to G_1$ be an epimorphism of groups such that $H \subseteq \ker f$, then show that G_1 is also a homomorphic image of G/H.

8. Find all subgroups of the groups $\mathbb{Z}/8\mathbb{Z}$, $\mathbb{Z}/24\mathbb{Z}$.

9. Show that if there exists an epimorphism from a finite group G onto the group $\mathbb{Z}_{35}$, then G has normal subgroups of index 7 and 5.

10. If there exists an epimorphism from a finite group G onto the group $\mathbb{Z}_8$, then show that G has normal subgroups of index 4 and 2.

11. Which of the following statements are true? Justify.

    (a) $\mathbb{Z}_6$ has six homomorphic images.

    (b)   The quotient group $5\mathbb{Z}/45\mathbb{Z}$ has three subgroups.

    (c) $4\mathbb{Z}/16\mathbb{Z}$ is a subgroup of $\mathbb{Z}/16\mathbb{Z}$.

    (d)   There are 5 subgroups of $\mathbb{Z}$ which contain $20\mathbb{Z}$ as a subgroup.

    (e)   Any epimorphism of $\mathbb{Z}$ onto $\mathbb{Z}$ is an isomorphism.

    (f)   There exists an epimorphism $f : \mathbb{Z}_{24} \to \mathbb{Z}_5$.

    Pick the correct option(s) from the following:

12. The number of subgroups of the group $\mathbb{Z}/10\mathbb{Z}$ is

    (i) 1 (ii) 10 (iii) 4 (iv) 5.

13. The number of subgroups of the quotient group $4\mathbb{Z}/12\mathbb{Z}$ is

    (i) 3 (ii) 2 (iii) 4 (iv) 1.

14. A group G is generated by the elements x, y with the relations $x^3 = y^2 = (xy)^2 = e$. The order of G is

    (i) 4   (ii) 6   (iii) 8   (iv) 12.

15. Let $\sigma = (1\ 2)(3\ 4\ 5)$ and $\tau = (1\ 2\ 3\ 4\ 5\ 6)$ be permutations in S_6, the group of permutations on six symbols. Then

    (i) the subgroups $\langle \sigma \rangle$ and $\langle \tau \rangle$ are isomorphic to each other.

    (ii) σ and τ are conjugate in S_6.

    (iii) $\langle \sigma \rangle \cap \langle \tau \rangle$ is the trivial group.

    (iv) σ and τ commute.

Chapter 7

Direct Product of Groups

In this section, we shall show that given n groups $G_1, G_2, \ldots, G_n$, we can construct a new group G, such that each G_i can be considered as a subgroup of this group.

7.1   Direct Product

Let G_1 and G_2 be two groups. Now, the Cartesian product of the sets G_1 and G_2 is the set $G_1 \times G_2$ of all ordered pairs (a_1, b_1), where $a_1 \in G_1$ and $b_1 \in G_2$. Define a binary operation $*$ on $G_1 \times G_2$ as follows:

$$(a_1, b_1) * (a_2, b_2) = (a_1 a_2, b_1 b_2) \text{ for all } (a_1, b_1), (a_2, b_2) \in G_1 \times G_2 \qquad (7.1.1)$$

Here $a_1 a_2$ denotes that product of a_1 and a_2 in the group G_1 and $b_1 b_2$ denotes the product of b_1 and b_2 in the group G_2.

Let us show that $G_1 \times G_2$ is a group under this binary operation, such that G_1 is isomorphic to a subgroup of this group and so is G_2.

Theorem 7.1.1. *Let G_1 and G_2 be two groups. Then the set*

$$G_1 \times G_2 = \left\{ (g_1, g_2) \,|\, g_1 \in G_1 \text{ and } y_2 \in G_2 \right\}$$

is a group under the binary operation defined in (7.1.1). Furthermore,

(i) $H_1 = \{(a_1, e_2) \in G_1 \times G_2 \,|\, e_2 \text{ is the identity element of } G_2\}$ is a normal subgroup of $G_1 \times G_2$ and $G_1 \simeq H_1$.

(ii) $H_2 = \{(e_1, b_2) \in G_1 \times G_2 \,|\, e_1 \text{ is the identity of } G_1\}$ is a normal subgroup of $G_1 \times G_2$ such that $G_2 \simeq H_2$.

(iii) $G_1 \times G_2 = H_1 H_2 = H_2 H_1$, $\quad H_1 \cap H_2 = \{(e_1, e_2)\}$.

Proof. Clearly, the operation defined in (7.1.1) is a well-defined binary operation on $G_1 \times G_2$. The associativity of this operation follows from the group operations of G_1 and G_2. Note that (e_1, e_2) is the identity element of $G_1 \times G_2$, where e_i is the identity element of G_i, $i = 1, 2$. Finally, (a_1^{-1}, b_1^{-1}) is the inverse of (a_1, b_1) for all $(a_1, b_1) \in G_1 \times G_2$. Hence $(G_1 \times G_2, *)$ is a group.

(i) Since $(e_1, e_2) \in H_1, H_1 \neq \phi$. Let $(a_1, e_2), (a_2, e_2) \in H_1$. Then $(a_1, e_2)^{-1}(a_2, e_2) = (a_1^{-1} a_2, e_2^{-1} e_2) = (a_1^{-1} a_2, e_2) \in H_1$, since $a_1^{-1} a_2 \in G_1$. Now, for any $(a_1, b_1) \in G_1 \times G_2$ and $(g_1, e_2) \in H_1$, we find that $(a_1, b_1) * (g_1, e_2) * (a_1, b_1)^{-1} = (a_1 g_1 a_1^{-1}, b_1 e_2 b_1^{-1}) = (a_1 g_1 a_1^{-1}, e_2) \in H_1$. Hence H_1 is a normal subgroup. Now the mapping $f_1 : G_1 \to H_1$, defined by $f_1(a_1) = (a_1, e_2)$ is a bijective mapping and for any $a_1, a_2 \in G_1$, $f_1(a_1 a_2) = (a_1 a_2, e_2) = (a_1, e_2) * (a_2, e_2) = f_1(a_1) f_1(a_2)$. Hence $G_1 \simeq H_1$.

(ii) The proof is similar to (i).

(iii) This is a simple exercise and is left to the reader. □

Definition 7.1.2. The group $(G_1 \times G_2, *)$ of Theorem 7.1.1 is called the **external direct product** or simply **direct product** of the groups G_1 and G_2.

Henceforth, the statement "*the direct product $G_1 \times G_2$ of the groups G_1 and G_2*" will mean the group $(G_1 \times G_2, *)$. Although we have defined the direct product for a pair of groups G_1 and G_2, it is easy to see that we can extend the definition for any finite number of groups $G_1, G_2, \ldots, G_n$.

We now introduce another kind of product known as *internal direct product*.

Definition 7.1.3. Let H and K be two subgroups of a group G. G is said to be an **internal direct product** of H and K if

(a) $G = HK$,

(b) $H \cap K = \{e\}$ and

(c) $hk = kh$ for all $h \in H$ and $k \in K$.

Example 7.1.4. Consider the Klein's four-group $K_4 = \{e, a, b, ab = ba\}$. For this group, $H_1 = \{e, a\}$ and $H_2 = \{e, b\}$ are two subgroups such that $H_1 H_2 = \{e, a\}\{e, b\} = \{e, a, b, ab\} = K_4$, $H_1 \cap H_2 = \{e\}$ and $xy = yx$ for all $x \in H_1$ and $y \in H_2$. Hence G is an internal direct product of its subgroups H_1 and H_2.

Example 7.1.5. Consider the symmetric group $S_3 = \{e, (1\,2), (1\,3), (2\,3), (1\,2\,3), (1\,3\,2)\}$. For this group, $H_1 = \{e, (1\,2)\}$ and $H_2 = \{e, (1\,2\,3), (1\,3\,2)\}$ are two subgroups such that
$$H_1 H_2 = \{e, (1\,2\,3), (1\,3\,2), (1\,2), (1\,2)(1\,2\,3), (1\,2)(1\,3\,2)\}$$
$$= \{e, (1\,2\,3), (1\,3\,2), (1\,2), (2\,3), (1\,3)\} = S_3$$
and $H_1 \cap H_2 = \{e\}$. But $(1\,2)(1\,3\,2) = (1\,3) \neq (2\,3) = (1\,3\,2)(1\,2)$. Hence S_3 is not an internal direct product of the subgroups, H_1 and H_2.

Note that any group G is always an internal direct product of the trivial subgroups $\{e\}$ and G itself.

Theorem 7.1.6. *Let H and K be two subgroups of a group G. G is an internal direct product of H and K if and only if*

  (i) $G = HK$

  (ii) H and K are normal subgroups of G

  (iii) $H \cap K = \{e\}$.

Proof. Suppose that G is an internal direct product of the subgroups H and K. We show only that H and K are normal subgroups of G. Let $g \in G$ and $h \in H$. Since $G = HK$, there exist $h_1 \in H$ and $k_1 \in K$ such that $g = h_1 k_1$. Now $ghg^{-1} = h_1 k_1 h(h_1 k_1)^{-1} = h_1 k_1 h k_1^{-1} h_1^{-1} = h_1 h h_1^{-1} k_1 k_1^{-1}$ (since $hk = kh$ for all $h \in H, k \in K$) $= h_1 h h_1^{-1} \in H$. Hence H is a normal subgroup of G. Similarly, we can show that K is a normal subgroup of G.

Conversely, assume that all the conditions (i), (ii) and (iii) hold in G. To prove that G is an internal direct product, we have to prove only that $ab = ba$ for all $a \in H$ and $b \in K$. Consider $aba^{-1}b^{-1}$. Now $aba^{-1}b^{-1} \in a(bHb^{-1}) \subseteq aH = H$ (since $a \in H$) and $aba^{-1}b^{-1} \in (aKa^{-1})b^{-1} \subseteq Kb^{-1} = K$ (since $b^{-1} \in K$). Hence $aba^{-1}b^{-1} \in H \cap K = \{e\}$ and so $ab = ba$ for all $a \in H, b \in K$. Hence the proof. $\square$

Theorem 7.1.7. *Let G be a group and H, K be two subgroups of G. If G is an internal direct product of H and K then,*

  (i) $G \simeq H \times K$,

  (ii) $G/H \simeq K$ and $G/K \simeq H$.

Proof. (i)   Since G is an internal direct product of the subgroups H and K then $G = HK$, H and K are normal and $H \cap K = \{e\}$. Hence for every $g \in G$, there are unique (prove it!) elements $a \in H$ and $b \in K$ such that $g = ab$. So we can define $f : G \to H \times K$ by $f(g) = (a, b)$ when $g = ab, a \in H, b \in K$. Let $g_1 = a_1 b_1$ and $g_2 = a_2 b_2$ be two elements of G, where $a_1, a_2 \in H$ and $b_1, b_2 \in K$. Now $g_1 g_2 = a_1 b_1 a_2 b_2 = a_1 a_2 b_1 b_2$. Hence $f(g_1 g_2) = (a_1 a_2, b_1 b_2) = (a_1, b_1)(a_2, b_2) = f(g_1)f(g_2)$. This shows that f is a homomorphism. Since for every $g \in G$, there are unique elements $a \in H$ and $h \in K$ such that $g = ab$, it follows that f is an injective mapping. Again, if $(a, b) \in H \times K$, then $g = ab \in G$ and hence $f(g) = (a, b)$. Combining all these, we find that f is an isomorphism and so $G \simeq H \times K$.

(ii)   Since for each $g \in G$, there are unique elements $a \in H, b \in K$, the mapping $\psi : G \to H$ defined by $\psi(g) = \psi(ab) = a$, for all $g = ab \in G$ can be shown to be an epimorphism. Hence by the first isomorphism theorem $G/\ker \psi \simeq H$.

$$
\begin{aligned}
\text{Now, } ker\,\psi &= \{g \in G \,|\, \psi(g) = e\} \\
&= \{g = ab \in G \,|\, a \in H, b \in K \text{ and } \psi(g) = e\} \\
&= \{g = ab \in G \,|\, a \in H, b \in K \text{ and } a = e\} \\
&= \{g = eb \in G \,|\, b \in K\} = K.
\end{aligned}
$$

Thus $G/K \simeq H$. Similarly, we can show that $G/H \simeq K$. $\qquad\qquad\square$

Before concluding this section, we now show some applications of the concept of direct product.

Theorem 7.1.8. *Any commutative group G of order 8 is isomorphic to one of the groups $\mathbb{Z}_8, \mathbb{Z}_4 \times \mathbb{Z}_2$ or $\mathbb{Z}_2 \times \mathbb{Z}_2 \times \mathbb{Z}_2$, where no two of these groups are isomorphic to each other.*

Proof. Let G be a commutative group of order 8. Since $|G|$ is even, G has an element, say b, of order 2. Now G contains a finite number of elements. Hence there exists an element $a \in G$ such that $o(a) \geq o(x)$ for all $x \in G$. Clearly, $o(a) \geq 2$. Since $o(a) \mid 8$, we find that $o(a) = 8$ or 4 or 2.

Case I.   Suppose $o(a) = 8$. Then G is a cyclic group of order 8 and hence $G \simeq \mathbb{Z}_8$.

Case II.   Suppose $o(a) = 4$. Let $H = \langle a \rangle$. Then $|H| = 4$. Hence, $H \neq G$. Let $b \in G$ such that $b \notin H$. Now H is a normal subgroup of G and hence the quotient group G/H exists and $|G/H| = 2$. Then $bH \neq H$ but $(bH)^2 = H$. Then $b^2 H = H$. This implies that $b^2 \in H = \{e, a, a^2, a^3\}$. Now $o(a) = o(a^3) = 4$. If $b^2 = a$ or a^3, then $o(b) = 8$, which goes against our assumption that $o(a) \geq o(b)$. Hence either $b^2 = e$ or $b^2 = a^2$. If $b^2 = a^2$, then $o(ba^{-1}) = 2$ and $ba^{-1} \notin H$. Thus we find that there exists an element $c \in G$ such that $c \notin H$ and $o(c) = 2$. Let $K = \langle c \rangle$. Then (i) H and K are normal subgroups (ii) $H \cap K = \{e\}$ (iii) $G = HK$. Hence $G \simeq H \times K \simeq \mathbb{Z}_4 \times \mathbb{Z}_2$.

Case III. $o(a) = 2$. Then $o(x) = 2$ for all nonidentity elements $x \in G$. Let $a, b \in G \setminus \{e\}$. Then $A = \{e, a\}, B = \{e, b\}$ are normal subgroups of G. Now $AB = \{e, a, b, ab\}$ is a subgroup of G and $AB \simeq \mathbb{Z}_2 \times \mathbb{Z}_2$. Since $AB \neq G$, there exists $c \in G$ such that $c \notin AB$. Now $o(c) = 2$. Let $C = \langle c \rangle$. Clearly, $AB \cap C = \{e\}$ and $G = ABC$. Hence, $G \simeq (AB) \times C \simeq \mathbb{Z}_2 \times \mathbb{Z}_2 \times \mathbb{Z}_2$. Hence (upto isomorphism) there exist only three commutative groups of order 8. $\qquad\square$

We have seen that any commutative group of order 4 is either $\mathbb{Z}_4$ or $\mathbb{Z}_2 \times \mathbb{Z}_2$; any commutative group of order 6 is $\mathbb{Z}_3 \times \mathbb{Z}_2 \simeq \mathbb{Z}_6$ and now we find that any commutative group of order 8 is either $\mathbb{Z}_8$ or $\mathbb{Z}_4 \times \mathbb{Z}_2$ or else $\mathbb{Z}_2 \times \mathbb{Z}_2 \times \mathbb{Z}_2$. These examples lead us towards a growing conviction that *any finite commutative group is either a cyclic group or a direct product of cyclic groups*. Indeed this is true and this result is known as the *Fundamental Theorem of finite Abelian groups*.

Worked-out Exercises

◊ **Exercise 7.1.1.** Let G_1, G_2 be two groups. The direct product $G_1 \times G_2$ is commutative if and only if both G_1 and G_2 are commutative.

Solution. Suppose G_1 and G_2 are two commutative groups. Let (a_1, b_1) and (a_2, b_2) be two elements of the direct product $G_1 \times G_2$. Then $(a_1, b_1)(a_2, b_2) = (a_1 a_2, b_1 b_2) = (a_2 a_1, b_2 b_1) = (a_2, b_2)(a_1, b_1)$. Hence $G_1 \times G_2$ is a commutative group.

Conversely, assume that $G_1 \times G_2$ is a commutative group. Let $a_1, a_2 \in G_1$ and $b_1, b_2 \in G_2$. Now $(a_1, b_1), (a_2, b_2) \in G_1 \times G_2$ and so $(a_1, b_1)(a_2, b_2) = (a_2, b_2)(a_1, b_1)$, i.e., $(a_1 a_2, b_1 b_2) = (a_2 a_1, b_2 b_1)$. So we find that $a_1 a_2 = a_2 a_1$ and $b_1 b_2 = b_2 b_1$. Hence G_1 and G_2 are both commutative groups.

◊ **Exercise 7.1.2.** Show that the direct product of $S_3 \times \mathbb{Z}$ of the groups S_3 and $\mathbb{Z}$ is an infinite noncommutative group.

Solution. Since S_3 is a noncommutative group, from the Worked-out Exercise 7.1.1, it follows that the direct product $S_3 \times \mathbb{Z}$ is a noncommutative group. Now $\mathbb{Z}$ is an infinite group. Hence $S_3 \times \mathbb{Z}$ is an infinite noncommutative group.

◊ **Exercise 7.1.3.** Show that the direct product $\mathbb{Z} \times \mathbb{Z}$ is not a cyclic group.

Solution. Suppose $\mathbb{Z} \times \mathbb{Z}$ is a cyclic group. Let (n, m) be a generator of $\mathbb{Z} \times \mathbb{Z}$. We have $(1, 0), (0, 1) \in \mathbb{Z} \times \mathbb{Z}$. Thus there are integers r, s such that $(1, 0) = r(n, m)$ and $(0, 1) = s(n, m)$. But then $rn = 1$ and $sn = 0$, together imply that $s = 0$ (as $n \neq 0$, since $rn = 1$), which is a contradiction, since $sm = 1$. So it follows that $\mathbb{Z} \times \mathbb{Z}$ is not a cyclic group.

◊ **Exercise 7.1.4.** Show that the direct product $\mathbb{Z}_6 \times \mathbb{Z}_4$ of the cyclic groups $\mathbb{Z}_6$ and $\mathbb{Z}_4$ is not a cyclic group.

Solution. The elements of $\mathbb{Z}_6 \times \mathbb{Z}_4$ are the ordered pairs (u, v) where $u \in \mathbb{Z}_6$ and $v \in \mathbb{Z}_4$. Hence $|\mathbb{Z}_6 \times \mathbb{Z}_4| = 24$. In order that $\mathbb{Z}_6 \times \mathbb{Z}_4$ may be a cyclic group, it must contain an element of order 24. Now if $(a, b) \in \mathbb{Z}_6 \times \mathbb{Z}_4$, then we must have $6a = 0$ and $4b = 0$, whence $12(a, b) = (0, 0)$. This shows that order of (a, b) will not exceed 12. Hence $\mathbb{Z}_6 \times \mathbb{Z}_4$ has no element of order 24. Consequently, $\mathbb{Z}_6 \times \mathbb{Z}_4$ is not a cyclic group.

◊ **Exercise 7.1.5.** Let H and K be two finite cyclic groups of order m and n respectively. Prove that the direct product $H \times K$ is a cyclic group if and only if $gcd(m, n) = 1$.

Solution. Suppose $H \times K$ is a cyclic group and let $gcd(m, n) = d > 1$. Let $(a, b) \in H \times K$. Since $|H| = m$ and $|K| = n$, we find that $a^m = e$ and $b^n = e$. Now $\frac{m}{d}, \frac{n}{d}$ and $\frac{mn}{d}$ are integers and $\frac{mn}{d} < mn$.

$$(a, b)^{\frac{mn}{d}} = \left(a^{\frac{mn}{d}}, b^{\frac{mn}{d}}\right) = \left((a^m)^{\frac{n}{d}}, (b^n)^{\frac{m}{d}}\right) = (e, e).$$

This shows that the order of any element $(a, b) \in H \times K$ will be less than or equal to $\frac{mn}{d} < mn$. Hence $H \times K$, which is a group of order mn, does not contain any element of order mn. This contradicts our assumption that $H \times K$ is a cyclic group. Hence $gcd(m, n) = 1$.

Conversely, assume that $gcd(m, n) = 1$. Since H and K are both cyclic groups of order m and n respectively, there exist $a \in H$ and $b \in K$ such that $o(a) = m$, $o(b) = n$. Now we show that $o(a, b) = mn$. Since $(a, b)^{mn} = (a^{mn}, b^{mn}) = \left((a^m)^n, (b^n)^m\right) = (e, e)$, the order of (a, b) is less than or equal to mn. Let d be a positive integer such that $(a, b)^d = (e, e)$. Then $a^d = e$ and $b^d = e$. Since $o(a) = m$ and $o(b) = n$, we have $m \mid d$ and $n \mid d$. Now $gcd(m, n) = 1$. Hence $mn \mid d$ and so $mn \leq d$. Thus it follows that $o(a, b) = mn$ and hence $H \times K$ is a cyclic group.

◇ **Exercise 7.1.6.** Show that the multiplicative group $\mathbb{R}^*$ of all nonzero real numbers is an internal direct product of $\mathbb{R}^+$ and T, where $\mathbb{R}^+$ is the set of all positive real numbers and $T = \{1, -1\}$.

Solution. $\mathbb{R}^+$ and T are both normal subgroups of the multiplicative group $\mathbb{R}^*$. Let $a \in \mathbb{R}^*$ and $a > 0$. Then $a = a \cdot 1$ and if $a < 0$, then $a = (-a)(-1)$. Hence $\mathbb{R}^* = \mathbb{R}^+ T$. Also $\mathbb{R}^+ \cap T = \{1\}$ and $ab = ba$ for all $a \in \mathbb{R}^+$ and $b \in T$. Hence $\mathbb{R}^*$ is an internal direct product of $\mathbb{R}^+$ and T.

◇ **Exercise 7.1.7.** Find the number of elements of order 5 in $\mathbb{Z}_{15} \times \mathbb{Z}_5$.

Solution. We count the number of elements (a, b) in $\mathbb{Z}_{15} \times \mathbb{Z}_5$ with the property that $5 = o\left((a, b)\right) = lcm\left\{o(a), o(b)\right\}$ [cf. Problem 10 of Exercise 7.1]. If $lcm\left\{o(a), o(b)\right\} = 5$, then we have the following cases:

    Case I. $o(a) = 5, \quad o(b) = 5$

    Case II. $o(a) = 5, \quad o(b) = 1$

    Case III. $o(a) = 1, \quad o(b) = 5$

Case I. Since $\mathbb{Z}_{15}$ is cyclic, it contains only one subgroup of order 5 and $\mathbb{Z}_5$ is itself a subgroup of order 5 in $\mathbb{Z}_5$. In any subgroup of order 5, except identity element, every element is of order 5. Hence there are 4 choices of a and 4 choices of b. This gives 16 elements of order 5 in $\mathbb{Z}_{15} \times \mathbb{Z}_5$.

Case II. There are four choices of a and only one choice of b. This gives 4 elements of order 5 in $\mathbb{Z}_{15} \times \mathbb{Z}_5$.

Case III. There is only one choice of a and four choices of b. This gives 4 elements of order 5 in $\mathbb{Z}_{15} \times \mathbb{Z}_5$.

Thus we find that $\mathbb{Z}_{15} \times \mathbb{Z}_5$ contains 24 elements of order 5.

$\Diamond$ **Exercise 7.1.8.** Find all subgroups of order 7 of the group $\mathbb{Z}_7 \times \mathbb{Z}_{14}$.

Solution. Clearly the number of elements of order 7 in the group $\mathbb{Z}_7 \times \mathbb{Z}_{14}$ is 48. Subgroup generated by any one of these elements is a group of order 7. Suppose H_1 be one such subgroup. Now, consider an element of order 7 of the given group from outside H_1. This element will generate another subgroup, say H_2 of order 7. Clearly $H_1 \cap H_2 = \{e\}$, as $H_1 \cap H_2$ being a subgroup of both H_1 and H_2, its order can only be 1. In this way, it can be seen that there are 8 such subgroups $H_i, i = 1, 2, \ldots 8$ of order 7 each, such that $\bigcap_{i=1}^{8} H_i = \{e\}$. It is easy to see that $[2], [4], [6], [8], [10], [12]$ are the only elements of order 7 in $\mathbb{Z}_{14}$. Hence the 8 subgroups of order 7 in $\mathbb{Z}_7 \times \mathbb{Z}_{14}$ are $\mathbb{Z}_7 \times \{[0]_{14}\}$ and $\{[0]_7\} \times H$ where $H = \{[0]_{14}, [2], [4], [6], [8], [10], [12]\}$ is a subgroup of order 7 in $\mathbb{Z}_{14}$ and six other subgroups generated respectively by $([1]_7, [2]_{14}), ([1]_7, [4]_{14}), ([1]_7, [6]_{14}), ([1]_7, [8]_{14}), ([1]_7, [10]_{14}), ([1]_7, [12]_{14})$.

Remark. It is interesting to note that, while the first two subgroups of $\mathbb{Z}_7 \times \mathbb{Z}_{14}$ in the above solution are coming out as the direct product of subgroups of the respective groups $\mathbb{Z}_7$ and $\mathbb{Z}_{14}$, the other six possible cases are very different in nature. Each of these is a subset of $\mathbb{Z}_7 \times H$ but none can be expressed as a direct product as the first two.[1] We invite you to make a complete list of elements of each of these subgroups separately and observe their pattern of pairings, first one from $\mathbb{Z}_7$ and the second one from H as above.

$\Diamond$ **Exercise 7.1.9.** Find a homomorphism $f : U_{40} \to U_{40}$ with kernel $\{[1], [9], [17], [33]\}$ and $f([11]) = [11]$.

Solution. $|U_{40}| = \phi(40) = 16$. In fact $U_{40} = \{[1], [3], [7], [9], [11], [13], [17], [19], [21], [23], [27], [29], [31], [33], [37], [39]\}$. In U_{40}, $o([17]) = 4$ and $\langle [17] \rangle = \{[1], [9], [17], [33]\} = A$, say, which is normal, as U_{40} is commutative. Again, observe that $o([11]) = o([39]) =$

---

[1]Going ahead of ourselves, we take this opportunity to comment that this is unlike what happens in ring theory, where ideals of a direct product of two rings are found as direct product of the ideals of the rings concerned.

$o([29]) = 2$, whence $B = \{[1], [11], [39], [29]\}$ is also a normal subgroup here, with $A \cap B = \{[1]\}$. (Indeed, $[11] \cdot [39] = [29]$ and though $o(19) = 2$ but $[11] \cdot [19] = [9]$ motivated the choice of B.) As it can be verified that $U_{40} = AB$, so by Theorem 7.1.6 and Theorem 7.1.7, we conclude that $U_{40} \simeq A \times B$. Define $f : A \times B \to A \times B$ by $f(a, b) \mapsto ([1], b)$. Then f is a homomorphism (*projection*) with kernel A and $f(([1], [11])) = (([1], [11]))$. Now identify $([1], [11]) \in A \times B$ with $[11] \in U_{40}$ to appreciate $f : U_{40} \to U_{40}$ with the required property.

$\Diamond$ **Exercise 7.1.10.** Consider the centre $Z(G)$ of a group G. For each positive integer n, define $J_n = \{(g_1, g_2, \ldots, g_n) \in Z(G) \times Z(G) \times \ldots \times Z(G) : g_1 g_2 \cdots g_n = e\}$. As a subset of the direct product of groups $\underbrace{G \times G \times \ldots \times G}_{n-\text{ copies}}$, J_n is

(i) not necessarily a subgroup.

(ii) a subgroup but not necessarily a normal subgroup.

(iii) a normal subgroup.

(iv) isomorphic to the direct product $\underbrace{Z(G) \times Z(G) \times \ldots \times Z(G)}_{(n-1)-\text{copies}}$.

Solution. Since $Z(G)$ is a normal subgroup of G, one can easily prove that J_n is a normal subgroup of $G \times G \times \ldots \times G$. Finally, it is easy to verify that the mapping $\psi : \underbrace{Z(G) \times Z(G) \times \ldots \times Z(G)}_{(n-1)-\text{copies}} \longrightarrow J_n$ defined by

$$\psi(a_1, a_2, \ldots, a_{n-1}) = (a_1, a_2, \ldots, a_{n-1}, a_n),$$

where $a_n = (a_1 a_2 \ldots a_{n-1})^{-1}$ is an isomorphism. Therefore, options (iii) and (iv) are correct.

$\Diamond$ **Exercise 7.1.11.** Let $G = \mathbb{Z}_{10} \times \mathbb{Z}_{15}$. Pick the correct statement(s).

(i) G contains exactly one element of order 2.

(ii) G contains exactly five elements of order 3.

(iii) G contains exactly twenty four elements of order 5.

(iv) G contains exactly twenty four elements of order 10.

Solution. Now [5] is the only one element in $\mathbb{Z}_{10}$ of order 2 and $\mathbb{Z}_{15}$ does not contain any element of order 2. Hence $([5], [0]) \in \mathbb{Z}_{10} \times \mathbb{Z}_{15}$ is the unique element of order 2. Similarly, it can be shown that $([0], [5])$ and $([0], [10])$ are exactly two elements in $\mathbb{Z}_{10} \times \mathbb{Z}_{15}$ of order 3. Hence option (ii) is wrong. Again, $([a], [b]) \in \mathbb{Z}_{10} \times \mathbb{Z}_{15}$ is of order 10 iff either, (I) $o([a]) = 10$ in $\mathbb{Z}_{10}$ and $o([b]) = 1$ in $\mathbb{Z}_{15}$ or, (II) $o([a]) = 10$ in $\mathbb{Z}_{10}$ and $o([b]) = 5$ in $\mathbb{Z}_{15}$ or, (III) $o([a]) = 2$ in $\mathbb{Z}_{10}$ and $o([b]) = 5$ in $\mathbb{Z}_{15}$. Now, in $\mathbb{Z}_{10}$, there are

4 elements of order 10 and 1 element of order 2, whereas there are 4 elements of order 5 in $\mathbb{Z}_{15}$. So $\mathbb{Z}_{10} \times \mathbb{Z}_{15}$ contains 24 elements of order 10. Now $([a], [b]) \in \mathbb{Z}_{10} \times \mathbb{Z}_{15}$ is an element of order 5 if either $[a] = [0] \in \mathbb{Z}_{10}$ and $o([b]) = 5$ in $\mathbb{Z}_{15}$ or, $o([a]) = 5$ in $\mathbb{Z}_{10}$ and $[b] = [0] \in \mathbb{Z}_{15}$, or, both $[a] \in \mathbb{Z}_{10}$ and $[b] \in \mathbb{Z}_{15}$ are elements of order 5. In $\mathbb{Z}_{10}$, the elements of order 5 are $[2], [4], [6]$ and $[8]$. Similarly, in $\mathbb{Z}_{15}$, the elements of order 5 are $[3], [6], [9]$ and $[12]$. Hence there are exactly twenty-four elements in the group $\mathbb{Z}_{10} \times \mathbb{Z}_{15}$ of order 5. Therefore, options (i), (iii) and (iv) are correct.

◊ **Exercise 7.1.12.** Let S_3 be the group of permutations of three distinct symbols. The direct product $S_3 \times S_3$ has an element of order
(i) 4   (ii) 6   (iii) 9   (iv) 18.

Solution. Clearly S_3 contains elements of order 2 and 3. Let $a, b \in S_3$ such that $o(a) = 2$ and $o(b) = 3$. Then $(a, b) \in S_3 \times S_3$ such that $o(a, b) = 6$. But $S_3 \times S_3$ contains no element of order 4, 9 and 18. Therefore, option (ii) is correct.

◊ **Exercise 7.1.13.** Let S_n denote the symmetric group on n symbols. The group $S_3 \times \mathbb{Z}/2\mathbb{Z}$ is isomorphic to which of the following groups?
(i) $\mathbb{Z}/12\mathbb{Z}$ (ii) $\mathbb{Z}/6\mathbb{Z} \times \mathbb{Z}/2\mathbb{Z}$
(iii) A_4, the alternating group of order 12
(iv) D_6, the dihedral group of order 12.

Solution. $S_3 \times \mathbb{Z}/2\mathbb{Z}$ is a noncommutative group of order 12. Now $a = (\alpha, 1+2\mathbb{Z}), b = (\beta, 0+2\mathbb{Z}) \in S_3 \times \mathbb{Z}/2\mathbb{Z}$ are two elements such that $S_3 \times \mathbb{Z}/2\mathbb{Z} = \langle a, b \rangle$, where $\alpha = (1\ 2\ 3)$ and $\beta = (1\ 2)$. Also $o(a) = 6$ and $o(b) = 2$. Moreover, $ba = (\beta, 0 + 2\mathbb{Z})(\alpha, 1 + 2\mathbb{Z}) = (\gamma, 1 + 2\mathbb{Z})$ and $a^{-1}b = (\alpha, 1 + 2\mathbb{Z})^{-1}(\beta, 0 + 2\mathbb{Z}) = (\gamma, 1 + 2\mathbb{Z})$, where $\gamma = (2\ 3)$. Hence $S_3 \times \mathbb{Z}/2\mathbb{Z} \simeq D_6$. Therefore, option (iv) is correct.

Exercises

1. Show that $(\mathbb{C}, +) \simeq (\mathbb{R}, +) \times (\mathbb{R}, +)$.

2. For any two groups H and K, prove that $H \times K \simeq K \times H$.

3. Show that the Klein's four-group K_4 is isomorphic to $\mathbb{Z}_2 \times \mathbb{Z}_2$.

4. Prove that for any two groups H and K, $Z(H \times K) = Z(H) \times Z(K)$.

5. Show that the group $(\mathbb{Z}, +)$ cannot be expressed as an internal direct product of two nontrivial subgroups.

6. Prove that $\mathbb{Z}_m \times \mathbb{Z}_n \simeq \mathbb{Z}_{mn}$ if and only if $gcd\,(m, n) = 1$.

7. Let M and N be two normal subgroups of a group G. Show that there exists a monomorphism from the group $G/M \cap N$ into the group $G/M \times G/N$.

8. Let K_i be normal subgroups of G_i, $i = 1, 2$. Show that $K_1 \times K_2$ is a normal subgroup of $G_1 \times G_2$ and $(G_1 \times G_2)/(K_1 \times K_2) \simeq G_1/K_1 \times G_2/K_2$.

9. If G_1, G_2, H_1, H_2 be groups such that $G_1 \simeq H_1$ and $G_2 \simeq H_2$, then prove that $G_1 \times G_2 \simeq H_1 \times H_2$.

10. Let H and K be two finite groups. Prove that $o(a, b) = lcm\{o(a), o(b)\}$, where $(a, b) \in H \times K$.

11. Find the number of elements of order 5 in $\mathbb{Z}_{25} \times \mathbb{Z}_5$.

12. Find all subgroups of order 14 of the group $\mathbb{Z}_7 \times \mathbb{Z}_{14}$.

13. Show that the mapping $f : \mathbb{Z} \times \mathbb{Z} \to \mathbb{Z}$, defined by $f\big((a, b)\big) = a - b$ is a homomorphism. Find $ker f$.

14. Let G be a cyclic group of order mn where $gcd(m, n) = 1$. Show that there exist subgroups H and K of order m and n respectively, such that $G \simeq H \times K$.

15. Let $\mathbb{C}^*$ be the multiplicative group of nonzero complex numbers. If $\mathbb{R}^+$ is the set of positive real numbers and $T = \{z \in \mathbb{C}^* \,|\, |z| = 1\}$. Then show that $\mathbb{C}^*$ is the internal direct product of $\mathbb{R}^+$ and T.

16. Justify whether the following statements are true or false:
    (a) $\mathbb{Z} \times \mathbb{Z} \simeq \mathbb{Z}$.
    (b) $\mathbb{R}^* \times \mathbb{R}^* \simeq \mathbb{R}^*$.
    (c) There exists a noncyclic commutative group of order 28.
    (d) There exists a noncommutative group of order 24.
    (e) There exists a noncommutative group of order 30.
    (f) $\mathbb{Z}_6 \times \mathbb{Z}_4 \simeq \mathbb{Z}_{24}$.
    (g) $\mathbb{Z}_7 \times \mathbb{Z}_9 \simeq \mathbb{Z}_{63}$.

    Pick the correct option(s) from the following:

17. The number of subgroups of order 2 in the group $\mathbb{Z}_2 \times \mathbb{Z}_2 \times \mathbb{Z}_2$ is
    (i) 8   (ii) 7   (iii) 4   (iv) 1.

18. The order of any nonidentity element of $\mathbb{Z}_3 \times \mathbb{Z}_3$ is
    (i)   3   (ii) 9   (iii) 6   (iv) none of these.

19. It is true that
    (i) $\mathbb{Z}_2 \times \mathbb{Z}_3$ is isomorphic to $\mathbb{Z}_6$
    (ii) $\mathbb{Z}_3 \times \mathbb{Z}_3$ is isomorphic to $\mathbb{Z}_9$
    (iii) $\mathbb{Z}_4 \times \mathbb{Z}_6$ is isomorphic to $\mathbb{Z}_{24}$
    (iv) $\mathbb{Z}_2 \times \mathbb{Z}_3 \times \mathbb{Z}_5$ is isomorphic to $\mathbb{Z}_{30}$.

20. For any group of order 36 and any subgroup H of G of order 4
    (i) $H \subset Z(G)$
    (ii) $H = Z(G)$
    (iii) H is a normal in G
    (iv) H is an Abelian group.

Chapter 8

Symmetry

In this chapter, we shall digress from our purely algebraic approach to the concept of group, and try to bring a geometric flavour in our discussion. Indeed, one general perception of geometric beauty lies in symmetry, and groups can be applied as a very useful tool, to study various geometrically symmetric patterns. It is not without reason, that a particular type of groups is called *symmetric group*! The possible interplay between algebra and geometry was first appreciated by Réne Descartes (1596-1650), who removed the *synthetic* bondage of Greek geometry, and opened up a new horizon by introducing the notion of analytic geometry, where study of geometry is done via the language of algebra. This interaction has reached an amazing depth, enriching both the branches to a great extent. In apt words of Sophie Germain: *the algebra is but a geometry in writing; the geometry is but an algebra enfigured.*

Before we proceed further, we would like to state that an analysis of the concept of symmetry in its fullest flourish, so as to encompass the modern study of all the *ornamental groups*, like *wallpaper groups*[1] or the problem of *tiling of the plane* is beyond the scope of this text. We would rather describe the initial concepts required for this study, in the language of the so called *transformation geometry*, with special attention towards describing the symmetric group S_3 of **symmetries of an equilateral triangle** or dihedral group D_4 of **symmetries of a square**. Furthermore, we shall not take up the axiomatic treatment of the subject, rather we shall take the liberty of an intuitive approach.

---

[1] It was formally proved in 1891 by E. S. Fedorov that there exist only 17 non-isomorphic groups of symmetry types of wallpaper patterns, though modern research indicates that this fact was implicitly known to the Moors of the later Middle age, who took a fancy of applying these designs to decorate their forts, palaces and mosques.

8.1   Isometry

We begin with the concept of transformation of a set.

Definition 8.1.1. A ***transformation of a set*** X means a permutation of the set X, i.e., a bijective mapping f from the set X onto itself.

It then goes without saying that everything that has already been proved for a permutation of a set, is naturally true in the present context also. Indeed, the set of all transformations of a set with more than two elements, form in general, a noncommutative group under the natural composition of transformations, which is essentially a composition of bijective mappings.

In a somewhat lofty proposition, Felix Klein (1849-1925), an illustrious student of Camille Jordan, upon his acceptance of the chair at the University of Erlangen, observed[2] that ***geometry*** *is the study of those properties of a set that remain invariant under some fixed subgroup* (group of symmetry, as we shall later call them) *of the full transformation group*. Though with the introduction of various other geometries, this belief that every geometry can be classified in terms of their symmetry groups is no longer tenable, nonetheless Klein's model of non-Euclidean geometries helped us to appreciate the place for non-Euclidean geometries in the body of mathematics as a whole. However, the said correspondence for the classical geometries and their groups of symmetry still remains valid.

To look into Euclidean geometry from this perspective, we first note that here we have sets for which a concept of *distance between elements* is defined. Let $\mathcal{P}$ denote a plane and suppose for every pair of points A, B of $\mathcal{P}$, distance $d(A, B)$ between those points, which is some non negative real number, is defined.

A ***rigid motion*** of the plane or an isometry[3], as we shall prefer to call it, is any way of moving all the points in the plane in such a manner that the relative distance between the points remains the same and the relative position of the points stays the same. More formally, we have the following definition:

Definition 8.1.2. A transformation $\alpha : \mathcal{P} \to \mathcal{P}$ is called an ***isometry*** or a ***rigid motion*** if it preserves distance, in the sense that for every pair of points $A, B \in \mathcal{P}$, $d(A, B) = d\big(\alpha(A), \alpha(B)\big)$.

Example 8.1.3. Trivially, the ***identity transformation*** of $\mathcal{P}$ onto itself, given by $i : \mathcal{P} \to \mathcal{P}$ such that $i(A) = A$ for all $A \in \mathcal{P}$ is an isometry.

---

[2]This address is famous in the history of mathematics as the *Erlanger Programme*.

[3]The origin of the word is from Greek *isos* (equal) and *metron* (measure).

Definition 8.1.4. A transformation of order 2 is called an **involution**. This means that if α is an involution then, $\alpha^2 = i$ but $\alpha \neq i$, i.e., in other words, $\alpha = \alpha^{-1}$. Observe that, by definition i is not an involution.

It can be shown, the subset of the full transformation group, consisting of all isometries of some set, on which the idea of distance is defined, is a subgroup. We denote it by $\mathfrak{S}$. In the light of Klein's definition, one may say that *Euclidean geometry is the study of those properties of line, line segment, triangle, angle etc. that remain invariant under the group of isometries.*

Going ahead of ourselves here, we may point out that translations, rotations, reflections and glide reflections, as we shall introduce shortly, are examples of such isometries. Indeed, it is remarkable that *any isometry of the plane $\mathcal{P}$ is either of these four types.*

Definition 8.1.5. If an isometry α carries a figure F (i.e., a subset of $\mathcal{P}$) to itself, it is called a **symmetry** of F.

A little reflection at the back of the mind shows that the set of all symmetries of F again forms a subgroup $\mathfrak{G}$ of $\mathfrak{S}$, called the **group of symmetries** of the figure F.

Definition 8.1.6. A point $P \in \mathcal{P}$ (line $l \subseteq \mathcal{P}$) is said to be a **fixed point** (resp. **fixed line**) of some transformation α of $\mathcal{P}$, if α fixes P (resp. l), i.e., $\alpha(P) = P$ (resp. $\alpha(l) = l$). Clearly, every point (resp. line) of $\mathcal{P}$ is fixed under the identity transformation i.

8.2 Four Isometries of the Plane

Let us now describe the above mentioned isometries one by one, in a somewhat informal manner, with the help of diagrams. We would rather state some important facts about them, without giving explicit proof. We begin with the isometry called **translation**.

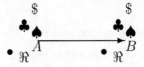

Fig. 16 *Translation through* $\overrightarrow{AB}$

In a translation, every point of $\mathcal{P}$ is moved by the same distance in the same direction, so that the line segments joining the initial and final positions of respective points are equal in length and parallel.

Example 8.2.1. In the language of Cartesian coordinates, a translation $\tau_{(a,b)}$ takes a point (x, y) to the point $(x + a, y + b)$. It can be justified that if $A \neq B$, then there is no fixed point of the translation $\tau_{(\overrightarrow{AB})}$, where $\tau_{(\overrightarrow{AB})}$ stands for the translation in the direction $\overrightarrow{AB}$ through the magnitude $d(A, B)$ (Fig. 16). However, all those lines that are parallel to the line AB are fixed. Since the composition of two translations is again so, it is not difficult to see that *translations of $\mathcal{P}$ form an abelian group*, where the translation through a null vector plays the role of identity.

Next we take up the isometry called **rotation**. Intuitively, a rotation fixes only one point of the plane and everything else rotates by the same amount around that point. Examine the following diagram (Fig. 17):

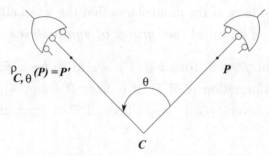

Fig. 17 *Rotation through an angle q*

Example 8.2.2. A rotation $\rho_{C,\theta}$ about a point $C \in \mathcal{P}$, through an angle θ (measured anticlockwise), where $0 \leq \theta < 2\pi$, (or, simply ρ_θ where C is understood from the context) is a transformation such that it fixes C and maps any other point $P \in \mathcal{P}$ to such a point $P' \in \mathcal{P}$ that, $d(C, P) = d(C, P')$ and the angle measure of the angle made by $\overrightarrow{CP}$ and $\overrightarrow{CP'}$ is θ.

The point C is called the **centre of rotation**. We merely comment here that the composition of two rotations about the same centre is again a rotation with that very centre, whence these *rotations with same centre form a subgroup of the group* $\mathfrak{S}$ *of isometries*. However, in case of rotations with different centres C and D, such a subgroup is not attained, as here the set is not closed under the composition[4].

A special kind of rotation is called **halfturn** as we shall describe now.

---

[4]It can be shown that the composition of two rotations with two different centres may either be a rotation with a new centre or may turn out to be a translation in a certain case.

Example 8.2.3. A halfturn H_C is nothing but a rotation $\rho_{C,\theta}$ with centre C and $\theta = 180°$ and hence it is an involution. So composition of two halfturns about the same centre is the identity transformation, which in turn tells us that halfturns do not form a group by themselves. However composition of two halfturns with different centres can be proved to be a translation and a translation can be looked upon as a product of two halfturns with suitable centres, whence union of the translations and the halfturns form a group.

We now describe another isometry of the plane, called the **reflection about a line** or line reflection, in short.

Example 8.2.4. A line reflection σ_m, about a line $m \subseteq \mathcal{P}$ is a transformation such that it fixes all the points $P \in m$, whereas any other $Q \in \mathcal{P}$ is mapped to such a $Q' \in \mathcal{P}$ that, the line m becomes the perpendicular bisector of the line segment QQ' (Fig. 18). Here $\sigma_m(Q) = Q'$ is called the *image* of Q under the reflection σ_m and m is called the **line of reflection**.

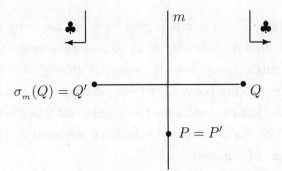

Fig. 18 *Reflection about a line* m

Observe that $\sigma_m \neq i$ but $\sigma_m^2 = i$, whence reflection is an involution. Observe that a halfturn H_C can also be looked upon as a *reflection in the point* C, denoted by σ_C [5]. Indeed, $H_C = \sigma_C = \sigma_C^{-1}$. Note further that reflection σ_m interchanges the half-planes of m. The points on m are the only fixed points of σ_m. However, it fixes the line m point-wise and also fixes every line that is perpendicular to m. A significant property of reflection is that, unlike translation or rotation, it reverses the orientation in the sense that it flips the plane over.

---

[5]Imitating the definition of σ_m, one may define σ_C as a transformation that fixes the point C only and any other $Q \in \mathcal{P}$ is mapped to such a $Q' \in \mathcal{P}$ that C is the midpoint of the line segment QQ'.

Definition 8.2.5. The line m is called a *line of symmetry* of a figure F (which is essentially a set of points in $\mathcal{P}$), if $\sigma_m(F) = F$, i.e., if σ_m fixes F. We shall refer to σ_m as a *linear symmetry* of F.

Definition 8.2.6. A point P is called a *centre of symmetry* of a figure F if there is a rotation $\rho_{P,\theta}$ about P through some angle θ that leaves the figure F unchanged, while its parts may be permuted. The smallest angle θ for which this happens is called the *angle of rotational symmetry* of the figure F. Later we shall refer to $\rho_{P,\theta}$ as a *rotational symmetry* of F.

Remark 8.2.7. Similarly as the line of symmetry, one may define a point P to be a *point of symmetry* of some figure F if $\sigma_P(F) = (F)$. However, this should not be confused with the centre of symmetry, in general. Clearly, a point of symmetry is a type of centre of symmetry but the converse is not true.

It is not difficult to see that the a figure may or may not have a line (or, point) of symmetry and certain figures may have one or more such lines of symmetry. Try to appreciate that the following example forms the pictorial perspective of each geometrical figure.

Example 8.2.8. A scalene triangle or a parallelogram does not have any line of symmetry, whereas there are three lines of symmetry of an equilateral triangle (along three medians) and a circle has infinitely many lines of symmetry (along any of its diameters). Note carefully that, the meeting point of the diagonals of the parallelogram is its point of symmetry. Observe that the centroid of an equilateral triangle is its centre of symmetry, with an angle $120°$ as its angle of rotational symmetry. However, an equilateral triangle has no point of symmetry.

An interesting exercise may be to find the lines, points and centres of symmetry (when these exist) of each of the upper case English alphabets. Can you think of a figure that has exactly n lines of symmetry, for any given integral value of $n \geq 3$?

Remark 8.2.9. Interestingly, *every plane isometry can be expressed as a composition of at most three reflections.* This in turn tells us that reflection alone can generate the isometry group. Indeed, the product of two reflections σ_m and σ_k in parallel lines m, k can be shown to be a translation through twice the distance between the lines m and k, in the perpendicular direction to the lines m and k, the sense being from k towards m for $\sigma_m \sigma_k$ and from m towards k for $\sigma_k \sigma_m$. Again if the lines m and k intersect at some point $C \in \mathcal{P}$, then $\sigma_m \sigma_k = \rho_{C,2\theta}$ where θ is the angle between the intersecting lines. In particular, when $\theta = 90°$, this product becomes a halfturn H_C about the point C.

Finally, we take up the description of the isometry called the **glide reflection**.

Definition 8.2.10. A glide reflection is a reflection about a line followed by a translation in a direction parallel to the line of reflection (Fig. 19).

Note that the composition is to be counted as one motion. Since this involves translation, there is no fixed point of glide reflection. The line of reflection involved in glide reflection is called the **glide line** and it is the only fixed line of a glide reflection. Since translation preserves orientation and reflection reverses it, we see that glide reflection, which is a product of these two, reverses the orientation. This clearly indicates that this is a new isometry, which is neither a rotation nor a translation, as both these isometries preserve the orientation.

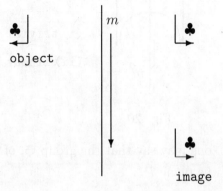

Fig. 19 *Glide Reflection about a line m*

8.3   Group of Symmetries

Now that we have described all the isometries of the plane, we can concentrate on finding the *group of symmetries* of a plane figure, where the group operation is taken to be the composition of isometries. However, we shall restrict our discussion within the finite figures in plane. Blissfully all the standard geometric shapes that you are acquainted with from your high school days fall in this category.

Definition 8.3.1. By a **finite figure**, we mean such a plane figure that does not have any nontrivial translational symmetry.

Let us recall the Definition 8.1.5. We have seen that a symmetry is an isometry which leaves a figure F in plane appearing exactly the same as before even after suffering the transformation.

Definition 8.3.2. The identity transformation can be considered as the ***trivial symmetry*** for any figure in the plane whatsoever. Note further that trivial symmetry can be looked upon as a rotational symmetry about any point of the plane, with an angle of rotation $0°$ or equivalently $360°$.

Example 8.3.3. Consider the symmetries of the following figure (Fig. 20). Clearly the group of symmetries of this figure is given by $\mathfrak{G} = \{i, \sigma_m\}$.

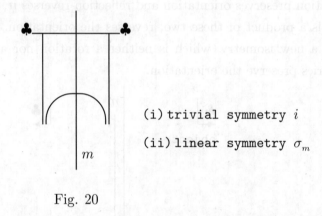

(i) trivial symmetry i

(ii) linear symmetry σ_m

Fig. 20

Remark 8.3.4. Observe that, one may say that the group $\mathfrak{G}$, of all the four isometries, is the group of symmetry of the plane $\mathcal{P}$.

Example 8.3.5. Let us consider a *rectangle which is not a square*. Fig. 21 shows that two lines along the perpendicular bisectors of opposite sides are precisely its lines of symmetry and their point of intersection is the centre of symmetry, while the angle of rotational symmetry is clearly $180°$.

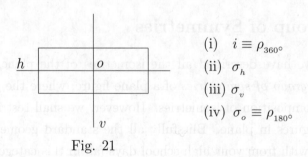

(i) $i \equiv \rho_{360°}$

(ii) σ_h

(iii) σ_v

(iv) $\sigma_o \equiv \rho_{180°}$

Fig. 21

This *group of symmetries of a rectangle which is not a square* is nothing but the **Klein's four-group** (Definition 5.1.13) upto isomorphism and is denoted[6] by $\mathcal{K}_4$. The Cayley table for this group in the present context can be constructed as follows, which is actually same as the one given in Example 5.1.20:

---

[6]Four-group in German is *Vierergruppe* and hence some authors use the name $\mathcal{V}_4$.

$\circ$	i	σ_h	σ_v	σ_o
i	i	σ_h	σ_v	σ_o
σ_h	σ_h	i	σ_o	σ_v
σ_v	σ_v	σ_o	i	σ_h
σ_o	σ_o	σ_v	σ_h	i

Example 8.3.6. Recall that in Example 4.1.4, we have described the **symmetric group** S_3 as the noncommutative group of six permutations of the set $\{1,2,3\}$ as follows:

$$S_3 = \{e, (1\,2), (1\,3), (2\,3), (1\,2\,3), (1\,3\,2)\},$$

whence we find that S_3 consists of one 1-cycle, three 2-cycles and two 3-cycles. To have a nice geometric description of this group, begin with an *equilateral triangle* and name its vertices as $1, 2$ and 3. It is then easy to see that the 1-cycle above is the trivial symmetry and each of the 2-cycles represents a linear symmetry about the lines along the medians, whereas the 3-cycles can be looked upon as rotational symmetries about the centroid through angles $120°$ and $240°$ respectively (Fig. 22).

Observe that the equilateral triangle has 6 symmetries altogether. Three of them are rotations about the centroid and three are line reflections about respective medians. If we denote the rotation $\rho_{120°}$ by ρ, then clearly $\rho^2 = \rho_{240°}$ and $\rho^3 = \rho_{360°} = i$. Again, if we denote a reflection say, σ_l by σ, it is not difficult to verify that $\sigma_n = \sigma\rho$ and $\sigma_k = \sigma\rho^2$.

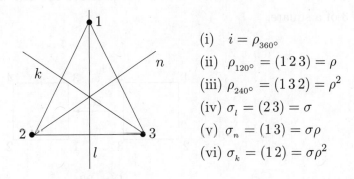

(i) $i = \rho_{360°}$

(ii) $\rho_{120°} = (1\,2\,3) = \rho$

(iii) $\rho_{240°} = (1\,3\,2) = \rho^2$

(iv) $\sigma_l = (2\,3) = \sigma$

(v) $\sigma_n = (1\,3) = \sigma\rho$

(vi) $\sigma_k = (1\,2) = \sigma\rho^2$

Fig. 22

The group $S_3 = \{i, \rho, \rho^2, \sigma, \sigma\rho, \sigma\rho^2\}$, can now be appreciated as the *group of symmetries of an equilateral triangle*, its Cayley table being as follows:

$\circ$	i	ρ	ρ^2	σ	$\sigma\rho$	$\sigma\rho^2$
i	i	ρ	ρ^2	σ	$\sigma\rho$	$\sigma\rho^2$
ρ	ρ	ρ^2	i	$\sigma\rho^2$	σ	$\sigma\rho$
ρ^2	ρ^2	i	ρ	$\sigma\rho$	$\sigma\rho^2$	σ
σ	σ	$\sigma\rho$	$\sigma\rho^2$	i	ρ	ρ^2
$\sigma\rho$	$\sigma\rho$	$\sigma\rho^2$	σ	ρ^2	i	ρ
$\sigma\rho^2$	$\sigma\rho^2$	σ	$\sigma\rho$	ρ	ρ^2	i

Remark 8.3.7. It is interesting to note that as $o(\rho) = 3$, the set $C_3 = \{i, \rho, \rho^2\}$ of rotations only, make a cyclic subgroup of the group S_3 with exactly half of the elements of S_3. Amazingly, for the Klein's four-group (Example 8.3.5) also, one can check that the rotations alone, given by $C_2 = \{i, \rho_{180°}\}$ form a cyclic subgroup, with exactly half of the elements of the group, though Klein's four-group does not match the requirements of S_2, since $|S_2| = 2! = 2$, but $|\mathcal{K}_4| = 4$. It seems we are yet to hit any pattern for generalization. Let us investigate further. We shall shortly see that there is a striking pattern that can be generalized elegantly.

At this stage, one may be tempted to think that the symmetries of a square should give us the group S_4. That this is *not* the case can be seen from the fact that the transformation on I_4 given by the permutation

$$\alpha = \begin{pmatrix} 1 & 2 & 3 & 4 \\ 2 & 3 & 1 & 4 \end{pmatrix} \in S_4$$

is not an isometry of the square. Check out in the following diagram (Fig. 23) that the above mentioned transformation does not preserve the distance between the vertices 1 and 3 of a square.

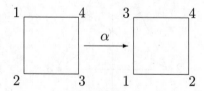

Fig. 23

So we have seen that all of the 24 members of the group S_4 do not fix the square, whence S_4 cannot be the group of symmetries of a square.[7]. So what are *the symmetries of a square?* Let us first examine geometrically.

---

[7]The group S_4, known as the *full tetrahedral group*, can be looked upon as the *group of symmetries of a regular tetrahedron.* This is a solid object with four faces, each an equilateral triangle.

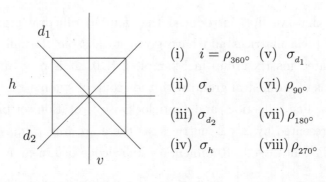

(i) $i = \rho_{360°}$ (v) σ_{d_1}

(ii) σ_v (vi) $\rho_{90°}$

(iii) σ_{d_2} (vii) $\rho_{180°}$

(iv) σ_h (viii) $\rho_{270°}$

Fig. 24

Example 8.3.8. A square is linearly symmetric about four lines of symmetry. These are precisely the two lines v and h, respectively along the vertical and horizontal perpendicular bisectors of its opposite sides and the two lines d_1 and d_2 along the diagonals, as shown in Fig. 24. Again, apart from the trivial symmetry (a rotation through 360°), it has three (anticlockwise) rotational symmetries about the meeting point of the diagonals, through angles 90°, 180° and 270° respectively. Denoting these eight symmetries as $\rho_{360°}, \rho_{90°}, \rho_{180°}, \rho_{270°}, \sigma_h, \sigma_v, \sigma_{d_1}, \sigma_{d_2}$, we now give the Cayley table of the group of symmetries of a square, where the group operation is as usual the composition of these isometries.

$\circ$	$\rho_{360°}$	$\rho_{90°}$	$\rho_{180°}$	$\rho_{270°}$	σ_h	σ_v	σ_{d_1}	σ_{d_2}
$\rho_{360°}$	$\rho_{360°}$	$\rho_{90°}$	$\rho_{180°}$	$\rho_{270°}$	σ_h	σ_v	σ_{d_1}	σ_{d_2}
$\rho_{90°}$	$\rho_{90°}$	$\rho_{180°}$	$\rho_{270°}$	$\rho_{360°}$	σ_{d_1}	σ_{d_2}	σ_v	σ_h
$\rho_{180°}$	$\rho_{180°}$	$\rho_{270°}$	$\rho_{360°}$	$\rho_{90°}$	σ_v	σ_h	σ_{d_2}	σ_{d_1}
$\rho_{270°}$	$\rho_{270°}$	$\rho_{360°}$	$\rho_{90°}$	$\rho_{180°}$	σ_{d_2}	σ_{d_1}	σ_h	σ_v
σ_h	σ_h	σ_{d_2}	σ_v	σ_{d_1}	$\rho_{360°}$	$\rho_{180°}$	$\rho_{270°}$	$\rho_{90°}$
σ_v	σ_v	σ_{d_1}	σ_h	σ_{d_2}	$\rho_{180°}$	$\rho_{360°}$	$\rho_{90°}$	$\rho_{270°}$
σ_{d_1}	σ_{d_1}	σ_h	σ_{d_2}	σ_v	$\rho_{90°}$	$\rho_{270°}$	$\rho_{360°}$	$\rho_{180°}$
σ_{d_2}	σ_{d_2}	σ_v	σ_{d_1}	σ_h	$\rho_{270°}$	$\rho_{90°}$	$\rho_{180°}$	$\rho_{360°}$

It can be shown that if $\rho_{90°}$ be taken as ρ and σ_h as σ, then the eight *symmetries of a square* can be represented by the group $\{i, \rho, \rho^2, \rho^3, \sigma, \sigma\rho, \sigma\rho^2, \sigma\rho^3\}$ where i is the identity, $\rho^4 = \sigma^2 = i$ and $\sigma\rho = \rho^3\sigma$. This group $\langle \rho, \sigma \rangle$ with eight elements is a noncommutative group and it is called the (fourth) **dihedral group** and is usually denoted by $\mathcal{D}_4$ (see Definition 5.1.9)[8] which now turns out to be the **group of symmetries of a square**. Note that the subset $C_4 = \{i, \rho, \rho^2, \rho^3\}$ of $\mathcal{D}_4$ is actually a cyclic subgroup as expected, consisting of all the rotational symmetries of the square.

---

[8]This group is also referred to as **octic group**.

Note: Recall that we first introduced the (fourth) dihedral group in Problem 6(b) of Exercise 3.1 via matrices and have given its abstract formulation as a particular finitely generated matrix group in Example 5.1.10. It is now time to correlate these representations of a dihedral group with the group of symmetries of a square. Indeed, the isometries 'line reflection' and (anticlockwise) 'rotation' of plane, i.e., $\mathbb{R}^2$ can be naturally represented by 2×2 matrices, as these are *linear transformations* from the vector space $\mathbb{R}^2$ onto itself. Rudimentary knowledge of Linear Algebra indicates that the matrices $r_k = \begin{bmatrix} c & -s \\ s & c \end{bmatrix}$, for $k = 0, 1, 2, 3$ where the symbols c and s respectively stand for $\cos\theta$ and $\sin\theta$, with $\theta = \frac{2\pi k}{4}$, represent the successive anticlockwise rotations (about the origin, e.g. the meeting point of the diagonals of the square in Fig.24) through angle θ. Similarly, the matrices $s_k = \begin{bmatrix} c & s \\ s & -c \end{bmatrix}$, for $k = 0, 1, 2, 3$ where c and s are as before, represent the line reflection in a line inclined at an angle $\frac{\theta}{2}$ with the positive direction of x-axis (e.g. the line h in Fig. 24). With this, all pieces of information fall in their own place and it is now easy to retrieve the eight matrices of Problem 6(b) of Exercise 3.1 as elements of $\mathcal{D}_4$. Furthermore, the generators of $\mathcal{D}_4$ given in Example 5.1.10 by $\boldsymbol{R} = \begin{bmatrix} 0 & -1 \\ 1 & 0 \end{bmatrix}$, and $\boldsymbol{S} = \begin{bmatrix} 0 & -1 \\ -1 & 0 \end{bmatrix}$ can easily be seen to be the matrices corresponding to rotational symmetry $\rho_{90°}$ and reflection symmetry σ_{d_1}, whence it is geometrically clear that $o(\boldsymbol{R}) = 4$, $o(\boldsymbol{S}) = 2$.

Remark 8.3.9. At this stage, an inquisitive mind might think about the word '*fourth*' used in the above discussion. Is it possible to talk about $\mathcal{D}_n$ in general? If so, then what is its geometric significance? Before we conclude this chapter, we would like to discuss this point in brief.

Definition 8.3.10. We have already pointed out that every isometry is a product of reflections. An isometry is **even** or **odd** according to it being a product of an even or odd number of reflections. Also every isometry is either even or odd, but never both.

Remark 8.3.11. We merely state that *every finite figure has either only rotational symmetry or else has an equal number of rotational and linear symmetries*. If a finite figure has exactly n rotational symmetries and no linear symmetry, then the figure is said to have a symmetry group C_n, whereas if a figure has exactly n rotational symmetries and exactly n linear symmetries, then the figure is said to have a symmetry group $\mathcal{D}_n$. The letter C stands for *cyclic* and the letter $\mathcal{D}$ stands for *dihedral*. Also note that $|C_n| = n$ and $|\mathcal{D}_n| = 2n$. The following figures as represented by Figs. 25 a, b, c, d and e along with their groups of symmetry written below them, may help to clear the conception.

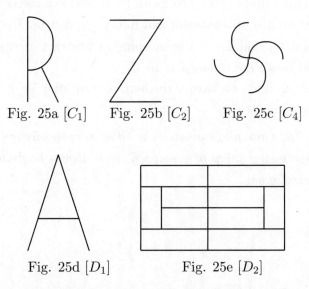

Fig. 25a $[C_1]$ Fig. 25b $[C_2]$ Fig. 25c $[C_4]$

Fig. 25d $[D_1]$ Fig. 25e $[D_2]$

Remark 8.3.12. We sum up this chapter by merely stating that it can be proved that the group $\mathcal{D}_n$, the nth dihedral group with $2n$ elements, is the symmetry group of a regular n-gon, which has exactly n linear symmetry and exactly n rotational symmetry[9]. In fact, one can show that for each positive integer n, there is a polygon having symmetry group $\mathcal{D}_n$ and a polygon having symmetry group C_n. Indeed, the group C_1 consists of only the identity element (trivial symmetry) and hence is the symmetry group of a scalene triangle, whereas the group $\mathcal{D}_1$ is the group of symmetry of an isosceles triangle which is not equilateral. The group C_2 contains only the identity and a halfturn, whence it is the symmetry group of a parallelogram which is not a rhombus, whereas, the group $\mathcal{D}_2$ is the symmetry group of a rectangle that is not a square. This makes $\mathcal{D}_2$ the same (i.e., isomorphic) as Klein's four-group $\mathcal{K}_4$ (see Example 5.1.21), just as $\boldsymbol{\mathcal{D}_3}$ **is the same (i.e., isomorphic) as** $\boldsymbol{S_3}$. Surely by now, the justification for the name $\mathcal{D}_4$ to the symmetry group of a square is clear. Observe that for any positive integer n, the collection of all even isometries in $\mathcal{D}_n$ (i.e., essentially the rotational symmetries about the centre of symmetry O) form a cyclic subgroup of $\mathcal{D}_n$, which is denoted[10] by $C_n = \langle \rho \rangle$, where $\rho = \rho_{(O, 360°/n)}$. All $\mathcal{D}_n$ for $n \geq 3$ are noncommutative groups. However

---

[9]If the elements of $\mathcal{D}_n$ given abstractly by $\langle \{r, s\} \rangle = \{r^0, r^1, r^2, \ldots r^{n-1}, s, rs, r^2 s \ldots r^{n-1} s\}$ where $o(r) = n$, $o(s) = 2$ and $sr = r^{n-1}s$, be looked upon respectively as n **rotations** $\rho_0, \rho_1, \ldots \rho_{n-1}$ and n **reflections** $\sigma_0, \sigma_1, \ldots \sigma_{n-1}$, then the group table may be computed by $\rho_i \rho_j = \rho_{i+j}$, $\rho_i \sigma_j = \sigma_{i+j}$, $\sigma_i \rho_j = \sigma_{i-j}$, $\sigma_i \sigma_j = \rho_{i-j}$, where the addition and subtraction in the subscripts are to be considered modulo n, as shown in Example 5.1.21 for $n = 2$.

[10]The finite groups of isometries C_n and $\mathcal{D}_n$ discussed above constitute a type of ornamental group known as ***rosette groups*** in the literature of group theory.

for $n \geq 4$, $\mathcal{D}_n$ is always a proper subgroup of S_n. Hence we have two infinite classes of finite symmetry groups: finite cyclic groups of rotational symmetries $C_1, C_2, C_3, \ldots$ and the finite dihedral groups of rotational and linear symmetries $\mathcal{D}_1, \mathcal{D}_2, \mathcal{D}_3, \ldots$ It is interesting to note that C_2 and D_1 are isomorphic as abstract groups as both have exactly 2 elements and hence are isomorphic to Z_2.

Turning the matter around, we have a theorem named after Leonardo Da Vinci[11] (1452-1519) which we merely state.

Theorem 8.3.13. *A finite group of isometries is either a cyclic group C_n or a dihedral group $\mathcal{D}_n$ and since symmetry group of a polygon must always be finite, it is either a cyclic group or a dihedral group.*

---

[11]Hermann Weyl (18885-1955) showed in his book *Symmetry* that Da Vinci had systematically studied the possible symmetries of regular polygon and applied it to the architectural constructions of his time.

Chapter 9

Finite Abelian Groups

We have already seen that every cyclic group is Abelian. Furthermore, it has also been proved that any two finite cyclic groups of the same order are isomorphic to each other, and for any positive integer n, the only cyclic group of order n (up to isomorphism) is $\mathbb{Z}_n$. Clearly, this determines all the finite cyclic groups of arbitrary order. However, turning the matter around, the additive groups $\mathbb{R}$, $\mathbb{Q}$ remind us that an Abelian group need not always be cyclic. But if we restrict our attention to *finite* Abelian groups, it is interesting to observe that any such group can be expressed as a direct sum of finite cyclic groups, as we will prove in this chapter. Thus, the structural properties of any finite Abelian group turns out to be nice, as that can be determined from the properties of finite cyclic groups, which are already well known.

In this chapter, we will use *additive notation* for the group operation. Accordingly, '0' and '$-a$' will denote respectively the identity element and the inverse of an element a.

9.1   Finite Abelian Groups

We begin our journey with the following definition.

Definition 9.1.1. An Abelian group G is said to be the ***internal direct sum*** or simply a ***direct sum*** of subgroups $G_1, G_2, \ldots, G_n$ if

   (i) $G = G_1 + G_2 + \cdots + G_n$

       (i.e., for all $g \in G$, $g = g_1 + g_2 + \cdots + g_n$ for some $g_i \in G_i$, $i = 1, 2, \ldots, n$) and

   (ii) $G_i \cap (G_1 + \cdots + G_{i-1} + G_{i+1} + \cdots + G_n) = \{0\}$ for all $i = 1, 2, \ldots, n$.

If G is a direct sum of subgroups $G_1, G_2, \ldots, G_n$ then we write

$$G = G_1 \oplus G_2 \oplus \cdots \oplus G_n.$$

It can be shown that a finite Abelian group G is a direct sum of subgroups G_1, G_2, $\ldots, G_n$ if and only if G is isomorphic to the direct product $G_1 \times G_2 \times \ldots \times G_n$ of groups $G_1, G_2, \ldots, G_n$. Hence, we find that

$$G = G_1 \oplus G_2 \oplus \cdots \oplus G_n \simeq G_1 \times G_2 \times \ldots \times G_n.$$

If $G = G_1 \oplus G_2 \oplus \cdots \oplus G_n$ and $G_i \simeq H_i$, where H_i is a group, $i = 1, 2, \ldots, n$, then

$$G \simeq H_1 \oplus H_2 \oplus \cdots \oplus H_n.$$

Definition 9.1.2. Let G be an Abelian group and A be a subgroup of G. Then A is called a ***direct summand*** of G, if there exists a subgroup B of G such that $G = A \oplus B$.

We now prove a theorem for finite Abelian group which gives a partial converse of Lagrange's theorem. This theorem is due to A. L. Cauchy and is known as **Cauchy's theorem for *finite* Abelian groups**.

Theorem 9.1.3. *Suppose G be a finite Abelian group of order n such that n is divisible by a prime p. Then G contains an element of order p (and consequently a subgroup of order p).*

Proof. The proof is by induction on the order of G. If $|G| = p$, a prime, then every element of G, other than 0, has order p. Thus, in particular, the theorem is true when $|G| = 2$. Now we make the induction hypothesis that the theorem is true for all groups of order r, where $2 \leq r < n$. Suppose G is an Abelian group of order n and p be a prime number such that $p \,|\, n$. Let $a \in G$ with $a \neq 0$ and let m denote the order of a. Then either p divides m or p does not divide m. If $p \mid m$, then $m = pk$ for some positive integer $k \, (< m)$. Since $o(a) = m$, and $k < m$, so $ka \neq 0$. Also $p(ka) = (pk)a = ma = 0$ implies ka is an element of order p. Now suppose p does not divide m. Since G is commutative, the cyclic subgroup $H = \langle a \rangle$ of G is of course a normal subgroup of G. Now $|G| = m \cdot [G : H]$. Since p does not divide m, we have $p \mid [G : H]$. Hence, p divides $|G/H|$. Since $|H| = m > 1$, we have $2 \leq |G/H| = \frac{n}{m} < n$, and hence by the induction hypothesis there exists $b + H \in G/H$ such that $o(b + H) = p$. Then

$$pb + H = p(b + H) = H.$$

Hence, $pb \in H$. Now $H = \langle a \rangle$ implies that $|H| = m$ and then, $p(mb) = m(pb) = 0$, so that, either $mb = 0$, or mb has order p. But $mb \neq 0$, else $m(b + H) = mb + H = H$, would yield $p \mid m$, a contradiction. Thus, mb has order p, whence mb is the desired element of G. $\square$

Next, we apply Cauchy's theorem to prove that **the converse of Lagrange's theorem holds for finite Abelian groups**.

Theorem 9.1.4. *Let G be a finite Abelian group of order n. If m is a positive integer such that $m \mid n$, then G has a subgroup of order m.*

Proof. If $m = 1$, then $\{e\}$ is the required subgroup of order m. If $n = 1$, then $m = n = 1$, and the result follows trivially. We now assume that $m > 1$, $n > 1$ and prove the result by induction on n. If $n = 2$, then $m = 2 = n$ and G itself is the required subgroup of order m. Suppose now that the theorem is true for all finite Abelian groups of order k such that $k < n$. Let G be a finite Abelian group of order n and m be a positive integer such that $m \mid n$. Let p be a prime number such that $p \mid m$. Then there exists an integer m_1 such that $m = pm_1$. By Cauchy's theorem, G has a subgroup H of order p. Since G is commutative, H is normal and hence G/H is a group. Now

$$1 \leq |G/H| = \frac{|G|}{|H|} < |G|$$

and

$$|G/H| = \frac{n}{p}.$$

Now $n = mm_2$ for some positive integer m_2. Thus,

$$|G/H| = \frac{pm_1 m_2}{p} = m_1 m_2$$

shows that m_1 divides $|G/H|$. Hence, from the induction hypothesis, G/H has a subgroup K/H such that $|K/H| = m_1$, where K is a subgroup of G containing H. Now $|K| = |K/H| \, |H| = m_1 p = m$. Hence, K is a subgroup of G of order m. $\square$

We merely state the following theorem and leave the proof as an exercise.

Theorem 9.1.5. *Let G be an Abelian group. Let $r \in \mathbb{Z}$ and p be a prime.*

(i)   *Let $G[r] = \{g \in G \mid rg = 0\}$. Then $G[r]$ is a subgroup of G.*

(ii) *Let $rG = \{rg \mid g \in G\}$. Then rG is a subgroup of G.*

(iii) *Let $G(p) = \{g \in G \mid g$ is of order p^s for some $s \geq 0\}$. Then $G(p)$ is a subgroup of G.*

(iv) *$G/G[r] \simeq rG$.*

The next theorem reveals the structural beauty of a finite Abelian group.

Theorem 9.1.6. *Let $G(\neq \{0\})$ be a finite Abelian group and let $|G| = p_1^{n_1} p_2^{n_2} \cdots p_k^{n_k}$, where the p_i's are distinct primes and the n_i's are positive integers. Then*

(i)   *$G = G(p_1) \oplus G(p_2) \oplus \cdots \oplus G(p_k)$,*

(ii) *$|G(p_i)| = p_i^{n_i}$ for each $i = 1, 2, \cdots, k$.*

Proof. (i)   Let $n = p_1^{n_1} p_2^{n_2} \cdots p_k^{n_k}$. Define

$$m_i = \frac{n}{p_i^{n_i}} \text{ for } i = 1, 2, \cdots, k.$$

Now $gcd(m_1, m_2, \cdots, m_k) = 1$. Hence there exist integers $t_1, t_2, \cdots, t_k$ such that $1 = t_1 m_1 + t_2 m_2 + \cdots + t_k m_k$. Let $g \in G$. Then

$$g = 1 \cdot g = t_1 m_1 g + t_2 m_2 g + \cdots + t_k m_k g.$$

Since $p_i^{n_i}(t_i m_i g) = t_i n g = t_i 0 = 0$, it follows that $t_i m_i g \in G(p_i)$ for $i = 1, 2, \cdots k$. Hence

$$G = G(p_1) + G(p_2) + \cdots + G(p_k).$$

Now $G(p_i) \cap G(p_j) = \{0\}$ for all $i \neq j$. We show that

$$G(p_i) \cap \Big(G(p_1) + \cdots + G(p_{i-1}) + G(p_{i+1}) + \cdots + G(p_k) \Big) = \{0\} \text{ for all } i = 1, 2, \ldots k.$$

Suppose

$$a \in G(p_i) \cap \Big(G(p_1) + \cdots + G(p_{i-1}) + G(p_{i+1}) + \cdots + G(p_k) \Big).$$

Then $a \in G(p_i)$ and $a \in \Big(G(p_1) + \cdots + G(p_{i-1}) + G(p_{i+1}) + \cdots + G(p_k) \Big)$. Hence,

$$a = a_1 + \cdots + a_{i-1} + a_{i+1} + \cdots + a_k,$$

where $a_j \in G_j$, for $j = 1, 2, \ldots, k; j \neq i$. Now for all $j \neq i$, $o(a_j) = p_j^{r_j}$ for some $r_j, 0 \leq r_j \leq n_j$. Let

$$r = p_1^{r_1} \cdots p_{i-1}^{r_{i-1}} p_{i+1}^{r_{i+1}} \cdots p_k^{r_k}.$$

Then $ra = 0$. Thus, $o(a)$ divides r. Since $a \in G_i$, $o(a)$ divides $p_i^{n_i}$. But r and $p_i^{n_i}$ are relatively prime. Therefore, $o(a) = 1$. This implies that $a = 0$. Hence,

$$G(p_i) \cap \Big(G(p_1) + \cdots + G(p_{i-1}) + G(p_{i+1}) + \cdots + G(p_k) \Big) = \{0\}.$$

(ii)   Each element of $G(p_i)$ has an order which is some power of p_i. Let t_i be the order of $G(p_i)$. Hence some power of p_i divides t_i. Let $q \neq p_i$ be a prime, such that q divides t_i. Then by Cauchy's theorem $G(p_i)$ has an element of order q, which is impossible. Hence the only prime divisor of t_i is p_i. This implies $G(p_i)$ has order some power of p_i, say $p_i^{t_i}$. Now from (i), $G = G(p_1) \oplus G(p_2) \oplus \cdots \oplus G(p_k)$. We know

$$G(p_1) \oplus G(p_2) \oplus \cdots \oplus G(p_k) \simeq G(p_1) \times G(p_2) \times \cdots \times G(p_k).$$

Hence

$$|G| = |G(p_1) \times G(p_2) \times \cdots \times G(p_k)| = |G(p_1)| \cdots |G(p_k)| = p_1^{t_1} p_2^{t_2} \cdots p_k^{t_k}.$$

But

$$|G| = n = p_1^{n_1} p_2^{n_2} \cdots p_k^{n_k}.$$

Hence $n = p_1^{t_1} p_2^{t_2} \cdots p_k^{t_k} = p_1^{n_1} p_2^{n_2} \cdots p_k^{n_k}$. Then uniqueness of prime factorization of n implies that $p_i^{t_i} = p_i^{n_i}$ for each $i = 1, 2, \cdots, k$. Hence $|G(p_i)| = p_i^{n_i}$ for each $i = 1, 2, \cdots, k$. $\square$

Let G be a finite Abelian group of order p^l for some $l \in \mathbb{N}$. Since the order of each element of G divides the order of G, the order of each element is p^r for some r, $0 \le r \le l$. Now, there exists $a \in G$ such that $o(a) \ge o(b)$ for all $b \in G$. In the following lemma, we show that $\langle a \rangle$ is a direct summand of G.

Lemma 9.1.7. *Let G be a finite Abelian group of order p^l for some $l \in \mathbb{N}$, where p is a prime. If $a \in G$ be such that $o(a) = p^k$ and it is the element of largest order in G, then the subgroup $\langle a \rangle$ is a direct summand of G, i.e., there exists a subgroup H of G such that $G = \langle a \rangle \oplus H$.*

Proof. Let $0 \ne x \in G$. Since $|G| = p^l$, $o(x) = p^t$ for some positive integer t. Also, $o(a) \ge o(x)$, so $t \le k$. Hence, $p^k x = 0$ for all $x \in G$. Let $\mathcal{C}$ be the collection of all subgroups B of G such that $\langle a \rangle \cap B = \{0\}$. Since $\{0\} \in \mathcal{C}, \mathcal{C} \ne \phi$. Also, $\mathcal{C}$ contains only a finite number of subgroups. Hence, $\mathcal{C}$ has a maximal element, say, H. We show that $G = \langle a \rangle \oplus H$. For this it suffices to show that $G = \langle a \rangle + H$, since $\langle a \rangle \cap H = \{0\}$. We prove this by contradiction. Let $G \ne \langle a \rangle + H$. Then there exists $g \in G$ such that $g \notin \langle a \rangle + H$. Since $p^k g = 0 \in \langle a \rangle + H$, there exists a positive integer s such that $p^s g \in \langle a \rangle + H$. Let n be the smallest positive integer such that $p^n g \in \langle a \rangle + H$, i.e., $p^n g \in \langle a \rangle + H$, but $p^{n-1} g \notin \langle a \rangle + H$. Write $d = p^{n-1} g$. Then $d \notin \langle a \rangle + H$ and $pd \in \langle a \rangle + H$. Now $pd = ta + b$ for some $t \in \mathbb{Z}$ and $b \in H$. Therefore, $0 = p^{k-1} pd = p^{k-1} ta + p^{k-1} b$. Thus, $p^{k-1} ta = -p^{k-1} b \in \langle a \rangle \cap H = \{0\}$, so $p^{k-1} ta = 0$. Then $o(a) - p^k$ must divide $p^{k-1} t$, so $p \mid t$. Let $t = pr$. Now $ra \in \langle a \rangle$. Then $pd = pra + b$ or $p(d - ra) = b \in H$. Write $x = d - ra$. Then $x = d - ra \notin H$. Consider the subgroup $\langle H, x \rangle$. Clearly $H \subset \langle H, x \rangle$ and this shows that $\langle a \rangle \cap \langle H, x \rangle \ne \{0\}$. Hence, there exist $m, s \in \mathbb{Z}$ and $b_1 \in H$ such that $0 \ne ma = b_1 + sx$. If $\gcd(p, s) \ne 1$, then $s = pq$ for some $q \in \mathbb{Z}$. Since $px = b \in H$, $ma = b_1 + q(px) \in H$, which contradicts the fact that $\langle a \rangle \cap H = \{0\}$. Therefore, $\gcd(p, s) = 1$, which implies that there exist $u, v \in \mathbb{Z}$ such that $1 = us + vp$. Thus, $x = u(sx) + v(px) = u(ma - b_1) + v(px) = uma + (-ub_1 + v(px)) \in \langle a \rangle + H$, i.e.,

$d - ra = x \in \langle a \rangle + H$. But then $d = ra + d - ra \in \langle a \rangle + H$, which is a contradiction since $d \notin \langle a \rangle + H$. Hence, $G = \langle a \rangle + H$. Thus $G = \langle a \rangle \oplus H$. $\square$

Definition 9.1.8. A finite Abelian group G is called a **p-group** if $|G| = p^n$ for some prime p and some nonnegative integer n.

In the following lemma, we prove that any nontrivial Abelian p-group can be expressed as a direct sum of nontrivial cyclic p-groups.

Lemma 9.1.9. *Every finite Abelian p-group $G \neq \{0\}$ is a direct sum of cyclic p-groups.*

Proof. Let $|G| = p^n$. We prove the result by induction on n. If $n = 1$, then G is a cyclic group of order p, so in this case the result holds trivially. Suppose the result is true for all p-groups of order p^t such that $1 \leq t < n$. Let G be a finite Abelian group of order p^n. Let $a \in G$ be such that $o(a)$ is the largest in G. Then by Lemma 9.1.7, there exists a subgroup B of G such that

$$G = \langle a \rangle \oplus B.$$

Now $\langle a \rangle \neq \{0\}$. Hence $|B| < |G|$. Because B is a p-group, therefore by the induction hypothesis, B is a direct sum of cyclic p-groups and it follows that G is a direct sum of cyclic p-groups. $\square$

From the following lemma we find that any nontrivial Abelian p-group can be expressed *uniquely* as a direct sum of nontrivial cyclic p-groups.

Lemma 9.1.10. *Let $G \neq \{0\}$ be a finite Abelian p-group. If*

$$G = G_1 \oplus G_2 \oplus \cdots \oplus G_r = H_1 \oplus H_2 \oplus \cdots \oplus H_s,$$

where G_i and H_j are cyclic p-groups with

$$|G_1| \geq |G_2| \geq \cdots \geq |G_r| > 1, \quad and \quad |H_1| \geq |H_2| \geq \cdots \geq |H_s| > 1,$$

then $r = s$ and $G_i \simeq H_i$, $1 \leq i \leq r$.

We omit the proof of the above lemma.

The theorem is called **the fundamental theorem of finite Abelian groups**.

Theorem 9.1.11. *$G \neq \{0\}$ be a finite Abelian group. Then G is a direct sum of cyclic p-groups.*

Proof. Let $G \neq \{0\}$ be a finite Abelian group and let $|G| = p_1^{n_1} p_2^{n_2} \cdots p_k^{n_k}$, where p_i's are distinct primes and n_i's are positive integers. Then by Theorem 9.1.6,

$$G = G(p_1) \oplus G(p_2) \oplus \cdots \oplus G(p_k),$$

and

$$|G(p_i)| = p_i^{n_i} \text{ for all } i = 1, 2, \ldots, k.$$

Now by Lemma 9.1.9, each $G(p_i)$ can be expressed as a direct sum of cyclic p-groups. Consequently G is a direct sum of cyclic p-groups. □

Theorem 9.1.12. *Any two decompositions of a finite Abelian group $G \neq \{0\}$ as a direct sum of cyclic p-groups are the same, except for the order in which the summands are arranged.*

Proof. Let $|G| = p_1^{n_1} p_2^{n_2} \cdots p_k^{n_k}$, where p_i's are distinct primes and n_i's are positive integers and

$$G = G_1 \oplus G_2 \oplus \cdots \oplus G_k$$

be a decomposition of G as a direct sum of cyclic p-groups. We prove the uniqueness of the direct summands by induction on k, the number of distinct primes in the factorization of $|G|$. If $k = 1$, then G is a p-group and the result is true by Lemma 9.1.10. Suppose the result is true for all nonzero finite Abelian groups H such that the number of distinct primes in the factorization of $|H|$ is less than k. Let G be a finite Abelian group such that the number of distinct prime factors of $|G|$ is k. Let

$$G = G_1 \oplus G_2 \oplus \cdots \oplus G_r = H_1 \oplus H_2 \oplus \cdots \oplus H_t$$

be two decompositions of G as a direct sum of nontrivial cyclic p-groups. Since we know that for groups A and B, $A \oplus B \simeq B \oplus A$, we may assume by rearranging (if necessary) that the summands $G_1, G_2, \ldots, G_m$ and $H_1, H_2, \ldots, H_s$ ($m \leq r$, $s \leq t$) are the cyclic p-groups for the prime p_1, the groups $G_{m+1}, \ldots, G_r$ and $H_{s+1}, \ldots, H_t$ are cyclic p-groups for the primes p different from p_1, where

$$|G_1| \geq |G_2| \geq \cdots \geq |G_m|, \text{and } |H_1| \geq |H_2| \geq \cdots \geq |H_s|.$$

Let $A = G_1 \oplus G_2 \oplus \cdots \oplus G_m$, $B = H_1 \oplus H_2 \oplus \cdots \oplus H_s$, $C = G_{m+1} \oplus \cdots \oplus G_r$, and $D = H_{s+1} \oplus \cdots \oplus H_t$. Then

$$G = A \oplus C = B \oplus D.$$

We now show that $A = B$. First note that the order of a nonzero element of A and that of a nonzero element of C are relatively prime. Similarly, the order of a nonzero element of B and that of a nonzero element of D are relatively prime. Let $a \in A$, $a \neq 0$. Then $a \in G = B \oplus D$. Thus, $a = b + d$ for some $b \in B$ and $d \in D$. If $a - b \neq 0$, then the order of $a - b$ is some positive multiple of p_1, whereas the order of d is different from any positive multiple of p_1. Therefore, we have a contradiction, whence $a - b = 0$, i.e., $a = b \in B$. This implies that $A \subseteq B$. Similarly, $B \subseteq A$, so $A = B$. An essentially similar argument shows that $C = D$. Now $A = B$ is a p-group and hence by Lemma 9.1.10, $m = s$ and

$$G_i \simeq H_i, \ i = 1, 2, \ldots, m.$$

Now $C = D$ is an Abelian group of order $p_2^{n_2} \cdots p_k^{n_k}$. Hence, by the induction hypothesis, it follows that the two decompositions

$$G_{m+1} \oplus \cdots \oplus G_r \text{ and } H_{s+1} \oplus \cdots \oplus H_t$$

of the group C are the same, except for the order in which the summands are arranged. Consequently, with an appeal to the induction argument we conclude that the above two decompositions of G are also the same, except for the order in which the summands are arranged. $\qquad \square$

Example 9.1.13. Let G be a noncyclic group of order p^2. Since $|G| = p^2$, G is Abelian. By Cauchy's theorem, there exists $a \in G$ such that $o(a) = p$. Since G is not cyclic, G does not contain any element of order p^2. Therefore, $o(a)$ is the largest in G. Thus, there exists a subgroup B of G such that

$$G = \langle a \rangle \oplus B.$$

Since $|G| = |\langle a \rangle| \cdot |B|$, it follows that $|B| = p$. This shows that B is a cyclic group of order p and $\langle a \rangle \simeq \mathbb{Z}_p \simeq B$. Hence, $G \simeq \mathbb{Z}_p \oplus \mathbb{Z}_p$.

Example 9.1.14. Let G be an Abelian group of order 8. We see that $8 = 2^3$, whence G is a 2-group. There exists $a \in G$ such that $o(a)$ is the largest in G. By Cauchy's theorem, G has an element of order 2. Thus, $o(a) \geq 2$, so $o(a) = 2, 4$ or 8. If $o(a) = 8$, then $G \simeq \mathbb{Z}_8$. If $o(a) = 4$, then $G \simeq \mathbb{Z}_4 \oplus \mathbb{Z}_2$. Now suppose that $o(a) = 2$. By Theorem 9.1.7, there exists a subgroup B of G such that $G = \langle a \rangle \oplus B$. Then $|B| = 4 = 2^2$, proving that B is a 2-group. Since $o(a)$ is the largest in G, B has no element of order 4. Thus, $B \simeq \mathbb{Z}_2 \oplus \mathbb{Z}_2$. Hence, $G \simeq \mathbb{Z}_2 \oplus \mathbb{Z}_2 \oplus \mathbb{Z}_2$. Now $\mathbb{Z}_8$ has an element of order 8, $\mathbb{Z}_4 \oplus \mathbb{Z}_2$ has no element of order 8, but has an element of order 4 and $\mathbb{Z}_2 \oplus \mathbb{Z}_2 \oplus \mathbb{Z}_2$ has no element of order 4 or 8. Thus, $\mathbb{Z}_8$, $\mathbb{Z}_4 \oplus \mathbb{Z}_2$ and $\mathbb{Z}_2 \oplus \mathbb{Z}_2 \oplus \mathbb{Z}_2$ are non-isomorphic groups. Hence, there are exactly three (up to isomorphism) Abelian groups of order 8.

Remark 9.1.15. We know that a finite Abelian group is called a p-group if $|G| = p^n$, ($n > 0$). Also we have proved that any finite Abelian p-group G of order p^n ($n > 0$) can be decomposed uniquely as $G = G(p_1) \oplus G(p_2) \oplus \cdots \oplus G(p_k)$, where each $G(p_i)$, is a cyclic group of order p^{n_i}, $1 \leq i \leq k$, and $n_1 \geq n_2 \geq \cdots \geq n_k > 0$. It is also true that $n = n_1 + n_2 + \cdots + n_k$. Therefore, $n_1, n_2, \ldots, n_k$ determine a **partition** of n. On the other hand, let $n = n_1 + n_2 + \cdots + n_k$, where each n_i is a positive integer and $n_1 \geq n_2 \geq \cdots \geq n_k$. Then

$$G = \mathbb{Z}_{p^{n_1}} \oplus \mathbb{Z}_{p^{n_2}} \oplus \cdots \oplus \mathbb{Z}_{p^{n_k}}$$

is an Abelian p-group of order $p^{n_1 + n_2 + \cdots + n_k} = p^n$. It now follows that *the number of non-isomorphic Abelian p-groups of order p^n ($n > 0$) is equal to the number of partitions of n*. Furthermore, the order of each of the constituent finite cyclic groups as direct summands of the Abelian group of order p^n is directly determined by each possible partition of n.

Example 9.1.16. Let $p = 2$ and $n = 4$. In this example, we want to describe all Abelian groups of order 2^4. Now 4, $3 + 1$, $2 + 2$, $2 + 1 + 1$ and $1 + 1 + 1 + 1$ are all possible partitions of 4. Thus, there are five non-isomorphic Abelian groups of order 2^4. They are

$$\mathbb{Z}_{2^4}$$
$$\mathbb{Z}_{2^3} \oplus \mathbb{Z}_{2^1}$$
$$\mathbb{Z}_{2^2} \oplus \mathbb{Z}_{2^2}$$
$$\mathbb{Z}_{2^2} \oplus \mathbb{Z}_{2^1} \oplus \mathbb{Z}_{2^1}$$
$$\mathbb{Z}_{2^1} \oplus \mathbb{Z}_{2^1} \oplus \mathbb{Z}_{2^1} \oplus \mathbb{Z}_{2^1}.$$

Worked-out Exercises

$\Diamond$ **Exercise 9.1.1.** Show that all Abelian groups of order 22 are cyclic.

Solution. Let G be an Abelian group of order 22. Now 11 and 2 are prime divisors of 22. Hence by Cauchy's theorem, G has an element a of order 11 and an element b of order 2. Since G is Abelian $o(ab) = o(a)o(b) = 22$. Thus G contains an element ab of order 22, whence it follows that G is a cyclic group.

$\Diamond$ **Exercise 9.1.2.** Describe all Abelian groups of order p^5 where p is a prime integer.

Solution. First we consider all partitions of 5, which are as follows:
$$5 = 4 + 1 = 3 + 2 = 3 + 1 + 1 = 2 + 2 + 1 = 2 + 1 + 1 + 1 = 1 + 1 + 1 + 1 + 1.$$

Thus, there are seven partitions of 5, so there exist seven non-isomorphic groups of order p^5. They are

$$\mathbb{Z}_{p^5}$$
$$\mathbb{Z}_{p^4} \oplus \mathbb{Z}_p$$
$$\mathbb{Z}_{p^3} \oplus \mathbb{Z}_{p^2}$$
$$\mathbb{Z}_{p^3} \oplus \mathbb{Z}_p \oplus \mathbb{Z}_p$$
$$\mathbb{Z}_{p^2} \oplus \mathbb{Z}_{p^2} \oplus \mathbb{Z}_p$$
$$\mathbb{Z}_{p^2} \oplus \mathbb{Z}_p \oplus \mathbb{Z}_p \oplus \mathbb{Z}_p$$
$$\mathbb{Z}_p \oplus \mathbb{Z}_p \oplus \mathbb{Z}_p \oplus \mathbb{Z}_p \oplus \mathbb{Z}_p.$$

$\diamond$ **Exercise 9.1.3.** Find all Abelian groups of order 96.

Solution. Let G be an Abelian group of order 96. Now $96 = 2^5 \cdot 3$. Hence $G = G(2) \oplus G(3)$ where $|G(2)| = 2^5$ and $|G(3)| = 3$. Clearly, $G(3) \simeq \mathbb{Z}_3$. Next, we consider $G(2)$ where $|G(2)| = 2^5$. Proceeding as in Exercise 9.1.2, we find that there exist seven non-isomorphic Abelian groups of order 2^5. They are

$$\mathbb{Z}_{2^5}$$
$$\mathbb{Z}_{2^4} \oplus \mathbb{Z}_2$$
$$\mathbb{Z}_{2^3} \oplus \mathbb{Z}_{2^2}$$
$$\mathbb{Z}_{2^3} \oplus \mathbb{Z}_2 \oplus \mathbb{Z}_2$$
$$\mathbb{Z}_{2^2} \oplus \mathbb{Z}_{2^2} \oplus \mathbb{Z}_2$$
$$\mathbb{Z}_{2^2} \oplus \mathbb{Z}_2 \oplus \mathbb{Z}_2 \oplus \mathbb{Z}_2$$
$$\mathbb{Z}_2 \oplus \mathbb{Z}_2 \oplus \mathbb{Z}_2 \oplus \mathbb{Z}_2 \oplus \mathbb{Z}_2.$$

Thus, there are seven non-isomorphic Abelian groups $G = G(2) \oplus G(3)$ of order 96 and they are

$$\mathbb{Z}_{2^5} \oplus \mathbb{Z}_3$$
$$\mathbb{Z}_{2^4} \oplus \mathbb{Z}_2 \oplus \mathbb{Z}_3$$
$$\mathbb{Z}_{2^3} \oplus \mathbb{Z}_{2^2} \oplus \mathbb{Z}_3$$
$$\mathbb{Z}_{2^3} \oplus \mathbb{Z}_2 \oplus \mathbb{Z}_2 \oplus \mathbb{Z}_3$$
$$\mathbb{Z}_{2^2} \oplus \mathbb{Z}_{2^2} \oplus \mathbb{Z}_2 \oplus \mathbb{Z}_3$$
$$\mathbb{Z}_{2^2} \oplus \mathbb{Z}_2 \oplus \mathbb{Z}_2 \oplus \mathbb{Z}_2 \oplus \mathbb{Z}_3$$
$$\mathbb{Z}_2 \oplus \mathbb{Z}_2 \oplus \mathbb{Z}_2 \oplus \mathbb{Z}_2 \oplus \mathbb{Z}_2 \oplus \mathbb{Z}_3.$$

$\diamond$ **Exercise 9.1.4.** Find all Abelian groups of order 1200.

Solution. Let G be an Abelian group of order 1200. We see that, $1200 = 2^4 \cdot 5^2 \cdot 3$. Hence

$$G = G(2) \oplus G(3) \oplus G(5)$$

where $|G(2)| = 2^4$, $|G(3)| = 5^2$, and $|G(3)| = 3$. Now it is easy to see that

$$4, \ 3+1, \ 2+2, \ 2+1+1 \ \text{ and } \ 1+1+1+1$$

are all possible partitions of 4. Thus, total number of partitions of 4 is five and hence there are five non-isomorphic Abelian groups of order 2^4. They are

$$\mathbb{Z}_{2^4}$$
$$\mathbb{Z}_{2^3} \oplus \mathbb{Z}_{2^1}$$
$$\mathbb{Z}_{2^2} \oplus \mathbb{Z}_{2^2}$$
$$\mathbb{Z}_{2^2} \oplus \mathbb{Z}_{2^1} \oplus \mathbb{Z}_{2^1}$$
$$\mathbb{Z}_{2^1} \oplus \mathbb{Z}_{2^1} \oplus \mathbb{Z}_{2^1} \oplus \mathbb{Z}_{2^1}.$$

Similarly, there are two partitions of 2, viz. 2 and $1 + 1$. Therefore,

$$\text{either } G(5) \simeq \mathbb{Z}_{5^2}; \quad \text{or, } G(5) \simeq \mathbb{Z}_5 \oplus \mathbb{Z}_5.$$

Since $|G(3)| = 3$,

$$G(3) \simeq \mathbb{Z}_3.$$

Hence, G is isomorphic to one of the following groups

$$\mathbb{Z}_{2^4} \oplus \mathbb{Z}_{5^2} \oplus \mathbb{Z}_3$$
$$\mathbb{Z}_{2^3} \oplus \mathbb{Z}_{2^1} \oplus \mathbb{Z}_{5^2} \oplus \mathbb{Z}_3$$
$$\mathbb{Z}_{2^2} \oplus \mathbb{Z}_{2^2} \oplus \mathbb{Z}_{5^2} \oplus \mathbb{Z}_3$$
$$\mathbb{Z}_{2^2} \oplus \mathbb{Z}_{2^1} \oplus \mathbb{Z}_{2^1} \oplus \mathbb{Z}_{5^2} \oplus \mathbb{Z}_3$$
$$\mathbb{Z}_{2^1} \oplus \mathbb{Z}_{2^1} \oplus \mathbb{Z}_{2^1} \oplus \mathbb{Z}_{2^1} \oplus \mathbb{Z}_{5^2} \oplus \mathbb{Z}_3$$
$$\mathbb{Z}_{2^4} \oplus \mathbb{Z}_5 \oplus \mathbb{Z}_5 \oplus \mathbb{Z}_3$$
$$\mathbb{Z}_{2^3} \oplus \mathbb{Z}_{2^1} \oplus \mathbb{Z}_5 \oplus \mathbb{Z}_5 \oplus \mathbb{Z}_3$$
$$\mathbb{Z}_{2^2} \oplus \mathbb{Z}_{2^2} \oplus \mathbb{Z}_5 \oplus \mathbb{Z}_5 \oplus \mathbb{Z}_3$$
$$\mathbb{Z}_{2^2} \oplus \mathbb{Z}_{2^1} \oplus \mathbb{Z}_{2^1} \oplus \mathbb{Z}_5 \oplus \mathbb{Z}_5 \oplus \mathbb{Z}_3$$
$$\mathbb{Z}_{2^1} \oplus \mathbb{Z}_{2^1} \oplus \mathbb{Z}_{2^1} \oplus \mathbb{Z}_{2^1} \oplus \mathbb{Z}_5 \oplus \mathbb{Z}_5 \oplus \mathbb{Z}_3.$$

◊ **Exercise 9.1.5.** Describe all Abelian groups of order 245. Show that there exists an element of order 35 in each of these groups.

Solution. Let G be an Abelian group of order $245 = 7^2 \cdot 5$. Then $G = G(7) \oplus G(5)$, where $G(7)$ is a group of order 7^2 and $G(5)$ is a group of order 5. Now two possible partitions of 2, viz. $2 = 1 + 1$ shows that either $G(7) \simeq \mathbb{Z}_{7^2}$ or $G(7) \simeq \mathbb{Z}_7 \oplus \mathbb{Z}_7$ and clearly $G(5) \simeq \mathbb{Z}_5$. Hence, $\mathbb{Z}_{7^2} \oplus \mathbb{Z}_5$ and $\mathbb{Z}_7 \oplus \mathbb{Z}_7 \oplus \mathbb{Z}_5$ are the only two non-isomorphic Abelian groups of order 245. Now in $\mathbb{Z}_{49} \oplus \mathbb{Z}_5$, $([7], [1])$ is an element of order 35 and in $\mathbb{Z}_7 \oplus \mathbb{Z}_7 \oplus \mathbb{Z}_5$, $([0], [1], [1])$ is an element of order 35.

◊ **Exercise 9.1.6.** Let G be a finite Abelian group of order 21. Choose the correct statement(s):

(i) G contains an element of order 7.

(ii) G contains seven elements of order 7.

(iii) G contains six elements of order 7.

(iv) G has no element of order 3.

Solution. Let G be an Abelian group of order $21 = 3 \cdot 7$. Then $G = G(3) \oplus G(7)$, where $G(3)$ is a group of order 3 and $G(7)$ is a group of order 7. Therefore $G(3) \simeq \mathbb{Z}_3$ and $G(7) \simeq \mathbb{Z}_7$. Hence, $G \simeq \mathbb{Z}_3 \oplus \mathbb{Z}_7 \simeq \mathbb{Z}_{21}$ whence any Abelian group of order 21 is cyclic. Now, $7 \mid 21$, and thus G has a unique cyclic subgroup of order 7. Hence G contains exactly 6 elements of order 7 which are $[3], [6], [9], [12], [15]$ and $[18]$. Also $[7]$ and $[14]$ are two elements of order 3. Hence options (i) and (iii) are correct.

◊ **Exercise 9.1.7.** Up to isomorphism, the number of Abelian groups of order 108 is
(i) 9   (ii) 12   (iii) 5   (iv) 6.

Solution. Let G be an Abelian group of order $108 = 2^2 \cdot 3^3$. Then $G = G(2) \oplus G(3)$. Now $G(2)$ is a group of order 4 and $G(3)$ is a group of order 27. Therefore either $G(2) \simeq \mathbb{Z}_{2^2}$ or $G(2) \simeq \mathbb{Z}_2 \oplus \mathbb{Z}_2$. Similarly, either $G(3) \simeq \mathbb{Z}_{3^3}$ or $G(3) \simeq \mathbb{Z}_{3^2} \oplus \mathbb{Z}_3$ or $G(3) \simeq \mathbb{Z}_3 \oplus \mathbb{Z}_3 \oplus \mathbb{Z}_3$. Thus G is either isomorphic to $\mathbb{Z}_4 \oplus \mathbb{Z}_{27}$ or isomorphic to $\mathbb{Z}_4 \oplus \mathbb{Z}_9 \oplus \mathbb{Z}_3$ or isomorphic to $\mathbb{Z}_4 \oplus \mathbb{Z}_3 \oplus \mathbb{Z}_3 \oplus \mathbb{Z}_3$ or isomorphic to $\mathbb{Z}_2 \oplus \mathbb{Z}_2 \oplus \mathbb{Z}_{27}$ or isomorphic to $\mathbb{Z}_2 \oplus \mathbb{Z}_2 \oplus \mathbb{Z}_9 \oplus \mathbb{Z}_3$ or isomorphic to $\mathbb{Z}_2 \oplus \mathbb{Z}_2 \oplus \mathbb{Z}_3 \oplus \mathbb{Z}_3 \oplus \mathbb{Z}_3$. Hence there are 6 non-isomorphic Abelian groups of order 108. Therefore, option (iv) is correct.

◊ **Exercise 9.1.8.** Let G be a finite Abelian group of order n. Pick each correct statement from below.

(i) If d divides n, there exists a subgroup of G of order d.

(ii) If d divides n, there exists an element of order d in G.

(iii) If every proper subgroup of G is cyclic, then G is cyclic.

(iv) If d divides n, there exists a cyclic subgroup of G of order d.

Solution. We know if G is a finite Abelian group of order n, then for each positive divisor d of n, there exists a subgroup of order d of G. Hence statement (i) is true. Now K_4 is an Abelian group of order 4 and 4 divides 4. But K_4 has no element of order 4. Moreover, K_4 is an Abelian group whose every proper subgroup is cyclic. But the whole group K_4 is non-cyclic. Finally, we consider the group $\mathbb{Z}_2 \oplus \mathbb{Z}_2 \oplus \mathbb{Z}_5$ of order 20 and $4 \mid 20$. But $\mathbb{Z}_2 \oplus \mathbb{Z}_2 \oplus \mathbb{Z}_5$ has no cyclic subgroup of order 4. Therefore, only option (i) is correct.

Exercises

1. Show that every Abelian group of order 35 is cyclic.

2. Show that any Abelian group of order 56 contains an element of order 14.

3. Show that any Abelian group of order 105 contains a cyclic subgroup of order 5.

4. Show that any Abelian group of order 105 contains a cyclic subgroup of order 7.

5. Show that any Abelian group of order 105 contains a cyclic subgroup of order 15.

6. Is it true that any Abelian group of order 105 contains an element of order 21? Justify.

7. Prove that any Abelian group of order pq, where p and q are distinct primes is a cyclic group. Is it true when $p = q$?

8. Find all Abelian groups of orders $121, 49, 81$ and 625.

9. Find all Abelian groups of orders $50, 80, 100$ and 200.

10. Find all Abelian groups of orders $30, 63, 78$ and 110.

11. Show that all Abelian groups of order 245 contains an element of order 35.

12. Find all Abelian groups of order pqr, where p, q and r are distinct primes.

13. Find all Abelian groups of order $p^2 q^3$, where p and q are distinct primes.

14. Find the number of Abelian groups of order 144 which have exactly three subgroups of order 2.

15. Let G be a finite Abelian group. Choose the correct statement(s):
    (i) If order of G is divisible by 4, then G contains a cyclic subgroup of order 4.
    (ii) If order of G is divisible by 6, then G contains a cyclic subgroup of order 6.
    (iii) There exists only (upto isomorphism) one group G of order 77.
    (iv) There exists only (upto isomorphism) one group G of order 12.

Choose the correct statement:

16. The number of nonisomorphic Abelian groups of order 72 is
    (i) 8   (ii) 6   (iii) 9   (iv) 18.

17. The number of Abelian groups of order 12 is
    (i) 1   (ii) 2   (iii) 3   (iv) 4.

18. The number of Abelian groups of order 120 is
    (i) 1   (ii) 2   (iii) 3   (iv) 4.

19. The number of Abelian groups of order 360 is
    (i) 3   (ii) 4   (iii) 5   (iv) 6.

Chapter 10

Sylow Theorems

We have shown in Chapter 5 that the converse of Lagrange's theorem is false in general. If G is a group of order $n > 1$ and m is a positive divisor of n, then G may not contain a subgroup of order m. However Cauchy's theorem and Sylow's theorems provide some information regarding partial converse of Lagrange's theorem. Indeed, as far as *finite Abelian groups* are concerned, we have already experienced this role of Cauchy's theorem in Chapter 9. Sylow theorems, as they are referred to, are due to the Norwegian mathematician Ludvig Sylow(1832-1918). He was a high school teacher up to his retirement at the age of 65. Only after that he accepted a chair at the Christiana University, which he held until death. In this chapter, we shall prove Cauchy's theorem and Sylow theorems. Further, we shall discuss some of the important consequences of all these theorems, in brief.

10.1   Group Actions

In this section we introduce the notion of a group acting on a set, formally known as *group action*, which is an extended notion of a permutation on a set and use different properties of this concept to study some important features of finite groups.

Definition 10.1.1. Let G be a group and S a nonempty set. A **(left) action** of G on S is a mapping $\bullet : G \times S \to S$ (usually denoted by $\bullet(g, x) \to g \bullet x$) such that

(i) $(g_1 g_2) \bullet x = g_1 \bullet (g_2 \bullet x)$, and

(ii) $e \bullet x = x$, where e is the identity of G

for all $x \in S$, $g_1, g_2 \in G$.

Note: When there is no scope of confusion, we shall write gx instead of $g \bullet x$ and it must not be confused with the group operation, often written by juxtaposition of the group elements.

If there is a left action of G on S, we say that G acts on S from the left and S is a **G-set**.

Example 10.1.2. Let G be a permutation group on a set S. Define a left action of G on S by

$$\sigma \bullet x = \sigma(x)$$

for all $\sigma \in G$, $x \in S$. Let $x \in S$. Now $e \bullet x = e(x) = x$, where e is the identity permutation on S. Let $\sigma_1, \sigma_2 \in G$. Then $(\sigma_1 \circ \sigma_2) \bullet x = (\sigma_1 \circ \sigma_2)(x) = \sigma_1(\sigma_2(x)) = \sigma_1 \bullet (\sigma_2(x)) = \sigma_1 \bullet (\sigma_2 \bullet x)$. Hence, S is a G-set.

Remark 10.1.3. From this example it is clear that the left-action of the group S_3 on the set $I_3 = \{1, 2, 3\}$ or, for that matter, the group D_4 on $I_4 = \{1, 2, 3, 4\}$ can be geometrically visualized as the study of symmetries of an equilateral triangle, or that of a square respectively, as we have described in Chapter 8. Indeed, one may say that the study of symmetries of an object is all about finding a suitable group to act on the object.

Example 10.1.4. Let G be a group and H be a normal subgroup of G. Define a left action of G on H by *conjugation* as

$$(g, h) \to g \bullet h = ghg^{-1}$$

for all $g \in G$, $h \in H$. Let $h \in H$. Now $e \bullet h = ehe^{-1} = ehe = h$. Let $g_1, g_2 \in G$. Then $(g_1 g_2) \bullet h = (g_1 g_2)h(g_1 g_2)^{-1} = (g_1 g_2)h(g_2^{-1} g_1^{-1}) = g_1(g_2 h g_2^{-1})g_1^{-1} = g_1(g_2 \bullet h)g_1^{-1} = g_1 \bullet (g_2 \bullet h)$. Hence, H is a G-set.

Theorem 10.1.5. *Let G be a group and S a G-set. A binary relation $\sim$ on S is defined by $a \sim b$ if and only if $ga = b$ for all $a, b \in S$, and for some $g \in G$. Then $\sim$ is an equivalence relation on S.*

Proof. For all $a \in S$, $ea = a$, implies that $a \sim a$ Thus, $\sim$ is reflexive. Let $a, b, c \in S$. Suppose $a \sim b$. Then $ga = b$ for some $g \in G$, which implies that $g^{-1}b = g^{-1}(ga) = (g^{-1}g)a = ea = a$. Hence, $b \sim a$ and so $\sim$ is symmetric. Now suppose $a \sim b$ and $b \sim c$. Then there exist $g_1, g_2 \in G$ such that $g_1 a = b$ and $g_2 b = c$. Then, $(g_2 g_1)a = g_2(g_1 a) = g_2 b = c$ and so $a \sim c$. Hence, $\sim$ is transitive. Consequently, $\sim$ is an equivalence relation on S. $\square$

Definition 10.1.6. Let S be a G-set, where G is a group and S is a nonempty set. The equivalence classes determined by the equivalence relation of Theorem 10.1.5, that partitions S, are called the **orbits** of G on S.

For $a \in S$, the orbit containing a is denoted by $[a]$. Clearly it consists of those elements of S on which a can be mapped to, under the action by some group element. For example, if we consider the action of D_n on the set $I_n = \{1, 2, 3, \ldots, n\}$, it is not difficult to appreciate geometrically that the orbit of each $i \in I_n$ is the whole of I_n. However, if we consider a group G to act on a set S of all its subgroups by the left action $(g, K) \mapsto gKg^{-1}$, for all $g \in G$ and $K \in S$, then the orbit of any normal subgroup H of G is just the singleton $\{H\}$. On the other hand, if the orbit of any subgroup is a singleton consisting itself, then the definition of normality ensures that it must be a normal subgroup.

Lemma 10.1.7. *Let G be a group and S be a G-set. For all $a \in S$, the subset*

$$G_a = \{g \in G \mid ga = a\}$$

is a subgroup of G.

Proof. Let $a \in S$. Since $ea = a$, $e \in G_a$ and so $G_a \neq \emptyset$. Let $g, h \in G_a$. Then $ga = a$ and $ha = a$. This implies that $(gh)a = g(ha) = ga = a$ and so $gh \in G_a$. Now $h^{-1}a = h^{-1}(ha) = (h^{-1}h)a = ea = a$. Thus, $h^{-1} \in G_a$. Hence, G_a is a subgroup of G. $\square$

The subgroup G_a of Lemma 10.1.7 is called the **stabilizer** of a or the **isotropy group** of a in G. These are those group elements that keep a fixed. For example, each vertex of a square is fixed by exactly two elements of D_4, the identity of D_4 (i.e., rotation through $360°$) and a reflection (along the diagonal through that vertex). So the diagonally opposite vertices of a square have the same stabilizer.

Example 10.1.8. Let G be a group. Consider the G-set G where the group action is defined as $g \bullet a = gag^{-1}$ for all $g, a \in G$. The stabilizer G_a of an element $a \in G$ in the G-set G is

$$G_a = \{g \in G \mid gag^{-1} = a\} = \{g \in G \mid ga = ag\} = C(a),$$

the *centralizer* of a.

Now if we again refer to the G-set S where S is the set of all subgroups of G and the group action is defined as before by $g \bullet K = gKg^{-1}$ for all $g \in G$ and $K \in S$, then for a subgroup K of G the stabilizer G_K is

$$G_K = \{g \in G \mid gKg^{-1} = K\} = N(K),$$

the *normalizer* of K.

We now describe a relation between the orbit $[a]$ and the isotropy group of a.

Lemma 10.1.9. *Let G be a group and S be a G-set. For all $a \in S$,*

$$[G : G_a] = ||[a]||.$$

Proof. Let $a \in S$. Let $\mathcal{L}$ be the set of all left cosets of G_a in G. Now

$$[a] = \{b \in S \mid a \sim b\} = \{b \in S \mid ga = b \text{ for some } g \in G\} = \{ga \mid g \in G\}.$$

We now show that there exists a one-one mapping from $\mathcal{L}$ onto $[a]$. Define

$$f : \mathcal{L} \to [a] \quad \text{by} \quad f(gG_a) = ga, \text{ for all } gG_a \in \mathcal{L}.$$

Let $g_1, g_2 \in G$. Then $g_1 G_a = g_2 G_a$ if and only if $g_2^{-1}g_1 \in G_a$ if and only if $g_2^{-1}(g_1 a) = (g_2^{-1}g_1)a = a$ if and only if $g_1 a = g_2 a$. Thus, f is a one-one mapping from $\mathcal{L}$ into $[a]$. Let $b \in [a]$. Then there exists $g \in G$ such that $ga = b$. Thus, $f(gG_a) = ga = b$. This implies that f is onto $[a]$. Consequently, $[G : G_a] = |\mathcal{L}| = ||[a]||$. $\qquad\square$

Remark 10.1.10. In case both G and S are finite, the result of Lemma 10.1.9 may be rephrased as

$$|G| = |G_a| \, ||[a]|| \quad \text{for all } a \in S,$$

which is often referred to as the **orbit-stabilizer theorem** in the literature of Group theory. An inquisitive mind must immediately note the striking similarity of this result with the celebrated Lagrange's theorem [Theorem 5.3.10] on finite group, which states that, for a subgroup H of a finite group G, we must have $|G| = |H|[G : H]$. Clearly, if we consider the set S to be the set of all left cosets gH of some subgroup H of a finite group G, then S can be easily seen to be a G-set under the action '*left multiplication*' by elements of G (viz. $(g_1, gH) \mapsto g_1 gH$). Here the stabilizer of eH, i.e., $H \in S$ is $G_H = \{g \in G \mid gH = H\} = \{g \in G \mid g \in H\} = H$ and the orbit of eH, i.e., H in S consists of those elements of S where H can be mapped to, under the 'left multiplication' by elements of G, which is clearly the whole of S. The next theorem ensures $|S| = [G : H]$, whence Lagrange's theorem follows from the orbit-stabilizer theorem.

Theorem 10.1.11. *Let G be a group and S be a G-set. If S is finite, then*

$$|S| = \sum_{a \in A} [G : G_a],$$

where A is a subset of S containing exactly one element from each orbit $[a]$.

Proof. By Theorem 10.1.5, S can be partitioned as the union of orbits. Therefore,

$$S = \cup_{a \in A}[a].$$

Hence,

$$|S| = \sum_{a \in A} |[a]| = \sum_{a \in A} [G : G_a] \qquad (10.1.1)$$

by lemma 10.1.9. $\square$

Example 10.1.12. Consider the set S of nine dots named by $a, b, c, p, q, r, x, y, z$ arranged in a square formation as follows :

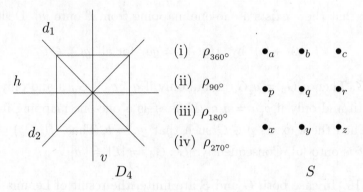

(i) $\rho_{360°}$

(ii) $\rho_{90°}$

(iii) $\rho_{180°}$

(iv) $\rho_{270°}$

$$D_4 \qquad\qquad\qquad\qquad\qquad S$$

Let the dihedral group D_4 of symmetries of a square [Example 8.3.8] act on the set S. Since the four axes of line symmetry passes through q making it the centre of rotational symmetry of the four rotations, we have that $[q] = \{q\}$, i.e., $|[q]| = 1$ (indeed one may call it a *fixed point* of this action, in the sense that $g \bullet q = q$ for all group elements $g \in D_4$). Note that there are only two other orbits $\{a, c, z, x\}$ and $\{b, r, y, p\}$ as can be easily verified geometrically. Hence we have $9 = 1 + 4 + 4$ that verifies the first part of equation 10.1.1. For the second part, note that $|D_4| = 8$ and observe that $D_{4(a)} = \{d_1, \rho_{360°}\}$ and $D_{4(b)} = \{v, \rho_{360°}\}$, while $D_{4(q)} = D_4$. Hence, $[D_4 : D_{4(a)}] = \frac{8}{2} = 4$, $[D_4 : D_{4(b)}] = \frac{8}{2} = 4$ and $[D_4 : D_{4(q)}] = \frac{8}{8} = 1$, justifies the claim.

Theorem 10.1.13. *Let G be a group of order p^n (where p is a prime). If S is a finite G-set and $S_0 = \{a \in S \mid ga = a \text{ for all } g \in G\}$, then*

$$|S| \equiv |S_0| \,(mod\,p).$$

Proof. From the Theorem 10.1.11, we find

$$|S| = \sum_{a \in A} [G : G_a],$$

where A is a subset of S containing exactly one element from each orbit $[a]$ of G. Now $a \in S_0$ if and only if $ga = a$ for all $g \in G$, i.e., if and only if $[a] = \{a\}$. Hence,

$$|S| = |S_0| + \sum_{a \in A \setminus S_0} \frac{|G|}{|G_a|}.$$

Now $|G_a| \neq |G|$ for all $a \in A \backslash S_0$. So $\frac{|G|}{|G_a|}$ is some power of p for all $a \in A \backslash S_0$. Thus, $\frac{|G|}{|G_a|}$ is divisible by p, proving that $|S| \equiv |S_0| \pmod{p}$. □

Theorem 10.1.14. *Let G be a finite group and H be a subgroup of G such that $|H| = p^k$, where p is a prime and k is a nonnegative integer. Then*

$$[G : H] \equiv [N(H) : H] \pmod{p}.$$

*where $N(H) = \{g \in G \mid gHg^{-1} = H\}$ is the **normalizer** of H in G.*

Proof. Let $S = \{xH \mid x \in G\}$. Define a left action of H on S by $h(xH) = (hx)H$ for all $h \in H$, $xH \in S$. Then S is an H-set. Let $S_0 = \{xH \in S \mid h(xH) = xH \text{ for all } h \in H\}$. By Theorem 10.1.13, $|S| \equiv |S_0| \pmod{p}$. Now $xH \in S_0$ if and only if $h(xH) = xH$ for all $h \in H$ if and only if $x^{-1}hx \in H$ for all $h \in H$ if and only if $x^{-1}Hx \subseteq H$. Now $|x^{-1}Hx| = |H|$. Hence, $xH \in S_0$ if and only if $x^{-1}Hx \subseteq H$ if and only if $x^{-1}Hx = H$ (since H is finite and $|x^{-1}Hx| = |H|$) if and only if $x \in N(H)$. This shows that S_0 is the set of all left cosets of H in $N(H)$. Thus, $|S_0| = [N(H) : H]$. Also, $|S| = [G : H]$. Hence, $[G : H] \equiv [N(H) : H] \pmod{p}$. □

We now prove the following theorem, which is known as the *Extended Cayley's theorem*, by group action technique.

Theorem 10.1.15. [***Extended Cayley's theorem***]: *Let G be a group and H be a subgroup of G. Let $S = \{aH \mid a \in G\}$. Then there exists a homomorphism ψ from G into $A(S)$ (the group of all permutations on S) such that $\ker \psi \subseteq H$.*

Proof. First we define a left action of G on S by $g(aH) = (ga)H$ for all $g \in G$. It can be routinely verified that S is a G-set under this group action.

Let $g \in G$. Define $\tau_g : S \to S$ by $\tau_g(a) = ga$ for all $a \in S$. Let $a, b \in S$. Then $\tau_g(a) = \tau_g(b)$ if and only if $ga = gb$ if and only if $a = b$. Therefore, τ_g is a one-one mapping. Now $b = g(g^{-1}b) = \tau_g(g^{-1}b)$ and $g^{-1}b \in S$. This shows that τ_g is onto S. Thus, $\tau_g \in A(S)$. Let $g_1, g_2 \in G$. Then

$$\tau_{g_1 g_2}(a) = (g_1 g_2)a = g_1(g_2 a) = \tau_{g_1}(g_2 a) = \tau_{g_1}(\tau_{g_2}(a)) = (\tau_{g_1} \circ \tau_{g_2})(a)$$

for all $a \in S$. This implies that $\tau_{g_1 g_2} = \tau_{g_1} \circ \tau_{g_2}$. Define

$$\psi : G \to A(S)$$

by

$$\psi(g) = \tau_g \text{ for all } g \in G.$$

Now

$$\psi(g_1 g_2) = \tau_{g_1 g_2} = \tau_{g_1} \circ \tau_{g_2} = \psi(g_1) \circ \psi(g_2) \text{ for all } g_1, g_2 \in G.$$

This proves that ψ is a homomorphism. Now,

$$
\begin{aligned}
ker\,\psi &= \{g \in G \mid \psi(g) = \tau_g = \text{the identity mapping on } S\} \\
&= \{g \in G \mid \tau_g(aH) = aH \text{ for all } aH \in S\} \\
&= \{g \in G \mid g(aH) = aH \text{ for all } aH \in S\}.
\end{aligned}
$$

Let $g \in ker\,\psi$. Then $g(aH) = aH$ for all $aH \in S$. In particular, $gH = H$. Thus, $g \in H$. Hence, $ker\,\psi \subseteq H$.   □

Now taking the subgroup $H = \{e\}$ in G, *Cayley's theorem* [refer to 6.1.18] follows from it immediately, thereby justifying the nomenclature.

Corollary 10.1.16. [*Cayley*]: *Every group is isomorphic to some subgroup of the group $A(S)$ of all permutations of some set S.*

Corollary 10.1.17. *Let G be a group and H be a subgroup of G of index n. Then there exists a homomorphism ψ from G into S_n such that $ker\,\psi \subseteq H$.*

Proof. Because $[G : H] = n$, the group $A(S)$ of all permutations on S is isomorphic to S_n. Hence the corollary follows from the Theorem 10.1.15 above.   □

Worked-out Exercises

◇ **Exercise 10.1.1.** Let G be a group of order $2m$, where m is an odd integer. Show that G has a normal subgroup of order m.

Solution. Since G is a group of even order so there exists an element $g \in G$ such that $o(g) = 2$. Now by Cayley's theorem G is isomorphic to a subgroup H of $A(G)$ where $\psi : G \longrightarrow A(G)$ is given by $\psi(x) = \tau_x$, $\tau_x(a) = xa$, $\forall\, x, a \in G$. Now $\tau_g(ga) = g(ga) = g^2 a = a$. Hence τ_g is a product of transpositions of the form $(a\ ga)$. Since $|G| = 2m$, the number of transpositions appearing in the factorization of τ_g is m. Thus τ_g is an odd permutation. Hence H contains an odd permutation. We now define $f : H \longrightarrow \{1, -1\}$ by

$$
f(\sigma) = \begin{cases} 1, & \text{if } \sigma \text{ is an even permutation} \\ -1, & \text{if } \sigma \text{ is an odd permutation} \end{cases}
$$

where $\{1, -1\}$ is a group under multiplication.

It is easy to verify that f is an epimorphism from H onto $\{1, -1\}$. Hence $H/ker\, f \simeq$ $\{1, -1\}$. Thus, $|H/ker\, f| = 2$, i.e., $|ker\, f| = \frac{|H|}{2} = \frac{2m}{2} = m \left[\text{ since } H \simeq G \text{ so } |H| = |G| = 2m\right]$.

So H has a normal subgroup, viz., $ker\, f$, of order m and consequently, G has a normal subgroup of order m.

$\lozenge$ **Exercise 10.1.2.** Let S be a finite G-set, where G is a group of order p^n (where p is a prime) such that p does not divide $|S|$. Show that there exists $a \in S$ such that $ga = a$ for all $g \in G$.

Solution. Let $S_0 = \{a \in S \mid ga = a \text{ for all } g \in G\}$. By Theorem 10.1.13,

$$|S| \equiv |S_0| \,(mod\, p).$$

Since p does not divide $|S|$, p does not divide $|S_0|$. Thus, $|S_0| \neq 0$. This shows that there exists $a \in S_0$. Thus, $ga = a$ for all $g \in G$.

$\lozenge$ **Exercise 10.1.3.** Let G be a finite group and H be a subgroup of G of index n such that $|G|$ does not divide $n!$. Then G contains a nontrivial normal subgroup.

Solution. Let $S = \{aH : a \in G\}$. Since G is finite then so is S, whence

$$|S| = [G : H] = n.$$

We define

$$\bullet : G \times S \longrightarrow S \text{ by } g \bullet (aH) = (ga)H \text{ for all } g \in G, \text{ for all } aH \in S.$$

Under this action S is a G-set. Then by Extended Cayley's theorem there exists a homomorphism $\psi : G \to A(S)$ such that $ker\, \psi \subseteq H$. Now $G/ker\, \psi$ is isomorphic to a subgroup of $A(S)$. So $|G/ker\psi|$ divides $n!$. As it is given that $|G|$ does not divide $n!$, hence $|ker\psi| \neq 1$, proving that $ker\, \psi$ is a non trivial normal subgroup of G. Hence G contains a nontrivial normal subgroup.

$\lozenge$ **Exercise 10.1.4.** Let G be a finite group. Let H be a subgroup of G of index p, where p is the smallest prime dividing the order of G. Show that H is a normal subgroup of G.

Solution. Let $S = \{aH \mid a \in G\}$. Since $[G : H] = p$, we see that $|S| = p$. Now, by Extended Cayley's theorem there exists a homomorphism $\psi : G \to A(S)$ such that $ker\, \psi \subseteq H$. Now $G/ker\, \psi$ is isomorphic to a subgroup of $A(S)$. Therefore, $|G/ker\, \psi|$ divides $|A(S)| = p!$. Let $|G/ker\, \psi| = n$. Then $n = [G : H][H : ker\, \psi] \geq p$. Let

$n = p_1 p_2 \cdots p_k$, where p_i are prime integers, $i = 1, 2, \ldots, k$. Since p_i divides $|G|$ and p is the smallest prime dividing the order of G, $p_i \geq p$ for all $i = 1, 2, \ldots, k$. Since n divides $p!$, we have each p_i divides $p!$. Since each p_i is a prime and $p_i \geq p$, we must have $i = 1$ and $p_i = p$. Thus, $n = p$. This implies that $[H : ker \, \psi] = 1$. Hence, $H = ker \, \psi$ and so H is a normal subgroup of G.

$\Diamond$ **Exercise 10.1.5.** Let G be a finite group of order pn where p is a prime and $p \geq n$. If H is a subgroup of G of order p, then prove that H is a normal subgroup of G.

Solution. It is given that $|H| = p$. So $[G : H] = n$. Let $S = \{aH : a \in G\}$. Then $|S| = [G : H] = n$. We define $\bullet : G \times S \longrightarrow S$ by $g \bullet (aH) = (ga)H$ for all $g \in G$, for all $aH \in S$. Then under this action S is a G-set and by Extended Cayley's theorem there exists a homomorphism $\psi : G \to A(S)$ such that $ker \, \psi \subseteq H$. Now, $|H| = p$ and $ker \, \psi \subseteq H$ implies either $|ker \, \psi| = 1$ or $|ker \, \psi| = p$. Now if $|ker \, \psi| = 1$ then ψ must be a monomorphism. But then G is isomorphic to a subgroup of $A(S)$, whence $|G|$ must divide $n!$, i.e., pn must divide $n!$, i.e., p must divide $(n-1)!$. But this is impossible, as it is given that p is a prime and $p \geq n$. Hence $|ker \, \psi| \neq 1$. So $|ker \, \psi| = p = |H|$. Also, $ker \, \psi \subseteq H$. This implies $H = ker \, \psi$. Since $ker \, \psi$ is a normal subgroup of G, so H is a normal subgroup of G.

Exercises

1. Consider the symmetric group S_3 on the set $I_3 = \{1, 2, 3\}$. Define the left action of S_3 on $I_3 = \{1, 2, 3\}$ by $\sigma a = \sigma(a)$ for all $\sigma \in S_3$, $a \in I_3$. Describe all distinct orbits of I_3.

2. Let G be the permutation group $\{(1), (1\,2\,3), (1\,3\,2), (4\,5), (1\,2\,3)(4\,5), (1\,3\,2)(4\,5)\}$ on the set $I_5 = \{1, 2, 3, 4, 5\}$. Define the left action of G on I_5 by $\sigma a = \sigma(a)$ for all $\sigma \in G, a \in I_5$. Describe all distinct orbits of I_5.

3. Consider the left action of the group $G = GL(2, \mathbb{R})$ on $G = GL(2, \mathbb{R})$ by conjugation. Find the orbit and stabilizer of $\begin{bmatrix} 1 & 0 \\ 0 & 4 \end{bmatrix}$.

4. Let G be group and S be a G-set. For any $x \in S$, G_x denotes the stabilizer of x. Prove that $G_{b \bullet x} = b \, G_x \, b^{-1}$ for all $b \in G$ and $x \in S$.

5. Let H be a subgroup of a group G. If $|H| = 13$ and index of H in G is 4, prove that H is a normal subgroup of G.

6. Let H be a subgroup of a group G. If $|H| = 17$ and $|G| = 85$, prove that H is a normal subgroup of G.

7. Let the index of a subgroup H of a group G be n. If H does not contain any nontrivial normal subgroup of G, prove that H is isomorphic to a subgroup of S_n.

8. Let G be a group acting on a set S containing at least two elements. Assume that G is *transitive*, i.e., given any $x, y \in S$, there exists $g \in G$ such that $gx = y$. Prove that,
   (i) for $x \in S$, the orbit $[x]$ of x is S;
   (ii) all the stabilizers G_x (for $x \in S$) are conjugate;
   (iii) if G has the property : $\{g \in G \mid gx = x \text{ for all } x \in S\} = \{e\}$ (which is the case if G is a subgroup of S_n for some n and $S = \{1, 2, 3, \ldots, n\}$) and if N is a normal subgroup of G and N is a subgroup of G_x for some $x \in S$, then $N = \{e\}$.

9. Let G be a group of order 77 acting on a set S of 20 elements. Show that G must have a fixed point.

10. Let G be a group. The left action of G on the set G is defined by conjugation, i.e., $(g, x) \to gxg^{-1}$ for all $g, x \in G$. Show that the kernel of the homomorphism $\psi : G \to A(G)$ induced by this action is $Z(G)$.

11. Let G be a finite group. Which of the following statements are true?
    (i) G is isomorphic to a subgroup of S_n for some positive integer n.
    (ii) G is isomorphic to a subgroup of A_n for some positive integer n.
    (iii) G is isomorphic to a cyclic subgroup of S_n for some positive integer n.
    (iv) G is isomorphic to a cyclic subgroup of A_n for some positive integer n.

10.2 Class Equation and Cauchy's Theorem

Let G be a group. On the set G, let us define the following relation:

$$\rho = \{(a, b) \in G \times G \mid b = xax^{-1} \text{ for some } x \in G\}.$$

It is easy to see that ρ is an equivalence relation, called the **conjugacy relation** and the equivalence class for an element $a \in G$ with respect to this relation ρ is called the **conjugacy class** of a, which is denoted by $cl(a)$. So

$$cl(a) = \{b \in G \mid b \rho a\} = \{b \in G \mid b = xax^{-1} \text{ for some } x \in G\} = \{xax^{-1} \mid x \in G\}.$$

Remark 10.2.1. If a group G acts on itself by *conjugation* [vide Example 10.1.4], the orbit of an element a of G under this action is precisely the conjugacy class of that element.

Suppose, G is a finite group. Then the number of conjugacy classes is finite. If $a_1, a_2, \ldots, a_k$ are representatives from each of the distinct conjugacy classes, then

$$G = cl(a_1) \cup cl(a_2) \cup \ldots \cup cl(a_k).$$

Let a be an element of G such that $a \in Z(G)$, the *centre* of G. Then

$$cl(a) = \{xax^{-1} \mid x \in G\} = \{a\}.$$

In this case, the conjugacy class is said to be *trivial*. Conversely, if $cl(a) = \{a\}$, then $xax^{-1} = a$ for all $x \in G$, which implies $xa = ax$ for all $x \in G$ and so $a \in Z(G)$. Thus we find that if $a \notin Z(G)$, then $cl(a) \cap Z(G) = \emptyset$ and $a \in Z(G)$, if and only if $cl(a) = \{a\}$. Hence we can partition G as follows $G = Z(G) \cup cl(x_1) \cup cl(x_2) \cup \ldots \cup cl(x_t)$ where $x_1, x_2, \ldots, x_t$ are representatives from each of the distinct conjugacy classes $cl(x_i)$, such that $cl(x_i) \cap Z(G) = \emptyset$, i.e., $cl(x_i)$ are those conjugacy classes which contain more than one element. Hence

$$|G| = |Z(G)| + \sum_{i=1}^{t} |cl(x_i)|,$$

where $x_1, x_2, \ldots, x_t$ are representatives for each of the nontrivial conjugacy classes. This equation is called the **class equation** of a finite group G.

Example 10.2.2. Consider the group S_3. The elements of S_3 are

$$e, (1\,2), (1\,3), (2\,3), (1\,2\,3) \text{ and } (1\,3\,2).$$

Now $cl(e) = \{e\}$, whence $e \in Z(S_3)$; indeed here $Z(S_3) = \{e\}$. Also we have,

$$cl\big((1\,2)\big) = \{x\,(1\,2)\,x^{-1} \mid x \in S_3\} = \{e\,(1\,2)\,e^{-1}, (1\,2)(1\,2)(1\,2)^{-1}, (1\,3)(1\,2)(1\,3)^{-1},$$

$$(2\,3)(1\,2)(2\,3)^{-1}, (1\,2\,3)(1\,2)(1\,2\,3)^{-1}, (1\,3\,2)(1\,2)(1\,3\,2)^{-1}\}$$

$$= \big\{(1\,2), (1\,3), (2\,3)\big\}.$$

Similarly, it can be shown that, $cl\big((1\,2\,3)\big) = \{(1\,2\,3), (1\,3\,2)\}$.
Hence,

$$S_3 = \{e\} \cup \{(1\,2), (1\,3), (2\,3)\} \cup \{(1\,2\,3), (1\,3\,2)\}$$

and so

$$6 = |S_3| = |\{e\}| + |\{(1\,2), (1\,3), (2\,3)\}| + |\{(1\,2\,3), (1\,3\,2)\}| = 1 + 3 + 2$$

is the class equation of S_3.

Example 10.2.3. In Exercise 3.1.6(a), we have introduced the Quaternion group $\mathcal{Q}_8 = \{\pm 1, \pm i, \pm j, \pm k\}$ as a non-Abelian group with eight elements governed by the rules $i^2 = j^2 = k^2 = ijk = -1$, where 1 is the identity element. If $\mathcal{Q}_8$ acts on itself by conjugation, the conjugacy classes must be the distinct orbits, as we have already pointed out. Let us find the class equation of $\mathcal{Q}_8$. Observe that $1, -1 \in Z(\mathcal{Q}_8)$ as it can be easily checked that the orbit of 1 is $cl(1) = \{x1x^{-1} \mid x \in \mathcal{Q}_8\} = \{1\}$ and similarly orbit of -1 is $cl(-1) = \{-1\}$. Again, for all $x, y \in \mathcal{Q}_8$, we have, using the benifit of $-1 \in Z(\mathcal{Q}_8)$,

$$-xy(-x)^{-1} = (-1)xy\left((-1)x\right)^{-1} = (-1)xyx^{-1}(-1)^{-1} = xyx^{-1}(-1)(-1)^{-1} = xyx^{-1},$$

which tells that the outcome of y conjugated by $-x$ (i.e., $-xy(-x)^{-1}$) is same as that of y conjugated by x (i.e., xyx^{-1}), whence the computations for the following *conjugation table* are considerably reduced. Note that, the elements y in the first column conjugated by the elements x of the top row, make the body of the table. The last column indicates the conjugacy classes of the corresponding first column element.

y ($\downarrow$) conjugated by $x(\rightarrow)$	1	i	j	k	Conjugacy Class
1	1	1	1	1	$\{1\}$
-1	-1	-1	-1	-1	$\{-1\}$
i	i	i	$-i$	$-i$	$\{i, -i\}$
$-i$	$-i$	$-i$	i	i	$\{i, -i\}$
j	j	$-j$	j	$-j$	$\{j, -j\}$
$-j$	$-j$	j	$-j$	j	$\{j, -j\}$
k	k	$-k$	$-k$	k	$\{k, -k\}$
$-k$	$-k$	k	k	$-k$	$\{k, -k\}$

Clearly there are two trivial conjugacy classes, whence $\{1, -1\} = Z(\mathcal{Q}_8)$. Also we have three distinct non-trivial conjugacy classes, viz., $cl(i) = cl(-i) = \{i, -i\}, cl(j) = cl(-j) = \{j, -j\}$ and $cl(k) = cl(-k) = \{k, -k\}$. Hence the class equation of $Z(\mathcal{Q}_8)$ is $8 = |\mathcal{Q}_8| = |Z(\mathcal{Q}_8)| + |cl(i)| + |cl(j)| + |cl(k)| = (1+1) + 2 + 2 + 2$.

Remark 10.2.4. Note that, a given partition of some $n = (1 + 1 + \cdots + 1) + n_1 + n_2 + \ldots + n_k$, $(n_i > 1)$, may be immediately rejected as a valid *class equation* of some group G of order n, if one of the n_i's fail to divide n, or the sum of the 1's at the beginning (which indicates the order of $Z(G)$) fails to divide n. For example, $10 = 1 + 2 + 3 + 4$ or, $10 = (1 + 1 + 1 + 1) + 2 + 4$ may be rejected by the above argument, as in the first case 3, and in the second case 4 do not divide 10. However, any one of these criterion, though sufficient for the rejection, is not necessary.

Recall that, for an element $a \in G$, the **centralizer** of a [Definition 5.1.28] is the subset $C(a) = \{x \in G \,|\, xa = ax\} = \{x \in G \,|\, xax^{-1} = a\}$. Clearly, $e, a \in C(a)$ and we have proved in Theorem 5.1.29 that $C(a)$ is a subgroup of G such that $Z(G) \subseteq C(a)$. The following theorem shows that, in a finite group, the index of the centralizer of an element is same as the order of the corresponding conjugacy class.

Theorem 10.2.5. *Let G be a finite group and $a \in G$. Then $[G : C(a)] = |cl(a)|$.*

Proof. Let $\mathcal{L}$ be the set of all left cosets of $C(a)$ in G. Now, $\mathcal{L} = \{xC(a) \mid x \in G\}$ and $cl(a) = \{xax^{-1} \mid x \in G\}$. Now the mapping

$$f : \mathcal{L} \to cl(a), \quad \text{defined by } f\left(xC(a)\right) = xax^{-1}$$

is a well-defined bijective mapping. Indeed,

$$xC(a) = yC(a) \iff x^{-1}ya = ax^{-1}y \iff xax^{-1} = yay^{-1}.$$

Thus it follows that

$$|\mathcal{L}| = |cl(a)| \text{ and hence, } [G : C(a)] = |cl(a)|.$$

$\square$

Note that in Example 10.2.2, $C\left((1\,2)\right) = \{e, (1\,2)\}$, which corroborates with

$$[S_3 : C\left((1\,2)\right)] = 3 = |cl(1\,2)| = |\{(1\,2), (1\,3), (2\,3)\}|;$$

again $C\left((1\,2\,3)\right) = \{e, (1\,2\,3), (1\,3\,2)\}$, whence,

$$[S_3 : C\left((1\,2\,3)\right)] = 2 = |cl(1\,2\,3)| = |\{(1\,2\,3), (1\,3\,2)\}|.$$

We leave it to the reader to find a similar verification for Example 10.2.3 using the conjugation table.

By virtue of the Theorem 10.2.5 above, the class equation of a finite group can be written as

$$|G| = |Z(G)| + \sum_{i=1}^{t}\left[G : C(x_i)\right] = |Z(G)| + \sum_{i=1}^{t}\frac{|G|}{|C(x_i)|},$$

where $x_1, x_2, \ldots, x_t$ are class representatives from each of the distinct nontrivial conjugacy classes.

We point out that the class equation is an important tool to study finite groups.

Theorem 10.2.6. *If G is a group of order p^n $(n > 0)$, where p is a prime, then $Z(G) \neq \{e\}$.*

Proof. Consider the class equation of the group G.

$$|G| = |Z(G)| + \sum_{i=1}^{t}\frac{|G|}{|C(x_i)|}, \tag{10.2.1}$$

where $x_1, x_2, \ldots, x_t$ are representatives from each conjugacy classes $cl(x_i)$ such that $x_i \notin Z(G)$.

If $x_i \notin Z(G)$, then $C(x_i) \neq G$ and $|C(x_i)| = p^{r_i}$ where $0 < r_i < n$, $(r_i \in \mathbb{N})$. Hence,

$$\frac{|G|}{|C(x_i)|} = p^{n-r_i},$$

which is divisible by p. So in (10.2.1), $\sum_{i=1}^{t} \frac{|G|}{|C(x_i)|}$ is divisible by p and also p divides $|G|$. Consequently, p divides $|Z(G)|$. Since $|Z(G)| \geq 1$, it follows that $|Z(G)| \geq p$ and hence $Z(G) \neq \{e\}$. $\qquad\square$

We have seen in Corollary 5.3.11 that *every group of prime order is cyclic* and hence commutative. But a group of order p^2, where p is prime, may not be cyclic. Indeed, Klein's four-group is a noncyclic group of order 2^2. However, the following theorem shows that every group of order p^2 is commutative.

Theorem 10.2.7. *For any prime number p, every group of order p^2 is commutative.*

Proof. Let G be a group of order p^2. Then $Z(G) \neq \{e\}$ and so $|Z(G)| = p$ or p^2. Suppose $|Z(G)| = p$. There exists $a \in G$ such that $a \notin Z(G)$. Now $C(a) = \{x \in G \,|\, xa = ax\}$ is a subgroup of G, such that $Z(G) \subseteq C(a)$. Since $a \in C(a)$, $Z(G) \neq C(a)$. Hence $|Z(G)| < |C(a)|$. But $|C(a)|$ divides $|G|$. Consequently, $|C(a)| = p^2$ which implies that $C(a) = G$. As a result, $a \in Z(G)$, a contradiction. Hence $|Z(G)| = p^2$ and so $G = Z(G)$ is a commutative group. $\qquad\square$

Now we shall prove **Cauchy's theorem for any finite group**. We shall discuss some applications of this theorem, which are instrumental in the development of the theory of finite groups. In Chapter 9 we have proved Cauchy's Theorem for finite Abelian group [Theorem 9.1.3]. We restate this result in the following lemma.

Lemma 10.2.8. *Let G be a finite Abelian group and p be a prime number. If $p \,|\, |G|$, then G has an element of order p and hence a subgroup of order p.*

Theorem 10.2.9. *[Cauchy] Let G be a finite group of order n such that n is divisible by a prime p. Then G contains an element of order p and hence a subgroup of order p.*

Proof. The proof is by induction on n. If $n = 2$, then G is commutative and the result follows from Lemma 10.2.8. Make the induction hypothesis that the result is true for all groups of order m such that $2 \leq m < n$. Now, the class equation for a group G of order n, by virtue of Theorem 10.2.5 is

$$|G| = |Z(G)| + \sum_{a \notin Z(G)} [G : C(a)] \qquad (10.2.2)$$

where $Z(G)$ denotes the centre of G and the summation runs over a complete set of representatives a of the distinct conjugacy classes like $cl(a)$, where none of these representatives belong to $Z(G)$.

Case 1: If $G = Z(G)$, then G is commutative and the result follows from Lemma 10.2.8.

Case 2: If $G \neq Z(G)$, then there exists $a \in G$ such that $a \notin Z(G)$. For such an element a, $G \neq C(a)$, whence $|G| > |C(a)| \geq 2$, where the first inequality holds as $C(a)$ is a subgroup of G, while $e, a \in C(a)$ justify the second.

Subcase (i): If p divides $|C(a)|$, then by the induction hypothesis, $C(a)$ and thus G has an element of order p.

Subcase (ii): If p does not divide $|C(a)|$ for all $a \notin Z(G)$, then as p is a prime number which divides $|G|$ and by Lagrange's theorem 5.3.10 we have

$$|G| = [G : C(a)] \cdot |C(a)|, \tag{10.2.3}$$

we see that p must divide $[G : C(a)]$ for all $a \notin Z(G)$. Consequently, in the class equation (10.2.2), p must divide each term of the summation. But as p divides $|G|$, it follows that p divides $|Z(G)|$. Since $Z(G)$ is commutative, we have again by Lemma 10.2.8 that there exists $a \in Z(G)$ of order p and hence G contains an element of order p.   □

Note that, the primality of p in Cauchy's theorem for finite groups is indispensable. Indeed, there is no element of order 6 in the group A_4 of 12 elements, as we have already seen while investigating the failure of the converse of Lagrange's theorem. However, if we consider finite *Abelian* groups, then in Theorem 9.1.4 we have proved the following result to show that the converse of Lagrange's theorem holds for this class of groups.

Theorem 10.2.10. *Let G be a finite Abelian group of order n. If m is a positive integer such that $m \mid n$, then G has a subgroup of order m.*

Let us now discuss some of the interesting applications of Cauchy's theorem.

Proposition 10.2.11. *For a prime p, every group of order p^n $(n > 0)$ contains a normal subgroup of order p.*

Proof. Let G be a group of order p^n, $(n > 0)$. Then $Z(G) \neq \{e\}$. Hence $|Z(G)| = p^t$ for some $0 < t \leq n$. Then by Cauchy's theorem, $Z(G)$ has an element a of order p. Let $H = \langle a \rangle$. Since $H \subseteq Z(G), gH = Hg$ for all $g \in G$, whence H is a normal subgroup of G of order p.   □

Proposition 10.2.12. *If G is a group of order pn, where p is a prime such that $p \geq n$, then G has a normal subgroup of order p.*

Proof. If $p = n$, then $|G| = p^2$ and hence G is commutative. So, by Cauchy's theorem, G has an element a of order p and hence a subgroup $H = \langle a \rangle$ of order p. Since G is commutative, H is a normal subgroup. Now, if $p > n$, then by Cauchy's theorem, G has a subgroup H of order p. We show that the number of subgroups of order p in G is only one. Let H and K be two distinct subgroups order p in G. Then,

$$|HK| = \frac{|H| \, |K|}{|H \cap K|}$$

$$= \frac{p \cdot p}{1} \qquad \text{(since } H \neq K \text{ and } |H \cap K| \text{ divides } |H| \text{ and } |K|\text{)}$$

$$> pn, \qquad \text{—a contradiction.}$$

Hence G has only one subgroup H of order p. It then follows that H is a normal subgroup. $\square$

Proposition 10.2.13. *Let G be a group of order p^n, where p is a prime and $n \geq 1$. Then any subgroup of G of order p^{n-1} is normal in G.*

Proof. We will prove the result by induction on n. If $n = 1$, then G is a group of prime order and hence commutative. Here the only subgroup is $\{e_G\}$, which is trivially normal. Thus, the result is true for $n = 1$. Suppose the result is true for all groups of order p^m, where $1 \leq m < n$. Let G be a group of order p^n and H be a subgroup of order p^{n-1}. Consider $N(H) = \{x \in G \mid xHx^{-1} = H\}$. We know $N(H) = H$ if and only if $Z(G) \subseteq H$ and $N(H) = G$ if and only if H is a normal subgroup. If $H \neq N(H)$, then $|N(H)| > p^{n-1}$. Thus, $|N(H)| = p^n$, so $N(H) = G$. Hence, in this case H is normal in G. Suppose $H = N(H)$. Then $Z(G)$, the centre of G, is a subset of H and by Theorem 10.2.6, $Z(G) \neq \{e\}$. By Cauchy's theorem there exists $a \in Z(G)$ such that $o(a) = p$. Let $K = \langle a \rangle$. Then K is a normal subgroup of G of order p. Now $|H/K| = p^{n-2}$ and $|G/K| = p^{n-1}$. Thus, by the induction hypothesis, H/K is a normal subgroup of G/K. Hence, by Theorem 6.2.9 (v), H is a normal subgroup of G. $\square$

Remark 10.2.14. The aforesaid Proposition 10.2.13 can also be proved alternatively by using Theorem 10.1.14. Indeed, $[G : H] \equiv [N(H) : H] (mod \, p)$ implies $p \equiv [N(H) : H] (mod \, p)$. Since $1 \leq [N(H) : H] \leq p$, we must have $[N(H) : H] = p = [G : H]$. This implies $|G| = |N(H)|$. Since G is finite and $N(H) \subseteq G$, we must have $N(H) = G$. Hence H is normal in G.

Worked-out Exercises

◇ **Exercise 10.2.1.** Let G be a finite group. Prove that if there exists an element $a \in G$ with exactly two conjugates, then G contains a nontrivial normal subgroup.

Solution.   According to the given condition, $[G : C(a)] = |cl(a)| = 2$. Thus $C(a)$ is a nontrivial subgroup and the index of the subgroup $C(a)$ is 2. Hence $C(a)$ is normal in G.

◇ **Exercise 10.2.2.** Prove that a subgroup H of a group G is a normal subgroup if and only if H is a union of some conjugacy classes of G.

Solution.   Let H be a normal subgroup of G. Now we know that for all $a \in G$, $a \in cl(a)$ always holds. So, for all $a \in H$, $a \in cl(a)$, whence $H \subseteq \bigcup_{a \in H} cl(a)$. Also, as H is normal, we have, for all $g \in G$, $a \in H$, $gag^{-1} \in H$. Hence $cl(a) \subseteq H$ for all $a \in H$. Thus

$$H = \bigcup_{a \in H} cl(a).$$

Conversely, assume that $H = \bigcup_{a \in S} cl(a)$ for some subset S of G. Let $h \in H$. Then there exists $a \in S$ such that $h \in cl(a)$. Thus $h = xax^{-1}$ for some $x \in G$. Now for all $g \in G$, we see that

$$ghg^{-1} = g(xax^{-1})g^{-1} = (gx)a(x^{-1}g^{-1}) = (gx)a(gx)^{-1} \in cl(a) \subseteq H.$$

Hence $gHg^{-1} \subseteq H$. Consequently H is a normal subgroup of G.

◇ **Exercise 10.2.3.** Let G be a finite group that has only two conjugacy classes. Show that $|G| = 2$.

Solution.   Let $|G| = n$. Let $a \in G$ and $a \neq e$. Then $G = cl(e) \cup cl(a)$. Since $|cl(e)| = 1$, $|cl(a)| = n - 1$. Hence, $n - 1 = |cl(a)| = [G : C(a)]$ divides $|G| = n$. (Since in case of a finite group, order of the group is equal to the product of the order of a subgroup and its index). Writing $n = (n - 1) + 1$, this means, $\frac{1}{n-1}$ must be an integer. This is possible only if $n = 2$.

◇ **Exercise 10.2.4.** Find the conjugacy classes $cl((1\,2))$, $cl((1\,2\,3))$, $cl((1\,2\,3\,4))$, and $cl((1\,2)(3\,4))$ in S_4. Hence write the class equation of S_4.

Solution.   The group S_4 has 24 elements. In fact,

$$S_4 = \{(1\,2),(1\,3),(1\,4),(2\,3),(2\,4),(3\,4),(1\,2\,3),(1\,3\,2),$$
$$(1\,2\,4),(1\,4\,2),(1\,3\,4),(1\,4\,3),(2\,3\,4),(2\,4\,3),(1\,2\,3\,4),$$
$$(1\,2\,4\,3),(1\,3\,2\,4),(1\,3\,4\,2),(1\,4\,2\,3),(1\,4\,3\,2),$$
$$(1\,2)(3\,4),(1\,4)(2\,3),(1\,3)(2\,4),e=(1)\}.$$

It is known that [vide Theorem 4.1.18] two permutations α and β of S_n are conjugate if and only if they have the same cyclic structure. Hence

$$cl((1\,2)) = \{(1\,2),(1\,3),(1\,4),(2\,3),(2\,4),(3\,4)\},$$
$$cl((1\,2\,3)) = \{(1\,2\,3),(1\,3\,2),(1\,2\,4),(1\,4\,2),(1\,3\,4),(1\,4\,3),(2\,3\,4),(2\,4\,3)\},$$
$$cl((1\,2\,3\,4)) = \{(1\,2\,3\,4),(1\,2\,4\,3),(1\,3\,2\,4),(1\,3\,4\,2),(1\,4\,2\,3),(1\,4\,3\,2)\},$$
$$cl((1\,2)(3\,4)) = \{(1\,2)(3\,4),(1\,4)(2\,3),(1\,3)(2\,4)\},$$
$$\text{and}$$
$$cl\{e\} = \{e\}.$$

Thus, we find that S_4 has five conjugacy classes. In S_4, we know that e is the only element in the centre. Hence, the class equation of S_4 is

$$|S_4| = |cl\{e\}| + |cl((12))| + |cl((123))| + |cl((1234))| + |cl((12)(34)|$$
$$24 = \quad 1 \quad + \quad 6 \quad + \quad 8 \quad + \quad 6 \quad + \quad 3$$

$\Diamond$ **Exercise 10.2.5.** Find all normal subgroups of S_4.

Solution.   From Exercise 10.2.2 we find that a subgroup H of S_4 is a normal subgroup if and only if H is a union of some conjugacy classes of S_4. Now, the conjugacy classes of S_4 are

$$C_1 = cl((12)) = \{(1\,2),(1\,3),(1\,4),(2\,3),(2\,4),(3\,4)\},$$
$$C_2 = cl((123))= \{(1\,2\,3),(1\,3\,2),(1\,2\,4),(1\,4\,2),(1\,3\,4),(1\,4\,3),(2\,3\,4),(2\,4\,3)\},$$
$$C_3 = cl((1234))= \{(1\,2\,3\,4),(1\,2\,4\,3),(1\,3\,2\,4),(1\,3\,4\,2),(1\,4\,2\,3),(1\,4\,3\,2)\},$$
$$C_4 = cl((12)(34))= \{(1\,2)(3\,4),(1\,4)(2\,3),(1\,3)(2\,4)\},$$
$$\text{and}$$
$$C_5 - cl\{e\}- \{e\}.$$

Thus, we find that S_4 has five conjugacy classes C_1,C_2,C_3,C_4,C_5 and

$$|C_1| = 6,\ |C_2| = 8,\ |C_3| = 6,\ |C_4| = 3,\ |C_5| = 1.$$

Hence H has to be the union of some of C_1,C_2,C_3,C_4,C_5. Also H needs to contain e and $|H|$ must be the sum of some of $6,8,6,3,1$. Further, $|H|$ has to divide 24. Hence, H may be one of

$$C_1 \cup C_2 \cup C_3 \cup C_4 \cup C_5,\ C_2 \cup C_4 \cup C_5,\ C_4 \cup C_5 \text{ and } C_5.$$

But each of these subsets is a subgroup and hence these four subgroups are the only normal subgroups of S_4.

◊ **Exercise 10.2.6.** Describe the conjugacy class $cl((1\ 2)(3\ 4))$ in A_5, given that there are 15 permutations of the form $(a\ b)(c\ d)$ in A_5.

Solution. To describe the conjugacy class $cl((1\ 2)(3\ 4))$ in A_5, we first note that [using Theorem 4.1.18] two permutations α and β of S_5 have the same cycle structure if and only if α and β are conjugate in S_5. Hence, the elements of A_5 that have different cycle structure cannot be conjugate. Let $\alpha = (1\ 2)(3\ 4)$. Then $cl(\alpha)$ contains only permutations of the form $(a\ b)(c\ d)$. There are 15 permutations of the form $(a\ b)(c\ d)$ in A_5. We now show that all these 15 permutations of the form $(a\ b)(c\ d)$ of A_5 are in $cl(\alpha)$.

Let $(a\ b)(c\ d) \in A_5$ and let $\pi \in S_5$ be such that $\pi(1) = a$, $\pi(2) = b$, $\pi(3) = c$ and $\pi(4) = d$. Now $\pi \circ \alpha \circ \pi^{-1} = \pi \circ ((1\ 2)(3\ 4)) \circ \pi^{-1} = (a\ b)(c\ d)$ [vide Theorem 4.1.17]. If $\pi \in A_5$, then α and $(a\ b)(c\ d)$ are conjugate in A_5.

Suppose $\pi \notin A_5$. Then π is an odd permutation. Let $\psi = \pi \circ (1\ 2)$. Clearly, $\psi \in A_5$. It can be easily checked that, $\psi \circ ((1\ 2)(3\ 4)) \circ \psi^{-1} = (a\ b)(c\ d)$. Thus α and $(a\ b)(c\ d)$ are conjugate in A_5 and hence $cl((1\ 2)(3\ 4))$ in A_5 consists of all the 15 permutations of the form $(a\ b)(c\ d)$.

◊ **Exercise 10.2.7.** Show that the set of twenty-four 5-cycles of A_5 splits into two different conjugacy classes with twelve elements each.

Solution. Let $\alpha = (1\ 2\ 3\ 4\ 5)$. It is known that the number of elements in a conjugacy class of a finite group G divides the order of the group G. Now, the order of A_5 is 60. There are twenty-four 5-cycles and 24 does not divide 60. Hence the set of twenty-four 5-cycles of A_5 does not form a single conjugacy class.

Let us now find $cl(1\ 2\ 3\ 4\ 5)$. As $\alpha = (1\ 2\ 3\ 4\ 5)$ is a five cycle, so the cyclic group $\langle \alpha \rangle$ is a group of order 5. It can be shown that no other elements of A_5 outside $\langle \alpha \rangle$ commute with α. Hence, centralizer $C(\alpha)$ contains only 5 elements. Then

$$|cl(1\ 2\ 3\ 4\ 5)| = \frac{|A_n|}{|C(\alpha)|} = \frac{60}{5} = 12.$$

Again $\beta = (1\ 3\ 5\ 2\ 4)$ is not an element of $cl(1\ 2\ 3\ 4\ 5)$. Proceeding as above, we can show that $|cl(1\ 3\ 5\ 2\ 4)| = 12$. Hence, A_5 splits into two different conjugacy classes with twelve elements each.

◊ **Exercise 10.2.8.** Show every group of order 14 contains 6 elements of order 7.

Solution. Let G be a group order 14. Since 7 divides $|G|$ and 7 is a prime, by Cauchy's Theorem G has a subgroup H of order 7. Suppose there exist two distinct subgroups H and K of order 7. Then $|H \cap K| = 1$ and hence

$$|HK| = \frac{|H||K|}{|H \cap K|} = 49 > 14 = |G|.$$

Consequently G has only one subgroup H of order 7. Let $a \in G$ be such that $o(a) = 7$, whence $H = \langle a \rangle$, which implies that $a \in H$. Hence every element of order 7 of G lies in H. Now all non-identity elements of H are of order 7 and there are six such elements in H. Hence G contains 6 elements of order 7.

◊ **Exercise 10.2.9.** Find all the groups of order 22 up to isomorphism.

Solution. Let G be a group of order 22. Since 11 divides $|G|$ and 11 is a prime, by Cauchy's theorem G has a subgroup H of order 11. Clearly H is a cyclic subgroup generated by an element, say a of order 11. Again 2 divides $|G|$, hence G must have an element, say b, of order 2. Clearly $b \notin H$ as $o(b)$ does not divide $|H|$. Since $[G : H] = 2$, H is a normal subgroup of G. Hence $b\,ab^{-1} \in H$. Therefore $b\,ab^{-1} = a^i$, $0 \le i < 11$. This implies that $a = b^{-1}a^i b = b\,a^i b^{-1}$ [since $b = b^{-1}$] $= (b\,ab^{-1})^i = (a^i)^i = a^{i^2}$. Hence $a^{i^2 - 1} = e$. Since $o(a) = 11$, we find that $11 \,|\, i^2 - 1 = (i - 1)(i + 1)$. But 11 is a prime, whence, either $11 \,|\, (i - 1)$ or $11 \,|\, (i + 1)$. But here $0 \le i < 11$, so either $i = 1$ or $i = 10$.

If $i = 1$, then $b\,ab^{-1} = a$, which implies that $b\,a = ab$ and so $o(ab) = o(a)\,o(b)$ as gcd $(11, 2) = 1$. This shows that G has an element of order 22. Consequently G is a cyclic group of order 22 and hence G is isomorphic to Z_{22}.

If $i = 10$, then $b\,ab^{-1} = a^{10}$, which implies that $b\,a = a^{10}b$. Now $[G : H] = 2$, hence $G = H \cup bH = \langle a \rangle \cup b\langle a \rangle = \langle a, b \rangle$. So G is generated by two elements a, b such that $o(a) = 11$, $o(b) = 2$ and $ba = a^{10}b$, i.e., $G \simeq D_{11}$. Hence we see that up to isomorphism there exist two groups of order 22.

◊ **Exercise 10.2.10.** Let G be a group of order 99. Prove that,

(a) G has a unique normal subgroup H of order 11.

(b) $H \subseteq Z(G)$.

Solution. (a) By Cauchy's theorem, G has a subgroup of order 11, say, H. Suppose K is any other subgroup of G of order 11. Suppose $H \ne K$. It follows that $|H \cap K| = 1$. Hence,

$$|HK| = \frac{|H||K|}{|H \cap K|} = \frac{11 \cdot 11}{1} = 121 > |G|, \quad \text{a contradiction.}$$

Hence, $H = K$ and so H is unique. Since H is the only subgroup of order 11, H is a normal subgroup of G.

(b)   Since $|H|$ is prime, H is cyclic. Let $H = \langle a \rangle$ for some $a \in H$. Then $gag^{-1} \in H$ for all $g \in G$. Thus, $gag^{-1} = a^i$ for some i, $0 \le i < 11$. Clearly $i \ne 0$. We claim that $i = 1$. Towards proving our claim, we first observe that

$$g^2ag^{-2} = g(gag^{-1})g^{-1} = ga^ig^{-1} = (gag^{-1})^i = (a^i)^i = a^{i^2}.$$

With an appeal to mathematical induction, we now conclude that

$$g^rag^{-r} = a^{i^r} \text{ for all } r \in \mathbb{N}. \tag{10.2.4}$$

Now by Cauchy's theorem again, we see that, G must contain an element of order 3, say, b. Then $a = b^3ab^{-3} = a^{i^3}$, by equation (10.2.4). Hence, $a^{i^3-1} = e$. Since $o(a) = 11$, we must have $11 \mid (i^3 - 1)$ i.e., $i^3 \equiv 1 \pmod{11}$, whence $i^9 \equiv 1 \pmod{11}$ indicates $i^{10} \equiv i \pmod{11}$. But by Fermat's little theorem we have,

$$i^{10} \equiv 1 \pmod{11}.$$

Thus, $i \equiv 1 \pmod{11}$. Since $1 \le i \le 10$, we must have $i = 1$. Thus, $gag^{-1} = a$, i.e., $ga = ag$. Hence, $H \subseteq Z(G)$.

$\diamond$ **Exercise 10.2.11.** Determine which of the following cannot be the class equation of a group:

(i) $10 = 1 + 1 + 1 + 2 + 5$.   (ii) $4 = 1 + 1 + 2$.

(iii) $8 = 1 + 1 + 3 + 3$.   (iv) $6 = 1 + 2 + 3$.

Solution. Let G be a group of order 10 with class equation $10 = 1 + 1 + 1 + 2 + 5$. Then there exist elements $a, b, d, x, y \in G$ such that $[G : C(a)] = 1, [G : C(b)] = 1, [G : C(d)] = 1, [G : C(x)] = 2$ and $[G : C(y)] = 5$. Now $[G : C(a)] = 1$ implies $G = C(a)$, i.e., $a \in Z(G)$. Similarly, we can show that $b, d \in Z(G)$. Hence $Z(G) = \{a, b, d\}$ contains three elements, a contradiction. Hence there does not exist any group with class equation $10 = 1 + 1 + 1 + 2 + 5$.

We know every group of order 4 is Abelian and thus class equation of any group of order 4 is $4 = 4$ or $4 = 1 + 1 + 1 + 1$.

Let G be a group of order 8 with class equation $8 = 1 + 1 + 3 + 3$. Then there exist elements $a, b, x, y \in G$ such that $[G : C(a)] = 1, [G : C(b)] = 1, [G : C(x)] = 3$ and $[G : C(y)] = 3$. Now $[G : C(x)] = 3$ implies $3 \mid 8$, a contradiction. Hence there does not exist any group with class equation $8 = 1 + 1 + 3 + 3$.

Now S_3 is a group with class equation $6 = 1 + 2 + 3$. Therefore, options (i), (ii) and (iii) are correct.

Exercises

1. Prove that the conjugacy relation on a group is an equivalence relation.

2. Let G be a group and $a \in G$. Prove that $a \in Z(G)$ if and only if $cl(a) = \{a\}$.

3. Let G be a group, H a subgroup of G, and $a \in G$. Prove that $N(aHa^{-1}) = aN(H)a^{-1}$.

4. Let H and K be subgroups of a group G. Prove that H is normal in K if and only if $H \subseteq K \subseteq N_G(H)$.

5. Let G be a group and H and K be subgroups of G. Prove that if H and K are conjugates, then $N(H)$ and $N(K)$ are conjugates.

6. In $D_4 = \langle a, b \mid o(a) = 4, o(b) = 2, \text{ and } ba = a^3b \rangle$, find all the elements of the conjugacy class $cl(a)$.

7. Find the class equation of the groups (i) Z_8 (ii) D_4 (iii) A_4 (iv) A_5 (v) S_5.

8. Find the number of elements of the conjugacy class $cl(1\ 2\ 3))$ in A_5.

9. Find all normal subgroups of S_5.

10. Show that every group of order 20 contains a normal subgroup of order 5.

11. Let G be a group of order pq where p, q are primes. Show that G contains a nontrivial normal subgroup.

12. Prove that every group of order 8 contains a nontrivial normal subgroup.

13. Let G be a non-commutative group of order p^3 where p is a prime. Prove that $\mid Z(G) \mid = p$.

14. Let G be a group of order p^3 where p is prime. Prove that $x^p \in Z(G)$ for all $x \in G$.

15. Show that every group of order 26 contains a normal subgroup of order 13.

16. Prove that every group of order 51 is cyclic.

Choose the right option(s) from the following statements:

17. The class equation of a group of order 10 cannot be

    (i) $10 = 1 + 1 + 1 + 2 + 5$.

    (ii) $10 - 1 + 2 + 3 + 4$.

    (iii) $10 = 1 + 2 + 2 + 5$.

    (iv) $10 = 1 + 1 + 2 + 2 + 2 + 2$.

18. It is true that

    (i) the centre of D_4 contains four elements.

    (ii) A_4 has a subgroup of order six.

    (iii) class equation of any non-Abelian group of order six is $6 = 1 + 2 + 3$.

    (iv) there exist non-Abelian groups of order eight.

10.3   Sylow Theorems

M. L. Sylow's work in determining the structure of finite groups is considered to be of fundamental importance in Abstract Algebra. These results provide useful insight towards partial converse of Lagrange's celebrated theorem on finite groups. It is interesting to note that while Sylow was working on these results sometimes around 1871-72, the concept of an *abstract group* was a relatively recent proposition by Jordan, yet to get a stronghold among mathematical circles and like many other contemporaries, groups for Sylow used to be what we may call now *subgroups of symmetric groups* [then known as 'conjugate system of substitution' as defined by Cauchy] and Sylow originally proved these theorems in 1872 for such *permutation groups*. Later, George Frobenius (1849-1917), influenced by Cayley's theorem, established those results in the present general setting.

Let us now discuss the Sylow theorems one by one and present some of their interesting applications.

Theorem 10.3.1. [*Sylow's First Theorem*] : *Let G be a group of order $p^n m$, where p is prime and $gcd(p,m) = 1$. For each $0 \leq i \leq n$, G has a subgroup of order p^i.*

Proof. It is sufficient to prove that, *if p^i divides $|G|$, then G has a subgroup of order p^i $(0 \leq i \leq n)$.* Choose such an i with $0 \leq i \leq n$, and fix it for the subsequent argument.

We prove this theorem by induction on $|G|$. The result holds trivially for $|G| = 1$. We assume that the result holds for all groups of order $k < |G|$. Now if G has a proper subgroup H such that p^i divides $|H|$, then by induction hypothesis, H has a subgroup of order p^i, and as $H \subseteq G$, hence the result follows.

Thus assume that G does not have a proper subgroup H such that p^i may divide $|H|$. Now the class equation (10.2.1) of G is:

$$|G| = |Z(G)| + \sum_{j=1}^{t} \frac{|G|}{|C(x_j)|},$$

where $x_1, x_2, \ldots, x_t$ are representatives from each conjugacy classes $cl(x_j)$ such that $x_j \notin Z(G)$. Since $C(x_j)\,[1 \leq j \leq t]$ is a proper subgroup of G, by our assumption p^i does not divide $|C(x_j)|$. But since $|C(x_j)|$ must divide $|G|$, $|C(x_j)|$ has to be of the form $p^k \cdot s$ for some positive integers $k < i$ and s. Then from the class equation above we see that p divides $\frac{|G|}{|C(x_j)|}$. But this implies p divides $|Z(G)|$.

Then by Cauchy's theorem (for finite Abelian groups), $Z(G)$ must have an element a (say), of order p. Let N be the cyclic subgroup generated by a. Since $N \subseteq Z(G)$,

N is a normal subgroup of G. Also $[G : N] = \frac{|G|}{p}$ and so p^{i-1} divides $|G/N|$. Then by induction hypothesis, G/N has a subgroup T (say), of order p^{i-1}. Therefore by Theorem 6.2.9, G has a subgroup $T_1 \supseteq N$, such that $T = T_1/N$. Now $|T_1| = |T| \cdot |N| = p^{i-1} \cdot p = p^i$. This completes the proof. □

Remark 10.3.2. From Sylow's first theorem, we find that for any finite group G and for any prime p, if p^i divides $|G|$ for $i \geq 0$, then G has a subgroup of order p^i. *This result is a partial converse of Lagrange's theorem* 5.3.10.

Definition 10.3.3. Let G be a finite group of order $p^n m$, where p is prime and $\gcd(p, m) = 1$, i.e., p and m are relatively prime. A subgroup P of G is called a ***Sylow p-subgroup*** of G, if $|P| = p^n$.

Remark 10.3.4. It follows from the first Sylow theorem that every finite group G contains Sylow p-subgroups. Clearly, such subgroups of G are *maximal p-subgroups*, i.e., order of every element of these subgroups is a power of p [see Definition 9.1.8]. Now watch carefully the diagrams of regular polygons with their respective axes of symmetry as shown in Fig. 26. By now it should be clear to you that they are related to the geometrical representation of Dihedral groups from D_3 to D_8 respectively.

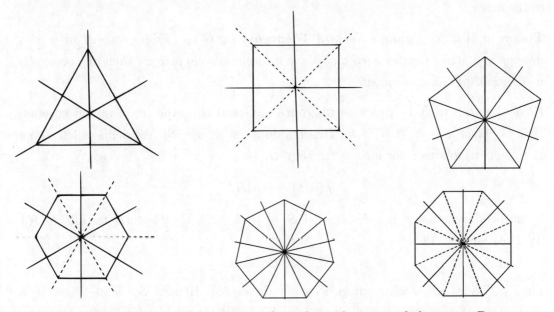

Fig. 26 *Axes of symmetry of regular polygons and the group* D_n

Surely you have noted the usage of two types of lines to represent these axes of symmetry in the above figures. Observe that the dashed ones always pass through a pair of opposite vertices, while bold ones do not. It is known that $|D_n| = 2n$.

When n *is odd*, e.g., in D_3 (equilateral triangle), in D_5 (regular pentagon) or in D_7 (regular heptagon), the largest power of 2 that divides the order of D_n is $2^1 = 2$, whence subgroups of order 2 are Sylow 2-subgroups in these cases. These subgroups are generated by reflections about the axes of symmetry passing through the vertex and perpendicularly bisecting the opposite side, represented by the *bold* lines in respective figures. [Recall that these group elements are of order 2 as two successive reflections about a same axis bring back the identity.] Direct counting in the respective figures reveal that in D_3 there are 3, in D_5 there are 5 and in D_7 there are 7 such subgroups. Are we hitting a pattern? Can the number of Sylow p-subgroups of a finite group G be counted by some formula? Let us wait and watch. In the meantime, we invite the reader to verify that these group elements are conjugate under '*rotation elements*' present in the respective D_n (with odd n), whence they belong to same conjugacy class.

Now turning our interest to those D_n where n *is even*, we see that in those cases e.g., in D_4 (square), in D_6 (regular hexagon) or in D_8 (regular octagon), the smallest power of 2 that divides the order of D_n is $2^2 = 4$, whence subgroups of order 2 are no more Sylow subgroups in these cases. They are still generated by reflections, but now they make two different conjugacy classes, *dashed* ones through opposite pair of vertices, belonging to one and *bold* ones bisecting the opposite pair of sides belonging to the other.

Theorem 10.3.5. [***Sylow's Second Theorem***] *Let G be a finite group of order $p^n m$, where p is a prime number such that p and m are relatively prime. Then any two Sylow p-subgroups of G are conjugate.*

Proof. Let H and K be Sylow p-subgroups of G and $\mathcal{S}$ be the set of all left cosets of H in G. Then $|\mathcal{S}| = [G : H] = m$. Hence p does not divide $|\mathcal{S}|$. We define a left action of K on $\mathcal{S}$ as follows : for all $k \in K$, $aH \in \mathcal{S}$,

$$k(aH) = (ka)H.$$

It can be shown that $\mathcal{S}$ is a K-set. Let $\mathcal{S}_0 = \{aH \in \mathcal{S} \mid k(aH) = aH \text{ for all } k \in K\}$. By Theorem 10.1.13,

$$|\mathcal{S}| \equiv |\mathcal{S}_0| (\mathrm{mod}\, p).$$

Then p divides $|\mathcal{S}| - |\mathcal{S}_0|$, but p does not divide $|\mathcal{S}|$. Hence, $|\mathcal{S}_0| \neq 0$. Then there exists $aH \in \mathcal{S}_0$ for some $a \in G$. Hence $k(aH) = aH$ for all $k \in K$. This implies that $a^{-1}kaH = H$ for all $k \in K$, so $a^{-1}ka \in H$ for all $k \in K$. Therefore, $a^{-1}Ka \subseteq H$. Now

$$|a^{-1}Ka| = |K| = |H|,$$

and $|H|$ is finite, so it follows that $a^{-1}Ka = H$. Thus H and K are conjugate. $\qquad \square$

Corollary 10.3.6. *Let G be a finite group and H be a Sylow p-subgroup of G. Then H is a unique Sylow p-subgroup of G if and only if H is a normal subgroup of G.*

Proof. Let G be a group of order $p^n m$, where p is a prime number and p and m are relatively prime. Suppose H is a unique Sylow p-subgroup of G. Now for any $g \in G$, gHg^{-1} is a subgroup and $|gHg^{-1}| = |H| = p^n$. It follows that gHg^{-1} is a Sylow p-subgroup of G. Hence from the assumption, we have $gHg^{-1} = H$ for all $g \in G$. Thus (by Theorem 5.4.3) we find that H is is a normal subgroup of G.

Conversely, assume that a Sylow p-subgroup H of G is normal. Let K be a Sylow p-subgroup of G. From the Sylow's second theorem $g^{-1}Hg = K$ for some $g \in G$. Since H is normal it follows that $g^{-1}Hg = H$. Hence $H = K$. $\square$

Example 10.3.7. The symmetric group S_4 has four Sylow 3-subgroups, namely

$$H_1 = \{(1), (1\,2\,3), (1\,3\,2)\}, \qquad H_2 = \{(1), (1\,2\,4), (1\,4\,2)\},$$

$$H_3 = \{(1), (1\,3\,4), (1\,4\,3)\}, \quad \text{and} \quad H_4 = \{(1), (2\,3\,4), (2\,4\,3)\}.$$

Thus, S_4 contains more than one Sylow 3-subgroup. Hence none of these subgroups are normal, but we can show that any two Sylow 3-subgroups of S_4 are conjugate. For example

$$((1\,2)(3\,4))^{-1}H_1((1\,2)(3\,4)) = \{(1), (1\,2\,4), (1\,4\,2)\} = H_2.$$

Theorem 10.3.8. [***Sylow's Third Theorem***] *Let G be a finite group of order $p^n m$, where p is a prime number such that p and m are relatively prime. Then the number n_p of Sylow p-subgroups of G satisfies*

(i) $n_p = 1 + kp$ for some nonnegative integer k and

(ii) n_p divides $|G|$.

Proof. Let $\mathcal{S}$ be the set of all Sylow p-subgroups of G. Let P be a Sylow p-subgroup of G, i.e., $P \in \mathcal{S}$. Then $|P| = p^n$. We define a left action of P on $\mathcal{S}$ by $g \bullet H = gHg^{-1}$, for all $g \in P$, and for all $H \in \mathcal{S}$. Since H is a subgroup of G then so is gHg^{-1}. Also, $|gHg^{-1}| = |H| = p^n$. Thus, $gHg^{-1} \subset \mathcal{S}$. One can easily check that $\mathcal{S}$ is a P-set.

Let $\mathcal{S}_0 = \{H \in \mathcal{S} : g \bullet H = H, \text{ for all } g \in P\} = \{H \in \mathcal{S} : gHg^{-1} = H, \text{ for all } g \in P\}$. Then by Theorem 10.1.13, we have

$$|\mathcal{S}| \equiv |\mathcal{S}_0| (\text{mod } p). \tag{10.3.1}$$

Let $Q \in \mathcal{S}_0$. Then, for all $g \in P$, we have $g \bullet Q = Q$, i.e., $gQg^{-1} = Q$, whence $g \in N(Q)$, the normalizer of Q. This shows that $P \subseteq N(Q)$. So P and Q are Sylow p-subgroups of $N(Q)$, as they are Sylow p-subgroups of G. Thus, by Sylow's second theorem, $aQa^{-1} = P$ for some $a \in N(Q)$. But then $P = Q$. Thus, $\mathcal{S}_0 = \{P\}$, so $|\mathcal{S}_0| = 1$.

Therefore, from (10.3.1), we have $n_p \equiv 1 \pmod{p}$, i.e., $n_p = 1 + kp$ for some $k \geq 0$. Hence $n_p = 1 + kp$ for some non-negative integer k.

Again, we define a left action $\star : G \times \mathcal{S} \longrightarrow \mathcal{S}$ by $g \star H = gHg^{-1}$ for all $g \in G$ and for all $H \in \mathcal{S}$. Then $\mathcal{S}$ is a G-set under the left action $\star$.

By Sylow's second theorem, we know that any two Sylow p-subgroups are conjugate to each other. So there is only one orbit in $\mathcal{S}$. Let $H \in \mathcal{S}$. Then $[G : G_H] = ||[H]||$, i.e., $\frac{|G|}{|G_H|} = |\mathcal{S}| = n_p$ [since the number of orbit is one]. Therefore, $n_p \mid |G|$. $\qquad \square$

Following is an application of Sylow's theorems.

Proposition 10.3.9. *If G be a group of order pq, where p, q are primes such that $p > q$ and q does not divide $p - 1$, then G is a cyclic group.*

Proof. By Sylow's First Theorem, G has Sylow p-subgroups and Sylow q-subgroups. Let n_p be the number of Sylow p-subgroups and n_q be that of Sylow q-subgroups of G. By Sylow's Third Theorem, we must have $n_p = kp + 1, k \geq 0$, $n_q = tq + 1, t \geq 0$ and both n_p and n_q divide pq. Now $1, p, q$ and pq are the only divisors of pq. Since p does not divide $kp + 1$, we find that n_p is neither p nor pq. Again, $p > q$ implies that $n_p \neq q$. Thus we find that $n_p = 1$, whence G contains only one Sylow p-subgroup, say H. From the Corollary 10.3.6, it follows that H is a normal subgroup of order p. Now as p is prime, H must be cyclic and hence $H \simeq \mathbb{Z}_p$.

Again q does not divide $tq + 1$. Hence n_q is neither q nor pq. If $tq + 1 = p$, then q divides $p - 1$. This implies that $n_q \neq p$ and so $n_q = 1$. Thus we find that G has only one Sylow q-subgroup, say K. Hence K is a normal subgroup of order q, whence, as before, we may have $K \simeq \mathbb{Z}_q$. Now $H \cap K = \{e\}$ and hence,

$$|HK| = \frac{|H||K|}{|H \cap K|} = pq.$$

Consequently, H and K are two normal subgroups of G such that $G = HK$ and $H \cap K = \{e\}$. Hence,

$$G \simeq H \times K \simeq \mathbb{Z}_p \times \mathbb{Z}_q \simeq \mathbb{Z}_{pq} \text{ (since } gcd(p, q) = 1),$$

which shows that G is a cyclic group. $\qquad \square$

Worked-out Exercises

$\Diamond$ **Exercise 10.3.1.** Let G be a finite group of order $p^n m$, where p is a prime number, such that p and m are relatively prime. Let H be a subgroup of G with $|H| = p^i$, $1 \le i < n$. Then show that there exists a subgroup K of G such that $|K| = p^{i+1}$ and H is a normal subgroup of K.

Solution. We know that

$$[N(H) : H] \equiv [G : H](\text{mod } p).$$

Since p divides $[G : H]$, p divides $|N(H)/H|$. Thus, by Cauchy's theorem, $N(H)/H$ has a subgroup K/H of order p . Now

$$|K| = |H| \, |K/H| = p^{i+1}.$$

Since H is normal in $N(H)$ and $H \subseteq K \subseteq N(H)$, H is normal in K.

$\Diamond$ **Exercise 10.3.2.** Let G be a finite group of order $p^n m$, where p is a prime number, such that p and m are relatively prime. Let H be a subgroup of G. Then prove that H is a Sylow p-subgroup of G if and only if H is a p-subgroup and is not properly contained in any other p-subgroup of G, i.e., H is a maximal p-subgroup of G.

Solution. Suppose H is a Sylow p-subgroup. Then $|H| = p^n$. Since $|G| = p^n m$ and p and m are relatively prime, it follows that H is a maximal p-subgroup of G.

Conversely, suppose that H is a maximal p-subgroup of G. As H is a p-subgroup of G, so $|H| = p^k$ for some positive integer k. Suppose $k \ne n$. By Exercise 10.3.1, there exists a subgroup K of G such that $H \subset K$ and $|K| = p^{k+1}$. This implies that H is not a maximal p-subgroup of G, a contradiction. Thus, $k = n$.

$\Diamond$ **Exercise 10.3.3.** Show that every group of order 35 is cyclic.

Solution. Let G be a group of order 35. Now, $35 = 7 \cdot 5$ and we see that $7 > 5$ and 5 does not divide $7 - 1$. Hence by Proposition 10.3.9, we find that G is a cyclic group.

$\Diamond$ **Exercise 10.3.4.** Find all the Sylow 2-subgroups of S_3.

Solution. $|S_3| = 6 = 2 \cdot 3$. By the Sylow theorem, S_3 has Sylow 2-subgroups and the order of each of these Sylow 2-subgroups is 2. Now any subgroup H of order 2 is a cyclic subgroup generated by an element of order 2 and if a is an element of order 2, then $K = \langle a \rangle$ is a subgroup of order 2. In S_3, an element α is of order 2 if and only if α is a 2-cycle. Now $(1\,2)$, $(1\,3)$ and $(2\,3)$ are the only 2-c'sycles of S_3. Hence the subgroups of order 2 are : $\{e, (1\,2)\}$, $\{e, (1\,3)\}$ and $\{e, (2\,3)\}$. Hence, these three subgroups are the Sylow 2-subgroups of S_3.

◇ **Exercise 10.3.5.** Find all Sylow 3-subgroups of A_4.

Solution. $|A_4| = 12 = 3 \cdot 4$. By the Sylow's first theorem, A_4 has Sylow 3-subgroups and the order of each of these Sylow 3-subgroups is 3. Now any subgroup $H \subseteq A_4$ of order 3 is a cyclic subgroup generated by an element of order 3 and thus $H = \langle a \rangle$ for some element $a \in A_4$, such that $o(a) = 3$. In A_4, an element α is of order 3 if and only if α is a 3-cycle. Now $(1\,2\,3)$, $(1\,3\,2)$, $(1\,2\,4)$, $(1\,4\,2)$, $(1\,3\,4)$, $(1\,4\,3)$, $(2\,3\,4)$ and $(2\,4\,3)$ are the only 3-cycles of A_4. Hence the subgroups of order 3 are: $\{e, (1\,2\,3), (1\,3\,2)\}$, $\{e, (1\,2\,4), (1\,4\,2)\}$, $\{e, (1\,3\,4), (1\,4\,3)\}$ and $\{e, (2\,3\,4), (2\,4\,3)\}$. Hence these 4 subgroups are the Sylow 3-subgroups of A_4.

◇ **Exercise 10.3.6.** If a group G of order 68 contains a normal subgroup of order 4, show that G is a commutative group.

Solution. Suppose G contains a normal subgroup H of order 4. Then H is a commutative group. Now $|G| = 17 \cdot 4$. Let n_{17} denote the number of Sylow 17-subgroups of G. Then $n_{17} = 17k + 1$ for some integer $k \geq 0$ and n_{17} divides 68. Thus, $n_{17} = 1$, so G contains a unique Sylow 17-subgroup, say, A. Then A is a normal subgroup of order 17 and $A \cap H = \{e\}$. Since $|AH| = \frac{|A||H|}{|A \cap H|} = 68$, we find that $G = A \times H$. Since A and H are both commutative, G is also commutative.

◇ **Exercise 10.3.7.** Show that every group of order 99 has a normal subgroup of order 9.

Solution. Let G be a group of order $99 = 3^2 \cdot 11$ and n_3 denote the number of Sylow 3-subgroups of G. Then $n_3 = 3k + 1$ for some integer $k \geq 0$ and n_3 divides 99. If $k = 0$, then $n_3 = 1$, which divides 99. But for any $k > 0$, n_3 does not divide 99. Hence, G contains a unique Sylow 3-subgroup H of order 9. Consequently, G has a normal subgroup of order 9.

◇ **Exercise 10.3.8.** Show that every noncyclic group of order 21 contains only 14 elements of order 3.

Solution. Let G be a noncyclic group of order 21. Since $21 = 7 \cdot 3$, G has Sylow 7-subgroup(s), each of order 7. If n_7 denotes the number of Sylow 7-subgroups, then $n_7 = 7k + 1$, $k \geq 0$ and $n_7 \mid 21$. Hence $n_7 = 1$ and so G has a unique Sylow 7-subgroup H, which must then be normal. Note that H is a cyclic subgroup of order 7. Now G has Sylow 3-subgroups also. If n_3 is the number of Sylow 3-subgroups, then $n_3 = 3k + 1$, $k \geq 0$ and $n_3 \mid 21$. Hence $n_3 = 1$ or 7. If $n_3 = 1$, then there exists a normal subgroup K of order 3 in G. Since $H \cap K$ must be a subgroup of both H

and K, $|H \cap K|$ must divide both 7 and 3, whence we find that $|H \cap K| = 1$. Then $|HK| = |H||K| = 7 \cdot 3 = 21 = |G|$. Thus it follows that $G = HK$, where H and K are normal subgroups of G and $H \cap K = \{e\}$. Hence,

$$G \simeq H \times K \simeq \mathbb{Z}_7 \times \mathbb{Z}_3 \simeq \mathbb{Z}_{21} \quad (\text{since } gcd(7,3) = 1).$$

But this contradicts the given condition that G is not cyclic. Hence $n_3 = 7$, which implies that G has 7 distinct subgroups of order 3, say $A_1, A_2, \ldots, A_7$. Now $A_i \cap A_j = \{e\}$ for all $1 \le i \ne j \le 7$. Hence $\bigcup_{i=1}^{7} A_i$ contains 15 elements including the identity element e. If $a \in A_i$ and $a \ne e$, then $o(a) = 3$. Hence $\bigcup_{i=1}^{7} A_i$ contains 14 elements of order 3. Now any element of order 3 in G belongs to one of the subgroups A_i. Hence G has exactly 14 elements of order 3.

$\lozenge$ **Exercise 10.3.9.** Show that a group of order 48 has a normal subgroup of order 16 or 8.

Solution. Let G be a group of order $48 = 2^4 \cdot 3$. Let n_2 denote the number of Sylow 2-subgroups of G. Now $n_2 = 2k + 1$ for some integer $k \ge 0$ and n_2 divides 48. Then $n_2 = 1$ or 3. If $n_2 = 1$, then G contains a unique Sylow 2-subgroup of order $2^4 = 16$, whence this subgroup of order 16 must be a normal subgroup. Suppose $n_2 = 3$. Then G has three Sylow 2-subgroups, say A, B and C, each of order 16. Let us now show that $|A \cap B| = 8$. Since $A \ne B$ and $|A \cap B|$ divides $|A|$, we see that $|A \cap B| = 1, 2, 4$, or 8. If $|A \cap B| \le 4$, then $|AB| = \frac{|A||B|}{|A \cap B|}$ shows that $|AB| \ge \frac{16 \cdot 16}{4} = 64 > 48 = |G|$, a contradiction. Hence, $|A \cap B| = 8$. Since $[A : A \cap B] = 2$ and $[B : A \cap B] = 2$, $A \cap B$ is a normal subgroup of A and B. Thus $A, B \subseteq N(A \cap B)$ whence, $AB \subseteq N(A \cap B)$. This implies that

$$|N(A \cap B)| \ge |AB| = \frac{|A||B|}{|A \cap B|} = \frac{16 \cdot 16}{8} = 32.$$

Since $N(A \cap B)$ is a subgroup of G, it follows that $|N(A \cap B)| = 48 = |G|$, which means $N(A \cap B) = G$, so that $A \cap B$ is a normal subgroup of G of order 8.

$\lozenge$ **Exercise 10.3.10.** Let G be a group of order $70 = 2 \cdot 5 \cdot 7$.

    (i) Show that a Sylow 7-subgroup of G is normal in G.

    (ii) Show that a Sylow 5-subgroup of G is normal in G.

    (iii) Show that G has a cyclic subgroup of order 35.

    (iv) Let H be a Sylow 7-subgroup of G, K be a Sylow 5-subgroup of G, and L be a Sylow 2-subgroup of G. Show that $G = HKL$.

    (v) If G/K is commutative, show that $H \subseteq Z(G)$.

Solution. By Theorem 10.3.1, G has at least one Sylow 7-subgroup, at least one Sylow 5-subgroup, and at least one Sylow 2-subgroup.

(i) The number of Sylow 7-subgroups is $1 + 7k$, where $(1 + 7k)$ divides $2 \cdot 5$. Hence $k = 0$, whence the number of Sylow 7-subgroups is 1. Let H be the Sylow 7-subgroup of G. Since H is a unique Sylow 7-subgroup of G, H is normal in G.

(ii) The number of Sylow 5-subgroups is $1 + 5k$, where $(1 + 5k)$ divides $2 \cdot 7$. Hence $k = 0$, whence the number of Sylow 5-subgroups is 1. Let K be the Sylow 5-subgroup of G. Since K is a unique Sylow 5-subgroup of G, K is normal in G.

(iii) Since H and K are normal subgroups of G, HK is a normal subgroup of G. Now $H \cap K = \{e\}$. Thus, $|HK| = 5 \cdot 7 = 35$. Since H and K are subgroups of order 5 and 7 respectively, H and K are cyclic groups. Note that $\gcd(5, 7) = 1$. Hence, HK is a cyclic group of order 35.

(iv) Let L be a Sylow 2-subgroup of G. Then $L \cap (HK) = \{e\}$ since non-identity elements in L are of order 2 and non-identity elements in HK are of order 5, 7, or 35. Now

$$|HKL| = \frac{|HK| \cdot |L|}{|L \cap (HK)|} = \frac{35 \cdot 2}{1} = 70 = |G|.$$

Hence, $G = HKL$.

(v) Since H and K are normal subgroups of G and $H \cap K = \{e\}$, $hk = kh$ for all $h \in H, k \in K$. It is given that G/K is commutative. Let $a \in L$ and $b \in H$ be nonidentity elements. Then $a, b \notin K$. Since G/K is commutative, $(aK)(bK) = (bK)(aK)$ or $(ab)K = (ba)K$. Hence, $(ab)^{-1}(ba) \in K$, so $b^{-1}a^{-1}ba \in K$. Since H is a normal subgroup of G and $b \in H$, $b^{-1}a^{-1}ba \in H$. This implies that $b^{-1}a^{-1}ba \in H \cap K = \{e\}$. Hence, $b^{-1}a^{-1}ba = e$, so $ba = ab$. Let $x \in G$ and $h \in H$. Now $G = HKL$, whence $x = abc$ for some $a \in H$, $b \in K$, and $c \in L$. Now $xh = (abc)h = ab(ch) = ab(hc) = a(bh)c = a(hb)c = (ah)bc = (ha)bc = hx$. Therefore, $h \in Z(G)$. Hence, $H \subseteq Z(G)$.

◊ **Exercise 10.3.11.** Let G be a group of order 65. Then the centre of the group is isomorphic to   (i) $\mathbb{Z}_1$ (ii) $\mathbb{Z}_5$ (iii) $\mathbb{Z}_{13}$ (iv) $\mathbb{Z}_{65}$.

Solution. By Proposition 10.3.9, we must have the group G of order 65 is cyclic and hence $G \simeq \mathbb{Z}_{65}$. Thus $Z(G) = G \simeq \mathbb{Z}_{65}$. Therefore, option (iv) is correct.

◊ **Exercise 10.3.12.** Let G be a finite group of order 20 in which the conjugacy classes have sizes $1, 4, 5, 5, 5$. Then which of the following statement(s) is(are) true?
(i) G contains a normal subgroup of order 5.
(ii) G contains a non-normal subgroup of order 5.

(iii) G contains a subgroup of order 10.

(iv) G contains a normal subgroup of order 4.

Solution. Here G is a non-Abelian group such that $Z(G) = \{e\}$. Now $|G| = 20 = 2^2 \cdot 5$ implies G contains Sylow 5-subgroups. It is easy to prove that the Sylow 5-subgroup H is unique and hence normal in G. Again, G contains a subgroup of order 2. Let A be a subgroup of order 2 of G. Since H is normal, it follows that $HA = \{ha : h \in H, a \in A\}$ is again a subgroup of G of order 10. Finally, G has no normal subgroup K of order 4. Otherwise $G \simeq H \times K \simeq \mathbb{Z}_5 \times \mathbb{Z}_4$, a contradiction, since G is non-Abelian. Therefore, options (i) and (iii) are correct.

$\Diamond$ **Exercise 10.3.13.** Let G be a group of order 125. Which of the following statement(s) are necessarily true?

(i) G has a non-trivial Abelian subgroup.

(ii) The centre of G is a proper subgroup.

(iii) The centre of G has order 5.

(iv) There is a subgroup of order 25.

Solution. Since $5 \mid |G|$, it follows that G has an element of order 5 and hence a subgroup H of order 5. Again, since $|H| = 5$, it follows that H is Abelian. If G is itself Abelian, then the centre coincides with whole group G, i.e., $|Z(G)| = 125$. Hence if G is Abelian, the centre is not a proper subgroup G. Finally, since $|G| = 125 = 5^3$, by Sylow's First theorem, it follows that G contains subgroups of order $1, 5, 5^2 (= 25)$ and 5^3. Therefore, options (i) and (iv) are correct.

Exercises

1. Find all Sylow 5-subgroups of A_5.

2. Find all Sylow 2-subgroups of A_4.

3. Let p be a prime number. Prove that a finite group G is a p-group if and only if $|G| = p^r$ for some nonnegative integer r.

4. Let H be a normal subgroup of a finite group G. Let p be a prime number. Prove that G is a p-group if and only if both G and G/H are p-groups.

5. Prove that every group of order 15 is cyclic.

6. Find all groups of order 65.

7. Show that there exists only one group of 33.

8. Find the number of groups of order 1001.

9. Prove that every group of order 175 is commutative.

10. Show that any group of order 20 contains exactly 4 elements of order 5.

11. Show that every group of order 45 contains a normal subgroup of order 9.

12. Let G be a group of order 100. If G has a unique Sylow 2-subgroup, then prove that G is a commutative group.

13. Find all groups of order 26.

14. Let G be a group of order 63. If G contains a unique subgroup of order 9 in G, then prove that G is a commutative group.

15. Let G be a group of order $231 = 3 \cdot 7 \cdot 11$.
    (a) Show that a Sylow 11-subgroup of G is normal in G.
    (b) Show that a Sylow 7-subgroup of G is normal in G.
    (c) Show that G has a cyclic subgroup of order 77.
    (d) Let H be a Sylow 11-subgroup of G, K be a Sylow 7-subgroup of G, and L be a Sylow 3-subgroup of G. Show that $G = HKL$.
    (e) Show that $H \subseteq Z(G)$.

16. Let G be a group of order p^n, where p is prime, $n > 1$ and H is a normal subgroup of G with $|H| > 1$. Then show that $|H \cap Z(G)| \neq \{e\}$. In particular, if $|H| = p$, then $H \subseteq Z(G)$

17. Let G be a finite group such that all Sylow subgroups are normal. Then show that G is isomorphic to the direct product of its Sylow subgroups.

18. Let G be a finite group, H be a Sylow p-subgroup of G. Prove that the number of Sylow p-subgroups of G is $[G : N(H)]$.

19. Let G be a finite commutative group. Prove that the number of solutions of $x^n = e$ in G (where $n > 0$ and n divides $|G|$) is a multiple of n.

20. Consider the symmetric group S_{20} and its subgroup A_{20} consisting of all even permutations. Let H be a Sylow 7-subgroup of A_{20}. Find the correct statement(s) from the following:

    (i) $|H| = 49$.

    (ii) H must be cyclic.

    (iii) H is a normal subgroup of A_{20}.

    (iv) Any Sylow 7-subgroup of S_{20} is a subset of A_{20}.

21. Let G denote the group $S_4 \times S_3$. Find the correct statement(s) from the following:
    (i) a Sylow 2-subgroup of G is normal
    (ii) a Sylow 3-subgroup of G is normal
    (iii) G has a nontrivial normal subgroup
    (iv) G has a normal subgroup of order 72.

22. Write the proof if the following statement is true, or else give a counter example.
    (i)   There exists only one (up to isomorphism) group of order 65.
    (ii) If a prime number p divides the order of a group G, then G contains a normal subgroup of order p.
    (iii) Every group of order 76 contains a unique element of order 19.
    (iv) Upto isomorphism, there exist only two groups of order 10.

(v)   In any group G, the elements ab and ba, (where $a, b \in G$), belong to the same conjugacy class.

(vi)   Every group of order 99 is commutative.

Choose the right option(s) in the following statements:

23. The number of Sylow 2-subgroups of S_4 is
    (i) 4 (ii) 1 (iii) 3 (iv) 2

24. The number of Sylow 2-subgroups of A_4 is
    (i) 4 (ii) 1 (iii) 3 (iv) 2

25. The number of normal subgroups of S_4 is
    (i) 4 (ii) 1 (iii) 3 (iv) 2

26. The number of Sylow 3-subgroups of A_4 is
    (i) 3 (ii) 1 (iii) 4 (iv) 2

27. The total number of non-isomorphic groups of order 122 is
    (i) 2   (ii) 1   (iii) 61   (iv) 4.

Chapter 11

Simple Groups

The notion of simple groups also was introduced by Galois. It was Galois who first observed that all alternating groups $A_n, n \geq 5$ are simple groups and this observation played the pivotal role in disposing off the long standing problem of a radical solution of a general quintic and further higher degree polynomials, in the negative. The class of simple groups enjoys peerless distinction in the theory of groups due to the fact that, every finite group can, in some special sense, be *factorized*[1] into simple groups, where the factorization is unique up to the order of factors. This result has a striking similarity with the so called *fundamental theorem of arithmetic*, which establishes the prime integers as the universal building block for any integer and that too in a unique way. A search for finding the *complete list of all the primes* was proved to be futile by Euclid himself over two millennium ago, as he had shown them to be infinitely many. Also a classification of all the primes[2] is till date out of reach. However, a search for a complete determination and classification of all the finite simple groups (upto isomorphism) was not in vein. This is considered as one of the most fundamental achievements of abstract algebra in recent times. The problem that has engaged hundreds of mathematicians all over the world for almost thirty years came to a brilliant end in January, 1981. The final crowning glory went to Daniel Gorenstein (1923-1992) and his co-workers. It is amazing to know that the final proof of this complete list of classification took about 10,000 printed pages!

It is not very difficult to see that a commutative simple group must be isomorphic to $\mathbb{Z}_p$, for some prime p, as we shall shortly show. The problem really was to classify the non-commutative simple groups. Five such groups of a particular nature were found as early as in 1861, in the works of E. Mathieu, which are presently

---

[1]A detailed treatment of this concept is out of scope of the present text.

[2]More on prime numbers in **Appendix C.**

called *sporadic groups*. Later on, a few more sporadic groups of huge order were constructed, the most fascinating one being due to R. L. Griess in the beginning of 1980. Aptly called *Monster* by J. H. Conway, this sporadic simple group has the order $808,017,424,794,512,875,886,459,904,961,710,757,005,754,368,000,000,000$. It has more elements than the number of elementary particles in the universe !

However, the first remarkable breakthrough towards the classification problem was the famous Feit-Thompson[3] theorem of 1963, which actually proved the so-called Burnside conjecture of 1911 that *a non-commutative simple group must have an even order*. Among others, remarkable contribution in this field were also made by Michael Aschbacher (1944-) during the late seventies, that paved the path towards the final goal achieved by Gorenstein and his team.

11.1 Simple Groups

Definition 11.1.1. A group G is called a ***simple group*** if $G \neq \{e\}$ and G has no nontrivial (i.e., other than $\{e\}$ and G) normal subgroups.

What is the class of groups that are simple? Investigating in this direction, the following theorem describes the family of all *commutative* simple groups.

Theorem 11.1.2. *A commutative group G is a simple group if and only if $G \simeq \mathbb{Z}_p$, for some prime p.*

Proof. For any prime p, $\mathbb{Z}_p$ is a cyclic group of order p. Since 1 and p are the only positive divisors of p, by Lagrange's theorem we find that $\mathbb{Z}_p$ has no normal subgroups other than $\mathbb{Z}_p$ and $\{[0]\}$. Hence $\mathbb{Z}_p$ is a simple group. Now, let G be a simple group. Hence $G \neq \{e\}$. There exists an element $a \in G$ such that $a \neq e$. Let $H = \langle a \rangle$. Since G is a commutative group, H is a normal subgroup of G such that $H \neq \{e\}$. Now G is a simple group, hence $G = H$. So we find that G is a cyclic group. If G is an infinite cyclic group, we find that $G \simeq \mathbb{Z}$. Since the group $\mathbb{Z}$ contains nontrivial normal subgroups, such that $2\mathbb{Z}, 3\mathbb{Z}$ etc., it follows that G also contains nontrivial normal subgroups. This goes against our assumption that G is a simple group. Hence G must be a finite cyclic group. Let $|G| = m$. Since $G \neq \{e\}$, $m > 1$. If m is composite, then in the cyclic group G, for every prime divisor q of m there exists a subgroup and hence a normal

---

[3]John Thompson (1932-) received the **Fields Medal** in 1970 and the **Abel Prize** in 2008 for his contributions to the theory of Simple Groups. These are among the most prestigious international awards in mathematics, the former being rated by many as the 'Nobel prize' of Mathematics. An interested reader may find more on these and some other prizes of international repute in mathematics in **Appendix D**.

subgroup of order q and in that case G cannot be simple. Consequently, m must be a prime number, say, p. Thus we find that G is a cyclic group of prime order p and hence $G \simeq \mathbb{Z}_p$, by Theorem 6.2.3. □

The above theorem conclusively describes all simple commutative groups. We find that there are infinitely many simple commutative groups and these are precisely $\mathbb{Z}_p$, where p is any prime number. Unfortunately, it is not so easy to describe all the noncommutative simple groups.

In what follows, we shall describe some methods to test the simplicity of finite groups.

Example 11.1.3. Let G be a group of order $25 = 5^2$. Then G is commutative. Now for the prime factor 5, G has a subgroup H of order 5, which must be normal in G as G is commutative. Thus, we find that a group of order 25 is not a simple group.

In Example 11.1.3, we have shown that a group of order $25 = 5^2$ is not simple. In general it follows from the Proposition 10.2.11 that if G is a p-group of order p^n, $n > 1$, then G is not simple.

Next we consider the following example.

Example 11.1.4. Let G be a group of order 10. Now $10 = 5 \cdot 2$. Let n_5 denote the number of Sylow 5-subgroups of G. From Sylow Theorem 10.3.8, $n_5 = 5k + 1$ for some integer $k \geq 0$ and n_5 divides $|G| = 10$. Thus, $n_5 = 1$, so there exists only one Sylow 5-subgroup, say, H in G. Since H is a unique Sylow 5-subgroup, H is a normal subgroup of G by Corollary 10.3.6, proving that G is not simple. Thus, no group of order 10 is simple.

In general, we have the following result.

Theorem 11.1.5. *Let p and q be two prime numbers. Then no group of order pq is simple.*

Proof. Let G be a group of order pq. If $p = q$, then $|G| = p^2$, so by Proposition 10.2.11, G is not simple. Suppose now $p \neq q$. Let $p > q$. Let n_p denote the number of Sylow p-subgroups of G. Then $n_p = pk + 1$ for some integer $k \geq 0$ and n_p divides pq. Since $\gcd(1 + kp, p) = 1$, n_p does not divide p. Hence, n_p divides q. Thus, $1 + kp \leq q$. But $p > q$. Therefore, $1 + kp \leq q$ holds only if $k = 0$. This implies that $n_p = 1$, so G contains a unique Sylow p-subgroup of order p, which must be normal by Corollary 10.3.6. Hence, G is not simple. □

Test by Cayley's Theorem

By using Cayley's Theorem we have proved the following result in the Worked-out Exercise 10.1.1

Proposition 11.1.6. *If G is a finite group of order $2n$, where n is an odd integer, then G contains a normal subgroup of order n and hence G is not simple, for $n > 1$.*

Next example can be settled as a direct consequence of this result.

Example 11.1.7. Let G be a group of order 30. Since $30 = 2 \cdot 15$, G contains a normal subgroup of order 15. Hence G is not a simple group.

Test by Extended Cayley's Theorem

We recall the following result which is the Corollary 10.1.17 to Cayley's theorem and discuss its application towards testing the simplicity of a group.

Proposition 11.1.8. *Let G be a finite group and let H be a subgroup of G of index n. Then there exists a homomorphism $f : G \to S_n$ such that $\ker f \subseteq H$.*

Using this result we have proved the following one in Worked-out Exercise 10.1.3

Corollary 11.1.9. *Let G be a finite group and H a subgroup of G of index $n \neq 1$. If $|G|$ does not divide $n!$, then G has a nontrivial normal subgroup.*

Example 11.1.10. Let G be a group of order 12. Note that, $12 = 2^2 \cdot 3$. Hence by Sylow's First Theorem, G has a subgroup H of order 2^2. Now $[G : H] = \frac{|G|}{|H|} = 3$. Observe that $|G| = 12$ does not divide $3!$, whence by Corollary 11.1.9, we may conclude that G has a nontrivial normal subgroup, so that G is not simple. Hence we may conclude that, *there does not exist a simple group of order* 12.

Remark 11.1.11. The result of the above example may be obtained directly as well. Indeed, here $12 = 2^2 \cdot 3$. Hence by Sylow's First Theorem, G has a subgroup H of order 2^2. Now $[G : H] = \frac{|G|}{|H|} = 3$. Hence by the Extended Cayley's theorem, there exists a homomorphism $f : G \to S_3$ such that $\ker f \subseteq H$. If $\ker f = \{e\}$, then f is a monomorphism and hence G is isomorphic to a subgroup K of S_3. Now $|K| = |G| = 12 > 6 = |S_3|$ shows that S_3 cannot contain the subgroup K of order 12. Consequently, $\ker f \neq \{e\}$. Since $|H| = 4$, $1 < |\ker f| \leq 4 < 12$. So we find that G contains a nontrivial normal subgroup $\ker f$ and hence G is not simple.

At this point let us recall the Proposition 10.2.12, which states that, *if G is a group of order pn, where p is prime such that $p \geq n$, then G has a normal subgroup of order p.*

Let G be a group of order $n \leq 60$. Applying the above results, we find that if $n = 6$ $(= 3 \cdot 2)$, 10 $(= 5 \cdot 2)$, 14 $(= 7 \cdot 2)$, 15 $(= 5 \cdot 3)$, 20 $(= 5 \cdot 4)$, 21 $(= 7 \cdot 3)$, 22 $(= 11 \cdot 2)$, 26 $(= 13 \cdot 2)$, 28 $(= 7 \cdot 4)$, 33 $(= 11 \cdot 3)$, 34 $(= 17 \cdot 2)$, 35 $(= 7 \cdot 5)$, 38 $(= 19 \cdot 2)$, 39 $(= 13 \cdot 3)$, 42 $(= 7 \cdot 6)$, 44 $(= 11 \cdot 4)$, 46 $(= 23 \cdot 2)$, 51 $(= 17 \cdot 3)$, 52 $(= 13 \cdot 4)$, 55 $(= 11 \cdot 5)$, 57 $(= 19 \cdot 3)$, or 58 $(= 29 \cdot 2)$, then G is not simple.

Test by Sylow Theorems

We can use the Sylow theorems to test the simplicity of finite groups.

Example 11.1.12. Let G be a group of order 50. We show that no group of order 50 is simple. Now $50 = 5^2 \cdot 2$. Hence G has Sylow 5-subgroups. Let n_5 be the number of Sylow 5-subgroups. Then by Sylow's third theorem, (see Theorem 10.3.8) $n_5 = 5k + 1$, $k \geq 0$ and $n_5 \mid 50$. Hence $n_5 = 1$. So there exists only one Sylow 5-subgroup, say H of order 5^2 in G. Hence by Corollary 10.3.6, H is a normal subgroup of order 25 in G. Thus it follows that G is not a simple group.

Example 11.1.13. In this example, we show that no group of order 40 is simple. Let G be a group of order $40 = 5 \cdot 8$. Let n_5 denote the number of Sylow 5-subgroups of G. By Sylow's third theorem (see Theorem 10.3.8), $n_5 = 5k + 1$ for some integer $k \geq 0$ and n_5 divides 40. Hence, $n_5 = 1$. Thus, G has a unique Sylow 5-subgroup which must be normal by Corollary 10.3.6. Hence, G is not simple.

Thus using the above tests for simplicity of groups we can show that **a group of order $n < 60$ is a simple group if and only if G is of prime order**.

Now the alternating group A_5 is of order 60. We show that A_n $(n \geq 5)$ is a simple group. Towards the proof, we first note that A_n $(n \geq 3)$ is generated by 3-cycles (vide Theorem 5.1.23). Further we have the following lemma.

Lemma 11.1.14. *Let H be a normal subgroup of A_n $(n \geq 5)$. If H contains a 3-cycle, then $H = A_n$.*

Proof. Let $\alpha = (a\,b\,c)$ be a 3-cycle in H and let $\beta = (u\,v\,w)$ be any 3-cycle in A_n. Now there exists a permutation $\delta \in S_n$ such that $\delta(a) = u, \delta(b) = v$ and $\delta(c) = w$. Now $\delta(a\,b\,c)\delta^{-1} = (u\,v\,w)$. If δ is an even permutation, then $\delta \in A_n$ and hence $(u\,v\,w) = \delta(a\,b\,c)\delta^{-1} \in H$. Suppose δ is an odd permutation. Since $n \geq 5$, there exist $d, f \in I_n = \{1, 2, \ldots, n\}$ such that $d, f \notin \{a, b, c\}$. Now $\delta(d\,f) \in A_n$ and $\delta(d\,f)(a\,b\,c)(\delta(d\,f))^{-1} \in H$. But we see that

$$\delta(d\,f)(a\,b\,c)(\delta(d\,f))^{-1}$$
$$= \delta(d\,f)(a\,b\,c)(d\,f)\delta^{-1}$$
$$= \delta(d\,f)(d\,f)(a\,b\,c)\delta^{-1} \quad \text{(since } (a\,b\,c) \text{ and } (d\,f) \text{ are disjoint cycles)}$$
$$= \delta(a\,b\,c)\delta^{-1}$$
$$= (u\,v\,w).$$

Hence $(u\,v\,w) \in H$. Since H contains all the 3-cycles, by Theorem 5.1.23, we find that $H = A_n$. $\qquad \square$

Example 11.1.15. A_3 is a group with 3 elements. Hence $\boldsymbol{A_3}$ **is a simple group.**

Example 11.1.16. A_4 is a group with 12 elements. A_4 contains a unique subgroup $K_4 = \{e, (1\,2)(3\,4), (1\,3)(2\,4), (1\,4)(2\,3)\}$ of order 4. Hence K_4 is a non trivial normal subgroup of A_4 . Thus $\boldsymbol{A_4}$ **is not a simple group.**

Example 11.1.17. In this example we show that $\boldsymbol{A_5}$ **is a simple group.**

Let $H \neq \{e\}$ be a normal subgroup of A_5. There exists $\alpha \in H$ such that $\alpha \neq \{e\}$. Since $\alpha \in A_5$, we find that either of the following must be the case:
(i) α is a 3-cycle; (ii) α is a 5-cycle; (iii) α is a product of two disjoint 2-cycles.
Case I : From Lemma 11.1.14, it follows that $H = A_5$.
Case II : Let $\alpha = (a\,b\,c\,u\,v)$ be a 5-cycle. Since $(a\,b\,c) \in A_5$, so $(a\,b\,c)(a\,b\,c\,u\,v)\,(a\,b\,c)^{-1} \in H$, whence $(a\,b\,c)(a\,b\,c\,u\,v)(a\,c\,b) \in H$, i.e., $(a\,u\,v\,b\,c) \in H$. Therefore $(a\,b\,c\,u\,v)^{-1}(a\,u\,v\,b\,c) \in H$, i.e., $(v\,u\,c\,b\,a)(a\,u\,v\,b\,c) \in H$ i.e., $(a\,c\,v) \in H$. So by Lemma 11.1.14, $H = A_5$.
Case III : Let $\alpha = (a\,b)(c\,d)$. There exists $w \in I_5 = \{1, 2, \ldots, 5\}$ such that $w \notin \{a, b, c, d\}$. Now $(c\,d\,w) \in A_n$ and $(c\,d\,w)\alpha(c\,d\,w)^{-1} \in H$. Now $(c\,d\,w)(a\,b)(c\,d)\,(c\,d\,w)^{-1} = (c\,d\,w)(a\,b)(c\,d)(c\,w\,d) = (w\,d)(a\,b)$. Since H is a subgroup, we find that $(a\,b)(c\,d)(w\,d)(a\,b) \in H$, i.e., $(c\,d\,w) \in H$. Hence by lemma 11.1.14, $H = A_5$. Thus we find that A_5 is a simple group.

We now show that $\boldsymbol{A_n}$ **is a simple group for all** $\boldsymbol{n \geq 5}$. Towards proving this, we first establish the following lemma.

Lemma 11.1.18. *Let H be a normal subgroup of A_n, $n \geq 5$. If H contains a product of two disjoint transpositions, then $H = A_n$.*

Proof. Suppose $(a\,b)(c\,d) \in H$, where $(a\,b)$ and $(c\,d)$ are disjoint transpositions. Let $w \in I_n$ be such that $w \notin \{a, b, c, d\}$. Let $\pi = (c\,d\,w)$. Since π is a 3-cycle, $\pi \in A_n$. Since H is a normal subgroup of A_n, we have $\pi(a\,b)(\,c\,d)\pi^{-1} \in H$. But $\pi\,(a\,b)(c\,d)\pi^{-1} = (d\,w)(a\,b)$, so $(d\,w)(a\,b) \in H$. Since H is a subgroup, $(c\,d\,w) = (a\,b)(c\,d)(d\,w)(a\,b) \in H$. Hence, H contains a 3-cycle, so by Lemma 11.1.14, $H = A_n$. $\qquad \square$

Theorem 11.1.19. A_n *is a simple group for all* $n \geq 5$.

Proof. Let H be a normal subgroup of A_n and $H \neq \{e\}$. Let $\pi(\neq e) \in H$ be a permutation that moves the smallest number of elements, say, m. Then $m \geq 3$. We claim that $m = 3$, in which case the result follows by Lemma 11.1.14. Suppose $m > 3$. Write $\pi = \pi_1 \pi_2 \ldots \pi_k$ as a product of disjoint cycles.

Suppose π_i is a transposition for all $i = 1, 2, \ldots, k$. Then $k \geq 2$. Let $\pi_1 = (a\ b)$ and $\pi_2 = (c\ d)$. Let $f \in I_n$ be such that $f \notin \{a, b, c, d\}$ and let $\sigma = (c\ d\ f)$. Since $\sigma \in A_n$ and H is a normal subgroup of A_n,

$$\pi' = \pi^{-1} \sigma \pi \sigma^{-1} \in H.$$

Clearly $\pi'(a) = a$ and $\pi'(b) = b$. If $u \in I_n$ and $u \notin \{a, b, c, d, f\}$ is such that $\pi(u) = u$, then $\pi'(u) = u$. Since $\pi'(f) = c$, $\pi' \neq e$. Thus, $\pi' \in H$, $\pi' \neq e$, and π' moves fewer elements than π, which is a contradiction. Hence, for some i, $1 \leq i \leq k$, π_i is a cycle of length ≥ 3. Since disjoint cycles commute, by renumbering if necessary, we may assume that $i = 1$. Then $\pi_1 = (a\ b\ c \cdots)$. If $m = 4$, then π is a cycle of length of 4 and hence an odd permutation, a contradiction. Thus, $m \geq 5$. Hence, π moves at least five elements. Let $d, f \in I_n$ and $d, f \notin \{a, b, c\}$. Let $\sigma = (c\ d\ f)$. As before, $\pi' = \pi^{-1} \sigma \pi \sigma^{-1} \in H$. Since $\pi'(b) = \pi^{-1}(d) \neq b$, $\pi' \neq e$. Now for any $u \notin \{a, b, c, d, f\}$, if $\pi(u) = u$, then $\pi'(u) = u$. Clearly $\pi'(a) = a$. Hence, π' moves fewer elements than π, which is again a contradiction. Hence, $m = 3$. Therefore H contains a 3-cycle and hence by 11.1.14, it follows that $H = A_n$. Consequently A_n $(n \geq 5)$ is a simple group.   □

We take this opportunity to merely point out that there does not exist any simple group whose order is a composite number less than 60. Note that the group A_5 is a simple group of oredr 60. We end this section by showing that this simple group of order 60 is unique upto isomorphism.

Lemma 11.1.20. *For* $n \geq 3$, A_n *is unique subgroup of* S_n *of index 2.*

Proof. Let H be any subgroup of S_n such that $[S_n : H] = 2$. Then H is a normal subgroup of S_n and the quotient group S_n/H is a group of order 2. Let $\alpha \in S_n$ be any 3-cycle. Now we consider the element $\alpha H \in S_n/H$. Since $|S_n/H| = 2$, we must have $(\alpha H)^2 = H$, i.e., $\alpha^2 \in H$. Since α is a 3-cycle, we have $\alpha^3 = e$, i.e., $\alpha^2 = \alpha^{-1}$. Thus $\alpha^{-1} \in H$ implies $\alpha \in H$. Since α is any 3-cycle, it follows that H contains all 3-cycles. But we know A_n is generated by all the 3-cycles. Hence $A_n \subseteq H$. Since H contains finite number of elements and $|A_n| = \frac{n!}{2} = |H|$, we must have $H = A_n$.   □

Proposition 11.1.21. *Every simple group of order 60 is isomorphic to A_5.*

Proof. Let G be a simple group of order 60. Then by Exercise 12 of section 11.1, it follows that G contains a subgroup H of order 12 and hence $[G : H] = 5$. Therefore, by Corollary 10.1.17, it follows that there exists a homomorphism $\psi : G \longrightarrow S_5$ such that $\ker \psi \subseteq H$. Since G is a simple group, we must have $\ker \psi = \{e\}$ and thus ψ is a monomorphism. Hence $G \simeq Im\psi$ and thus $|Im\psi| = |G| = 60$. Now $Im\psi$ is a subgroup of S_5 of order 60. Hence $[S_5 : Im\psi] = 2$. Therefore, by Lemma 11.1.20, we must have $Im\psi = A_5$. Consequently, $G \simeq A_5$. $\qquad\square$

From Theorem 11.1.2, we have seen that there are infinitely many *commutative simple groups* $\mathbb{Z}_p$, where p is any prime number and now from Theorem 11.1.19, we find that there are infinitely many *noncommutative simple groups* $A_n, n \geq 5$. However, it is also true that there exist noncommutative simple groups other than $A_n, n \geq 5$ as well.

Worked-out Exercises

◇ **Exercise 11.1.1.** Show that no group of order 70 is a simple group.

Solution. Let G be a group of order 70. Now $70 = 2 \cdot 35$ and 35 is an odd integer. Hence by the Proposition 11.1.6, we find that G contains a normal subgroup of order 35. Hence G is not a simple group.

◇ **Exercise 11.1.2.** Show that no group of order 36 is simple.

Solution. Let G be a group of order 36. Now $36 = 3^2 \cdot 2^2$. Hence by Sylow's First theorem, G has a subgroup H of order 3^2. Now $[G : H] = 4$. Hence by the Extended Cayley's Theorem, there exists homomorphism $f : G \to S_4$ such that $\ker f \subseteq H$. If $\ker f = \{e\}$, then f is a monomorphism and hence G is isomorphic to a subgroup K of S_4. In that case, $|K| = |G| = 36$ implies that S_4 contains a subgroup of order 36 which is impossible, since $|S_4| = 24$. Hence $1 < |\ker f| \leq |H| = 9$. Therefore G has a nontrivial subgroup $\ker f$. Thus we find that G is not a simple group.

◇ **Exercise 11.1.3.** Show that no group of order 56 is a simple group.

Solution. Let G be a group of order 56. Now $56 = 7 \cdot 2^3$. Then G has Sylow 7-subgroups and Sylow 2-subgroups. Let n_7 and n_2 denote respectively, the numbers of Sylow 7-subgroups and Sylow 2-subgroups of G. Then by Sylow's Third theorem, we have $n_7 = 7m + 1, m \geq 0$, $n_2 = 2k + 1, k \geq 0$ and further, both n_7 and n_2

must divide 56. This gives us $n_7 = 1$ or 8. If $n_7 = 1$, then G has a unique Sylow 7-subgroup of order 8, which must then be normal, due to its uniqueness, whence G is not simple. However, if $n_7 = 8$, then G has 8 Sylow 7-subgroups, say $A_1, A_2, \ldots, A_8$. Now $|A_i| = 7, i = 1, 2, \ldots, 8$. Also, $A_i \cap A_j = \{e\}$ for $i \neq j$ and for all $a \neq e, a \in A_i, o(a) = 7$. Thus, G contains 48 elements of order 7.

Now, $n_2 = 1$ or 7. Again, if $n_2 = 1$, then G has a unique Sylow 2-subgroup of order 8, which then must be normal, whence G is not simple. If however, $n_2 = 7$, then G has seven Sylow 2-subgroups, say $B_1, B_2, \ldots, B_7$, where $|B_i| = 8$, for each $i = 1, 2, \ldots, 8$. Since $B_1 \neq B_2$, $|B_1 \cap B_2| \leq 4$. This implies that $B_1 \cup B_2$ contains at least 12 elements, none of which is of order 7. Hence $|G| \geq 48 + 12 = 60$ which is a contradiction. Thus we find that either $n_7 = 1$ or $n_2 = 1$, in each of which case, we have already seen that G has a normal subgroup. Consequently, G is not simple.

◊ **Exercise 11.1.4.** Show that no group of order 108 is a simple group.

Solution. Let G be a group of order 108. Now $108 = 3^3 \cdot 2^2$. Hence G has Sylow 3-subgroups as well as Sylow 2-subgroups. Let n_3 be the number of Sylow 3-subgroups. Then by Sylow's Third Theorem $n_3 = 3k + 1$, $k \geq 0$ and $n_3 \mid 108$. Hence $n_3 = 1$ or 4. If $n_3 = 1$, then G has a unique Sylow 3-subgroup H of order 3^3, which must then be normal, whence G is not simple. Suppose $n_3 = 4$. Let A and B be two distinct Sylow 3-subgroups of G. Now $|A \cap B|$ divides $|A|$. Hence $|A \cap B| = 1, 3, 9$ or 27. Since $A \neq B$, $|A \cap B| \neq 27$. If $|A \cap B| \leq 3$, then

$$|AB| = \frac{|A|\,|B|}{|A \cap B|} \geq \frac{27 \cdot 27}{3} = 243 > 108.$$

Hence $|A \cap B| = 9$ and $|AB| = 81$.

Now $|A \cap B| = 3^2$ and $|A| = 3^3$. Hence $A \cap B$ is a normal subgroup in A. Similarly, $A \cap B$ is a normal subgroup in B. Hence $A \subseteq N(A \cap B)$ and $B \subseteq N(A \cap B)$, where $N(A \cap B) = \{g \in G \mid g(A \cap B)g^{-1} = A \cap B\}$ is a subgroup of G.

Hence $AB \subseteq N(A \cap B)$. Now $81 = |AB| \leq |N(A \cap B)|$ and $|N(A \cap B)|$ divides 108. Hence $|N(A \cap B)| = 108$. This implies that $N(A \cap B) = G$ and so $|A \cap B| = 9$ and it is a non trivial normal subgroup of G. Therefore G is not simple.

◊ **Exercise 11.1.5.** Show that no group of order 105 is a simple group.

Solution. Let G be a group of order $105 = 7 \cdot 5 \cdot 3$. Let n_7 be the number of Sylow 7-subgroups in G. Then $n_7 = 7k + 1$, $k \in \mathbb{N}_0$ and $n_7 \mid 105$. Therefore $n_7 = 1$ or 15. If $n_7 = 1$, then G has only one Sylow 7-subgroup of order 7. Hence G contains a normal subgroup of order 7 and this implies that G is not simple.

If $n_7 \neq 1$, then $n_7 = 15$. Then G has 15 subgroups $H_1, H_2, \ldots, H_{15}$ such that $|H_i| = 7$, for all $i = 1, 2, \ldots 15$. Now $H_i \cap H_j \subseteq H_i$ and hence if $i \neq j$, $H_i \cap H_j = \{e\}$, where $1 \leq i, j \leq 15$. Also, we see that every nonidentity element of H_i is an element of order 7. Hence each H_i contains 6 elements of order 7. Then $\bigcup_{i=1}^{15} H_i$ must contain $15 \times 6 = 90$ elements of order 7.

Now consider Sylow 5-subgroups of G. Let n_5 denote the number of Sylow 5-subgroups of G. Then $n_5 = 5k + 1$, $k \in \mathbb{N}_0$ and $n_5 \mid 105$. Hence $n_5 = 1$ or 21. If $n_5 = 1$, then G has only one Sylow 5-subgroup of order 5. This implies that G has a normal subgroup of order 5 whence G is not simple.

On the other hand, suppose $n_5 = 21$. Then G has 21 subgroups $K_1, K_2, \ldots K_{21}$ such that $|K_i| = 5$ for all $i = 1, 2, \ldots, 21$. Each nonidentity element of K_i is of order 5. Hence each K_i contains 4 elements of order 5. Also we find that $K_i \cap K_j = \{e\}$ when $i \neq j$. Thus we find that $\bigcup_{i=1}^{21} K_i$ contains 84 elements of order 5.

So if $n_7 = 15$ and $n_5 = 21$, then G must contain 90 elements of order 7 and 84 elements of order 5. Then $|G| \geq 90 + 84 = 174 > 105$, a contradiction. Hence either $n_7 = 1$ or $n_5 = 1$. Consequently, either G has a normal subgroup of order 7 or a normal subgroup of order 5. Therefore G is not simple.

$\Diamond$ **Exercise 11.1.6.** Let G be a simple group of order 60. Pick the right option:

(i) G has six Sylow-5 subgroups.   (ii) G has four Sylow-3 subgroups.

(iii) G has a cyclic subgroup of order 6.   (iv) G has a unique element of order 2.

Solution. Here $|G| = 60 = 2^2 \cdot 3 \cdot 5$. So G contains Sylow 5-subgroups of order 5. Let n_5 denote the number of Sylow 5-subgroups of G. Then $n_5 = 5k + 1$ for some non-negative integer k and $n_5 \mid 12$. From this it follows that $n_5 = 1$ or 6. Since G is simple, so $n_5 \neq 1$. Hence $n_5 = 6$ and G has six Sylow-5 subgroups. Similarly, we can show that G has either four or ten Sylow-3 subgroups. Hence option (ii) is wrong.

If G contains unique element of order 2, then G has a unique subgroup H of order 2 and hence H is normal, a contradiction, since G is simple. Hence option (iv) is wrong.

Again, since G is simple, so $G \simeq A_5$. We now prove that A_5 has no cyclic subgroup of order 6. Otherwise, let K be cyclic subgroup of A_5 of order 6. Hence, A_5 must have an element σ of order 6, i.e., in (disjoint) cycle decomposition of σ there must be a 3-cycle and at least two transpositions, which is impossible in A_5. Hence G has no cyclic subgroup of order 6. Therefore, option (i) is correct.

◇ **Exercise 11.1.7.** Let G be a simple group of order 168. The number of subgroups of order 7 is (i) 1   (ii) 7   (iii) 8   (iv) 28.

Solution. Here $|G| = 168 = 2^3 \cdot 3 \cdot 7$. So G contains Sylow 7-subgroups of order 7. Let n_7 denote the number of Sylow 7-subgroups of G. Then $n_7 = 7k + 1$ for some non-negative integer k and $n_7 \mid 24$. From this it follows that $n_7 = 1$ or 8. Since G is simple so $n_7 \neq 1$. Therefore $n_7 = 8$ and thus G contains 8 subgroups of order 7. Therefore, option (iii) is correct.

Exercises

1. Show that no groups of order 9, 18, 40, 42, 58, 125, 165, 525, 595 are simple groups.

2. If G is a group of order $2 \cdot 3 \cdot 31$, then show that G is not a simple group.

3. Let G be a group of order $p^2 q$, where p and q are distinct primes and $p > q$. Show that G is not a simple group.

4. Let G be a group of order 48. Then show that G contains a normal subgroup H, where $|H|$ is 16 or 8.

5. Let G be a group of order 255. Show that G is not simple.

6. Show that there is no simple group of order $3^3 5^3$.

7. Show that no group of order 77 is simple.

8. † Let G be a group and H be a subgroup of finite index. Show that G contains a normal subgroup of finite index.

9. Let G be a group of order n and p be the least prime factor of n. Prove that any subgroup of index p is normal in G.

10. Show that any group G of order 38 must have a normal subgroup of order 19.

11. Let G be a finite group and H be a subgroup of G such that $[G : H]$ is the least prime factor of $|G|$. Then show that H is a normal subgroup of G.

12. Prove that every simple group of order 60 has a subgroup of order 12.

13. Write the proof if the following statement is true or else justify your answer by giving a counter example whenever necessary.

    (i) Any group of order pq, where p, q are distinct prime numbers, is cyclic.

    (ii) Any group of order 60 is simple.

    (iii) The group A_n is a simple group for all $n > 1$.

    (iv) A_5 contains a subgroup of order 30.

    (v) A_5 contains a subgroup of order 20.

    (vi) A_5 contains a subgroup of order 15.

    (vii) There exists a simple abelian group of order 50.

    (viii) There exists a simple abelian group of order 31.

    (ix) A group of order 12 is not simple.

Find the correct statement(s) out of the following:

14. It is true that
    (i) $(\mathbb{Z}, +)$ is a simple group.   (ii) $(\mathbb{Q}, +)$ is a simple group.
    (iii) $(\mathbb{Z}_8, +)$ is a simple group.   (iv) $(\mathbb{Z}_{71}, +)$ is a simple group.

15. It is true that
    (i) A_4 is a simple group.   (ii) A_3 is a simple group.
    (iii) S_3 is a simple group.   (iv) S_4 is a simple group.

16. It is true that
    (i) Every commutative group is a simple group.
    (ii) Every finite group is a simple group.
    (iii) Every group of prime order is a simple group.
    (iv) Every noncommutative group is a simple group.

17. It is true that
    (i) Every group of order 49 is a simple group.
    (ii) Every group of order 49 is a cyclic group.
    (iii) Every group of order 49 is a commutative group.
    (iv) There exists a noncommutative group of order 49.

18. It is true that
    (i) Every group of order 30 is a simple group.
    (ii) Every group of order 30 is a commutative group.
    (iii) There exists a noncommutative group of order 30.

19. The number of normal subgroups of a non-Abelian group G of order 21, other than the identity subgroup $\{e\}$ and G is
    (i) 0   (ii) 1   (iii) 3   (iv) 7.

20. Let G be a group of order 45. Then
    (i) G has an element of order 9.
    (ii) G has a subgroup of order 9.
    (iii) G has a normal subgroup of order 9.
    (iv) G has a normal subgroup of order 5.

Chapter 12

Rings

12.1 Elementary Properties

In the very beginning of our school life we learn addition, subtraction and multiplication of integers. Considering this set along with these operations as a model, if we want to build up an algebraic structure, then the following facts are revealed:

(i) The set of integers is closed[1] under addition and multiplication.

(ii) Addition is associative and commutative.

(iii) There is an additive identity, namely, zero.

(iv) There is an additive inverse corresponding to each element of the set.

(v) Multiplication is associative and distributes over addition.

There are many other algebraic properties that enrich this fantastic age old mathematical object. For the time being, we only abstract the above five properties to define a ring.

Definition 12.1.1. A **ring** [2] R is an algebraic structure $(R, +, \cdot)$ consisting of a nonempty set R together with two binary operations $+$ and $\cdot$ (called **addition** and **multiplication**) such that $(R, +)$ is an Abelian group, $(R, \cdot)$ is a semigroup and $a \cdot (b + c) = (a \cdot b) + (a \cdot c)$, $(b + c) \cdot a = (b \cdot a) + (c \cdot a)$ for all $a, b, c \in R$.

---

[1]That is $m + n$ and mn, both are integers for all integers m, n.

[2]Although David Hilbert introduced the term "ring," it was A. E. Noether (1882-1935) who under the influence of Hilbert, set down the axioms for rings. In 1914, Fraenkel gave the first definition of a ring. However, it is no longer commonly used.

We denote the identity element of the group $(R, +)$ by the symbol 0 and the (additive) inverse of a by $-a$ for all $a \in R$. If $R = \{0\}$, then R is called the **trivial ring**.

Considering this, we now write the definition of a ring in the following way:

A ring is an ordered triple $(R, +, \cdot)$ such that R is a nonempty set where $+$ and $\cdot$ are two binary operations on R (i.e., for each pair (a, b) of elements of R, there exist unique elements $a + b$ and $a \cdot b$ in R), satisfying the following axioms for all $a, b, c \in R$:

(i) $a + b = b + a$ *(commutative law for addition)*;

(ii) $a + (b + c) = (a + b) + c$ *(associative law for addition)*;

(iii) there exists an element $0 \in R$ such that $a + 0 = a$ for all $a \in R$
                                            (existence of additive identity);

(iv) for each $a \in R$, there exists an element $-a \in R$ such that $a + (-a) = 0$
                                            (existence of additive inverse);

(v) $a \cdot (b \cdot c) = (a \cdot b) \cdot c$ for all $a, b, c \in R$
                                (associative law for multiplication);

(vi) $a \cdot (b + c) = (a \cdot b) + (a \cdot c)$ and $(b + c) \cdot a = (b \cdot a) + (c \cdot a)$ for all $a, b, c \in R$
(distributive laws).

Definition 12.1.2. A ring R is called **commutative** if $ab = ba$ for all $a, b \in R$ and R is said to have an **identity** (or a **unity**) if there exists an element $1 \in R$ such that $a \cdot 1 = 1 \cdot a = a$, for all $a \in R$. We denote the element $a + a$ by $2a$ and in general, $a + a + \cdots + a$ (n copies of a added) by na, ($n \in \mathbb{N}$). It follows clearly from distributive laws that in a ring with identity, $na = (n1) \cdot a$.

Now it is clear that the set of integers $(\mathbb{Z}, +, \cdot)$ with usual addition and multiplication is a commutative ring with identity. In the following, we list some other examples of rings:

Example 12.1.3. Set of rational numbers, real numbers or complex numbers are commutative rings with identity under the usual addition and multiplication.

Example 12.1.4. Let $\mathbb{Z}_n$ be the set of integers modulo n, where n is a positive integer. We define binary operations $+$ and $\cdot$ on $\mathbb{Z}_n$ by

$$[a] + [b] = [a + b] \quad \text{and} \quad [a] \cdot [b] = [ab],$$

for all $[a], [b] \in \mathbb{Z}_n$. We have shown before that these two operations are well-defined and proved further that $(\mathbb{Z}_n, +)$ is an Abelian group (cf. Example 3.1.5) and $(\mathbb{Z}_n, \cdot)$ is a commutative semigroup (cf. Example 3.1.6) with identity. Now for all elements $[a], [b], [c] \in \mathbb{Z}_n$,

$$
\begin{aligned}
[a] \cdot ([b] + [c]) &= [a] \cdot [b + c] && \text{(definition of } + \text{ in } \mathbb{Z}_n) \\
&= [a(b + c)] && \text{(definition of } \cdot \text{ in } \mathbb{Z}_n) \\
&= [ab + ac] && \text{(property of } \mathbb{Z}) \\
&= [ab] + [ac] && \text{(definition of } + \text{ in } \mathbb{Z}_n) \\
&= ([a] \cdot [b]) + ([a] \cdot [c]) && \text{(definition of } \cdot \text{ in } \mathbb{Z}_n).
\end{aligned}
$$

Since the multiplication is commutative, it follows that

$$([b] + [c]) \cdot [a] = ([b] \cdot [a]) + ([c] \cdot [a]),$$

for all $[a], [b], [c] \in \mathbb{Z}_n$. Hence $\mathbb{Z}_n$ is a commutative ring with identity. Previously (cf. Example 3.1.5), we have noted that $\mathbb{Z}_n$ consists of n distinct elements $[0], [1], [2], \ldots, [n-1]$ only. So $(\mathbb{Z}_n, +, \cdot)$ is a finite ring with n elements.

Example 12.1.5. Let $\mathbb{Z}[i] = \{a + ib \in \mathbb{C} \mid a, b \in \mathbb{Z},\ i^2 = -1\}$. Define addition and multiplication on $\mathbb{Z}[i]$ as follows:

$$
\begin{aligned}
(a + ib) + (c + id) &= (a + c) + i(b + d), \\
(a + ib) \cdot (c + id) &= (ac - bd) + i(ad + bc).
\end{aligned}
$$

If $a, b, c, d \in \mathbb{Z}$, then $a+c, b+d, ac-bd, ad+bc \in \mathbb{Z}$. Thus $+$ and $\cdot$ defined above are two binary operations on $\mathbb{Z}[i]$. Also note that these are the usual addition and multiplication of complex numbers. Hence the following properties hold for any $z_1, z_2, z_3 \in \mathbb{Z}[i]$:

$$
\begin{aligned}
z_1 + z_2 = z_2 + z_1,\ z_1 + (z_2 + z_3) = (z_1 + z_2) + z_3,\ z_1 z_2 = z_2 z_1, \\
z_1(z_2 z_3) = (z_1 z_2) z_3,\ z_1(z_2 + z_3) = z_1 z_2 + z_1 z_3.
\end{aligned}
$$

Now $0 = 0 + i0 \in \mathbb{Z}[i]$ and $z + 0 = z$ for all $z \in \mathbb{Z}[i]$. Thus 0 is the additive identity of $\mathbb{Z}[i]$. Further for any $z = a + ib \in \mathbb{Z}[i]$, let $-z = (-a) + i(-b)$. Then $z + (-z) = 0$. Finally $1 = 1 + i0 \in \mathbb{Z}[i]$ and $(a + ib)(1 + i0) = a + ib$ for all $a + ib \in \mathbb{Z}[i]$. All these verifications show that $\mathbb{Z}[i]$ is a commutative ring with identity. This ring is called the **ring of Gaussian integers**.

It is easy to build up rings from Abelian groups:

Example 12.1.6. Let $(G, +)$ be an Abelian group, written additively. Define $a \cdot b = 0$ for all $a, b \in G$, where 0 is the identity of the group G. Then $(G, +, \cdot)$ becomes a ring, called a **null ring**.

Example 12.1.7. Let $(G, +)$ be an Abelian group and R be the set of all endomorphisms of G. Define

$$(f + g)(x) = f(x) + g(x) \quad \text{and} \quad (f \circ g)(x) = f(g(x))$$

for all $f, g \in R$ and for all $x \in G$. Then $(R, +, \circ)$ is a ring (which is called the **ring of endomorphisms** of G).

In order to verify this, we first note that for any $x, y \in G$ and for any $f, g \in R$,

$$(f \circ g)(x + y) = f(g(x + y)) = f(g(x) + g(y)) = f(g(x)) + f(g(y))$$
$$= (f \circ g)(x) + (f \circ g)(y).$$

This implies, $f \circ g$ is an endomorphism of the group G and hence $f \circ g \in R$ for all $f, g \in R$. The commutative and associative laws for addition follow from the definition of addition and the corresponding properties of the Abelian group $(G, +)$. The additive identity of R is the null mapping, say θ which sends all the elements of G to 0_G, i.e., $\theta(x) = 0_G$ for all $x \in G$ and for each $f \in R$, $(-f)$ is the map defined by $(-f)(x) = -f(x)$ for all $x \in G$ (verify!).

The associativity for multiplication follows from the fact that the composition of mapping is associative. Let us verify distributive laws:

Let $f, g, h \in R$ and $x \in G$ be an arbitrary element. Then,

$$
\begin{aligned}
(f \circ (g + h))(x) &= f(g(x) + h(x)) \\
&= f(g(x)) + f(h(x)) \quad \text{[as } f \text{ is a homomorphism]} \\
&= (f \circ g)(x) + (f \circ h)(x) \\
&= ((f \circ g) + (f \circ h))(x).
\end{aligned}
$$

Thus $f \circ (g + h) = (f \circ g) + (f \circ h)$. Again,

$$
\begin{aligned}
((g + h) \circ f)(x) &= (g + h)(f(x)) = g(f(x)) + h(f(x)) \\
&= (g \circ f)(x) + (h \circ f)(x) = ((g \circ f) + (h \circ f))(x)
\end{aligned}
$$

which implies $(g + h) \circ f = (g \circ f) + (h \circ f)$. This completes the verification. Hence $(R, +, \circ)$ is a ring.

We now concentrate on building new rings from the given rings:

Example 12.1.8. Let R_1 and R_2 be two rings. Define on $R = R_1 \times R_2$,

$$(a, b) + (c, d) = (a + c, b + d) \quad \text{and} \quad (a, b) \cdot (c, d) = (ac, bd).$$

Then $(R, +, \cdot)$ is a ring where $(0_{R_1}, 0_{R_2})$ is the additive identity element and $-(a, b) = (-a, -b)$ for all $a \in R_1$, $b \in R_2$. This ring R is called the **direct product of rings** R_1 and R_2.

Example 12.1.9. For a commutative ring R with identity, consider the *formal sum* $a_0 + a_1 x + a_2 x^2 + \cdots + a_n x^n = f(x)$, say, where $a_i \in R$ and $n \in \mathbb{N}$. It is called a **polynomial** [3] over R in the *indeterminate* x, where $a_i, i = 0, 1, 2, \ldots, n$ are called coefficients of the above polynomial, some of which may be considered to be 0_R. The highest power of x (with a non zero coefficient) in a given $f(x)$ is called the degree of $f(x)$. The non-zero elements of R are regarded as constant polynomials (sometimes called a monomial) with degree zero, while 0_R is considered as a monomial for which degree is undefined. Let $R[x]$ be the set of all such polynomials. Define for any $f(x) = a_0 + a_1 x + a_2 x^2 + \cdots + a_n x^n$, $g(x) = b_0 + b_1 x + b_2 x^2 + \cdots + b_m x^m \in R[x]$,

$$f(x) + g(x) = (a_0 + b_0) + (a_1 + b_1)x + (a_2 + b_2)x^2 + \cdots + (a_p + b_p)x^p$$
$$f(x)g(x) = c_0 + c_1 x + c_2 x^2 + \cdots + c_{m+n} x^{m+n},$$

where $p = \max\{m, n\}$ (considering $a_r = 0_R$ for all $r > n$ and $b_s = 0_R$ for all $s > m$) and $c_k = \sum_{\substack{i,j=0 \\ i+j=k}}^{k} a_i b_j$ for each $k = 0, 1, 2, \ldots, m + n$.

Then $(R[x], +, \cdot)$ forms a ring with the above addition and multiplication of polynomials, which is called the **polynomial ring over** R (in the indeterminate x).

As a particular case of the above example, let $\mathbb{R}$ be the set of all real numbers. Denote the set of all polynomials (in the indeterminate x) with real coefficients by $\mathbb{R}[x]$. It is easy to verify that $(\mathbb{R}[x], +, \cdot)$ is a commutative ring with identity with the usual addition and multiplication of polynomials with real coefficients.

Example 12.1.10. Let $M_n(\mathbb{R})$ be the set of all $n \times n$ real matrices ($n \in \mathbb{N}$). Then we see that $M_n(\mathbb{R})$ is closed under the usual addition and multiplication of matrices. We know that for any three matrices $A, B, C \in M_n(\mathbb{R})$,

$$A + B = B + A, \ A + (B + C) = (A + B) + C,$$
$$A + O_n = A, \ A + (-A) = O_n,$$
$$A(BC) = (AB)C, \ A(B + C) = AB + AC$$
$$\text{and} \ (B + C)A = BA + CA,$$

where O_n is the null matrix of order $n \times n$. So $(M_n(\mathbb{R}), +, \cdot)$ is a ring.

More generally, let R be a ring with identity. Let $M_n(R)$ be the set of all square matrices of order n with entries from R, ($n \in \mathbb{N}$). Define for any $A = (a_{ij})$, $B = (b_{ij}) \in$

---

[3]For details and more rigorous treatment, see Definition 15.1.1 and Theorem 15.1.3.

$M_n(R)$, $A + B = (c_{ij})$ and $AB = (d_{ij})$ where,

$$c_{ij} = a_{ij} + b_{ij} \quad \text{and} \quad d_{ij} = \sum_{k=1}^{n} a_{ik} b_{kj}.$$

Then exactly in a similar way as above (i.e., for $R = \mathbb{R}$), one can verify that $(M_n(R), +, \cdot)$ satisfies all the properties required to be a ring with the addition and multiplication defined above. This ring is called the **ring of matrices over** R.

Which of the above rings are noncommutative? Which of the above rings have an identity?

We now prove some basic properties of rings. Before that we point out the following conventions which we shall follow henceforth:

Let $(R, +, \cdot)$ be a ring and $a, b, c, d \in R$.

1. We often drop the symbol $\cdot$ for multiplication and write $a \cdot b$ simply as ab.

2. Multiplication is assumed to be performed before addition [accordingly, $ab + cd$ stands for $(ab) + (cd)$].

3. We write $a - b$ instead of $a + (-b)$.

4. We refer to a ring $(R, +, \cdot)$ as a ring R under the operations $+$ and $\cdot$ or as a ring R together with the operations $+$ and $\cdot$ or simply as a ring R.

Theorem 12.1.11. *Let R be a ring and $a, b \in R$. Then*

(i) $a \cdot 0 = 0 \cdot a = 0$;

(ii) $a(-b) = (-a)b = -ab$;

(iii) $(-a)(-b) = ab$.

Proof. (i) $a \cdot 0 + a \cdot 0 = a(0 + 0) = a \cdot 0$ which implies $a \cdot 0 = 0$ as $(R, +)$ is a group. Similarly $0 \cdot a = 0$.

(ii) $ab + a(-b) = a(b + (-b)) = a \cdot 0 = 0$ which implies $a(-b) = -ab$. The proof is similar for the other part.

(iii) $(-a)(-b) = -(-a)b = -(-(ab))$, by using (ii). Now in the group $(R, +)$, $-(-x) = x$ for all $x \in R$, whence it follows that $-(-(ab)) = ab$. Hence the proof. $\square$

In particular, one should notice that $(-a)^2 = a^2$ for all $a \in R$ and if the ring R has an identity 1, then $1 \cdot (-1) = (-1) \cdot 1 = -1$ and $(-1)(-1) = 1$.

Considering the property (i), the additive identity 0 is called the *zero* element of the ring R. Also we note that if $1 = 0$ in a ring R, then $a = a \cdot 1 = a \cdot 0 = 0$ for all $a \in R$. So in this case R becomes the trivial ring $\{0\}$.

The following identities are easy applications of distributive laws:

Theorem 12.1.12. *Let R be a ring and $a, b, c, d \in R$. Then*

(i) $(a + b)(c + d) = ac + bc + ad + bd$;

(ii) $(a - b)(c - d) = ac - bc - ad + bd$;

(iii) $(a + b)^2 = a^2 + ab + ba + b^2$;

(iv) $(a - b)^2 = a^2 - ab - ba + b^2$;

(v) $(a + b)(a - b) = a^2 - ab + ba - b^2$.

One should note that the condition: $a + b = b + a$ in the definition of a ring is *redundant* in the case of a ring with identity. If R is a ring with identity 1, then using the distributive laws we have $(a + b)(1 + 1) = (a + b)1 + (a + b)1 = a + b + a + b$ and also $(a + b)(1 + 1) = a(1 + 1) + b(1 + 1) = a + a + b + b$. Now, equating the right-hand sides and using cancellation laws for addition, we obtain $a + b = b + a$.

Now in any ring, 0 is an element which satisfies $0^2 = 0$ and in any ring with identity, 1 is another element satisfying $1^2 = 1$. In general, we define the following:

Definition 12.1.13. An element x in a ring R is called *idempotent* if $x^2 = x$.

Example 12.1.14. In $M_3(\mathbb{R})$, the ring of real square matrices of order 3 (cf. Example 12.1.10), the following matrices are idempotents:

$$\begin{bmatrix} 1 & 0 & 0 \\ 0 & 1 & 0 \\ 0 & 0 & 0 \end{bmatrix}, \begin{bmatrix} 2 & -2 & -4 \\ -1 & 3 & 4 \\ 1 & -2 & -3 \end{bmatrix}$$

There are rings in which every element is idempotent.

Definition 12.1.15. A ring R is called a *Boolean ring* if every element of R is idempotent, i.e., $x^2 = x$ for all $x \in R$.

We prove the following interesting properties of a Boolean ring:

Theorem 12.1.16. *Let R be a Boolean ring. Then*

(i) $2x = 0$ *for all* $x \in R$;

(ii) $xy = yx$ *for all* $x, y \in R$.

Proof. (i) Let $x \in R$. Then $-x \in R$ and so $x = x^2 = (-x)^2 = -x$ as R is a Boolean ring. Thus $2x = 0$ for all $x \in R$.

(ii) Let $x, y \in R$. Then $x + y = (x+y)^2 = x^2 + xy + yx + y^2 = x + xy + yx + y$, which implies that $xy = x + y - x - y - yx = -yx$. But since $yx \in R$, we have $yx = -yx$ by (i). Therefore $xy = yx$ for all $x, y \in R$. $\qquad\square$

The above theorem proves that *a Boolean ring is a commutative ring*. Note that the ring $\mathbb{Z}$ is a commutative ring which is not a Boolean ring.

We now define the *invertible* elements of a ring under multiplication.

Definition 12.1.17. Let R be a ring with identity 1 and $1 \neq 0$. Then an element $u \in R$ is called a **unit** (or **invertible**) if there exists $v \in R$ such that $uv - vu = 1$. v is called the **inverse** of u and is denoted by u^{-1}. Verify that the inverse of a unit u is unique.

Theorem 12.1.18. *Let R be a ring with identity 1 $(\neq 0)$. Then the set of units of R forms a group under multiplication in R.*

Proof. Let U be the set of units of R. We will show that $(U, \cdot)$ is a subgroup of the semigroup $(R, \cdot)$. Now $U \neq \emptyset$ as $1 \in U$. Also if $u \in U$, then there exists $u^{-1} \in R$ such that $uu^{-1} = u^{-1}u = 1$. This implies $u^{-1} \in U$. Further if $v \in U$, then $uv \cdot (v^{-1}u^{-1}) = u(vv^{-1})u^{-1} = u \cdot 1 \cdot u^{-1} = uu^{-1} = 1$. Similarly, $(v^{-1}u^{-1})uv = v^{-1}v = 1$. Therefore uv is a unit and $(uv)^{-1} = v^{-1}u^{-1}$. Thus U has an identity 1 and for each element $u \in U$, there exists an inverse u^{-1} of u; also U is closed under multiplication. That is to say, $(U,)$ is a subgroup of $(R, \cdot)$. $\qquad\sqcap$

Example 12.1.19. (i) Nonsingular matrices are units in $M_n(\mathbb{R})$. (ii) Any nonzero rational number is a unit in $\mathbb{Q}$.

In the ring $M_3(\mathbb{R})$, if we consider the matrices

$$A = \begin{bmatrix} 0 & 0 & 1 \\ 0 & 0 & 0 \\ 0 & 0 & 0 \end{bmatrix} \quad \text{and} \quad B = \begin{bmatrix} 1 & 1 & 3 \\ 5 & 2 & 6 \\ -2 & -1 & -3 \end{bmatrix},$$

then one can verify that $A^2 = O$ and $B^3 = O$, though neither A nor B is the zero (null) matrix. Thus in a ring there may be some nonzero element whose integral power is zero for some positive integer greater than 1.

Definition 12.1.20. An element x in a ring R is called **nilpotent** if $x^n = 0$ for some positive integer n. The smallest positive integer (for x) with this property is called the **degree of nilpotency** of the element x.

Theorem 12.1.21. *The sum of two nilpotent elements of a commutative ring is also nilpotent.*

Proof. Let R be a commutative ring and $a, b \in R$ be such that $a^m = 0$ and $b^n = 0$ for some positive integers m and n. Now

$$(a + b)^{m+n} = a^{m+n} + \binom{m+n}{1}a^{m+n-1}b + \cdots + \binom{m+n}{r}a^{m+n-r}b^r + \cdots + b^{m+n}$$

$$= a^m\left\{a^n + \binom{m+n}{1}a^{n-1}b + \cdots + \binom{m+n}{n}b^n\right\} + \left\{\binom{m+n}{n+1}a^{m-1}b + \cdots + b^m\right\}b^n$$

$$= 0.$$

This implies $a + b$ is nilpotent, as required. $\qquad\square$

Worked-out Exercises

$\Diamond$ **Exercise 12.1.1.** Let $\mathbb{R}$ be the set of all real numbers and R be the set of all real-valued continuous functions defined on $\mathbb{R}$. Define

$$(f + g)(x) = f(x) + g(x) \quad \text{and} \quad (f \cdot g)(x) = f(x)g(x)$$

for all $f, g \in R$ and for all $x \in \mathbb{R}$. Show that $(R, +, \cdot)$ is a ring under the binary operations defined above.

Solution. Clearly, the set R is nonempty. Also since the sum and product of two (real-valued) continuous functions are again (real-valued) continuous functions, we have R as closed under $+$ and $\cdot$. Now for any $x \in \mathbb{R}$ and for any $f, g, h \in R$, we have the following:

(i) $(f+g)(x) = f(x)+g(x) = g(x)+f(x) = (g+f)(x)$ which implies that $f+g = g+f$.

(ii) $\big((f + g) + h\big)(x) = (f + g)(x) + h(x) = \big(f(x) + g(x)\big) + h(x) = f(x) + g(x) + h(x) = f(x) + \big(g(x) + h(x)\big) = f(x) + (g + h)(x) = \big(f + (g + h)\big)(x)$. So, $(f + g) + h = f + (g + h)$.

(iii) The constant function, **0** (say), which sends all the elements of $\mathbb{R}$ to zero, satisfies $(f + \mathbf{0})(x) = f(x) + \mathbf{0}(x) = f(x) + 0 = f(x)$ for all $f \in R$. Therefore, $f + \mathbf{0} = f$ for all $f \in R$.

(iv) For each $f \in R$, define a function $-f : \mathbb{R} \longrightarrow \mathbb{R}$ by $(-f)(x) = -f(x)$. Then, $\big(f + (-f)\big)(x) = f(x) + (-f(x)) = 0 = \mathbf{0}(x)$, i.e., $f + (-f) = \mathbf{0}$.

(v) $\big((f \cdot g) \cdot h\big)(x) = (f \cdot g)(x)h(x) = \big(f(x)g(x)\big)h(x) = f(x)g(x)h(x) = f(x)\big(g(x)h(x)\big)$
$= f(x)(g \cdot h)(x) = \big(f \cdot (g \cdot h)\big)(x)$. Thus $(f \cdot g) \cdot h = f \cdot (g \cdot h)$.

(vi) $\big(f \cdot (g + h)\big)(x) = f(x)(g + h)(x) = f(x)\big(g(x) + h(x)\big) = f(x)g(x) + f(x)h(x) =$
$(f \cdot g)(x) + (f \cdot h)(x) = \big((f \cdot g) + (f \cdot h)\big)(x)$. Hence $f \cdot (g + h) = (f \cdot g) + (f \cdot h)$.
Similarly, one can show that $(g + h) \cdot f = (g \cdot f) + (h \cdot f)$.

Therefore $(R, +, \cdot)$ is a ring.

◊ **Exercise 12.1.2.** Which of the following algebraic structures $(R, +, \cdot)$ form a ring?

(i) Let X be any set and $R = \mathscr{P}(X)$, the power set of X. Define $A + B = A \triangle B$ and $A \cdot B = A \cap B$ for all $A, B \in R$.

(ii) In the above set R, define $A + B = A \cup B$ and $A \cdot B = A \cap B$ for all $A, B \in R$.

(iii) Let R be the set of all real-valued continuous functions defined on $\mathbb{R}$. Define $(f + g)(x) = f(x) + g(x)$ and $(f \circ g)(x) = f(g(x))$ for all $f, g \in R$ and for all $x \in \mathbb{R}$.

Solution. (i) First note that $R \neq \emptyset$ as $X \in R$. Let $A, B \in R = \mathscr{P}(X)$. Then $A \triangle B, A \cap B \in \mathscr{P}(X) = R$, which implies R is closed under addition and multiplication. The following results are inferred from set theory:

$$A \triangle B = B \triangle A, \; A \triangle (B \triangle C) = (A \triangle B) \triangle C, \; A \triangle \emptyset = A, \; A \triangle A = \emptyset,$$
$$A \cap (B \cap C) = (A \cap B) \cap C, \; A \cap B = B \cap A,$$
$$A \cap (B \triangle C) = (A \cap B) \triangle (A \cap C)$$

for all $A, B, C \in R$. Thus R is a commutative ring. Also since $A \cap X = A$ for all $A \in R$, it follows that R has an identity, namely X. Finally, note that $A \cap A = A$ for all $A \in R$ shows that R is a Boolean ring.

(ii) Note that the empty subset, $\emptyset$ is the identity with respect to addition as $A \cup \emptyset = A$ for all $A \in R$. But for any $\emptyset \neq A \in R$, there is no element $B \in R$ so that $A \cup B = \emptyset$. Thus, in this case, $(R, +)$ is not a group unless $X = \emptyset$. Therefore R is not a ring if $X \neq \emptyset$. Otherwise R is the trivial ring consisting of a single element, namely $\emptyset$.

(iii) It is easy to verify that R satisfies all the properties of a ring *except* distributive laws. For example, consider $f, g, h \in R$ defined by $f(x) = x^2$, $g(x) = 2x$, $h(x) = 3x$.

Then, $(f \circ (g+h))(x) = f(g(x)+h(x)) = f(2x+3x) = 25x^2$ whereas, $(f \circ g + f \circ h)(x) = (f \circ g)(x) + (f \circ h)(x) = (2x)^2 + (3x)^2 = 13x^2$. Therefore R is not a ring.

◊ **Exercise 12.1.3.** If $R = \{a, b, c, d\}$ is a ring, then complete the multiplication table of R, where

+	a	b	c	d
a	a	b	c	d
b	b	a	d	c
c	c	d	a	b
d	d	c	b	a

and

·	a	b	c	d
a	a	a	a	a
b	a	b		
c	a		a	
d	a	b	c	

Is R commutative? Does it have an identity?

Solution. First note that a is the additive identity and is the zero of the ring R. Also since $2b = 2c = 2d = a = 0$, we have $x = -x$ for all $x \in R$. Now $(b+c)b = b^2 + cb$ by distributive law. Then $db = b + cb$. This implies that $cb = 0 = a$, as $db = b$. Next consider the equality: $d(c+d) = dc + d^2$. This implies that $d^2 = d(d+c) - dc = db - c = b - c = b + c = d$. Similarly $c(c+d) = c^2 + cd$ implies that $c^2 = 0 = a$ as $c(c+d) = cb = 0 = a = cd$. Again from $(b+c)c = bc + c^2$, it follows that $c = dc = (b+c)c = bc + 0 = bc$. Finally, $bd = b(b+c) = b^2 + bc = b + c = d$. Therefore the complete multiplication table is

·	a	b	c	d
a	a	a	a	a
b	a	b	**c**	**d**
c	a	**a**	**a**	a
d	a	b	c	**d**

Clearly, R is not commutative and it does not have an identity.

◊ **Exercise 12.1.4.** Prove that a ring can have at most one identity (i.e., identity element of a ring is unique).

Solution. Suppose e_1 and e_2 to be two identities of a ring R. Then,

$$xe_1 = e_1 x = x \qquad \text{and} \qquad xe_2 = e_2 x = x \qquad \text{for all } x \in R.$$

Then from the first equation, replacing x by e_2, we get $e_1 e_2 = e_2$ and from the second equation, replacing x by e_1, we get $e_1 e_2 = e_1$. Thus $e_1 = e_2$. Hence identity of a ring is unique.

◊ **Exercise 12.1.5.** Let R be a ring. Define $e_1 \in R$, a **left identity** if $e_1 x = x$ for all $x \in R$. If e_1 is unique, then show that e_1 is also a right identity (defined dually).

Solution. Let R be a ring with a unique left identity, e_1. We have to show that $xe_1 = x$ for all $x \in R$. Let $x \in R$. Then for all $y \in R$, we have $(xe_1 - x + e_1)y = xe_1y - xy + e_1y = xy - xy + y = y$, which implies that $(xe_1 - x + e_1)$ is a left identity. Since e_1 is the unique left identity in R, we have $xe_1 - x + e_1 = e_1$. This implies that $xe_1 = x$, as required.

♦ **Exercise 12.1.6.** If R is a ring with identity such that $(xy)^2 = x^2y^2$ for all $x, y \in R$, then show that R is commutative. Set an example to show that the above result may be false if R does not have an identity.

Solution. Let R be a ring with identity such that $(xy)^2 = x^2y^2$ for all $x, y \in R$. Let $x, y \in R$. Now $(x(1 + y))^2 = x^2(1 + y)^2$, which implies that $x^2 + xyx + x^2y + (xy)^2 = x^2 + 2x^2y + x^2y^2$. Since $(xy)^2 = x^2y^2$, we get $x^2y - xyx = 0$. Thus,

$$x(xy - yx) = 0 \quad \text{for all} \quad x, y \in R.$$

Therefore $(1 + x)((1 + x)y - y(1 + x)) = 0$. This implies that $(1 + x)(xy - yx) = 0$, i.e., $(xy - yx) + x(xy - yx) = 0$. Thus $xy - yx = 0$, i.e., $xy = yx$ for all $x, y \in R$ and hence R is commutative.

Now let $R = \left\{ \begin{bmatrix} a & b \\ 0 & 0 \end{bmatrix} \mid a, b \in \mathbb{R} \right\} \subset M_2(\mathbb{R})$. It is easy to verify that R is a noncommutative ring. Indeed,

$$\begin{bmatrix} 0 & 1 \\ 0 & 0 \end{bmatrix} \begin{bmatrix} 1 & 0 \\ 0 & 0 \end{bmatrix} = \begin{bmatrix} 0 & 0 \\ 0 & 0 \end{bmatrix} \quad \text{and} \quad \begin{bmatrix} 1 & 0 \\ 0 & 0 \end{bmatrix} \begin{bmatrix} 0 & 1 \\ 0 & 0 \end{bmatrix} = \begin{bmatrix} 0 & 1 \\ 0 & 0 \end{bmatrix}.$$

Let $A, B \in R$. Then,

$$A = \begin{bmatrix} a & b \\ 0 & 0 \end{bmatrix}, \quad B = \begin{bmatrix} c & d \\ 0 & 0 \end{bmatrix}$$

for some $a, b, c, d \in \mathbb{R}$. Verify that

$$(AB)^2 - A^2B^2 = \begin{bmatrix} a^2c^2 & a^2cd \\ 0 & 0 \end{bmatrix}.$$

Note that $\begin{bmatrix} 1 & 0 \\ 0 & 0 \end{bmatrix}$ is a left identity of R and R has no right identity.

◊ **Exercise 12.1.7.** Find the group of units in the ring $\mathbb{Z}_8$.

Solution. We have $\mathbb{Z}_8 = \{[0], [1], [2], [3], [4], [5], [6], [7]\}$. Verify that

$$[1][1] = [1], \quad [3][3] = [1], \quad [5][5] = [1] \quad \text{and} \quad [7][7] = [1].$$

These imply that $[1], [3], [5]$ and $[7]$ are the units of $\mathbb{Z}_8$. On the other hand $[0], [2], [4]$ and $[6]$ are not units of $\mathbb{Z}_8$ as there are no such elements $[i] \in \mathbb{Z}_8$ so that $[k][i] = [1]$ for $k = 0, 2, 4$ or 6. Therefore the group of units of $\mathbb{Z}_8$ is given by $\{[1], [3], [5], [7]\}$. Note that this group is isomorphic to the Klein's four-group.

$\Diamond$ **Exercise 12.1.8.** Show that $[x] \in \mathbb{Z}_n$ is a unit if and only if $\gcd(x, n) = 1$.

Solution. Suppose $[x] \in \mathbb{Z}_n$ be such that $\gcd(x, n) = 1$. Then there exist integers a, b such that $xa + nb = 1$. So $xa = 1 + n(-b) \equiv 1 \pmod{n}$ which implies $[x][a] = [1]$, i.e., $[x]$ is a unit in $\mathbb{Z}_n$.

Conversely, if $[x]$ is a unit in $\mathbb{Z}_n$, then there exists $[a] \in \mathbb{Z}_n$ such that $[x][a] = [1]$. Then $xa \equiv 1 \pmod{n}$. Thus $xa = nk + 1$ for some integer k and hence x and n are relatively prime to each other, i.e., $\gcd(x, n) = 1$.

$\Diamond$ **Exercise 12.1.9.** Prove that a ring R has no nonzero nilpotent elements if and only if 0 is the only solution of the equation $x^2 = 0$ in R.

Solution. If R has no nonzero nilpotent elements, then certainly the equation $x^2 = 0$ has only one solution $x = 0$. Conversely, let $x^2 = 0$; this implies that $x = 0$ in R. Now if possible, let a be a nilpotent element of R. Let n be the least positive integer such that $a^n = 0$. If $n \leq 2$, then $a = 0$. Let $n > 2$. Then n must be odd, for otherwise by hypothesis, $a^{\frac{n}{2}} = 0$ contradicting the minimality of n. Let $n = 2m + 1$. Then $m > 0$ and so $m + 1 < n$. Now $(a^{m+1})^2 = a^{2m+2} = a^n a = 0$. But then $a^{m+1} = 0$, which again contradicts the minimality of n. This completes the proof.

$\Diamond$ **Exercise 12.1.10.** Let R be a ring with identity. For $a \in R$, the element $x \in R$ is called a **right inverse** of a, if $ax = 1$. If $a \in R$ has a right inverse, then prove that the following conditions are equivalent:
(i) a has at least two right inverses;
(ii) a is not a unit;
(iii) there exists $0 \neq b \in R$ such that $ab = 0$.

Solution. (i) $\implies$ (ii) : Let $x, y \in R$ be such that $ax = 1 = ay$ and $x \neq y$. Now if a is a unit in R, then $a^{-1}ax = a^{-1}ay$ which implies $x = y$. Thus a is not a unit in R.

(ii) $\implies$ (iii) : Let x be a right inverse of a. Since a is not a unit, $xa \neq 1$, i.e., $xa - 1 \neq 0$. Let $b = xa - 1$. Then $ab = a(xa - 1) = axa - a = a - a = 0$.

(iii) $\implies$ (i) : If x is a right inverse of a, then $a(x - b) = ax - ab = 1 - 0 = 1$. But $x \neq b$ as $ax = 1$ and $ab = 0$. Thus $x - b$ is another right inverse of a.

◇ **Exercise 12.1.11.** Which of the following statement is true?

(i) Every ring is commutative.   (ii) Every ring is finite.

(iii) Every ring is additively commutative. (iv) Every finite ring is commutative.

Solution. Consider the ring $M_2(\mathbb{Z}_n)$ of all 2×2-matrices with entries from $\mathbb{Z}_n$, where n is a positive integer. Then $M_2(\mathbb{Z}_n)$ is a finite noncommutative ring. Again $(\mathbb{Z}, +, \cdot)$ is an infinite ring. From the definition of a ring, it follows that every ring is additive commutative. Hence option (iii) is correct.

◇ **Exercise 12.1.12.** Let R be a non-zero ring with identity such that $a^2 = a$ for all $a \in R$. Which of the following statements are true?

(i) $2a = 0$ for all $a \in R$.

(ii) $ab = ba$ for all $a, b \in R$

(iii) $3a = 0$ for all $a \in R$.

Solution. Here R is a Boolean ring and thus by Theorem 12.1.16, it follows that $2a = 0$ for all $a \in R$ and $ab = ba$ for all $a, b \in R$. Hence options (i) and (ii) are correct.

Exercises

1. Which of the following algebraic structures $(R, +, \cdot)$ form a ring?

   (i) $R = \mathbb{Z}$, + denotes the usual addition, $a \cdot b = \max\{a, b\}$, $a, b \in \mathbb{Z}$.
   (ii) $R = \mathbb{Z}$, + denotes the usual addition, $a \cdot b = |a|b$, $a, b \in \mathbb{Z}$.
   (iii) $R = \mathbb{Z}[\sqrt{2}] = \{a + b\sqrt{2} \in \mathbb{R} \mid a, b \in \mathbb{Z}\}$,

   $$(a + b\sqrt{2}) + (c + d\sqrt{2}) = (a + c) + (b + d)\sqrt{2},$$
   $$(a + b\sqrt{2}) \cdot (c + d\sqrt{2}) = (ac + 2bd) + (ad + bc)\sqrt{2}.$$

   (iv) $R = \mathrm{GL}(2, \mathbb{R})$, the set of all nonsingular 2×2 matrices over $\mathbb{R}$, + and $\cdot$ are usual matrix addition and multiplication.

2. For any two integers m, n, define $m \oplus n = m + n - 1$ and $m \odot n = m + n - mn$. Prove that the set of integers $\mathbb{Z}$ forms a commutative ring with identity with these two binary operations.

3. Let R be the set of all even integers. Define addition as usual and multiplication by $a \cdot b = \frac{1}{2}ab$. Show that R is a ring. Is there an identity in R ?

4. If $R = \{a, b, c, d\}$ is a ring, then complete the multiplication table of R, where $(R, +)$ is the same as Worked-out Exercise 12.1.3 :

$\cdot$	a	b	c	d
a	a	a	a	a
b	a	b		
c	a			c
d	a	b	c	

Is R commutative? Does it have an identity? Prove that R satisfies $x^2 = x$ for all $x \in R$.

5. Determine which of the following sets of real-valued functions on $\mathbb{R}$ form a ring under the operations defined in Worked-out Exercise 12.1.1:

  (i) the set of constant functions;

  (ii) the set of integer-valued functions;

  (iii) the set of even integer-valued functions;

  (iv) the set of twice differentiable functions having second derivative zero at $x = 0$;

  (v) the set of infinitely differentiable functions having first k derivatives zero at $x = 1$.

6. Let R be a ring. If $a, b \in R$, then prove that

  (i) $-(-a) = a$;

  (ii) $-(a - b) = -a + b$.

7. Let R be a ring and $m, n \in \mathbb{Z}$. Show that

  (i) $n(ab) = (na)b = a(nb)$;

  (ii) $(ma)(nb) = (mn)ab$;

  (iii) $n(-a) = (-n)a$.

8. Prove that a ring R is commutative if and only if $(a+b)^2 = a^2 + 2ab + b^2$ for all $a, b \in R$.

9. Prove that a ring R is commutative if and only if $(a+b)(a-b) = a^2 - b^2$ for all $a, b \in R$.

10. Give an example of a ring which contains elements a, b such that

  (i) $(a+b)^2 \neq a^2 + 2ab + b^2$.

  (ii) $(a+b)(a-b) \neq a^2 - b^2$.

11. Show that the binomial theorem holds for any commutative ring with identity; i.e., show that

$$(a+b)^n = \sum_{i=0}^{n} \binom{n}{i} a^{n-i} b^i \text{ for all } n \in \mathbb{Z}^+.$$

12. Let $(R, +, \cdot)$ be a mathematical system with two operations, addition and multiplication, which satisfies all the conditions of a ring except the commutative property of addition. Suppose there exists an element $c \in R$ such that $ca = cb \implies a = b$ (i.e., c can be left cancelled) for each $a, b \in R$. Then prove that $(R, +, \cdot)$ is a ring.

13. Show that a direct product of two commutative rings with identity is a commutative ring with identity.

14. † If in a ring R, $x^3 = x$ for all $x \in R$, then show that R is commutative.

15. † Prove that any ring of order 15 is commutative.

16. † Let $\mathcal{H}$ be the set of all symbols $a_0 + a_1 i + a_2 j + a_3 k$, where $a_r \in \mathbb{R}$, $r = 0, 1, 2, 3$. Two symbols $a_0 + a_1 i + a_2 j + a_3 k$ and $b_0 + b_1 i + b_2 j + b_3 k$ are considered to be equal if and only if $a_r = b_r$, $r = 0, 1, 2, 3$. Define addition and multiplication as a formal sum and product using the following relations:

$$i^2 = j^2 = k^2 = -1, \ ij = -ji = k, \ jk = -kj = i, \ ki = -ik = j.$$

Prove that $\mathcal{H}$ is a non-commutative ring with identity (this ring is called the **ring of real quaternions**).

17. Prove that a ring R with identity is a Boolean ring if and only if $a(a + b)b = 0$ for all $a, b \in R$.

18. Suppose $m, n > 1$ are positive integers which are relatively prime. Prove that $\mathbb{Z}_{mn}$ has at least four idempotent elements.

19. Find all idempotent elements of the rings $\mathbb{Z}_6$, $\mathbb{Z}_8$ and $\mathbb{Z}_{12}$.

20. † Find the positive integers n for which $\mathbb{Z}_n$ does not have a nonzero nilpotent element.

21. † Find the positive integers n for which $\mathbb{Z}_n$ does not have an idempotent element other than $[0]$ and $[1]$.

22. If a is an idempotent element of a ring R, then prove that for any $b \in R$, the product $(1 - a)ba$ is nilpotent.

23. In a ring R with identity 1, show that

   (i) $a(-1) = (-1)a = -a$ for all $a \in R$;

   (ii) if a is a unit in R, then $-a$ is also a unit in R and $(-a)^{-1} = -a^{-1}$.

   (iii) if $ab + ba = 1_R$ and $a^3 = a$, then $a^2 = 1_R$.

24. (a) Find the group of units in each of the following rings: (i) $\mathbb{Z}_7$, (ii) $\mathbb{Z}_{12}$, (iii) $\mathbb{Z}_n$.
   (b) Find all the units of $M_2(\mathbb{Z})$.
   (c) Prove that the units of $\mathbb{Z}[x]$ and $\mathbb{Z}$ are the same.

25. In a ring R with identity, if every idempotent is central, then prove that $ab = 1$, $(a, b \in R)$, implies that $ba = 1$.

26. (a) In a finite ring R with identity, show that $ab = 1$ $(a, b \in R)$ implies that $ba = 1$.
   (b) Let R be a ring with identity 1_R and $a \in R$. If there exists a unique $b \in R$ such that $ab = 1_R$. Prove that $ba = 1_R$.
   (c) Prove that a finite ring R with prime number of elements is commutative.

27. Let R be a ring and let $x \in R$. If there exists a unique $a \in R$ such that $xa = x$ for all x, prove that $ax = x$.

28. In a ring R with identity, if $a^2 = a$, $a \in R$, then show that $1 - 2a$ is a unit.

29. Show that the units of the ring $\mathbb{R}[x]$ of polynomials over $\mathbb{R}$ (cf. Example 12.1.9) are nonzero constant polynomials.

30. † Let R be a commutative ring with identity. Let $a, b \in R$ be such elements that a is invertible and b is nilpotent. Prove that $a + b$ is invertible. Is the result true for a noncommutative ring?

31. If a is a nilpotent element of a ring R with identity 1, then show that $1 + a$ and $1 - a$ are units of R.

32. Let R be a ring and $a, b \in R$ be such that $1 - ab$ is a unit. Prove that $1 - ba$ is also a unit and $(1 - ba)^{-1} = 1 + b(1 - ab)^{-1}a$.

33. †(**Kaplansky**) Suppose that an element a of a ring R has two or more right inverses. Let b be one of them. Prove that $x \longmapsto b + 1 - xa$ (x is a right inverse of a) is an injective mapping of the set of right inverses of a into itself and hence show that a has infinitely many right inverses.

34. Write the proof if the following statements are true or else give counter examples:

    (i) In a ring R, for all $a, b \in R$. $-(ab) = (-b)(-a)$.

    (ii) In a ring R, if a, b are idempotents, then $a + b$ is an idempotent.

    (iii) In a ring R, if a, b are idempotents, then ab is an idempotent.

    (iv) In a ring R, if a, b are zero divisors, then $a + b$ is a zero divisor.

    (v) Every finite ring has an identity element.

    (vi) Every finite ring is a commutative ring.

    (vii) For every positive integer n, there exists a ring with n elements.

35. Which of the following statement is true?
    (i) Every ring contains non-zero nilpotent element.
    (ii) Every ring contains at least one invertible element.
    (iii) Every finite ring contains nonzero idempotent elements.
    (iv) Every ring contains an idempotent element.
    Pick the correct option from the following:

36. The number of unit elements of the ring $\mathbb{Z}$ is
    (i) 1   (ii) 2   (iii) finite but more than 2   (iv) infinite.

37. The number of unit elements of the ring $\mathbb{Z}[i]$ is
    (i) 1   (ii) 2   (iii) 4   (iv) infinite.

38. The number of unit elements of the ring $\mathbb{Z}_7$ is
    (i) 0   (ii) 1   (iii) 6   (iv) 7.

39. The number of unit elements of the ring $\mathbb{Z}_{10}$ is
    (i) 0   (ii) 4   (iii) 5   (iv) 9.

40. The number of idempotent elements in $\mathbb{Z}$ is
    (i) 0   (ii) 1   (iii) 2   (iv) 3.

41. The number of idempotent elements in $\mathbb{Z}_8$ is
    (i) 0   (ii) 1   (iii) 2   (iv) 4.

42. The number of solutions of $x^2 - [4]x + [3] = 0$ in $\mathbb{Z}_{12}$ is
    (i) 2   (ii) 4   (iii) 6   (iv) none of these.

12.2   Integral Domains, Division Rings and Fields

In this section, we develop rings with certain special conditions. To begin with, let us consider the finite ring $\mathbb{Z}_6$, the ring of integers modulo 6. In this ring, if we take the product of two nonzero elements, $[2]$ and $[3]$ (modulo 6), then we have $[2] \cdot [3] = [6] = [0]$. Thus this ring has some nonzero elements whose product is zero (additive identity) of the ring. Also in $M_2(\mathbb{R})$, the ring of 2×2 matrices over the set of real numbers, we have

$$\begin{bmatrix} 1 & 0 \\ 0 & 0 \end{bmatrix} \begin{bmatrix} 0 & 0 \\ 0 & 1 \end{bmatrix} = \begin{bmatrix} 0 & 0 \\ 0 & 0 \end{bmatrix},$$

but none of the elements in the left hand side is zero (null matrix) of the ring. In general, we define the following:

Definition 12.2.1. Let R be a ring. An element $a \in R$ is called a ***zero divisor*** in R, if $a \neq 0$ and there exists a nonzero element $b \in R$ such that $ab = 0$ or $ba = 0$.

Remark 12.2.2. In the above definition b is also a zero divisor in R.

Definition 12.2.3. A ring R is said to satisfy **left [right] cancellation** property if for all $a, b, c \in R$, $a \neq 0$ and $ab = ac$ [resp. $ba = ca$] implies that $b = c$.

The following theorem establishes a relation between cancellation property for multiplication and zero divisors in a ring R.

Theorem 12.2.4. *Let R be a ring. Then the following conditions are equivalent:*
(i) R has no zero divisor;
(ii) R satisfies left cancellation property;
(iii) R satisfies right cancellation property.

Proof. (i) $\implies$ (ii) : Suppose the ring R has no zero divisor. Let $a, b, c \in R$, $a \neq 0$ and $ab = ac$. Then $a(b - c) = 0$ which implies $b - c = 0$, as $a \neq 0$ and R has no zero divisor. So we have $b = c$.

(ii) $\implies$ (i) : Let the ring R satisfy the left cancellation property. Let $a \in R$ be such that $a \neq 0$. Suppose $b \in R$ such that $ab = 0$. Then $ab = 0 = a \cdot 0$ which implies that $b = 0$ by the left cancellation property. Now if $ba = 0$, then for $b \neq 0$, $ba = 0 = b \cdot 0$ implies that $a = 0$, which is a contradiction. Thus $ba = 0$ implies that $b = 0$. So a is not a zero divisor.

Similarly, one can show that (i) $\iff$ (iii). $\qquad\qquad\qquad\square$

Now a ring may or may not have zero divisors. In fact, the ring of integers, rationals, reals or complex numbers do not have zero divisors. Consequently, the rings without zero divisors deserve particular attention.

Definition 12.2.5. A commutative ring R with identity $1 \neq 0$ is called an ***integral domain*** (in short, ***ID***) if R has no zero divisors.

Example 12.2.6. The ring of integers $\mathbb{Z}$, ring of rational numbers $\mathbb{Q}$, ring of real numbers $\mathbb{R}$ and the ring of complex numbers $\mathbb{C}$ are integral domains.

Example 12.2.7. The ring $\mathbb{Z}_6$ of integers modulo 6 is not an integral domain.

Example 12.2.8. If R is an integral domain, then the polynomial ring $R[x]$ over R is an integral domain.[4]

---
[4]For a proof, see Theorem 15.1.10.

Remark 12.2.9. $R_1 \times R_2$ is not necessarily an integral domain, even if R_1 and R_2 are integral domains, since $(a,0) \cdot (0,b) = (0,0)$ for any $a \in R_1, b \in R_2$.

For the ring $\mathbb{Z}_n$ of all integers modulo a positive integer n, we have the following nice characterization:

Theorem 12.2.10. *For any positive integer n, the ring $\mathbb{Z}_n$ of all integers modulo n is an integral domain if and only if n is a prime integer.*

Proof. Let $\mathbb{Z}_n$ be an integral domain. Then $[1] \neq [0]$ in $\mathbb{Z}_n$ and hence $n > 1$. If n is not prime, then $n = pq$ for some integers p, q where $1 < p, q < n$. So we have $[p][q] = [n] = [0]$, but neither $[p]$ nor $[q]$ is zero of the ring $\mathbb{Z}_n$. This contradiction shows that n must be prime.

Conversely, consider $\mathbb{Z}_n$ for a prime integer n. Let $[a], [b] \in \mathbb{Z}_n \smallsetminus \{[0]\}$. Now if $[a][b] = [0]$, then $[ab] = [0]$, i.e., n divides ab. Since n is prime, we have either $n \mid a$ or $n \mid b$. Both the cases are not possible as $[a], [b] \neq [0]$. Therefore $\mathbb{Z}_n$ is an integral domain. $\square$

Though the next theorem follows immediately from Theorem 12.2.4, we provide an independent proof of it.

Theorem 12.2.11. *A commutative ring R with identity $1 \neq 0$ is an integral domain if and only if the cancellation law holds for multiplication (i.e., $ab = ac$, $a, b, c \in R$, $a \neq 0 \implies b = c$)*

Proof. Let R be an integral domain. Let $a, b, c \in R$ $a \neq 0$ and $ab = ac$. Then $a(b-c) = 0$ which implies that $b - c = 0$, as R is an integral domain and $a \neq 0$. So we have $b = c$.

Conversely, let R be a commutative ring with identity, in which the cancellation law holds. Let $a, b \in R$ be such that $a \neq 0$ and $ab = 0$. Then $ab = 0 = a \cdot 0$ which implies $b = 0$. Thus R has no zero divisors. Hence R is an integral domain. $\square$

In view of the above theorem, we note that if every nonzero element of a commutative ring R with identity is a unit, then R satisfies the cancellation law and hence R is an integral domain.

Definition 12.2.12. A ring R with identity $1 \neq 0$ is called a ***division ring*** (also called a ***skew field***) if every nonzero element of R is a unit (i.e., if for any $a \in R$, $a \neq 0$, there exists an element $b \in R$ such that $ab = ba = 1$).

Note that if R is a division ring, the set of all nonzero elements of R forms a group under multiplication (cf. Theorem 12.1.18).

Definition 12.2.13. A commutative division ring is called a **field**, i.e., a ring R with identity $1 \neq 0$ is called a field if R is commutative and every nonzero element of R is a unit.

Example 12.2.14. The rings $\mathbb{Q}, \mathbb{R}, \mathbb{C}$ are division rings which are fields.

Remark 12.2.15. While the underlying set of the field $\mathbb{C}$ can be looked upon as $\mathbb{R} \times \mathbb{R}$ with addition defined componentwise for the ordered pairs of reals, it is the typical multiplication rule of these pairs given by $(a, b)(c, d) = (ac - bd, ad + bc)$ that makes $\mathbb{R}^2$ into the field $\mathbb{C}$. It is worth pointing out that, this multiplication rule has no generalization for higher n-tuples when $n > 2$, though the componentwise addition of pairs can easily be generalized even in those cases. Indeed, if $\mathbb{R}^n$ (with componentwise addition) be a field, then it can be proved that n must either be 1 or 2.

Note that there are division rings which are not fields. We have the following examples:

Example 12.2.16. Let

$$R = \left\{ \begin{bmatrix} \alpha & -\overline{\beta} \\ \beta & \overline{\alpha} \end{bmatrix} \in M_2(\mathbb{C}) \mid \overline{\alpha}, \overline{\beta} \text{ denote the conjugates of } \alpha, \beta \right\}.$$

Define addition $+$ and multiplication $\cdot$ in R by usual matrix addition and matrix multiplication. We now show that R is a division ring but not a field.

Let

$$A = \begin{bmatrix} a + id & -b - ic \\ b - ic & a - id \end{bmatrix}, \quad B = \begin{bmatrix} r + it & -u - iv \\ u - iv & r - it \end{bmatrix} \in R.$$

Then,

$$A + B = \begin{bmatrix} (a + r) + i(d + t) & -(b + u) - i(c + v) \\ (b + u) - i(c + v) & (a + r) - i(d + t) \end{bmatrix} \in R;$$

also it is a routine calculation to check that $AB \in R$ (verify!). Observe that $O = \begin{bmatrix} 0 & 0 \\ 0 & 0 \end{bmatrix} \in R$ is the zero element and for any $A \in R$, we have $-A \in R$ such that $A + (-A) = O$. Further, the distributive properties hold[5]. Hence R is a ring with identity $I = \begin{bmatrix} 1 & 0 \\ 0 & 1 \end{bmatrix} \in R$. Now,

$$\begin{bmatrix} i & 1 \\ -1 & -i \end{bmatrix}, \begin{bmatrix} 1 & i \\ i & 1 \end{bmatrix} \in R$$

---

[5]We leave the verification as an exercise.

and

$$\begin{bmatrix} i & 1 \\ -1 & -i \end{bmatrix} \begin{bmatrix} 1 & i \\ i & 1 \end{bmatrix} = \begin{bmatrix} 2i & 0 \\ 0 & -2i \end{bmatrix}$$

$$\begin{bmatrix} 1 & i \\ i & 1 \end{bmatrix} \begin{bmatrix} i & 1 \\ -1 & -i \end{bmatrix} = \begin{bmatrix} 0 & 2 \\ -2 & 0 \end{bmatrix}$$

This clearly shows that R is a noncommutative ring with $I \neq O$. Let

$$\begin{bmatrix} a + id & -b - ic \\ b - ic & a - id \end{bmatrix}$$

be a nonzero element of R. Then either $a + id \neq 0$ or, $-b - ic \neq 0$ i.e., either $a^2 + d^2 \neq 0$ or $b^2 + c^2 \neq 0$. Hence $a^2 + b^2 + c^2 + d^2 \neq 0$. Let $k = a^2 + b^2 + c^2 + d^2$. Observe that

$$\frac{1}{k} \begin{bmatrix} a - id & b + ic \\ -b + ic & a + id \end{bmatrix} \in R$$

is the inverse of $\begin{bmatrix} a + id & -b - ic \\ b - ic & a - id \end{bmatrix} \in R$. Hence each nonzero element of R has an inverse in R, whence R is a division ring. But as R is noncommutative, clearly R is not a field.

Example 12.2.17. The ring $\mathcal{H}$ of real quaternions given in Problem 16 of Exercise 12.1 is a division ring which is *not* a field.

While it can be established directly[6] by manipulation of symbols representing real quaternions, viz. $a_0 + a_1 i + a_2 j + a_3 k$, where $a_r \in \mathbb{R}$, $r = 0, 1, 2, 3$, using the stipulated rules like $i^2 = j^2 = k^2 = -1$, $ij = -ji = k$, $jk = -kj = i$, $ki = -ik = j$, it is interesting to note that if we consider the matrices

$$\mathbf{1} = \begin{bmatrix} 1 & 0 \\ 0 & 1 \end{bmatrix}, \; \mathbf{i} = \begin{bmatrix} 0 & -1 \\ 1 & 0 \end{bmatrix}, \; \mathbf{j} = \begin{bmatrix} 0 & -i \\ -i & 0 \end{bmatrix}, \; \mathbf{k} = \begin{bmatrix} i & 0 \\ 0 & -i \end{bmatrix}$$

then the symbol $a_0 \mathbf{1} + a_1 \mathbf{i} + a_2 \mathbf{j} + a_3 \mathbf{k}$, where $a_r \in \mathbb{R}$, $r = 0, 1, 2, 3$ may be looked upon equivalently as a 2×2 complex matrix

$$\begin{bmatrix} a_0 + a_3 i & -a_1 - a_2 i \\ a_1 - a_2 i & a_0 - a_3 i \end{bmatrix}$$

which is clearly similar to Example 12.2.16. Furthermore, here the matrix $\mathbf{1}$ behaves like the number 1, while $\mathbf{i}^2 = \mathbf{j}^2 = \mathbf{k}^2 = -\mathbf{1}$ and also $\mathbf{ij} = -\mathbf{ji} = \mathbf{k}, \mathbf{jk} = -\mathbf{kj} = \mathbf{i}$,

---

[6]We leave it as a routine exercise.

$ki = -ik = j$, each of which can be checked by usual rule of matrix multiplication. Hence this example[7] follows from Example 12.2.16 above.

Theorem 12.2.18. *Any field is an integral domain.*

Proof. Let R be a field and $a, b \in R$ such that $a \neq 0$ and $ab = 0$. In R, a is a unit and hence a^{-1} exists in R. Then $0 = a^{-1} \cdot 0 = a^{-1}(ab) = (a^{-1}a)b = 1 \cdot b = b$. Thus we find that R is a commutative ring with $1 \neq 0$ and without zero divisors. Hence R is an integral domain. $\square$

Now what about the converse? Clearly the ring $\mathbb{Z}$ is an integral domain which is not a field (e.g., 2 has no inverse in $\mathbb{Z}$). But in the following, we show that any finite integral domain is a field.

Theorem 12.2.19. *Any finite integral domain is a field.*

Proof. Let R be a finite integral domain. Suppose $R = \{a_1, a_2, \ldots, a_n\}$. Let $a \in R$, $a \neq 0$ and we consider the set $S = \{aa_1, aa_2, \ldots, aa_n\}$. Then $S \subseteq R$, since R is closed under product. If $aa_i = aa_j$, $(0 < i, j \leqslant n)$, then by Theorem 12.2.11, we have $a_i = a_j$ (as $a \neq 0$) which implies that elements of S are distinct. Then $S = R$, as $S \subseteq R$ and $|S| = n = |R|$. Now since R contains 1, we have $1 = aa_j$ for some j $(1 \leqslant j \leqslant n)$, which implies a is a unit and since this happens for every nonzero element a of R, we have R is a field. $\square$

Corollary 12.2.20. *For any positive integer n, $\mathbb{Z}_n$ is a field if and only if n is a prime integer.*

Proof. If $\mathbb{Z}_n$ is a field, then from Theorem 12.2.18, $\mathbb{Z}_n$ is an integral domain and hence from Theorem 12.2.10, n is a prime integer.

Conversely, suppose n is prime. Then $\mathbb{Z}_n$ is a finite integral domain by Theorem 12.2.10. Hence from Theorem 12.2.19, it follows that $\mathbb{Z}_n$ is a field. $\square$

---

[7]The algebra of quaternions $\mathcal{H}$ was discovered by William Rowan Hamilton in 1843. Towards finding an efficient method for computation of rotations in $\mathbb{R}^3$, his initial attempt was to establish an algebraic structure for triplets like $a + bi + cj$, which would generalize the algebra of complex numbers $a + ib$ governed by $i^2 = -1$. However, after relentless efforts for more than 13 years he could not generalize the multiplication operation that would give a field structure in tandem with the natural addition for the triplets and finally considered $ij = k$, which paved the path towards the skew field of real quadruples, that he named *quaternions*. It is interesting to note that the complex number $a_0 + a_1 i$ turns out to be a special case of the corresponding quaternion, if we put $a_2 = a_3 = 0$, and this leads to a matrix representation of a complex number $a + ib$ as $\begin{bmatrix} a & -b \\ b & a \end{bmatrix}$, which follows from the matrix representation of a quaternion.

We have started our discussion in this section with a finite ring, namely $\mathbb{Z}_6$, the ring of integers modulo 6. Now it is clear that $\mathbb{Z}_6$ is not an integral domain, but $\mathbb{Z}_5$ is an integral domain and hence by Corollary 12.2.20 above, $\mathbb{Z}_5$ is a field as well. In this ring, $\mathbb{Z}_5 = \{[0], [1], [2], [3], [4]\}$, $[1]$ is the identity and simple verification reveals that $[2]^{-1} = [3]$, as $[2] \cdot [3] = [6] = [1]$ and $[4]^{-1} = [4]$ as $[4][4] = [16] = [1]$.

One interesting fact about the finite ring $\mathbb{Z}_n$ is that, for any $a \in \mathbb{Z}_n$, $na = a + a + \cdots + a$ (n numbers of a) $= [0]$, for if $a = [k]$ $(0 \leqslant k \leqslant n)$, then $na = n[k] = [nk] = [0]$, since $nk \equiv 0 \,(\mathrm{mod}\ n)$. Thus there are rings in which some (fixed) integral multiple of every element is zero. In general, we have the following definition:

Definition 12.2.21. Let R be a ring. If there exists a positive integer n such that $na = 0$ for all $a \in R$, then the least such positive integer is called the **characteristic** of the ring R. If there exists no such positive integer n with the above property, then the ring R is said to be of **characteristic** 0 *(zero)*. It is a convention that a ring is said to be of **finite characteristic** if its characteristic is nonzero.

Remark 12.2.22. Note that any ring of characteristic zero is infinite. In other words any finite ring must be of finite characteristic. For if R is a finite ring, the (additive) group $(R, +)$ is finite as well. So it follows from group theory that every element $a \in R$ satisfies $|R|a = 0$, i.e.,

$$\underbrace{a + a + \cdots + a}_{|R| \text{ copies}} = 0.$$

Thus R is of a finite characteristic.

Example 12.2.23. (i) The characteristic of $\mathbb{Z}_n$ is n ($n \in \mathbb{N}$). (ii) The ring $\mathbb{Z}$ and the fields $\mathbb{Q}, \mathbb{R}, \mathbb{C}$ are of characteristic 0.

Previously in Theorem 12.2.10, we noticed that $\mathbb{Z}_p$ is an integral domain when p is prime. So this finite integral domain has a prime characteristic. Is it true for any integral domain? In fact, it is.

Theorem 12.2.24. *The characteristic of an integral domain is either prime or zero. In particular, characteristic of a field is either prime or zero.*

Proof. Let R be an integral domain. If the characteristic of R is 0, then we are done. So suppose the characteristic of R is $n \neq 0$. Then $na = 0$ for all $a \in R$ and so $n1 = 0$ but $m1 \neq 0$ for any $m < n$ ($m \in \mathbb{N}$), for otherwise $ma = 0$ for all $a \in R$, which would contradict the minimality of n. Now suppose n is composite (i.e., not prime). Then $n = pq$ for some integers p, q where $1 < p, q < n$. Now $(p1)(q1) = (pq)1 = n1 = 0$.

Since R is an integral domain, either $p\,1 = 0$ or $q\,1 = 0$, none of which is true. Therefore n can never be composite and so n is prime. Since every field is an integral domain, the result is also true for a field. □

Corollary 12.2.25. *The characteristic of a finite field is a prime integer.*

Proof. Follows immediately from the above theorem and Remark 12.2.22. □

We bring an end to this section with the following diagram (Fig. 27) that shows the relationship among the various algebraic structures introduced in this section.

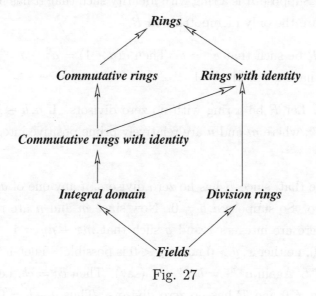

Fig. 27

Worked-out Exercises

◇ **Exercise 12.2.1.** Find the elements in $\mathbb{Z}_{12}$ which are zero divisors.

Solution. Verify that in $\mathbb{Z}_{12}$, $[0] = [2][6] = [3][4] = [8][3] = [9][4] = [10][6]$. Thus $[2], [3], [4], [6], [8], [9]$ and $[10]$ are zero divisors of $\mathbb{Z}_{12}$. For $k = 1, 5, 7$ or 11, $[k]$ is a unit in $\mathbb{Z}_{12}$ as in these cases $\gcd(k, 12) = 1$ (cf. Exercise 12.1.8). So these elements are not zero divisors.

◇ **Exercise 12.2.2.** Is there any integral domain which has six elements?

Solution. Let R be an integral domain. If $|R| = 6$, then $(R, +)$ is an abelian group of order 6, which must be isomorphic to $\mathbb{Z}_6$. Then $(R, +)$ is cyclic. Suppose it is generated by $a \in R$. Then $2a, 3a \neq 0$ but $2a \cdot 3a = 6a^2 = 0$, as the order of $(R, +)$ is 6. Thus there is no integral domain with 6 elements.

◊ **Exercise 12.2.3.** Let R_1 and R_2 be two rings. Show that $R_1 \times R_2$ is an integral domain if and only if any one of them is an integral domain and the other contains only a zero element.

Solution. If either of R_1 and R_2 is an integral domain and the other contains only a zero element, then clearly $R_1 \times R_2$ is an integral domain. Conversely, let $R_1 \times R_2$ be an integral domain. Suppose R_1 contains nonzero elements. Let $a \in R_1 \setminus \{0\}$. Since $(a, 0)(0, b) = (0, 0)$ for any $b \in R_2$, we have $b = 0$ which implies $R_2 = \{0\}$.

◊ **Exercise 12.2.4.** Suppose R is a ring with identity such that R has no zero divisors. Prove that 0 and 1 are the only idempotents in R.

Solution. Let $a \in R$ be such that $a^2 = a$. Then $a(a - 1) = a^2 - a = 0$. Since R has no zero divisors, we have $a = 0$ or $a = 1$.

◊ **Exercise 12.2.5.** Let R be a ring with no zero divisors. If $a, b \in R$ be such that $a^m = b^m$ and $a^n = b^n$, where m and n are relatively prime positive integers, then show that $a = b$.

Solution. First note that, since R has no zero divisors, if any one of a, b is zero, then the other is also zero. So suppose $a, b \neq 0$. Now since m and n are relatively prime positive integers, there are integers x and y such that $mx + ny = 1$. Let $x \geq 0$ and $y \leq 0$ (since $m, n > 0$, neither $x, y > 0$ nor $x, y < 0$ is possible). Then $a^{mx} = b^{mx}$ which implies $a^{1-ny} = b^{1-ny}$. Again $a^{-ny} = b^{-ny} = c$ (say). Then $ca = cb$, i.e., $c(a - b) = 0$. Certainly $c \neq 0$ as $a \neq 0$ and R has no zero divisors. Thus $a - b = 0$, i.e., $a = b$ as required. The proof for the case $x \leq 0$ and $y \geq 0$ is similar.

◊ **Exercise 12.2.6.** Let R be a finite ring without zero divisors and $|R| > 1$. Then show that R is a division ring.

Solution. Suppose $R = \{a_1, a_2, \ldots, a_n\}$. Let $a \in R$, $a \neq 0$ and consider the set $S = \{aa_1, aa_2, \ldots, aa_n\}$. Then $S \subseteq R$, since R is closed under product. If $aa_i = aa_j$ $(0 \leqslant i, j \leqslant n)$, then $a(a_i - a_j) = 0$ which implies that $a_i = a_j$ as $a \neq 0$ and R has no zero divisors. But then elements of S are distinct. So $S = R$, as $S \subseteq R$ and $|S| = n = |R|$.

Thus $a = aa_i$ for some i $(0 \leqslant i \leqslant n)$. Similarly considering the set $T = \{a_1a, a_2a, \ldots, a_na\}$, one can show that $R = T$. Thus for any $b \in R$, there exists $a_r \in R$ so that $b = a_r a$. Then $ba_i = a_r aa_i = a_r a = b$, whence it follows that a_i is a right identity of R. Dually, one can obtain a left identity, say a_j in R. But then $a_i = a_j a_i = a_j$. This implies that R has a (two-sided) identity and we denote it, as usual, by 1.

Now since $1 \in R = S = T$, we have $a_k, a_t \in R$ so that $aa_k = 1 = a_t a$. Now $a_k = 1 \cdot a_k = a_t a a_k = a_t \cdot 1 = a_t$. Thus a has a two-sided inverse and so a is a unit. Therefore, every nonzero member of R is a unit which implies R is a division ring.

$\Diamond$ **Exercise 12.2.7.** Let $(G, +)$ be a simple abelian group. Prove that the ring of endomorphisms of G (cf. Example 12.1.7) is a division ring.

Solution. Let R be the ring of endomorphisms on G. Note that the zero of R is the function θ (say) which maps all elements of G to 0, the identity of G. Let $\theta \neq f \in R$. Now the kernel of f is a normal subgroup of G. But G is simple. Thus $\ker f = \{0\}$ or G. Since $f \neq \theta$, $\ker f \neq G$. So $\ker f = \{0\}$ which implies that f is injective. Also $f(G)$ is a subgroup of G (hence a normal subgroup of G, as G is Abelian) and since $f \neq \theta$, we have $f(G) = G$, proving that f is a bijective endomorphism, i.e., an automorphism. Hence $f^{-1} \in R$ for all $f \neq \theta$ in R, i.e., R is a division ring.

$\blacklozenge$ **Exercise 12.2.8.** Show that a ring R with $|R| > 1$ is a division ring if it satisfies the following condition:

for each $0 \neq a \in R$, there exists a *unique* element $x \in R$ such that $axa = a$.

Solution. It is required to show that $(R^*, \cdot)$ is a group, where $R^* = R \smallsetminus \{0\}$. Let $a, b \in R^*$. We show that $ab \in R^*$. Let x be the unique element in R so that $axa = a$. Now if $ab = 0$, then $a(b + x)a = aba + axa = 0 + a = a$ which implies that $b + x = x$, i.e., $b = 0$. This contradiction proves that R^* is closed under the multiplication.

Let $a \in R^*$ and $axa = a$ for a unique $x \in R$. Certainly, $x \in R^*$ for otherwise $a = axa = 0$. Now $axax = ax$ which implies that R^* contains idempotents. Denote the set of idempotents in R^* by E. We show that $|E| = 1$. Let $e, f \in E$. Let $g \in R^*$ be the unique element such that $ef \cdot g \cdot ef = ef$. Now $ef \cdot ge \cdot ef = ef$ and $ef \cdot fg \cdot ef = ef$. These imply $g = ge = fg$. Also $ef(ge \cdot fg)ef = ef$ Then $ge \cdot fg = g$ which implies that $g^2 = g$. Therefore $geg = g = gfg$. But then $e = f$. Thus $|E| = 1$. Let $E = \{e\}$.

Finally for each $a \in R^*$, $ax = xa = e$, where x is the unique element satisfying $axa = a$. Thus $ae = ea = a$ which implies e is the identity of R and hence it follows that $x = a^{-1}$, i.e., a is a unit. Therefore R^* is a group and so R is a division ring.

$\Diamond$ **Exercise 12.2.9.** Let R be a ring with identity. Then show that R is of characteristic n if and only if n is the least positive integer such that $n1 = 0$.

Solution. Suppose R is of characteristic n, then $n1 = 0$ as $1 \in R$. Let $m1 = 0$ for some positive integer m. Then for any $a \in R$, $ma = (m1) \cdot a = 0 \cdot a = 0$. Thus $m \geq n$, by definition of the characteristic. Thus n is the least positive integer such that $n1 = 0$.

Conversely, if n is the least positive integer such that $n1 = 0$, then $na = (n1) \cdot a = 0 \cdot a = 0$ for all $a \in R$. Also, if m is a positive integer such that $ma = 0$ for all $a \in R$, then $m1 = 0$. Hence by the given condition, $m \geq n$. Therefore n is the least positive integer such that $na = 0$ for all $a \in R$, i.e., R is of characteristic n.

◇ **Exercise 12.2.10.** Show that the characteristic of a finite ring R divides $|R|$.

Solution. Let R be a finite ring with characteristic $n \in \mathbb{N}$. Since n is the least positive integer so that $nx = 0$ for all $x \in R$. Then there exist $a \in R$ such that $na = 0$ and $ma \neq 0$ for all $0 < m < n$. This implies the order of the element a in the group $(R, +)$ is n. Therefore n divides the order of the group, i.e., $|R|$.

◇ **Exercise 12.2.11.** Let R be a commutative ring with characteristic p, where p is a prime number. Prove that $(a + b)^p = a^p + b^p$.

Solution. Since R is commutative, we have

$$(a + b)^p = a^p + \binom{p}{1} a^{p-1} b + \cdots + \binom{p}{r} a^{p-r} b^r + \cdots \binom{p}{p-1} a b^{p-1} + b^p.$$

Now since p is prime, p divides $\binom{p}{r} = \dfrac{p!}{r!\,(p-r)!}$ for all $r = 1, 2, 3, \ldots, p-1$. Therefore

$$\sum_{r=1}^{p-1} \binom{p}{r} a^{p-r} b^r = 0$$

as the characteristic of R is p. Thus $(a + b)^p = a^p + b^p$.

◇ **Exercise 12.2.12.** Which of the following statement is true?
(i) Every ring contains nonzero zero divisor.
(ii) Every integral domain contains no nonzero zero divisor.
(iii) Every finite ring contains nonzero zero divisor.
(iv) Every integral domain is finite.

Solution. The ring $(\mathbb{Z}_5, +, \cdot)$ is a finite ring containing no nonzero zero divisor. Again $(\mathbb{Z}, +, \cdot)$ is an infinite integral domain. Hence option (ii) is correct.

◇ **Exercise 12.2.13.** Which of the following statement is true?
(i) Every ring with identity is an integral domain.
(ii) If R is a ring with identity such that characteristic of R is zero, then R contains infinite number of elements.
(iii) Every finite ring is of characteristic zero.
(iv) Every integral domain contains at least three idempotent elements.

Solution. The ring $(\mathbb{Z}_6, +, \cdot)$ is a ring with identity but not an integral domain. Let R be a finite ring containing n elements. Then by Worked-out Exercise 12.2.10, it follows that characteristic of R divides n and thus characteristic of R can not be zero. Let a be an idempotent in an integral domain. Then $a^2 = a$ implies $a(a-1) = 0$, i.e., either $a = 0$ or $a = 1$. Hence every integral domain contains exactly two idempotent elements. Finally, if R is a ring with identity such that characteristic of R is zero, then $\mathbb{Z} \subseteq R$ and thus R contains infinite number of elements. Hence option (ii) is correct.

◇ **Exercise 12.2.14.** Which of the following statements are true?

(i) $\mathbb{Z}_{10}$ is an integral domain.

(ii) $\mathbb{Z}_{11}$ is an integral domain.

(iii) $\mathbb{Z}_{12}$ is an integral domain.

(iv) $\mathbb{Z}_{13}$ is an integral domain.

Solution. We know $\mathbb{Z}_n$ is an integral domain if and only if n is prime. Hence options (ii) and (iv) are correct.

Exercises

1. Which elements are zero divisors in the rings $\mathbb{Z}_5, \mathbb{Z}_6, \mathbb{Z}_8$?

2. Which elements are zero divisors in $\mathbb{Z}_n$, the ring of integers modulo n?

3. Which elements are zero divisors in $\mathbb{Z}_5 \times \mathbb{Z}_{10}$, $\mathbb{Z}_4 \times \mathbb{Z}_6$?

4. Which elements are zero divisors in $\mathbb{Z}_m \times \mathbb{Z}_n$?

5. If R is a Boolean ring with $|R| > 2$, determine all the zero divisors of R.

6. Is there any integral domain which has ten elements?

7. Show that the ring $\mathbb{Z}[\sqrt{3}] = \{a + b\sqrt{3} \in \mathbb{R} \mid a, b \in \mathbb{Z}\}$ with usual addition and multiplication is an integral domain.

8. (a) Give an example of a commutative ring with identity which contains divisor of zero and whose characteristic is prime. Justify your answer.
   (b) Give an example of a commutative ring without identity element and without zero divisor.
   (c) Give an example of an integral domain which has an infinite number of elements, yet is of finite characteristic.
   (d) Prove that the ring of matrices of the form $\begin{pmatrix} x & y \\ 2y & x \end{pmatrix}$ contains no divisor of zero if $x, y \in \mathbb{Q}$ but contains divisor of zero if $x, y \in \mathbb{R}$.

9. Let R be a ring with $|R| > 1$. Suppose for any $a \in R \setminus \{0\}$ and any $b \in R$, there is an element $x \in R$ satisfying $ax = b$. Then prove that R is a division ring.

10. Let R be a ring with a right identity e. If for each $a \in R \setminus \{0\}$, there exists $x \in R$ such that $xa = e$, show that R is a division ring.

11. (a) Let R be a finite commutative ring with $|R| > 1$, which has no zero divisors. Show that R is a field.

(b) Let a, b be two elements in a skew field F. If $b \neq 0$ and $(ab)^2 = ab^2 + bab - b^2$, prove that $a = 1$.

12. † Let $(F, +, \cdot)$ be a field. Prove that the groups $(F, +)$ and $(F \setminus \{0\}, \cdot)$ are not isomorphic.

13. Show that a Boolean ring is a field if and only if it contains only 0 and 1.

14. Let R be an integral domain. Let $a \in R \setminus \{0\}$ be such that $na = 0$ for some positive integer n. Show that R is of a finite characteristic.

15. Let R be a ring with identity. Show that the ring $M_n(R)$, of all $n \times n$ matrices (cf. Example 12.1.10) has the same characteristic as that of R.

16. Let R be a commutative ring which has no zero divisors. Prove that the characteristic of R is either prime or zero.

17. Let R be a commutative ring with characteristic p, where p is a prime number. Prove that $(a \pm b)^{p^n} = a^{p^n} \pm b^{p^n}$ for any positive integer n.

18. † Let $H = \{r + \bar{x} \ : \ r \in \mathbb{R}, \bar{x} \in \mathbb{R}^3\}$. Define *addition* in H as $(r + \bar{x}) + (s + \bar{y}) = (r + s) + (\bar{x} + \bar{y})$, where the second addition is the componentwise addition in real vector space $\mathbb{R}^3$. Define *multiplication* in H as $(r + \bar{x})(s + \bar{y}) = rs + r\bar{y} + \bar{x}s + \bar{x}\bar{y}$ by stipulating rs as ordinary multiplication in $\mathbb{R}$, $r\bar{y}, \bar{x}s$ as external (or scalar) multiplication in the vector space $\mathbb{R}^3$ (where clearly $r\bar{y} = \bar{y}r$ etc.) and $\bar{x}\bar{y} = -(\bar{x} \cdot \bar{y}) + (\bar{x} \times \bar{y})$, where $\cdot$ and $\times$ respectively denote the *dot* and *cross* product of vectors in $\mathbb{R}^3$. Show that H is a skew field which is not a field[8].

19. Let S be any set and $\mathcal{P}(S)$ be the power set of S. Describe the units and zero divisors of $(\mathcal{P}(S), \triangle, \cap)$. Under what condition is $\mathcal{P}(S)$ a field?

20. Decide whether the following statements are correct. Justify your answer giving necessary examples whenever required.

   (i) There exists a field with five elements.

   (ii) There exists a field with six elements.

   (iii) Let R be a ring with identity which has no zero divisors and $a, b \in R$. Then $ab = 1$ if and only if $ba = 1$.

21. Which of the following statements are true?
   (i) Every field is an integral domain.
   (ii) Every integral domain is a feild.
   (iii) Every ring is an integral domain.
   (iv) Every finite integral domain is a field.

22. Let R and S denote commutative ring with identity and char(R) denote the characteristic of the ring R. Which of the following statements are true?
   (i) If R is a finite field, then char(R) is prime.
   (ii) If char(R) is prime, then R is a field.
   (iii) If S is a subring of R containing the identity of R, then char$(S) = $ char(R).

---

[8]Indeed this is another presentation of Hamilton's quaternions. Amazingly, the terms **scalar** and **vector** were first coined by Hamilton with reference to some special quaternions, when $\bar{x} = 0$ and $r = 0$ respectively.

23. Let F denote a field and char(F) denote the characteristic of the field F. Which of the following statement is true?
    (i) char(F) is always a prime number.
    (ii) char(F) is always zero.
    (iii) char(F) is either zero or a prime number
    (iv) char(F) may be a composite number.

12.3   Subrings and Subfields

In this section, we define substructures of the algebraic structures, viz., rings and fields, and study their properties.

Definition 12.3.1. A nonempty subset S of a ring $(R, +, \cdot)$ is called a **subring** of R if $(S, +)$ is a subgroup of the Abelian group $(R, +)$ and S is *closed* under multiplication, i.e., for all $a, b \in S$, $ab \in S$.

The smallest subring of a ring R is $\{0\}$ and the greatest one is R itself.

Example 12.3.2. In the following chain, the former is a subring of the later (with the usual addition and multiplication):

$$\mathbb{Z} \subseteq \mathbb{Q} \subseteq \mathbb{R} \subseteq \mathbb{C}.$$

Note that $\mathbb{Z}_n$, the ring of integers modulo n ($n \in \mathbb{N}$, $n > 1$) is *not* a subring of $\mathbb{Z}$, but $n\mathbb{Z} = \{nr : r \in \mathbb{Z}\}$ is a subring of $\mathbb{Z}$.

Example 12.3.3. The set $\mathbb{Z}[\sqrt{2}] = \{a + b\sqrt{2} \in \mathbb{R} \mid a, b \in \mathbb{Z}\}$ is a subring of $\mathbb{R}$. Clearly $S = \mathbb{Z}[\sqrt{2}]$ is nonempty as $0 = 0 + 0\sqrt{2} \in S$. Let $x, y \in S$. Then $x = a + b\sqrt{2}$ and $y = c + d\sqrt{2}$, where $a, b, c, d \in \mathbb{Z}$. Now $x - y = (a - c) + (b - d)\sqrt{2} \in S$ as $a - c, b - d \in \mathbb{Z}$. Thus $(S, +)$ is a subgroup of $(\mathbb{R}, +)$ by Theorem 5.1.5. Also $xy = (a + b\sqrt{2})(c + d\sqrt{2}) = (ac + 2bd) + (ad + bc)\sqrt{2} \in S$ as $ac + 2bd, ad + bc \in \mathbb{Z}$. Therefore S is a subring of $\mathbb{R}$.

Example 12.3.4. Let R_1 and R_2 be two rings and S_1 and S_2 be two subrings of R_1 and R_2 respectively. Then $S_1 \times S_2$ is a subring of $R_1 \times R_2$ (cf. Example 12.1.8).

Example 12.3.5. If R is a commutative ring with identity, then R is a subring of the polynomial ring, $R[x]$ (cf. Example 12.1.9). The set of all polynomials over R, which consist of only even powers of x, is also a subring of $R[x]$.

Example 12.3.6. The ring of Gaussian integers,

$$\mathbb{Z}[i] = \{a + ib \in \mathbb{C} \mid a, b \in \mathbb{Z}, \; i^2 = -1\}$$

is a subring of $\mathbb{C}$ (cf. Example 12.1.5).

A natural question that arises is how we can recognize that a nonempty subset of a ring is, indeed, a subring of it. The answer is the following:

Theorem 12.3.7. *Let R be a ring and S be a nonempty subset of R. A necessary and sufficient condition that S is a subring of R is*

$$a, b \in S \implies a - b, \, ab \in S. \tag{12.3.1}$$

Proof. Let S be a subring of R. Let $a, b \in S$. Since $(S, +)$ is a subgroup of $(R, +)$, we have $a - b \in S$. Also by definition, $ab \in S$.

Conversely, let S be a nonempty subset of R satisfying (12.3.1). Since for all $a, b \in S$, $a - b \in S$, we have $(S, +)$ is a subgroup of $(R, +)$ by Theorem 5.1.5. Also by (12.3.1), $ab \in S$ for all $a, b \in S$. Thus S is a subring of R.   □

It may happen that a ring with identity has a subring without an identity. Also it is *not* necessary that if a subring S of a ring R has an identity 1_S, then it is the identity 1_R of R. The following examples throw some light on this issue.

Example 12.3.8. The ring of integers $(\mathbb{Z}, +, \cdot)$ is a ring with identity 1, but its subring $(2\mathbb{Z}, +, \cdot)$ of even integers is a subring without any identity.

Example 12.3.9. The ring $(M_2(\mathbb{R}), +, \cdot)$ of 2×2 matrices over $\mathbb{R}$ is a ring with identity $\begin{bmatrix} 1 & 0 \\ 0 & 1 \end{bmatrix}$. However, the subring (check!) of the particular 2×2 matrices of the form $\begin{bmatrix} x & x \\ x & x \end{bmatrix}$ has the identity $\begin{bmatrix} \frac{1}{2} & \frac{1}{2} \\ \frac{1}{2} & \frac{1}{2} \end{bmatrix}$ (vide Worked-out Example 3.1.8).

Theorem 12.3.10. *Let $\{S_\alpha : \alpha \in \Lambda\}$ be a collection of subrings of a ring R. Then, $S = \bigcap_{\alpha \in \Lambda} S_\alpha$ is a subring of R.*

Proof. For each $\alpha \in \Lambda$, $0 \in S_\alpha$. So $0 \in S$ and S is nonempty. Now let $a, b \in S$. Then $a, b \in S_\alpha$ for each $\alpha \in \Lambda$. Since S_α is a subring, we have $a - b, ab \in S_\alpha$ for all $\alpha \in \Lambda$. Thus $a - b, ab \in S$. Therefore by Theorem 12.3.7, S is a subring of R.   □

What is the intersection of all the subrings $n\mathbb{Z}$ ($n \in \mathbb{N}$) of the ring $\mathbb{Z}$ of integers?

As in the case of subgroups of a group, here also the union of two subrings may not be a subring. For example, consider subrings $2\mathbb{Z}$ and $3\mathbb{Z}$ of $\mathbb{Z}$. Since $2 + 3 \notin 2\mathbb{Z} \cup 3\mathbb{Z}$, we have that $2\mathbb{Z} \cup 3\mathbb{Z}$ is not a subring of $\mathbb{Z}$.

Theorem 12.3.11. *Let R be a ring and X be a nonempty subset of R. Let $\{S_\alpha : \alpha \in \Lambda\}$ be the collection of subrings of R containing X. Then $S = \bigcap_{\alpha \in \Lambda} S_\alpha$ is the smallest [9] subring of R containing X.*

Proof. Certainly, S is a subring containing X by the above theorem. That is, S is a member in the collection $\{S_\alpha : \alpha \in \Lambda\}$ and since S is the intersection of all of them, it is the smallest one in this collection. $\qquad\square$

In a noncommutative ring, the following subset (in fact a subring) draws special attention.

Definition 12.3.12. Let R be a ring. Define

$$C(R) = \{a \in R \mid xa = ax \ \text{for all} \ x \in R\}.$$

$C(R)$ is called the **centre** of R. Note that $C(R) = R$ if and only if R is commutative.

Theorem 12.3.13. *The centre of a ring R is a subring of R.*

Proof. We have $C(R) \neq \emptyset$ as $0 \in C(R)$. Let $a, b \in C(R)$. Then $xa = ax$ and $xb = bx$ for all $x \in R$. These imply $x(a - b) = (a - b)x$ for all $x \in R$. That is, $a - b \in C(R)$. Moreover $xab = axb = abx$ for all $x \in R$. Thus $ab \in C(R)$. Then by Theorem 12.3.7, $C(R)$ is a subring of R. $\qquad\square$

Next we consider the substructure of the algebraic structure, field.

Definition 12.3.14. Let F be a field. A subring S of F is called a **subfield** of F if $1_F \in S$ and for each $0 \neq a \in S$, $a^{-1} \in S$ (where 1_F is the identity of F). Clearly a subfield S is itself a field.

Example 12.3.15. $\mathbb{Q}$ is a subfield of $\mathbb{R}$ and $\mathbb{R}$ is a subfield of $\mathbb{C}$.

Example 12.3.16. The set $\mathbb{Q}[\sqrt{2}] = \{a + b\sqrt{2} \in \mathbb{R} \mid a, b \in \mathbb{Q}\}$ is a subfield of $\mathbb{R}$. Indeed, $\mathbb{Q}[\sqrt{2}]$ is a subring of $\mathbb{R}$ in a similar way as in Example 12.3.3. Let $a + b\sqrt{2} \in \mathbb{Q}[\sqrt{2}] \smallsetminus \{0\}$. Now in the field, $\mathbb{R}$,

$$(a + b\sqrt{2})^{-1} = \frac{a}{a^2 - 2b^2} - \frac{b}{a^2 - 2b^2}\sqrt{2}.$$

Clearly the right hand side belongs to $\mathbb{Q}[\sqrt{2}]$. Note that since $a, b \in \mathbb{Q}$ and $a + b\sqrt{2} \neq 0$, $a^2 - 2b^2 \neq 0$. Thus $\mathbb{Q}[\sqrt{2}]$ is a subfield of $\mathbb{R}$.

---

[9] S is *smallest* in the sense that $S \subseteq T$ for all subring T of R with $X \subseteq T$. This theorem only describes the existence of the smallest subring S of a ring, containing a given nonempty subset X of the ring. But one cannot gather any idea about how it looks like, in terms of the elements of X. For a complete description, see Problem 16 of Exercise 12.3.

Example 12.3.17. Let A be the set of all complex numbers which satisfy a polynomial equation with rational coefficients, i.e.,

$$A = \left\{ \alpha \in \mathbb{C} \mid a_0 + a_1\alpha + a_2\alpha^2 + \cdots + a_n\alpha^n = 0, \ a_i \in \mathbb{Q}, \ n \in \mathbb{N}_0 \right\}.$$

Then A is a subfield of $\mathbb{C}$. Elements of A are called **algebraic numbers**[10].

Now we present a necessary and sufficient condition for a subset of a field F to be a subfield of F.

Theorem 12.3.18. *Let S be a subset of a field F. Then S is a subfield of F if and only if S satisfies the following conditions:*

$$|S| \geq 2 \tag{12.3.2}$$

$$a - b \in S \ \ \text{for all} \ \ a, b \in S; \tag{12.3.3}$$

$$ab^{-1} \in S \ \ \text{for all} \ \ a \in S, \ b \in S \smallsetminus \{0\}. \tag{12.3.4}$$

Proof. Let S be a subfield of F. Then S is a subring of F and so S is nonempty and satisfies (12.3.3). Then $0 \in S$. Also by definition, $1 \in S$ and $0 \neq 1$. Thus $|S| \geq 2$. Now since S is a subfield of F, for any b in $S \smallsetminus \{0\}$, we have $b^{-1} \in S$. So for any $a \in S$, $ab^{-1} \in S$, as S is a subring of F, which implies (12.3.4).

Conversely, let S be a subset of F which satisfies (12.3.2), (12.3.3) and (12.3.4). By (12.3.2), S is nonempty and there exists a nonzero element, say a in S. Then by (12.3.4), $1 = aa^{-1} \in S$. Now let $a, b \in S$ so that $b \neq 0$. Then $b^{-1} = 1b^{-1} \in S$ and so $ab = a(b^{-1})^{-1} \in S$ by (12.3.4). Also for any $a, b \in S$, $a - b \in S$ by (12.3.3). Thus S is a subring of F, $1 \in S$ and for any $b \in S \smallsetminus \{0\}$, $b^{-1} \in S$. Therefore S is a subfield of F. $\square$

The next theorem shows that intersection of subfields is again a subfield.

Theorem 12.3.19. *Let $\{S_\alpha : \alpha \in \Lambda\}$ be a collection of subfields of a field F. Then $S = \bigcap\limits_{\alpha \in \Lambda} S_\alpha$ is also a subfield of F.*

Proof. By Theorem 12.3.10, we have that S is a subring. Now since $1 \in S_\alpha$ for each $\alpha \in \Lambda$, we have $1 \in S$. Let $b \in S$ so that $b \neq 0$. Then $b \in S_\alpha \smallsetminus \{0\}$ and so $b^{-1} \in S_\alpha$ for all $\alpha \in \Lambda$. Thus $b^{-1} \in S$. Hence S is a subfield of F. $\square$

Here again we raise a question:

What is the intersection of all subfields of the field of real numbers, $\mathbb{R}$?

---

[10]Algebraic numbers play important roles in Field theory and Number theory. For a proof that the set of all algebraic numbers form a subfield of $\mathbb{C}$, consult any book on Number theory.

Worked-out Exercises

◊ **Exercise 12.3.1.** Suppose in a ring R, $e \in R$ is idempotent. Show that eRe is a subring of R with identity e.

Solution. We have $e^2 = e$. Then $e = eee \in eRe$ and so $eRe \neq \emptyset$. Let $x, y \in eRe$. Then $x = ere$ and $y = ese$ for some $r, s \in R$. Now $x - y = ere - ese = e(r - s)e \in eRe$ and $xy = ere \cdot ese = e(res)e \in eRe$. Thus eRe is a subring of R. Also $ex = e \cdot ere = ere = x$. Similarly $xe = x$. Therefore e is the identity of eRe.

◊ **Exercise 12.3.2.** Let $S = \{[0], [2], [4], [6], [8]\}$, where $[n]$ denotes the equivalence class of n modulo 10. Prove that S is a subring of $\mathbb{Z}_{10}$ with the usual operations of $\mathbb{Z}_{10}$. Also show that S has an identity which is different from that of $\mathbb{Z}_{10}$.

Solution. Let $[i], [j] \in S$. Then i, j are even. Let $[m] = [i] - [j]$ and $[n] = [i][j]$ where $0 \leq m, n < 10$. Then $i - j \equiv m(\bmod\, 10)$ and $ij \equiv n(\bmod\, 10)$ that is, $i - j = m + 10k_1$ and $ij = n + 10k_2$ for some integers k_1, k_2. This implies that m and n are both even. Hence $[i] - [j], [i][j] \in S$ and so S is a subring of $\mathbb{Z}_{10}$.

Now it is interesting to observe that $[6][n] = [n]$ for all $[n] \in S$. So $[6]$ is the identity of S which is different from the identity, $[1]$ of $\mathbb{Z}_{10}$.

◊ **Exercise 12.3.3.** Let $R = M_2(\mathbb{C})$, the ring of all 2×2 complex matrices and let S be a subset of R consisting of the matrices of the form $B = \begin{bmatrix} \alpha & \beta \\ -\bar{\beta} & \bar{\alpha} \end{bmatrix}$. Show that S is a subring of R. Find the centre of S.

Solution. By definition S is nonempty. Let

$$A = \begin{bmatrix} \alpha & \beta \\ -\bar{\beta} & \bar{\alpha} \end{bmatrix}, \quad B = \begin{bmatrix} \gamma & \delta \\ -\bar{\delta} & \bar{\gamma} \end{bmatrix} \in S$$

Then,

$$A - B = \begin{bmatrix} \alpha - \gamma & \beta - \delta \\ -(\bar{\beta} - \bar{\delta}) & \bar{\alpha} - \bar{\gamma} \end{bmatrix} \quad \text{and} \quad AB = \begin{bmatrix} \mu & \nu \\ -\bar{\nu} & \bar{\mu} \end{bmatrix}.$$

where $\mu = \alpha\gamma - \beta\bar{\delta}$ and $\nu = \alpha\delta + \beta\bar{\gamma}$. Hence $A - B, AB \in S$ and so S is a subring[11] of R.

Now let

$$A = \begin{bmatrix} \alpha & \beta \\ -\bar{\beta} & \bar{\alpha} \end{bmatrix} \in C(S) \quad \text{and} \quad B = \begin{bmatrix} \gamma & \delta \\ -\bar{\delta} & \bar{\gamma} \end{bmatrix} \quad \text{be any element of } S$$

---

[11]Though we have already proved that S is a ring (in fact, a division ring) in Example 12.2.16, we provide here a separate proof that S is a subring of $R = M_2(\mathbb{C})$.

where $C(S)$ is the centre of S. Then $AB = BA$ implies that

$$\begin{bmatrix} \alpha\gamma - \beta\bar{\delta} & \alpha\delta + \beta\bar{\gamma} \\ -\bar{\alpha}\bar{\delta} - \bar{\beta}\gamma & \bar{\alpha}\bar{\gamma} - \bar{\beta}\delta \end{bmatrix} = \begin{bmatrix} \gamma\alpha - \delta\bar{\beta} & \delta\bar{\alpha} + \beta\gamma \\ -\bar{\delta}\alpha - \bar{\beta}\bar{\gamma} & \bar{\gamma}\bar{\alpha} - \bar{\delta}\beta \end{bmatrix}$$

Thus we have $\beta\bar{z} = z\bar{\beta}$ for all $z \in \mathbb{C}$. Putting $z = 1$, we get $\beta = \bar{\beta}$ which implies β is real and then putting $z = i$, we get $-i\beta = i\beta$ which implies $\beta = 0$. Also we have, $(\alpha - \bar{\alpha})z = 0$ for all $z \in \mathbb{C}$, which gives $\alpha = \bar{\alpha}$, i.e., α is real. Therefore

$$C(S) = \left\{ \begin{bmatrix} \alpha & 0 \\ 0 & \bar{\alpha} \end{bmatrix} \mid \alpha \in \mathbb{R} \right\}.$$

◊ **Exercise 12.3.4.** Find the smallest subring of $\mathbb{R}$ containing $\frac{1}{2}$.

Solution. Consider the following subset S of $\mathbb{R}$:

$$S = \left\{ \frac{n}{2^k} \mid n, k \in \mathbb{Z}, \ k \geq 0 \right\}.$$

Firstly, $\frac{1}{2} \in S$ for $n = k = 1$. Next let $x, y \in S$. Then $x = \frac{m}{2^r}$ and $y = \frac{n}{2^s}$ for some $m, n, r, s \in \mathbb{Z}, \ r, s > 0$. Then,

$$x - y = \frac{2^s m - 2^r n}{2^{r+s}} \quad \text{and} \quad xy = \frac{mn}{2^{r+s}},$$

which imply that $x - y, xy \in S$. Thus S is a subring of $\mathbb{R}$ containing $\frac{1}{2}$. Suppose T is a subring of $\mathbb{R}$ containing $\frac{1}{2}$. Then $1 = \frac{1}{2} + \frac{1}{2} \in T$ and so $n \in T$ for all $n \in \mathbb{Z}$ as T is a subring of $\mathbb{R}$. Also since $\frac{1}{2} \in T$, we have $\frac{1}{2^k} \in T$ for every $k \in \mathbb{Z}, \ k \geq 0$. Therefore for each $n, k \in \mathbb{Z}$ with $k \geq 0$, $\frac{n}{2^k} \in T$ which implies $S \subseteq T$. So S is the smallest subring of $\mathbb{R}$ containing $\frac{1}{2}$.

◊ **Exercise 12.3.5.** Show that the field $\mathbb{Q}$ of rational numbers has no proper subfields.

Solution. Let S be a subfield of $\mathbb{Q}$. Then $1 \in S$. Since S is a subring of $\mathbb{Q}$, we also have $-1 \in S$. Let $x \in \mathbb{Q}$. Then there exist $p, q \in \mathbb{Z}$ and $q > 0$ such that $x = \frac{p}{q}$. Now if $p = 0$, then $x = 0$ and $0 \in S$, as S is a subring. If $p > 0$, then $p = 1 + 1 + \cdots + 1$ (p-times) and so $p \in S$. Again if $p < 0$, then $p = (-1) + (-1) + \cdots + (-1)$ ($|p|$-times). Thus $p \in S$. Similarly, $q \in S$ and since S is a subfield, $q^{-1} \in S$. But $q^{-1} = \frac{1}{q}$ in $\mathbb{Q}$. Thus $p, q^{-1} \in S$. Therefore $x = \frac{p}{q} = pq^{-1} \in S$. This implies that $\mathbb{Q} \subseteq S$. Hence $S = \mathbb{Q}$ which implies that $\mathbb{Q}$ has no proper subfields.

◇ **Exercise 12.3.6.** Let $\omega \neq 1$ be a root of $x^3 = 1$. Prove that $T = \{a + b\omega \in \mathbb{C} \mid a, b \in \mathbb{Q}\}$ is a subfield of the field $\mathbb{C}$.

Solution. We first note that $0 = 0 + 0\omega \in T$ and $1 = 1 + 0\omega \in T$. Thus $|T| \geq 2$. Next let $x, y \in T$. Then $x = a + b\omega$ and $y = c + d\omega$ for some $a, b, c, d \in \mathbb{Q}$. So $x - y = (a - c) + (b - d)\omega \in T$. Finally, for $y \neq 0$,

$$
\begin{aligned}
xy^{-1} &= (a + b\omega)(c + d\omega)^{-1} \\
&= \frac{a + b\omega}{c + d\omega} \\
&= \frac{(a + b\omega)(c + d\omega^2)}{(c + d\omega)(c + d\omega^2)} \\
&= \frac{ac + bc\omega + ad\omega^2 + bd}{c^2 + cd(\omega + \omega^2) + d^2} \\
&= \frac{(ac + bd - ad) + (bc - ad)\omega}{c^2 - cd + d^2} \\
&= \frac{ac + bd - ad}{c^2 - cd + d^2} + \frac{bc - ad}{c^2 - cd + d^2}\, \omega \in T.
\end{aligned}
$$

Note that since $c + d\omega \neq 0$, $c + d\omega^2 = \overline{c + d\omega} \neq 0$ and hence $c - cd + d^2 = (c + d\omega)(c + d\omega^2) \neq 0$. Therefore by Theorem 12.3.18, T is a subfield of $\mathbb{C}$.

◇ **Exercise 12.3.7.** Which one of the following is a subring of $\mathbb{Z}[i]$?
(i) $A = \{a + bi \in \mathbb{Z}[i] : a \text{ and } b \text{ are even integers}\}$.
(ii) $B = \{a + bi \in \mathbb{Z}[i] : a \geq 0\}$.
(iii) $C = \{a + bi \in \mathbb{Z}[i] : b \geq 0\}$.
(iv) $D = \{a + bi \in \mathbb{Z}[i] : a, b \geq 0\}$.

Solution. Clearly, $0 \in A$. Let $x = 2p + 2qi, y = 2u + 2vi \in A$. Then $x - y = 2(p - u) + 2(q - v)i \in A$ and $xy = 2(2up - 2vq) + 2(2vp + 2uq)i \in A$. Therefore, A is a subring of $\mathbb{Z}[i]$. Now $0, 2 + 3i \in B$, but $0 - (2 + 3i) = -2 - 3i \notin B$. Thus B is not a subring of $\mathbb{Z}[i]$. Similarly, one can check that C and D are also not subrings of $\mathbb{Z}[i]$. Hence option (i) is correct.

◇ **Exercise 12.3.8.** Which of the following is a subfield of the ring $M_2(\mathbb{R})$?

(i) $A = \left\{ \begin{pmatrix} a & 0 \\ b & c \end{pmatrix} : a, b, c \in \mathbb{R} \right\}$ (ii) $B = \left\{ \begin{pmatrix} a & b \\ -b & a \end{pmatrix} : a, b \in \mathbb{R} \right\}$

(iii) $C = \left\{ \begin{pmatrix} a & b \\ 0 & c \end{pmatrix} : a, b, c \in \mathbb{R} \right\}$ (iv) $D = \left\{ \begin{pmatrix} a & a \\ b & c \end{pmatrix} : a, b, c \in \mathbb{R} \right\}$.

Solution. One can check that B is a subfield of $M_2(\mathbb{R})$. Also, it is easy to verify that D is not closed under multiplication. Moreover, the inverse of the non-zero element $\begin{pmatrix} 1 & 0 \\ 0 & 0 \end{pmatrix}$ does not exist in A and C. Hence option (ii) is correct.

Exercises

1. In the ring $\mathbb{Z}$ of integers, find which of the subsets of $\mathbb{Z}$ are subrings:

   (i) The set of integers of the form $5k + 3$, $k \in \mathbb{Z}$.

   (ii) The set of integers of the form $5k$, $k \in \mathbb{Z}$.

   (iii) The set of integers of the form $5k + 1$, $k \in \mathbb{Z}$.

2. Which of the following subsets of $M_2(\mathbb{R})$ are subrings of the ring $(M_2(\mathbb{R}), +, \cdot)$? In case it is, check whether it has the same identity as the ring or not.

   (i) $A = \left\{ \begin{bmatrix} a & b \\ 0 & 0 \end{bmatrix} \mid a, b \in \mathbb{R} \right\}$

   (ii) $B = \left\{ \begin{bmatrix} 0 & 0 \\ 0 & r \end{bmatrix} \mid r \in \mathbb{R} \right\}$

   (iii) $C = \left\{ \begin{bmatrix} 1 & a \\ 0 & b \end{bmatrix} \mid a, b \in \mathbb{R} \right\}$

   (iv) $D = \left\{ \begin{bmatrix} a & b \\ c & d \end{bmatrix} \mid a, b, c, d \in \mathbb{Q} \right\}$.

3. Is $T = \left\{ \begin{bmatrix} a & a+b \\ a+b & b \end{bmatrix} \mid a, b \in \mathbb{R} \right\}$ a subring of $M_2(\mathbb{R})$?

4. In which of the following structures is S a subring of R?

   (i) $R = \mathbb{Q}$ and $S = \{ \frac{p}{q} \in \mathbb{Q} : 7 \nmid q \}$.

   (ii) Let R be the set of all real-valued functions on $\mathbb{R}$ and S be the set of all functions $f(x)$ of the form $a + b \cos nx + c \sin nx$, $a, b, c \in \mathbb{R}$, $n \in \mathbb{Z}$.

   (iii) $R = M_2(\mathbb{R})$ and S is a subset of R, consisting of the matrices of the form $\begin{bmatrix} a & b \\ -b & a \end{bmatrix}$.

   (iv) Let R be any ring and $a \in R$ be a fixed element. $S = \{x \in R | xa = ax\}$.

   (v) Let R be a ring and $a \in R$ be a fixed element. $S = \{x \in R : x \cdot a = 0\}$.

5. Let $R = \{(a, b, c, d) \mid a, b, c, d \in \mathbb{Q}\}$. Define for all (a, b, c, d), $(e, f, g, h) \in R$.

$$(a, b, c, d) + (e, f, g, h) = (a + e, b + f, c + g, d + h),$$
$$(a, b, c, d) \cdot (e, f, g, h) = (ae + bg, af + bh, ce + dg, cf + dh)$$

   Show that R is a noncommutative ring. If $S = \{(a, b, -b, a) \mid a, b \in \mathbb{Z}\}$, then prove that S is a commutative subring of R with the addition and multiplication as defined above.

6. Give an example of a subset S of $\mathbb{Z}$, which is closed under addition and multiplication, and which contains 0 and 1 but is not a subring of $\mathbb{Z}$.

7. If S is the set of all 2×2 matrices over $\mathbb{Z}$ of the form $\begin{bmatrix} a & b \\ 0 & c \end{bmatrix}$, then prove the following:

   (i) S is a subring of $M_2(\mathbb{Z})$.

   (ii) $\begin{bmatrix} a & b \\ 0 & c \end{bmatrix}^k = \begin{bmatrix} a^k & x \\ 0 & c^k \end{bmatrix}$ for some integer x and hence find the idempotent and nilpotent elements of S.

   (iii) the set of nilpotent elements of S forms a subring.

8. Find the smallest subring of $\mathbb{Z}$ containing 8.

9. Find all subrings of the ring $\mathbb{Z}$ of integers.

10. Find all subrings of $\mathbb{Z}_{10}$.

11. Find the smallest subring of $\mathbb{C}$ (the ring of complex numbers) which contains the real cube root of 3.

12. Show that a subring (with identity) of an integral domain is an integral domain.

13. † Find the centre of the ring $M_n(\mathbb{R})$.

14. Let R be a ring such that the equation $x^2 = 0$ has the only solution $x = 0$. Then prove that every idempotent of R is central.

15. Let R be a ring such that $x^2 - x \in C(R)$ for all $x \in R$. Prove that R is commutative.

16. † Let X be a nonempty subset of a ring R. Define

$$\begin{aligned} X_0 &= X \cup \{0\}, \\ X_{k+1} &= X_k \cup \{y \in R : y = a - b, \, a, b \in X_k\} \\ &\quad \cup \{z \in R : z = ab, \, a, b \in X_k\} \end{aligned}$$

for $k = 0, 1, 2, 3, \ldots$. Define $[X] = \bigcup\limits_{k=o}^{\infty} X_k$. Prove that $[X]$ is the smallest subring containing X (cf. Theorem 12.3.11).[12]

17. In the following, verify whether the subset S is a subfield of the field F:

   (i) $S = \mathbb{Z}$, $F = \mathbb{R}$.

   (ii) $S = \mathbb{Q}[\sqrt{3}] = \{a + b\sqrt{3} \in \mathbb{R} \mid a, b \in \mathbb{Q}\}$, $F = \mathbb{R}$.

   (iii) $S = \mathbb{Z}[i] = \{a + ib \in \mathbb{C} \mid a, b \in \mathbb{Z}, \, i^2 = -1\}$, $F = \mathbb{C}$.

   (iv) $S = \mathbb{Q}[i] = \{a + ib \in \mathbb{C} \mid a, b \in \mathbb{Q}, \, i^2 = -1\}$, $F = \mathbb{C}$.

   (v) $S = \{a + b\sqrt{2} \in \mathbb{R} \mid a, b \in \mathbb{Q} \text{ and } a, b \geqslant 0\}$, $F = \mathbb{R}$.

   (vi) $S = \{[0], [2], [4], [6], [8], [10]\}$, $F = \mathbb{Z}_{11}$.

18. Show that the field $\mathbb{Z}_p$ has no proper subfields.

19. Show that the field of real numbers has an infinite proper subfield but no finite subfields.

20. Does there exist a subfield S such that $\mathbb{R} \subset S \subset \mathbb{C}$?

21. Find a subfield S of $\mathbb{R}$ such that $\mathbb{Q} \subset S \subset \mathbb{R}$.

---

[12]From this construction, it is advisable to understand that the elements of $[X]$ are *all possible* finite sum (or difference) of (finite) products of the elements of X.

22. Prove that the characteristic of a subfield of a field is same as that of the field.

23. Prove that the intersection of all subfields of $\mathbb{R}$ is $\mathbb{Q}$.

24. Write the proof if the statement is correct or else give a counter example:

   (i) The ring $\mathbb{Z}_5$ is a subring of the ring $\mathbb{Z}_{10}$.

   (ii) The sum of two subfields of a field is a subfield of that field.

   (iii) The set $T = \{2^n \mid n \in \mathbb{Z}\}$ is a subfield of the field $\mathbb{Q}$.

   (iv) The ring $M_2(\mathbb{R})$ of all 2×2 real matrices contains a subring which is itself a field.

25. Which one of the following forms a field?

   (i) $A = \left\{ \begin{pmatrix} a & 0 \\ 0 & 0 \end{pmatrix} : a \in \mathbb{R} \right\}$,   (ii) $A = \left\{ \begin{pmatrix} a & 0 \\ 0 & b \end{pmatrix} : a, b \in \mathbb{R} \right\}$,

   (iii) $A = \left\{ \begin{pmatrix} a & b \\ 0 & 0 \end{pmatrix} : a, b \in \mathbb{R} \right\}$,   (iv) $A = \left\{ \begin{pmatrix} a & 0 \\ b & c \end{pmatrix} : a, b, c \in \mathbb{R} \right\}$.

26. Suppose $\mathbb{Z}_n$ is a ring under addition modulo n and multiplication modulo n, where $n = pm$ such that p is a prime and $gcd(p, m) = 1$. Show that $m\mathbb{Z}_n$ is a subring of $\mathbb{Z}_n$. Find $|m\mathbb{Z}_n|$ and also find the unity of $m\mathbb{Z}_n$.

Chapter 13

Ideals and Homomorphisms of Rings

Often it has happened in the history of the development of mathematical ideas, that an intriguing problem with a deceptively simple look was posed by someone and immediately some solutions were suggested, only to be found incorrect or inadequate in due course of time. Gradually, the depth of the problem became apparent and then the masters in that area from all over the places engaged themselves in finding a solution to it, but still the solution eluded them for decades and even for centuries! However, in every such instance, almost without exception, the subject as such was immensely enriched with their masterly approach from various corners, and several new and powerful concepts of mathematics were born. One classical example is the concept of the *ideal* of a ring that plays the central role in analyzing and understanding the structure of a ring.

In 1637, while reading a copy of Diophantus' *Arithmetica*, through Bachet's translation, the French politician and scholar Pierre de Fermat (1601-1665), mentioned in the margin of the book that *if n is an integer greater than 2, then there exist no positive integers x, y, z such that $x^n + y^n = z^n$*. He had emphatically noted further that he had "*assuredly found an admirable proof*" of this theorem, but unfortunately the "*margin is too narrow to contain it*". This result is referred to as the **Fermat's Last Theorem** (FLT, in brief). The stage was set and many a great mathematician tried his hand in solving the problem[1]. Among others, Ernst Edward Kummer(1810-1893), the then professor of mathematics in the University of Breslau, in 1843 thought that he

---

[1]It was finally settled after about 360 years, by Andrew Wiles (1953-) of Princeton University. In the 1998 ICM at Berlin, this effort brought special laurels to Wiles. The reader may refer to Appendix E for further details on FLT.

had found a proof of this result, which eventually was proved to be inadequate, in the sense that it was true for a particular class of prime numbers only. But he continued the effort and in the process he introduced the concept of *ideal complex numbers*, by means of which he was able to restore the unique factorization in a structure where the fundamental theorem of arithmetic does not hold[2]. His idea[3] eventually motivated Richard Dedekind (1831-1891) to define the concept of an *ideal of a ring*. Kronecker (1823-1891) also played a very significant role in the development of the ring theory.

13.1 Ideals and Quotient Rings

It is a very common experience to all of us that multiplication of an even integer with any integer always produces an even integer. Going further, we see that the same thing happens to the set of all multiples of a fixed positive integer. Suppose n is a positive integer. Let $n\mathbb{Z}$ be the set of all multiples of n in the ring of integers, $\mathbb{Z}$. Take any integer m and any $nz \in n\mathbb{Z}$. Then $mnz \in n\mathbb{Z}$. Certainly, this set $n\mathbb{Z}$ is a subring of $\mathbb{Z}$. Now the above fact shows that it is something more. It is a subring with a special condition that it absorbs elements of the ring under multiplication.

This now leads to the following definition of subrings with the special property mentioned above.

Definition 13.1.1. Let R be a ring. A subring I is called a **left [right] ideal** of R, if for all $r \in R$ and for all $x \in I$, $rx \in I$ [resp. $xr \in I$]. If I is a left ideal as well as a right ideal of R, then I is called a **two-sided ideal** or simply an **ideal** of R.

Certainly, there is no distinction between left and right ideals in the case of commutative rings. We have already shown that in the ring $\mathbb{Z}$, for any integer n, $n\mathbb{Z}$ is an ideal of $\mathbb{Z}$.

Example 13.1.2. Consider the ring $M_2(\mathbb{Z})$. Let

$$I_1 = \left\{ \begin{bmatrix} a & 0 \\ b & 0 \end{bmatrix} \mid a, b \in \mathbb{Z} \right\},$$

$$I_2 = \left\{ \begin{bmatrix} a & b \\ 0 & 0 \end{bmatrix} \mid a, b \in \mathbb{Z} \right\},$$

---

[2]For an English translation of the original German paper on ideal complex numbers, interested readers may refer to *A Source Book in Mathematics* by David Eugene Smith.

[3]In the language of Professor E.T.Bell, "*Kummer's introduction of ideals into arithmetic was, beyond all dispute, one of the greatest mathematical advances of the nineteenth century.*"

$$I_3 = \left\{ \begin{bmatrix} a & c \\ b & d \end{bmatrix} \mid a, b, c \text{ and } d \text{ are even integers} \right\},$$

and

$$I_4 = \left\{ \begin{bmatrix} a & 0 \\ 0 & 0 \end{bmatrix} \mid a \in \mathbb{Z} \right\}.$$

Since $\begin{bmatrix} 0 & 0 \\ 0 & 0 \end{bmatrix} \in I_1$, $I_1 \neq \emptyset$. Let $\begin{bmatrix} a & 0 \\ b & 0 \end{bmatrix}, \begin{bmatrix} c & 0 \\ d & 0 \end{bmatrix} \in I_1$ and $\begin{bmatrix} x & y \\ z & w \end{bmatrix} \in M_2(\mathbb{Z})$. Then,

$$\begin{bmatrix} a & 0 \\ b & 0 \end{bmatrix} - \begin{bmatrix} c & 0 \\ d & 0 \end{bmatrix} = \begin{bmatrix} a-c & 0 \\ b-d & 0 \end{bmatrix} \in I_1$$

and

$$\begin{bmatrix} x & y \\ z & w \end{bmatrix} \begin{bmatrix} a & 0 \\ b & 0 \end{bmatrix} = \begin{bmatrix} xa+yb & 0 \\ za+wb & 0 \end{bmatrix} \in I_1,$$

proving thereby that I_1 is a left ideal of $M_2(\mathbb{Z})$. Now $\begin{bmatrix} 1 & 0 \\ 1 & 0 \end{bmatrix} \in I_1$ and $\begin{bmatrix} 0 & 1 \\ 0 & 0 \end{bmatrix} \in M_2(\mathbb{Z})$, but

$$\begin{bmatrix} 1 & 0 \\ 1 & 0 \end{bmatrix} \begin{bmatrix} 0 & 1 \\ 0 & 0 \end{bmatrix} = \begin{bmatrix} 0 & 1 \\ 0 & 1 \end{bmatrix} \notin I_1.$$

Hence I_1 is not a right ideal of $M_2(\mathbb{Z})$. Similarly, I_2 is a right ideal of $M_2(\mathbb{Z})$ but not a left ideal, I_3 is an ideal of $M_2(\mathbb{Z})$ and I_4 is a subring but not an ideal of $M_2(\mathbb{Z})$.

Before giving some other important examples, we must note that every ring R has at least one ideal, namely, $\{0\}$ which is called the **zero ideal** and is denoted by (0). Certainly R is an ideal of itself and any nontrivial ring R $(R \neq \{0\})$ has at least two ideals, (0) and R. These two ideals are called **trivial ideals** and any ideal other than these two is called **nontrivial**. A left [right, two-sided] ideal I of R is called **proper**, if $I \neq R$.

Example 13.1.3. Let R be a ring. Define $2R = \{2x \mid x \in R\}$ and verify that $2R$ is an ideal of R. In general, $nR = \{nx \mid x \in R\}$, $(n \in \mathbb{N})$ [4] is an ideal of R.

Example 13.1.4. Let R be a ring and $S = R \times R$. Then $R \times \{0\}$ and $\{0\} \times R$ are ideals of S. Also, for any left [right, two-sided] ideals I_1 and I_2 of R, $I_1 \times I_2$ is a left [resp. right, two-sided] ideal of S. In fact, if R has an identity, then the only left [right, two-sided] ideals of S are of this type. (prove!)

---

[4]Recall that $nx = x + x + \cdots + x$ (n number of x added together)

Example 13.1.5. Consider the polynomial ring[5] $\mathbb{R}[x]$ over the field $\mathbb{R}$ of all reals. Let I be the set of all polynomials whose constant terms are zero, i.e.,

$$I = \left\{ a_0 + a_1 x + a_2 x^2 + \cdots + a_n x^n \mid a_i \in \mathbb{R}, \ a_0 = 0, \ n \in \mathbb{Z}_0^+ \right\}.$$

Then I is an ideal of $\mathbb{R}[x]$.

In view of Theorem 12.3.7 and Definition 13.1.1, it follows that a necessary and sufficient condition for a nonempty set I to be an ideal of a ring R is

$$a, b \in I, \ r \in R \implies a - b, \ ra, \ ar \in I. \tag{13.1.1}$$

Theorem 13.1.6. *Let R be a ring and $\{I_\alpha \mid \alpha \in \Lambda\}$ be a collection of left [right, two-sided] ideals of R. Then $I = \bigcap\limits_{\alpha \in \Lambda} I_\alpha$ is a left [resp. right, two-sided] ideal of R.*

Proof. Let $\{I_\alpha \mid \alpha \in \Lambda\}$ be a collection of left ideals of R. Since each I_α is a subring of R, by Theorem 12.3.10, we have that I is a subring of R. Let $x \in I$ and $r \in R$. Then $x \in I_\alpha$ and hence $rx \in I_\alpha$ for each $\alpha \in \Lambda$ since I_α is a left ideal of R. Thus $rx \in I$. This implies that I is a left ideal of R. The proof for right ideals and two-sided ideals are similar. $\qquad\square$

As usual, union of ideals may not be an ideal. Indeed, $2\mathbb{Z}$ and $3\mathbb{Z}$ are ideals of $\mathbb{Z}$, but $2\mathbb{Z} \cup 3\mathbb{Z}$ is not.

Definition 13.1.7. Let R be a ring. Let I and J be two ideals of R. Define $I + J = \{a + b \mid a \in I, \ b \in J\}$ and

$$IJ = \left\{ \sum_{i=1}^{n} a_i b_i \mid a_i \in I, \ b_i \in J, \ n \in \mathbb{N} \right\}.[6]$$

Theorem 13.1.8. *Let R be a ring and I, J be two ideals of R. Then $I + J$ and IJ are ideals of R. Moreover, $IJ \subseteq I \cap J$ and $I \cup J \subseteq I + J$. Indeed $I + J$ is the smallest ideal containing $I \cup J$.*

Proof. Let $a, c \in I$, $b, d \in J$ and $r \in R$. Then $(a+b) - (c+d) = (a-c) + (b-d) \in I+J$ and $r(a+b) = ra + rb \in I+J$ since I and J are ideals of R. Similarly, $(a+b)r \in I+J$ and so $I + J$ is an ideal of R.

---

[5]You will come to know about the ring of polynomials more formally in Chapter 15. However, to appreciate this example your present knowledge of polynomials should suffice.

[6]Though the addition of ideals is a set addition, the product is not a set product. It consists of all finite sums of elements of the set product.

Again, since $-(ab) = a(-b) \in IJ$ for any $a \in I$ and $b \in J$, it is a routine to verify that the difference of any two elements of IJ belongs to IJ. Further note that $r(ab) = (ra)b$ and $(ab)r = a(br)$ are products of elements of I and J as $ra \in I$ and $br \in J$. Then simple application of distributive laws proves that for each $r \in R$ and $x \in IJ$, $rx, xr \in IJ$. Thus IJ is an ideal of R.

Now since I and J are ideals of R, we have $IJ \subseteq I \cap J$. Again for any element $a \in I$, $a = a + 0 \in I + J$. So $I \subseteq I + J$. Similarly $J \subseteq I + J$. Thus $I \cup J \subseteq I + J$. Finally, let K be any ideal of R containing both I and J. Then obviously $I + J \subseteq K$, proving that $I + J$ is the smallest ideal of R containing $I \cup J$. $\square$

For a given set X of R, the smallest ideal containing X is the intersection of all ideals of R containing X. This ideal is called the ideal **generated** by X and is denoted by (X). If X is finite, then (X) is called **finitely generated**. The same is true for left and right ideals also.

Now, what is the smallest ideal which contains a fixed element? Naturally, the answer is that, it is the intersection of all ideals containing that element. Then how does it look like?

Theorem 13.1.9. *Let R be a ring and $x \in R$. Denote the smallest ideal containing x by (x). Then*

$$(x) = \left\{ rx + xs + \sum_{i=1}^{m} s_i x t_i + nx \mid r, s, s_i, t_i \in R;\ m \in \mathbb{N},\ n \in \mathbb{Z} \right\}.^{7}$$

If R has an identity, then

$$(x) = \left\{ \sum_{i=1}^{m} s_i x t_i \mid s_i, t_i \in R;\ m \in \mathbb{N} \right\}$$

and if R is a commutative ring with identity, then

$$(x) = Rx = \{ rx \mid r \in R \}.$$

We leave the proof as an exercise to the reader.

Definition 13.1.10. The ideal (x) of a ring R as described above is called the **principal ideal** generated by the element $x \in R$.

Definition 13.1.11. A ring R with identity is called a **principal ideal ring** if every ideal of R is a principal ideal. An integral domain in which every ideal is a principal ideal is called a **principal ideal domain**, (**PID**, in brief).

---

[7]If n is a negative integer, then by nx we mean $(-n)(-x)$ and by $0x$ we mean 0.

Example 13.1.12. Consider the ring $\mathbb{Z}$ of all integers. It has been shown in Worked-out Exercise 5.1.4 that all the subgroups of $\mathbb{Z}$ are of the form $n\mathbb{Z}$, for $n = 0, 1, 2, \ldots$ It can be shown that these are ideals of the ring $\mathbb{Z}$. Thus it follows that the ideals of $\mathbb{Z}$ are precisely $n\mathbb{Z} = (n)$, where $n = 0, 1, 2, \ldots$ Hence $\mathbb{Z}$ is a PID.

Note that, in a ring R with identity, $R = (1)$ and hence for any ideal I of R, $1 \in I$ if and only if $I = R$. Thus in this case R has trivial ideals (0) and (1). So next we raise the question as to what are the rings which have only trivial ideals?

Definition 13.1.13. A ring R is called *simple* if $R^2 \neq \{0\}$ and R has no nontrivial ideals.

Theorem 13.1.14. *A commutative ring R with identity is simple if and only if R is a field.*

Proof. Let R be a field. Since $1 \neq 0$ in R, we find that $R^2 \neq \{0\}$. Let $I \neq (0)$ be any ideal of R. Then there exists $a \in I$ such that $a \neq 0$ and hence $1 = a^{-1}a \in I$ which implies $r = r1 \in I$ for all $r \in R$. Hence $R \subseteq I$. But $I \subseteq R$. Therefore $I = R$. Hence R is simple.

Conversely, let R be a commutative simple ring with identity. In order to show that R is a field, we show that each nonzero element $0 \neq a \in R$ is a unit. Let $a \in R \setminus \{0\}$. Consider the ideal (a) of R. Certainly $(a) \neq (0)$. Since R is simple, it follows that $(a) = R$ and so $1 \in (a)$. Since R is commutative, $(a) = Ra$. Hence there exists $r \in R$ such that $ra = 1$. Since R is commutative, we have $ar = 1$, proving that a is a unit in R. Hence R is a field. $\square$

It is *not* always true that a simple ring with identity is a division ring, as the ring of matrices $M_n(K)$ over a field K is such an example. That $M_n(K)$ is simple, follows from the facts that, ideals of $M_n(K)$ must be of the form $M_n(I)$, where I is an ideal of K (cf. Worked-out Exercise 13.1.9) and K is simple. However, if R has no nontrivial left ideals (or equivalently no nontrivial right ideals) and has an identity, then it is a division ring (cf. Worked-out exercise 13.1.11).

Ideals play almost the same role in the theory of rings as normal subgroups do in the theory of groups. Let I be an ideal of a ring R. Then I is a subring of R and also $RI \subseteq I$, and $IR \subseteq I$. Since $(R, +)$ is an Abelian group, I is a normal subgroup of the group $(R, +)$. Consequently by Theorem 5.4.5, there is a well-defined quotient group R/I, elements of which are the cosets $r + I, r \in R$ and the binary operation, addition is defined by $(a+I)+(b+I) = (a+b)+I$ for all $a, b \in R$. In fact, R/I becomes a ring.

Theorem 13.1.15. *Let R be a ring and I be an ideal of R. Define the sets $a + I = \{a + x \mid x \in I\}$ for each $a \in R$ and $R/I = \{a + I \mid a \in R\}$. Then R/I forms a ring with addition and multiplication defined by*

$$(a + I) + (b + I) = (a + b) + I \quad and \quad (a + I)(b + I) = ab + I \qquad (13.1.2)$$

for all $a, b \in R$.

Proof. First we show that the binary operations defined in (13.1.2) are well-defined. Let $a_1, a_2, b_1, b_2 \in R$ be such that $a_1 + I = a_2 + I$ and $b_1 + I = b_2 + I$. Then $a_1 = a_1 + 0 = a_2 + i_1$ for some $i_1 \in I$. Similarly, $b_1 = b_2 + i_2$ for some $i_2 \in I$. Thus $a_1 + b_1 = a_2 + b_2 + i_1 + i_2 \in (a_2 + b_2) + I$, which implies that $(a_1 + b_1) + I \subseteq (a_2 + b_2) + I$. Similar arguments show that $(a_2 + b_2) + I \subseteq (a_1 + b_1) + I$, i.e., $(a_1 + b_1) + I = (a_2 + b_2) + I$, as required.

Again $a_1 b_1 = a_2 b_2 + i_1 b_2 + a_2 i_2 + i_1 i_2 \in a_2 b_2 + I$, as I is a (two-sided) ideal of R. Then $a_1 b_1 + I \subseteq a_2 b_2 + I$. Similarly we have $a_2 b_2 + I \subseteq a_1 b_1 + I$, proving that $a_1 b_1 + I = a_2 b_2 + I$. Thus both the operations defined in (13.1.2) are well-defined.

Now it is a routine matter to verify that both the operations are associative and that multiplication distributes over addition. Also the addition is commutative. Moreover $I \, (= 0 + I)$ acts as the zero element and for each $a + I \in R/I$, $(-a) + I = -(a + I)$. All these simple verifications are left to the reader. But what follows from them is the fact that R/I is a ring under the operations defined above. $\qquad \square$

Definition 13.1.16. Let R be a ring and I be an ideal of R. Then the ring R/I of the above theorem is called the **quotient ring** or **factor ring** of R by I.

Let us now look at some examples of quotient ring.

Example 13.1.17. Consider the ring $\mathbb{Z}$. In this ring, $5\mathbb{Z} = \{5k \mid k \in \mathbb{Z}\}$ is an ideal of $\mathbb{Z}$. Then $\mathbb{Z}/5\mathbb{Z} = \{n + 5\mathbb{Z} \mid n \in \mathbb{Z}\}$. Now $\mathbb{Z}/5\mathbb{Z}$ is a ring where addition and multiplication are defined by

$$(n + 5\mathbb{Z}) + (m + 5\mathbb{Z}) = (n + m) + 5\mathbb{Z}$$

and

$$(n + 5\mathbb{Z})(m + 5\mathbb{Z}) = nm + 5\mathbb{Z}.$$

This ring is the quotient ring of $\mathbb{Z}$ by the ideal $5\mathbb{Z}$. Now $\mathbb{Z}$ is a commutative ring with identity. Hence $\mathbb{Z}/5\mathbb{Z}$ is also a commutative ring with identity. In group-theory, we have seen that the number of distinct cosets in $\mathbb{Z}/5\mathbb{Z}$ is five, which are $0 + 5\mathbb{Z}, 1 + 5\mathbb{Z}, 2 + 5\mathbb{Z}, 3 + 5\mathbb{Z}, 4 + 5\mathbb{Z}$. Hence this is a ring with five elements.

Example 13.1.18. Consider the ring $\mathbb{Z} \times \mathbb{Z}$ (cf. Example 12.1.8). Let $I = \{(n, 0) \mid n \in \mathbb{Z}\}$. Then I is an ideal of $\mathbb{Z} \times \mathbb{Z}$. The elements of the quotient ring $(\mathbb{Z} \times \mathbb{Z})/I$ of the ring $\mathbb{Z} \times \mathbb{Z}$ by the ideal I are the cosets $(n, m) + I$, $(n, m) \in \mathbb{Z} \times \mathbb{Z}$ and the operations of addition and multiplication are defined by

$$\Big((n, m) + I\Big) + \Big((r, t) + I\Big) = (n + r, m + t) + I$$

and

$$\Big((n, m) + I\Big)\Big((r, t) + I\Big) = (nr, mt) + I.$$

Let n, m be two distinct integers. Then $(0, n), (0, m) \in \mathbb{Z} \times \mathbb{Z}$. If $(0, n) + I = (0, m) + I$ then

$$(0, n) - (0, m) \in I$$
$$\Rightarrow \quad (0, n - m) \in I$$
$$\Rightarrow \quad n - m = 0$$
$$\Rightarrow \quad n = m.$$

So, we find that $(0, n) + I \neq (0, m) + I$ when $n \neq m$. Hence the quotient ring $(\mathbb{Z} \times \mathbb{Z})/I$ is an infinite ring.

Theorem 13.1.19. *If R is a commutative ring with identity $1 \neq 0$ and I be a proper ideal of R, then the quotient ring R/I is also a commutative ring with identity (different from zero).*

Proof. Let $x, y \in R/I$. Then there are $a, b \in R$ such that $x = a + I$ and $y = b + I$. Now,

$$xy = (a + I)(b + I) = ab + I = ba + I = (b + I)(a + I) = yx.$$

Therefore R/I is commutative.

Next, for any $x = a + I \in R/I$, we have $(a + I)(1 + I) = a \cdot 1 + I = a + I$. Similarly, $(1 + I)(a + I) = a + I$. Thus $1 + I$ is the identity of R/I. Now since I is a proper ideal of R, $1 \notin I$ and so $0 + I \neq 1 + I$. This completes the proof. $\qquad \square$

Recall that in Definition 5.4.11 we have defined a congruence relation on a group and established its relationship with normal subgroups of that group. Following is the ring theoretic counterpart of that result.

Definition 13.1.20. Let R be a ring. An equivalence relation ρ on R is called a ***congruence relation on the ring*** R if $a \rho b$ implies $c + a \rho c + b$, $ca \rho cb$ and $ac \rho bc$ for all $a, b, c \in R$.

Theorem 13.1.21. *Let R be a ring.*

(i) If I is an ideal of R, then the relation ρ_I on R defined by $a\,\rho_I\,b$ if and only if for all $a, b \in R$, $a - b \in I$ is a congruence relation on R. For each $r \in R$, the ρ_I class of r is the coset $r + I$.

(ii) If ρ is a congruence on R, then $I = \rho(0)$ is an ideal of R, where $\rho(0)$ denotes the ρ congruence class containing the zero element 0 [which is the identity of the group $(R, +)$] and $\rho = \rho_I$.

Proof. (i) It can be shown easily that ρ_I is an equivalence relation on R. Let $a, b \in R$ such that $a\,\rho_I\,b$. Then $a - b \in I$. Let $c \in R$. Now $(c + a) - (c + b) = a - b \in I$, $ca - cb = c(a - b) \in I$ and $ac - bc = (a - b)c \in I$, as I is an ideal of R. Thus $a\,\rho_I\,b$ implies $c + a\,\rho_I\,c + b$, $ca\,\rho_I\,cb$ and $ac\,\rho_I\,bc$ for all $a, b, c \in R$. Hence the relation ρ_I is a congruence relation on R and ρ_I class of r is

$$\{a \in R \mid r\rho_I a\} = \{a \in R \mid r - a \in I\} = \{a \in R \mid a \in r + I\} = r + I.$$

(ii) Let ρ be a congruence on R. Suppose $a, b \in \rho(0)$. Then $a\rho0$ and $b\rho0$. Now $a - b\rho0 - b$ and $-b\rho0$. Thus $a - b\rho0$. Hence $a - b \in \rho(0)$. Now for any $a \in \rho(0)$, it follows that $a\rho0$. Hence for any $r \in R$, $ra\rho0$, $ar\rho0$. Hence $ra, ar \in \rho(0)$. It follows that $\rho(0)$ is an ideal of R.

Finally we show that the congruence relation ρ_I defined by the ideal $I = \rho(0)$ is identical with ρ. Let $a\,\rho_I\,b$ for $a, b \in R$. Then $a - b \in I = \rho(0)$. Hence $a - b\rho0$. This implies $b + (a - b)\rho b + 0$, i.e., $a\rho b$. Hence $\rho_I \subseteq \rho$. Suppose now $a\rho b$. Then $a - b\rho b - b = 0$. Hence $a - b \in \rho(0) = I$. This shows that $a\,\rho_I\,b$. Consequently $\rho \subseteq \rho_I$. Therefore $\rho_I = \rho$. $\square$

Remark 13.1.22. From the above theorem, it follows that there exists a one-to-one correspondence between the set of all ideals of a ring R and the set of all congruences on R. It is worth pointing out that since a Field is free from non-trivial ideals, there is no non-trivial congruence relation on a field.

Worked-out Exercises

◊ **Exercise 13.1.1.** Show that the set

$$I = \{a + b\sqrt{3} \in \mathbb{Z}[\sqrt{3}] \mid a - b \text{ is an even integer}\}$$

is an ideal in the ring $\mathbb{Z}[\sqrt{3}] = \{a + b\sqrt{3} \mid a, b \in \mathbb{Z}\}$.

Solution. Since $5+3\sqrt{3} \in I$, $I \neq \emptyset$. Let $x = a_1+b_1\sqrt{3}, y = a_2+b_2\sqrt{3}$ and $r = a_3+b_3\sqrt{3}$ be elements of $\mathbb{Z}[\sqrt{3}]$ such that $x, y \in I$. Then a_1-b_1 and a_2-b_2 are even integers. Hence $(a_1 - a_2) - (b_1 - b_2) = (a_1 - b_1) - (a_2 - b_2)$ is an even integer and so, $x - y = (a_1 - a_2) + (b_1 - b_2)\sqrt{3} \in I$. Again $rx = (a_3 + b_3\sqrt{3})(a_1 + b_1\sqrt{3}) = (a_3a_1 + 3b_3b_1) + (a_3b_1 + b_3a_1)\sqrt{3}$ and $a_3a_1 + 3b_3b_1 - (a_3b_1 + b_3a_1) = a_3(a_1 - b_1) + 2b_3b_1 + b_3(b_1 - a_1)$. Since $a_1 - b_1$ is an even integer, it follows that $(a_3a_1 + 3b_3b_1) - (a_3b_1 + b_3a_1)$ is an even integer. Hence $rx \in I$. Since $\mathbb{Z}[\sqrt{3}]$ is commutative, $xr \in I$. Hence I is an ideal of $\mathbb{Z}[\sqrt{3}]$.

$\diamondsuit$ **Exercise 13.1.2.** Consider the ring of integers, $\mathbb{Z}$. Prove that every ideal of $\mathbb{Z}$ is of the form $n\mathbb{Z} = (n)$ for some nonnegative integer n. Suppose a and b be two positive integers. Show that $(a) + (b) = (d)$ and $(a) \cap (b) = (c)$, where $d = \gcd(a, b)$ and $c = \text{lcm}(a, b)$.

Solution. We first verify that $n\mathbb{Z}$ is an ideal of the commutative ring $\mathbb{Z}$ for any non-negative integer n. Since $n = n \cdot 1 \in n\mathbb{Z}$, $n\mathbb{Z} \neq \emptyset$. Let $a, b \in n\mathbb{Z}$, $r \in \mathbb{Z}$. Then $a = nz_1$, $b = nz_2$ for some $z_1, z_2 \in \mathbb{Z}$. Thus $a - b = nz_1 - nz_2 = n(z_1 - z_2) \in n\mathbb{Z}$ and $ra = rnz_1 = nz_1r \in n\mathbb{Z}$ which imply that $n\mathbb{Z}$ is an ideal of $\mathbb{Z}$.

Conversely, let I be an ideal of $\mathbb{Z}$. If $I = \{0\}$, then $I = 0\mathbb{Z} = (0)$. So let $I \neq \{0\}$. Let $0 \neq n \in I$. Then $-n \in I$, as I is an ideal of $\mathbb{Z}$. Thus $|n| \in I$, i.e., I contains a positive integer. Let n_0 be the least positive integer contained in I. We show that $I = n_0\mathbb{Z}$. Since $n_0 \in I$, we have $n_0\mathbb{Z} \subseteq I$. Let $m \in I$. Let $m = n_0q+r$ for some integers q and r such that either $r = 0$ or $0 < r < n_0$. Now $r = m - n_0q \in I$ as $m, n_0 \in I$. Thus if $r > 0$, then $r \nless n_0$, since n_0 is the least positive integer contained in I. Therefore we have $r = 0$ and so $m = n_0q \in n_0\mathbb{Z}$. Then $I \subseteq n_0\mathbb{Z}$ and hence $I = n_0\mathbb{Z}$, as required.

Now suppose that a and b be two positive integers, $d = \gcd(a, b)$ and $c = \text{lcm}(a, b)$. Since $d \mid a$ and $d \mid b$, it is clear that $a, b \in (d)$ and so $(a) + (b) \subseteq (d)$. Also since $d = \gcd(a, b)$, there are two integers x and y such that $d = ax + by$. Thus $d \in (a) + (b)$ which implies that $(d) \subseteq (a) + (b)$. Therefore $(a) + (b) = (d)$.

Again since $a \mid c$ and $b \mid c$, we have $c \in (a) \cap (b)$. So $(c) \subseteq (a) \cap (b)$. Let $x \in (a) \cap (b)$, then $a \mid x$ and $b \mid x$. Since $c = \text{lcm}(a, b)$, we have $c \mid x$. Thus $x \in (c)$ which implies that $(a) \cap (b) \subseteq (c)$. Therefore $(a) \cap (b) = (c)$.

$\diamondsuit$ **Exercise 13.1.3.** Let R be a ring with identity. Show that a subset I of $R \times R$ is an ideal of R if and only if $I = I_1 \times I_2$ for some ideals I_1 and I_2 of R.

Solution. It is easy to check that $I_1 \times I_2$ is an ideal of $R \times R$, where I_1 and I_2 are ideals of R. Indeed, let $(a, b), (c, d) \in I_1 \times I_2$ and $(x, y) \in R \times R$. Then since I_1 is an ideal of R, $a - c, xa, ax \in I_1$. Similarly, $b - d, by, yb \in I_2$. Thus $(a - c, b - d), (xa, yb), (ax, by) \in I_1 \times I_2$, proving that $I_1 \times I_2$ is an ideal of $R \times R$.

Next, let I be an ideal of $R \times R$. Further let us consider $I_1 = \{a \in R \mid (a, b) \in I\}$ and $I_2 = \{b \in R \mid (a, b) \in I\}$. We show that I_1 and I_2 are ideals of R and $I = I_1 \times I_2$. Let $a_1, a_2 \in I_1$ and $r \in R$. Then there are $b_1, b_2 \in R$ such that $(a_1, b_1), (a_2, b_2) \in I$. Thus $(a_1 - a_2, b_1 - b_2) = (a_1, b_1) - (a_2, b_2) \in I$. Also $(ra_1, 0) = (r, 0)(a_1, b_1) \in I$. Similarly, $(a_1r, 0) \in I$. Therefore $a_1 - a_2, ra_1, a_1r \in I_1$. This implies that I_1 is an ideal of R. Similarly, verify that I_2 is an ideal of R.

Now for any $(a, b) \in I$, we have $a \in I_1$ and $b \in I_2$, that is $(a, b) \in I_1 \times I_2$. So $I \subseteq I_1 \times I_2$. Let $a \in I_1$ and $b \in I_2$. Then there are $c, d \in R$ such that $(a, c), (d, b) \in I$. This implies that $(a, 0) = (1, 0)(a, c) \in I$ and $(0, b) = (0, 1)(d, b) \in I$ since I is an ideal of $R \times R$. Then $(a, b) = (a, 0) + (0, b) \in I$ which implies that $I_1 \times I_2 \subseteq I$. Hence $I = I_1 \times I_2$ as required.

$\Diamond$ **Exercise 13.1.4.** Let R be a ring such that R has no zero divisors. If any subring of R is an ideal of R, then prove that R is commutative.

Solution. First note that $a \cdot 0 = 0 \cdot a = 0$ for all $a \in R$. Suppose $a \in R \smallsetminus \{0\}$. Consider the set $C(a) = \{x \in R \mid ax = xa\}$. We show that $C(a)$ is a subring of R. Since $a \in C(a)$, we have $C(a) \neq \emptyset$. Let $x, y \in C(a)$. Then $ax = xa$ and $ay = ya$. Then $a(x - y) = ax - ay = xa - ya = (x - y)a$ and $axy = xay = xya$ which implies that $x - y, xy \in C(a)$. Thus $C(a)$ is a subring of R and hence by the given condition, $C(a)$ is an ideal of R. Let $r \in R$. Then $ra \in C(a)$ as $a \in C(a)$. Then $ara = raa$ which implies that $(ar - ra)a = 0$. Since $a \neq 0$ and R has no zero divisor, we have $ar - ra = 0$, i.e., $ar = ra$. Thus a commutes with every element of R. Also, since a was chosen arbitrarily, R is commutative.

$\Diamond$ **Exercise 13.1.5.** Let R be a ring and $S \subseteq R$ be nonempty. Define

$$\mathrm{Ann}_l(S) = \{a \in R \mid ax = 0 \text{ for all } x \in S\},$$

which is called the **left annihilator** of S in R. Show that $\mathrm{Ann}_l(S)$ is a left ideal of R. Moreover if S is a left ideal of R, then prove that $\mathrm{Ann}_l(S)$ is an ideal of R.

Solution. Certainly $0 \in \mathrm{Ann}_l(S)$ and so $\mathrm{Ann}_l(S)$ is nonempty. Let $a, b \in \mathrm{Ann}_l(S)$ and $r \in R$. Then $ax = bx = 0$ for all $x \in S$. This implies that $(a - b)x = ax - bx = 0$ and $(ra)x = r(ax) = r \cdot 0 = 0$. Thus $\mathrm{Ann}_l(S)$ is a left ideal of R.

Suppose S be a left ideal of R. Let $a \in \mathrm{Ann}_l(S), r \in R$. Then $rx \in S$ for all $x \in S$ and so $(ar)x = a(rx) = 0$. Thus, in this case, $ar \in \mathrm{Ann}_l(S)$ and hence $\mathrm{Ann}_l(S)$ becomes an ideal of R.

◊ **Exercise 13.1.6.** Show that for each positive integer $n > 1$, $\mathbb{Z}_n$ is a PIR.

Solution. Let I be an ideal of $\mathbb{Z}_n = \{[0], [1], [2], \ldots, [n-1]\}$. Let i be the least positive integer such that $[i] \in I$. We show that I is generated by $[i]$, i.e., $I = ([i])$. Since $[i] \in I$, we have $([i]) \subseteq I$. On the other hand, let $[a] \in I$. Let $q, r \in \mathbb{Z}$ such that $a = qi + r$ where $r = 0$ or $0 < r < i$. Since $[i] \in I$, we have $[qi] = [q][i] \in I$ and so $[r] = [a - qi] = [a] - [qi] \in I$. Then by the choice of i in I, $r = 0$. So $[a] = [q][i] \in ([i])$. Therefore $I \subseteq ([i])$, i.e., $I = ([i])$. Hence $\mathbb{Z}_n$ is a PIR.

◊ **Exercise 13.1.7.** Prove that the polynomial ring $\mathbb{Q}[x]$ over the field of rational numbers is a PID.[8]

Solution. Let I be an ideal of $\mathbb{Q}[x]$. If $I = \{0\}$, then $I = (0)$. So let $I \neq \{0\}$. Again if I contains a nonzero constant, say q, then $1 = qq^{-1} \in I$ and so $I = \mathbb{Q}[x] = (1)$. Suppose I does not contain any nonzero constant. Let $f(x)$ be a polynomial in I with the least degree, say $m > 0$. We show that $I = (f(x))$. Obviously, $(f(x)) \subseteq I$ as $f(x) \in I$. Let $g(x) \in I$. If $g(x) = 0$, then $g(x) \in (f(x))$. Otherwise, we use induction on $\deg g(x)$ to show that $g(x) \in (f(x))$. Since $g(x) \in I$, we have $\deg g(x) \geq m$, by choice of f. Let

$$g(x) = a_0 + a_1 x + a_2 x^2 + \cdots + a_n x^n, \quad a_n \neq 0,$$
$$f(x) = b_0 + b_1 x + b_2 x^2 + \cdots + b_m x^m, \quad b_m \neq 0, \ (n \geq m).$$

Now (from school algebra)[9] dividing $g(x)$ by $f(x)$, we find the polynomials $q(x)$ and $r(x)$ in $\mathbb{Q}[x]$ such that $g(x) = q(x)f(x) + r(x)$ where either $r(x) = 0$ or $\deg r(x) < \deg f(x)$.

Now $q(x)f(x) \in I$ and $g(x) \in I$. Hence $r(x) = g(x) - q(x)f(x) \in I$. If $r(x) \neq 0$, I contains a polynomial $r(x)$ such that $\deg r(x) < \deg f(x)$. This contradicts the choice of $f(x)$. Hence $r(x) = 0$. Therefore $g(x) = q(x)f(x) \in (f(x))$. Hence $I = (f(x))$. Therefore $\mathbb{Q}[x]$ is a PID.

◊ **Exercise 13.1.8.** Prove that $M_2(\mathbb{R})$, the ring of all 2×2 matrices over the field of real numbers is simple.

Solution. Let I be an ideal of $M_2(\mathbb{R})$ such that $I \neq \left\{ \begin{bmatrix} 0 & 0 \\ 0 & 0 \end{bmatrix} \right\}$. We show that $I = M_2(\mathbb{R})$. Let $A = \begin{bmatrix} a & b \\ c & d \end{bmatrix} \in I$ where at least one of a, b, c, d is nonzero. Now verify that

$$\begin{bmatrix} a & b \\ c & d \end{bmatrix} \begin{bmatrix} 0 & 1 \\ 1 & 0 \end{bmatrix} = \begin{bmatrix} b & a \\ d & c \end{bmatrix}, \quad \begin{bmatrix} 0 & 1 \\ 1 & 0 \end{bmatrix} \begin{bmatrix} a & b \\ c & d \end{bmatrix} = \begin{bmatrix} c & d \\ a & b \end{bmatrix}$$

---

[8]Later in Theorem 15.1.12 we shall see that such a polynomial ring over any field is a PID.
[9]For a detailed and general proof see Theorem 15.1.12.

and $\begin{bmatrix} c & d \\ a & b \end{bmatrix} \begin{bmatrix} 0 & 1 \\ 1 & 0 \end{bmatrix} = \begin{bmatrix} d & c \\ b & a \end{bmatrix}$. Thus $\begin{bmatrix} b & a \\ d & c \end{bmatrix}, \begin{bmatrix} c & d \\ a & b \end{bmatrix}, \begin{bmatrix} d & c \\ b & a \end{bmatrix} \in I$, whence without any

loss of generality we may assume: $a \neq 0$. But then $\begin{bmatrix} 1 & 0 \\ 0 & 0 \end{bmatrix} = \begin{bmatrix} a^{-1} & 0 \\ 0 & 0 \end{bmatrix} \begin{bmatrix} a & b \\ c & d \end{bmatrix} \begin{bmatrix} 1 & 0 \\ 0 & 0 \end{bmatrix}$

$\in I$. Also since $\begin{bmatrix} d & c \\ b & a \end{bmatrix} \in I$, we have $\begin{bmatrix} 0 & 0 \\ 0 & 1 \end{bmatrix} = \begin{bmatrix} 0 & 0 \\ 0 & 1 \end{bmatrix} \begin{bmatrix} d & c \\ b & a \end{bmatrix} \begin{bmatrix} 0 & 0 \\ 0 & a^{-1} \end{bmatrix} \in I$. So

finally, we get $\begin{bmatrix} 1 & 0 \\ 0 & 1 \end{bmatrix} = \begin{bmatrix} 1 & 0 \\ 0 & 0 \end{bmatrix} + \begin{bmatrix} 0 & 0 \\ 0 & 1 \end{bmatrix} \in I$. Hence $I = M_2(\mathbb{R})$, as I is an ideal of

$M_2(\mathbb{R})$ which contains the identity. Therefore $M_2(\mathbb{R})$ is simple.

♦ **Exercise 13.1.9.** Let R be a ring with identity. Consider the ring of matrices, $M_n(R)$. Show that any ideal I of $M_n(R)$ is of the form $M_n(T)$ for some ideal T of R. Hence show that if R is a field, then $M_n(R)$ is simple.

Solution. Let E_{ij} be the $n \times n$ matrix in which the (i, j)-th. entry is 1 and all other entries are zero. Then we can write $(a_{ij}) = \sum_{i,j=1}^{n} a_{ij} E_{ij}$ and it can be easily verified that

$$E_{ij} E_{kl} = \delta_{jk} E_{il}, \quad \text{where } \delta_{jk} = \begin{cases} 0, & \text{if } j \neq k \\ 1, & \text{if } j = k. \end{cases}$$

Let I be an ideal of $M_n(R)$. Suppose $T = \{a \in R \mid a = a_{11} \text{ for some } (a_{ij}) \in I\}$. Since $I \neq \emptyset$, T is also nonempty. Clearly, if $a, b \in T$, then $a - b \in T$. Suppose $a \in T$ and $r \in R$. The $a = a_{11}$ for some $(a_{ij}) = \sum_{i,j=1}^{n} a_{ij} E_{ij} \in I$. Since I is an ideal,

$$raE_{11} = rE_{11}\left(\sum_{i,j=1}^{n} a_{ij} E_{ij}\right) E_{11} \in M,$$

$$arE_{11} = E_{11}\left(\sum_{i,j=1}^{n} a_{ij} E_{ij}\right) rE_{11} \in M.$$

Hence $ra, ar \in T$. Thus T is an ideal of R.

Let $A = (a_{ij}) = \sum_{r,s=1}^{n} a_{rs} E_{rs} \in I$. We have to show that $A \in M_n(T)$. Let $1 \leq i, j \leq n$. Now, $E_{1i}\left(\sum_{r,s=1}^{n} a_{rs} E_{rs}\right) E_{j1} = \sum_{r,s=1}^{n} a_{rs} E_{1i} E_{rs} E_{j1} = \sum_{r,s=1}^{n} a_{rs} \delta_{ir} E_{1s} E_{j1} = \sum_{r,s=1}^{n} a_{rs} \delta_{ir} \delta_{sj} E_{11} = a_{ij} E_{11}$. Hence $a_{ij} E_{11} \in I$. Therefore $a_{ij} \in T$. This implies that $A \in M_n(T)$. Thus $I \subseteq M_n(T)$.

Conversely, let $A = (a_{ij}) = \sum_{i,j=1}^{n} a_{ij}E_{ij} \in M_n(T)$. We show that $A \in I$. Since $a_{ij} \in T$, there exists $B = (b_{rs}) \in I$ such that $b_{11} = a_{ij}$. Then $E_{i1}BE_{1j} \in I$. Now,

$$
E_{i1}BE_{1j} = E_{i1}\left(\sum_{r,s=1}^{n} b_{rs}E_{rs}\right)E_{1j} = \sum_{r,s=1}^{n} b_{rs}E_{i1}E_{rs}E_{1j}
$$
$$
= \sum_{r,s=1}^{n} b_{rs}\delta_{1r}E_{is}E_{1j} = \sum_{r,s=1}^{n} b_{rs}\delta_{1r}\delta_{s1}E_{ij}
$$
$$
= b_{11}E_{ij} = a_{ij}E_{ij}.
$$

Thus $a_{ij}E_{ij} \in I$ and so $\sum_{i,j=1}^{n} a_{ij}E_{ij} \in I$ as I is an ideal. This implies that $A \in I$ as required. Therefore $I = M_n(T)$.

Now if R is a field, then R has only two ideals, namely, (0) and R itself. Thus by the above deduction, $M_n(R)$ also has only two ideals (the zero ideal and the whole ring), i.e., $M_n(R)$ is simple.

◊ **Exercise 13.1.10.** Let R be a commutative ring such that R has no nontrivial ideals. Then show that either R is a field or R is a finite ring with prime number of elements and $ab = 0$ for all $a, b \in R$.

Solution. Since R^2 denotes the set of all finite sums $a_1b_1 + a_2b_2 + \ldots + a_nb_n$ such that $a_i, b_i \in R$, and $n \in \mathbb{N}$, it is easy to check that R^2 is an ideal of R. Then either $R^2 = (0)$ or $R^2 = R$. If $R^2 = (0)$, then $ab = 0$ for all $a, b \in R$. In this case, every subgroup of $(R, +)$ is an ideal of R. But then $(R, +)$ has no nontrivial subgroup. So $(R, +)$ is a cyclic group of prime order.

On the other hand, suppose $R^2 = R$. Let $a \in R$, $a \neq 0$. Consider the ideal Ra. Now $Ra = (0)$ or R. Since $R^2 \neq (0)$, there is at least one $a \in R \setminus \{0\}$ such that $Ra \neq (0)$. Then for this element, $Ra = R$. So there exists $e \in R$ so that $ea = a$. Also for any $r \in R$, $r = xa$ for some $x \in R$. But then $re = xae = xa = r$. Since R is commutative, it follows that e is the identity of R. Therefore, R is a simple commutative ring with identity. Hence R is a field by Theorem 13.1.14.

◊ **Exercise 13.1.11.** Let R be a ring with identity $1 \neq 0$ such that R has no nontrivial left ideal. Show that R is a division ring.

Solution. Let $a \in R \setminus \{0\}$. Consider the left ideal Ra. By the given condition, we have $Ra = (0)$ or R. Now $a = 1 \cdot a \in Ra$ and $a \neq 0$. So $Ra = R$. Then there exists $b \in R$ such that $ba = 1$. Since $b \neq 0$ (for otherwise $0 = 1$), arguing as before, we get $xb = 1$ for some $x \in R$. Now $x = x \cdot 1 = xba = 1 \cdot a = a$. Therefore we have $ab = ba = 1$ which implies that a is a unit and so R is a division ring.

◊ **Exercise 13.1.12.** Let R be ring. An ideal I of R is called a *nil ideal* if every element of I is nilpotent. Prove the following:

(i) The ideal $I = \{[0], [4]\}$ in the ring $\mathbb{Z}_8$ is a nil ideal.

(ii) If R is a commutative ring and N is the set of all nilpotent elements of R, then N is a nil ideal and the quotient ring R/N has no nonzero nilpotent elements.

(iii) The sum of two nil ideals of a commutative ring is again a nil ideal.

Solution. (i) Since $[4]^2 = [16] = [0]$, we have that I is a nil ideal of $\mathbb{Z}_8$.

(ii) Since $0 \in N$, $N \neq \emptyset$. Let $x, y \in N$ and $r \in R$. Then there are positive integers m, n such that $x^m = y^n = 0$. Then by Theorem 12.1.21, $(x + y)^{m+n} = 0$. Also $(-y)^n$ is either y^n or $-y^n$, according as n is even or odd, whence $(-y)^n = 0$, and since R is commutative, $(xr)^m = x^m r^m = 0$ and $(rx)^m = r^m x^m = 0$. Thus $x - y, rx, xr \in N$ which implies that N is an ideal of R. Let $u \in R/N$ such that $u^k = 0_{R/N} = N$ for some integer $k > 0$. If $u = a + N$, then $a^k + N = N$ which implies that $a^k \in N$. Then $(a^k)^q = 0$ for some positive integer q. Thus $a^{kq} = 0$ and so $a \in N$. This implies that $u = a + N = N = 0_{R/N}$. Therefore R/N has no nonzero nilpotent element.

(iii) Let I and J be two nil ideals of R. Let $a \in I + J$. Then $a = b + c$ where $b \in I$ and $c \in J$. Since I and J are nil ideals, b and c are nilpotent elements. Then by Theorem 12.1.21, $a = b + c$ is also nilpotent as R is commutative. Therefore all elements of $I + J$ are nilpotent. Hence $I + J$ is a nil ideal.

◊ **Exercise 13.1.13.** Define $A = \{r \in R : r^n \in I \text{ for some positive integer } n\}$, where I is an ideal of a commutative ring R. Prove that A is an ideal of R.

Solution. Clearly $A \neq \emptyset$, as $0 \in A$. To show A is an ideal of R, let $a, b \in A$ and $c \in R$. Then there exist positive integers m and n such that $a^m \in I$ and $b^n \in I$. Now

$$
\begin{aligned}
(a - b)^{m+n} &= a^{m+n} - \binom{m+n}{1}a^{m+n-1}b + \cdots + (-1)^r \binom{m+n}{r} a^{m+n-r} b^r + \cdots + \\
&\qquad\qquad (-1)^{m+n} b^{m+n} \\
&= a^m \left\{ a^n - \binom{m+n}{1} a^{n-1} b + \cdots + (-1)^n \binom{m+n}{n} b^n \right\} + \\
&\qquad \left\{ (-1)^{n+1} \binom{m+n}{n+1} a^{m-1} b + \cdots + (-1)^{m+n} b^m \right\} b^n \\
&\in I.
\end{aligned}
$$

Hence $a - b \in A$.

Again $(ca)^m = c^m a^m \in I$. Hence A is a left ideal of R. Since R is commutative, it follows that A is an ideal of R.

◊ **Exercise 13.1.14.** Let R be a commutative ring with 1 and I, J be two ideals of R such that $I + J = R$. Prove that $IJ = I \cap J$.

Solution. Clearly $IJ \subseteq I \cap J$, as both I and J are ideals of the ring R.

To show the reverse inclusion, let $a \in I \cap J$. Now $1 \in R = I + J$ implies $1 = i + j$ for some $i \in I$ and $j \in J$. Then $a = a \cdot 1 = a(i + j) = a \cdot i + a \cdot j = i \cdot a + a \cdot j \in IJ$. Hence $I \cap J \subseteq IJ$ and consequently, $I \cap J = IJ$.

◊ **Exercise 13.1.15.** Consider the ring $R = M_2(\mathbb{Z})$ of all 2×2-matrices with integer entries and its subset S given by $S = \left\{ \begin{pmatrix} a & 0 \\ 0 & a \end{pmatrix} : a \in \mathbb{Z} \right\}$. Find the correct statement.

(i) S is a subring of R but not an ideal of R.
(ii) S is an ideal of R.
(iii) S is neither a subring nor an ideal of R.
(iv) S is an ideal of R but not a subring of R.

Solution. Let $A = \begin{pmatrix} a & 0 \\ 0 & a \end{pmatrix}$ and $B = \begin{pmatrix} b & 0 \\ 0 & b \end{pmatrix}$ be two elements of S, where $a, b \in \mathbb{Z}$.

Then $A - B = \begin{pmatrix} a - b & 0 \\ 0 & a - b \end{pmatrix}$ and $AB = \begin{pmatrix} ab & 0 \\ 0 & ab \end{pmatrix}$. Hence S is a subring of R.

Now, $\begin{pmatrix} 1 & 1 \\ 1 & 1 \end{pmatrix} \in R$ and $\begin{pmatrix} 1 & 0 \\ 0 & 1 \end{pmatrix} \in S$ but, $\begin{pmatrix} 1 & 1 \\ 1 & 1 \end{pmatrix} \begin{pmatrix} 1 & 0 \\ 0 & 1 \end{pmatrix} = \begin{pmatrix} 1 & 1 \\ 1 & 1 \end{pmatrix} \notin S$.

Thus S is not an ideal of R. Hence option (i) is correct.

◊ **Exercise 13.1.16.** Which of the following statement is true?
(i) The set of all nilpotent elements in a ring forms an ideal of the ring.
(ii) In a commutative ring, the set of all nilpotent elements forms an ideal of the ring.
(iii) The set of all nilpotent elements in a ring forms a subring of the ring.
(iv) In a commutative ring, the set of all nilpotent elements may not form an ideal of the ring.

Solution. By Exercise 13.1.12, it follows that in a commutative ring, the set of all nilpotent elements forms an ideal of the ring. We now cite an example to ensure that this result is not true in general if the ring is noncommutative. Consider the non-commutative ring $R = M_2(\mathbb{R})$, the ring of all 2×2-matrices with real entries. Here $A = \begin{pmatrix} 0 & 1 \\ 0 & 0 \end{pmatrix}$ and $B = \begin{pmatrix} 0 & 0 \\ 1 & 0 \end{pmatrix}$ are two nilpotent elements of R, but the sum $A + B = \begin{pmatrix} 0 & 1 \\ 1 & 0 \end{pmatrix}$ is not nilpotent as we have

$$(A + B)^n = \begin{cases} \begin{pmatrix} 0 & 1 \\ 1 & 0 \end{pmatrix}, & \text{if } n \text{ is odd} \\ \begin{pmatrix} 1 & 0 \\ 0 & 1 \end{pmatrix}, & \text{if } n \text{ is even.} \end{cases}$$

Hence option (ii) is correct.

◇ **Exercise 13.1.17.** Which of the following statement is true?

(i) Quotient ring of an integral domain is always an integral domain.

(ii) Quotient ring of an integral domain is always a field.

(iii) Quotient ring of an integral domain may not be an integral domain.

(iv) Quotient ring of an integral domain contains no nontrivial ideals.

Solution. We consider the integral domain $\mathbb{Z}$ and its one ideal $6\mathbb{Z}$. Then the corresponding quotient ring $\mathbb{Z}/6\mathbb{Z} \simeq \mathbb{Z}_6$ which is neither a field nor an integral domain. Moreover, $\mathbb{Z}/6\mathbb{Z} \simeq \mathbb{Z}_6$ contains nontrivial ideals $\{[0], [2], [4]\}$ and $\{[0], [3]\}$. Hence option (iii) is correct.

Exercises

1. In each of the following cases decide whether I is an ideal of the ring R. Justify your answer.

   (a) $R = \mathbb{Z} \times \mathbb{Z}, I = \{(3n, 8m) \mid n, m \in \mathbb{Z}\}$

   (b) $R = \mathbb{Z}, I = 9\mathbb{Z}$

   (c) $R = \mathbb{Z}[\sqrt{2}] = \{a + b\sqrt{2} \mid a, b \in \mathbb{Z}\}, I = \{b\sqrt{2} \mid b \in \mathbb{Z}\}$

   (d) $R = \mathbb{Z} \times \mathbb{Z}, I = \{(a, a) \mid a \in \mathbb{Z}\}]$

   (e) $R = M_2(\mathbb{Z}), I = \left\{ \begin{bmatrix} 0 & b \\ 0 & d \end{bmatrix} \mid b, d \in \mathbb{Z} \right\}$

   (f) $R = \mathbb{Z} \times \mathbb{Z}, I = \{(a, 0) \mid a \in \mathbb{Z}\}$.

2. In the ring $\mathbb{Z}[\sqrt{2}]$, show that the subset $I = \{a + b\sqrt{2} \mid a, b \in \mathbb{Z} \text{ and } a \text{ is an even integer}\}$ is an ideal.

3. Show that the set I of all integers is a subring of the ring $\mathbb{Q}$ but I is not an ideal of $\mathbb{Q}$.

4. Let $\mathbb{Z}[i\sqrt{5}] = \{a + bi\sqrt{5} \in \mathbb{C} \mid a, b \in \mathbb{Z}\}$ and

$$I = \left\{ a + bi\sqrt{5} \in \mathbb{Z}[i\sqrt{5}] \mid a - b \text{ is a multiple of } 2 \right\}.$$

   Show that I is an ideal of the ring $\mathbb{Z}[i\sqrt{5}]$.

5. Find all ideals of the ring $\mathbb{Z}_8, \mathbb{Z}_5$ and $\mathbb{Z}_9$.

6. Let R be a ring. If A is a left ideal and B is a right ideal of R, then prove that AB is an ideal of R.

7. Let R be a commutative ring with identity and $a, b \in R$. Show that $I = \{ra + tb \mid r, t \in R\}$ is an ideal of R.

8. Let R be a ring. Prove that for each $a \in R$, Ra and aR are the left ideal and right ideal of R respectively. Moreover, if R has an identity, then show that Ra [aR] is the smallest left ideal [resp. right ideal] containing a.

9. Let R be a ring and I, J be two ideals of R. Show that $I \cup J$ is an ideal of R if and only if either $I \subseteq J$ or $J \subseteq I$.

10. Write all the distinct elements of the ring $\mathbb{Z}/4\mathbb{Z}$. Write the multiplication table for this ring.

11. Let $I = \left\{ \begin{bmatrix} a & b \\ c & d \end{bmatrix} \in M_2(\mathbb{Z}) \mid a, b, c, d \text{ are even integers} \right\}$. Show that I is an ideal of $M_2(\mathbb{Z})$. Find the number of elements of the quotient ring $M_2(\mathbb{Z})/I$.

12. Let $T = \left\{ \frac{a}{b} \in \mathbb{Q} \mid a \text{ and } b \text{ are relatively prime and } 5 \nmid b \right\}$. Show that T is a ring under the usual addition and multiplication. Also prove that $I = \left\{ \frac{a}{b} \in T \mid 5 \text{ divides } a \right\}$ is an ideal of T and the quotient ring T/I is a field.

13. Show that the set $12\mathbb{Z}$ is an ideal of the ring $3\mathbb{Z}$. Describe the quotient ring $3\mathbb{Z}/12\mathbb{Z}$.

14. Let I be an ideal of a ring R. Define

$$(R : I) = \{x \in R \mid rx \in I \text{ for all } r \in R\}.$$

Show that $(R : I)$ is an ideal of R.

15. Consider the ring $\mathbb{Z}_{48}$, the ring of integers modulo 48. Let $I = \{[r] \mid 4 \text{ divides } r\}$. Show that I is an ideal of $\mathbb{Z}_{48}$ and determine its **annihilator**[10], Ann(I) (cf. Worked-out Exercise 13.1.5).

16. In the ring $\mathbb{Z}[i]$, show that $I = \{a + ib \in \mathbb{Z}[i] \mid a \text{ and } b \text{ are even}\}$ is an ideal. Find $Ann\, I$.

17. Let X be an infinite set. Prove that $(\mathscr{P}(X), \triangle, \cap)$ is a Boolean ring[11] in which the collection of all finite subsets of X forms an ideal. Also show that for any $Y \subseteq X$, $\mathscr{P}(Y)$ and $\mathscr{P}(X \setminus Y)$, both are principal ideals of $\mathscr{P}(X)$ with $\mathscr{P}(Y) \cap \mathscr{P}(X \setminus Y) = \{\emptyset\}$ and $\mathscr{P}(X) = \mathscr{P}(Y) + \mathscr{P}(X \setminus Y)$.

18. Let R be a commutative ring and I be an ideal of R. Define

$$\mathrm{Rad}I = \{r \in R \mid r^n \in I \text{ for some positive integer } n\}.[12]$$

Show that $\mathrm{Rad}I$ is an ideal of R containing I.

19. Prove that any integral domain with a finite number of ideals is a field.

20. † Show that the ring of matrices, $M_n(R)$ over a simple ring R with identity is simple.

21. † If R is a simple ring, prove that the characteristic of R is either prime or zero. Hence show that the characteristic of a division ring is either prime or zero.

---

[10]Since the concerned ring is commutative, we omit the term "left".

[11]The empty set $\emptyset$ is the zero element and the set X itself is the identity element of the ring respectively.

[12]$\mathrm{Rad}I$ is called the **radical** of the ideal I.

22. † Let R be a ring. An ideal I of R is called **nilpotent** if $I^n = \{0\}$ for some positive integer n. Prove that every nilpotent ideal is a nil ideal (cf. Worked-out Exercise 13.1.12).

23. † Let R be a ring. Prove that for any two ideals I and J of R, the following conditions are equivalent:

    (i) $IJ = (0) \implies I \cap J = (0)$;

    (ii) (0) is the only nilpotent ideal of R.

24. Let R be a ring and I be an ideal of R. Show that the quotient ring R/I is commutative if and only if $ab - ba \in I$ for all $a, b \in R$.

25. Find the correct statement from the following:

    (a) A field has no ideals.

    (b) A field has only two ideals.

    (c) A field has only one ideal.

    (d) An infinite field may contain an infinite number of ideals.

26. Let F be a field. Then the number of ideals of the ring $F \times F$ is

    (i) 0 (ii) 1 (iii) 2 (iv) 4

27. Find whether the following assertions are true or false. Justify your answer.

    (a) Let $I = \{a + bi \in \mathbb{Z}[i] \mid 2 \text{ divides } b\}$. Then I is an ideal of $\mathbb{Z}[i]$.

    (b) Let R be the ring of all continuous functions on $\mathbb{R}$, with pointwise operations. Then $I = \{f \in R \mid f(0) \text{ is an even integer}\}$ is an ideal of R.

    (c) Let I be an ideal of a ring R with identity such that I contains a unit element. Then $I = R$.

13.2 Homomorphisms

In group-theory, we have seen that one way to get some information about some group is to establish a connection with some other group by way of homomorphism. In this section, we shall extend this idea in the case of the ring-theory. Also from group-theory, we know that homomorphisms are characterized by normal subgroups, which are the kernels of homomorphisms and there is a one-to-one correspondence between the set of normal subgroups of a group and the set of homomorphisms defined on it. Likewise in the case of rings, we show that kernels of homomorphisms are ideals and here also the set of ideals of a ring corresponds bijectively with set of homomorphisms defined on the ring. Certainly, all these claims are subject to proof and we start doing that with the definition of homomorphism for rings.

Definition 13.2.1. Let R and S be two rings. A mapping $f : R \to S$ is called a *homomorphism* of R into S, if it satisfies the following:

   (i) $f(a+b) = f(a) + f(b)$,

   (ii) $f(ab) = f(a)f(b)$

for all $a, b \in R$. As usual, we call an injective [surjective] homomorphism a *monomorphism* [resp. *epimorphism*]. A bijective homomorphism is called an *isomorphism* and in this case we write $R \simeq S$. Any homomorphism of a ring R into itself is called an *endomorphism* and a bijective endomorphism is called an *automorphism*.

Example 13.2.2. Define a mapping $f : \mathbb{Z} \to \mathbb{Z}_n$ by $f(r) = [r]$ where $[r]$ denotes the equivalence class of r modulo n ($n \in \mathbb{N}$). Then by definition of addition and multiplication of $\mathbb{Z}_n$, it follows that for each $r, s \in \mathbb{Z}$, $f(r + s) = [r + s] = [r] + [s] = f(r) + f(s)$ and $f(rs) = [rs] = [r][s] = f(r)f(s)$ and hence f is a homomorphism of the ring $\mathbb{Z}$ onto the ring $\mathbb{Z}_n$.

Example 13.2.3. Let R be the ring of all real-valued continuous functions defined on $\mathbb{R}$ (cf. Worked Out Exercise 12.1.1). Define the mapping $\Phi : R \longrightarrow \mathbb{R}$ by $\Phi(f(x)) = f(0)$. Let $f(x), g(x) \in R$. Then,

$$\Phi((f+g)(x)) = (f+g)(0) = f(0) + g(0) = \Phi(f(x)) + \Phi(g(x));$$
$$\Phi((fg)(x)) = (fg)(0) = f(0)g(0) = \Phi(f(x)) \cdot \Phi(g(x)).$$

Therefore Φ is a homomorphism of R into $\mathbb{R}$. Also since constant functions are continuous, we have Φ is onto, i.e., an epimorphism.

Example 13.2.4. Consider the ring $\mathbb{Z}$. On $\mathbb{Z}$, define $f : \mathbb{Z} \to \mathbb{Z}$ by $f(n) = -n$. Let $n, m \in \mathbb{Z}$. Now $f(n+m) = -(n+m) = (-n)+(-m) = f(n)+f(m)$. This shows that f is a group homomorphism. Now $2, 3 \in \mathbb{Z}$ and $f(2 \cdot 3) = -(2 \cdot 3) \neq (-2)(-3) = f(2)f(3)$. Hence f is not a ring homomorphism.

Note that the mapping f in Definition 13.2.1 is a homomorphism of the abelian group $(R, +)$ into another abelian group $(S, +)$. Thus the following results follow immediately from the group-theory.

Theorem 13.2.5. *Let R and S be two rings and $f : R \to S$ be a homomorphism of R into S. Then,*

(i) $f(0_R) = 0_S$,

(ii) $f(-a) = -f(a)$ *and*

(iii) $f(a - b) = f(a) - f(b)$, *for all* $a, b \in R$.

Theorem 13.2.6. *Let R and S be two rings and $f : R \to S$ be a homomorphism of R into S. Then, the following assertions hold:*

(i) $f(R) = \{f(a) \mid a \in R\}$ is a subring of S;

(ii) If R is commutative, then so is the subring $f(R)$.

Moreover if R has an identity, then

(iii) $f(1_R) = 1_{f(R)}$.

Proof. Let $x, y \in f(R)$. Then $x = f(a)$ and $y = f(b)$ for some $a, b \in R$. Then $x - y = f(a) - f(b) = f(a - b)$, $xy = f(a)f(b) = f(ab)$. Also if R is commutative, then $xy = f(ab) = f(ba) = f(b)f(a) = yx$. So we have proved (i) and (ii). Now if R has an identity, then $x \cdot f(1_R) = f(a)f(1_R) = f(a \cdot 1_R) = f(a) = x$ and likewise $f(1_R) \cdot x = x$. Since this happens for all $x \in f(R)$, we have $f(1_R) = 1_{f(R)}$. $\qquad \square$

Remark 13.2.7. It is very important to understand that even if the rings R and S both have identities, then also $f(1_R)$ may *not* be equal to 1_S (cf. Example 13.2.14). However, equality holds in some special situations (e.g., if f is surjective).

Definition 13.2.8. Let R and S be two rings and $f : R \to S$ be a homomorphism of R into S. Then the set $\{x \in R \mid f(x) = 0_S\}$ is called the **kernel** of f and is denoted by $\ker f$.

In Example 13.2.2, the kernel of f is $n\mathbb{Z}$, which we know is an ideal of the ring $\mathbb{Z}$. The following theorem shows that kernels of homomorphisms defined on a ring are always ideals of the rings.[13]

Theorem 13.2.9. *Let R and S be two rings and $f : R \to S$ be a homomorphism of R into S. Then $\ker f$ is an ideal of R.*

Proof. First we note that $\ker f$ is nonempty as $0_R \in \ker f$, by Theorem 13.2.5(i). Let $x, y \in \ker f$ and $r \in R$. Then $f(x) = f(y) = 0_S$. Thus, $f(x - y) = f(x) - f(y) = 0_S$ which implies $x - y \in \ker f$. Again $f(rx) = f(r)f(x) = f(r) \cdot 0_S = 0_S$ and similarly $f(xr) = 0_S$. Thus, $rx, xr \in \ker f$. Therefore $\ker f$ is an ideal of R. $\qquad \square$

Example 13.2.10. Given any two rings R and S, there always exists a homomorphism of R into S which sends all the elements of R to the zero of S. This is called *trivial homomorphism*. In this case, $\ker f = R$. Otherwise a homomorphism is called *nontrivial*.

---

[13]Later on, we shall see that the converse of this statement also holds, i.e., every ideal of a ring is the kernel of some homomorphism defined on it (cf. Theorem 13.2.15).

On the other hand, the identity map ι_R on a ring R is an isomorphism of R onto itself and in this case $\ker \iota_R = \{0_R\}$.[14]

Theorem 13.2.11. *Let R and S be two rings. A homomorphism $f : R \to S$ is injective if and only if $\ker f = \{0_R\}$.*

Proof. If f is injective, then by definition, $\ker f = f^{-1}(0_S)$ is a singleton set and so by Theorem 13.2.5(i), it consists of only the zero element of R. Conversely, let $\ker f = \{0_R\}$. Let $x, y \in R$ be such that $f(x) = f(y)$. Then $f(x-y) = f(x) - f(y) = 0_S$ which implies that $x - y \in \ker f = \{0_R\}$. Thus $x = y$. Hence f is injective. $\qquad\square$

Therefore, a surjective homomorphism is an isomorphism if and only if its kernel is the zero ideal.

Example 13.2.12. Consider the ring of complex numbers, $\mathbb{C}$. Define $f : \mathbb{C} \to \mathbb{C}$ by $f(z) = \bar{z}$. Then for any $z_1, z_2 \in \mathbb{C}$, we have

$f(z_1 + z_2) = \overline{z_1 + z_2} = \overline{z_1} + \overline{z_2} = f(z_1) + f(z_2)$ and $f(z_1 z_2) = \overline{z_1 z_2} = \overline{z_1}\,\overline{z_2} = f(z_1)f(z_2)$, whence it follows that f is a homomorphism of $\mathbb{C}$ into itself. Moreover since $f(\bar{z}) = \bar{\bar{z}} = z$ for all $z \in \mathbb{C}$, f is surjective. Now $\ker f = \{z \in \mathbb{C} \mid \bar{z} = 0\} = \{0\}$. Thus f is an isomorphism on $\mathbb{C}$.

Example 13.2.13. Let $R[x]$ be the polynomial ring over a commutative ring R with identity. Define the mapping $\Phi : R[x] \to R$ by $\Phi\big(f(x)\big) = f(0)$. Verify that Φ is an epimorphism with $\ker \Phi = (x)$ which is the ideal I described in Example 13.1.5.

Example 13.2.14. Let us consider the mapping $f : \mathbb{Z} \to \mathbb{Z} \times \mathbb{Z}$ defined by $f(n) = (n, 0)$. Then f is a monomorphism with $\ker f = \{0\}$ and its image, $f(\mathbb{Z})$ is the subring $\mathbb{Z} \times \{0\}$. Note that $f(1) = (1, 0)$ which is not the identity of $\mathbb{Z} \times \mathbb{Z}$.

The following theorem shows that a quotient ring of a ring R by an ideal I of R is nothing but a homomorphic image of R where I is the kernel of the homomorphism.

Theorem 13.2.15. *Let R be a ring and I be an ideal of R. Define a mapping*

$$\phi : R \to R/I \quad by \quad \phi(a) = a + I \quad for \ all \ \ a \in R.$$

Then ϕ is an epimorphism[15] of R onto R/I with $\ker \phi = I$.

---

[14]For two rings $R \subseteq S$, the identity map on R (called ***inclusion map***) is a monomorphism of R into S.

[15]ϕ is called the ***canonical*** or ***natural epimorphism*** of R onto R/I.

Proof. Let $a, b \in R$. Then $\phi(a + b) = (a + b) + I = (a + I) + (b + I) = \phi(a) + \phi(b)$ and $\phi(ab) = (ab) + I = (a + I)(b + I) = \phi(a) \cdot \phi(b)$. This implies ϕ is a homomorphism. Also for any $x \in R/I$, $x = a + I = \phi(a)$ for some $a \in R$. Therefore ϕ is onto. Finally, $\ker \phi = \{a \in R \,|\, a + I = I\} = \{a \in R \,|\, a \in I\} = I$. $\qquad\square$

The converse is also true, i.e., any homomorphic image of a ring is a quotient ring of the given ring by the kernel of the homomorphism. This result is known as the **first isomorphism theorem**.[16]

Theorem 13.2.16. (First Isomprphism Theorem) *Let R and S be two rings and $f : R \to S$ be a ring homomorphism. Then $R/\ker f \simeq Imf$. Moreover, if $f : R \to S$ is an epimorphism, then $R/\ker f \simeq S$.*

Proof. Let $I = \ker f$. Define a mapping

$$\Psi : R/I \to Imf \text{ by } \Psi(a + I) = f(a).$$

We need to verify first that Ψ is well-defined. Let $a, b \in R$ be such that $a + I = b + I$. Then $a - b \in I = \ker f$. Therefore $f(a - b) = 0$. But this implies $f(a) - f(b) = 0$, i.e., $f(a) = f(b)$ and so $\Psi(a + I) = \Psi(b + I)$.

Now let $a, b \in R$. Then $\Psi\big((a + I) + (b + I)\big) = \Psi\big((a + b) + I\big) = f(a + b) = f(a) + f(b) = \Psi(a + I) + \Psi(b + I)$. Also $\Psi\big((a + I)(b + I)\big) = \Psi(ab + I) = f(ab) = f(a)f(b) = \Psi(a + I)\Psi(b + I)$. Thus Ψ is a homomorphism.

Next consider any $y \in Imf$. There exists $x \in R$ such that $f(x) = y$. Then $y = \Psi(x + I)$, proving that Ψ is onto. Finally,

$$
\begin{aligned}
\ker \Psi &= \{a + I \in R/I \,|\, \Psi(a + I) = 0_S\} \\
&= \{a + I \in R/I \,|\, f(a) = 0_S\} \\
&= \{a + I \in R/I \,|\, a \in I\} \qquad (\text{since } I = \ker f) \\
&= \{I\}
\end{aligned}
$$

Since $I = 0_{R/I}$, we have by Theorem 13.2.11, that Ψ is injective and hence Ψ is an isomorphism. Consequently, $R/\ker f \simeq Imf$.

Finally, if $f : R \to S$ is an epimorphism, then $Imf = S$ and hence $R/\ker f \simeq S$. $\quad\square$

The above two theorems establish the aforesaid bijective correspondence between the set of ideals in a ring and the set of homomorphisms that can be defined on it.

Now suppose I and J are two ideals of R. Hence $I + J$ is again an ideal of R and $J \subseteq I + J$. Since J is an ideal of R so is it of $I + J$, whence $(I + J)/J$ exists. Again J being an ideal of R, one can prove that $I \cap J$ is an ideal of I. Hence $I/(I \cap J)$ exists.

---

[16] Also called the **first homomorphism theorem** by some authors.

Theorem 13.2.17. (Second Isomorphism Theorem) *Let I and J be two ideals of a ring R. Then*

$$I/(I \cap J) \simeq (I + J)/J.$$

Proof. We define $\psi : I \longrightarrow (I + J)/J$ by $\psi(i) = i + J$ for all $i \in I$. To show ψ is a homomorphism, let $i_1, i_2 \in I$. Then $\psi(i_1 + i_2) = (i_1 + i_2) + J = (i_1 + J) + (i_2 + J) = \psi(i_1) + \psi(i_2)$ and $\psi(i_1 i_2) = i_1 i_2 + J = (i_1 + J)(i_2 + J) = \psi(i_1)\psi(i_2)$. Hence ψ is a ring homomorphism.

For the surjectivity of ψ, let $x + J \in (I+J)/J$. Then $x \in I+J$, i.e., $x = a+b$ for some $a \in I, b \in J$. Now, $x = a+b$ implies $a = x-b$. Also $\psi(a) = \psi(x-b) = (x-b)+J = x+J$ (since $b \in J$, it follows that $b + J = 0 + J$). Therefore, ψ is onto.

Hence by First Isomorphism theorem we have $I/\ker \psi \cong (I + J)/J$.

Now,
$$
\begin{aligned}
\ker \psi &= \{i \in I : \psi(i) = 0 + J\} \\
&= \{i \in I : i + J = 0 + J\} \\
&= \{i \in I : i \in J\} \\
&= I \cap J.
\end{aligned}
$$

Consequently, $I/(I \cap J) \cong (I + J)/J.$ ☐

Observe that, if I and J are two ideals of R, then R/I and R/J exist. Again, since J is an ideal of R containing I, it can be shown that J/I is an ideal of R/I. Hence $(R/I)/(J/I)$ exists.

Theorem 13.2.18. (Third Isomorphism Theorem) *Let I and J be two ideals of a ring R so that $I \subseteq J$. Then*

$$(R/I)/(J/I) \simeq R/J.$$

Proof. We define $\varphi : R/I \longrightarrow R/J$ by $\varphi(a + I) = a + J$,   for all $a + I \in R/I$.

Now, let $a + I, b + I \in R/I$ be such that $a + I = b + I$. Then $a - b \in I \subseteq J$. This implies $a + J = b + J$. Thus the mapping φ is well defined.

Now, let $x + I, y + I \in R/I$. Then
$$
\begin{aligned}
\varphi\big((x + I) + (y + I)\big) &= \varphi\big((x + y) + I\big) \\
&= (x + y) + J \\
&= (x + J) + (y + J) \\
&= \varphi(x + I) + \varphi(y + I)
\end{aligned}
$$

and

$$\varphi\big((x+I)(y+I)\big) = \varphi(xy+I)$$
$$= xy + J$$
$$= (x+J)(y+J)$$
$$= \varphi(x+I)\,\varphi(y+I).$$

Let $z + J \in R/J$. Then there exists $z + I \in R/I$ such that $\varphi(z+I) = z + J$. Thus φ is onto. Hence by First Isomorphism theorem, we have $(R/I)\big/\ker\varphi \cong R/J$.

Now,

$$\ker\varphi = \{a + I \in R/I : \varphi(a+I) = 0 + J\}$$
$$= \{a + I \in R/I : a + J = 0 + J\}$$
$$= \{a + I \in R/I : a \in J\}$$
$$= J/I.$$

Therefore, $(R/I)/(J/I) \cong R/J$. $\qquad\square$

Theorem 13.2.19. (Correspondence Theorem) *Let $f : R \to S$ be an epimorphism of a ring R onto a ring S. Let*

$$\mathcal{I} = \{I \mid I \text{ is an ideal of } R \text{ that contains } \ker f\}$$

and

$$\mathcal{J} = \{J \mid J \text{ is an ideal of } S\}.$$

Then the mapping $f^* : \mathcal{I} \to \mathcal{J}$ defined by $f^*(I) = f(I)$ for all $I \in \mathcal{I}$ is an inclusion preserving [17] bijective mapping.

Proof. Clearly, $f(I) \neq \emptyset$, since $0_S = f(0_R) \in f(I)$. To show $f(I)$ is an ideal of S, let $f(a), f(b) \in f(I)$ for some $a, b \in I$ and $s \in S$. Since f is onto, there exists an element $r \in R$ such that $s = f(r)$. Also as I is an ideal of R, it follows that $a - b, ra, ar \in I$. Now, $f(a) - f(b) = f(a - b) \in f(I)$ and $sf(a) = f(r)f(a) = f(ra) \in f(I)$. Similarly, one can show that $f(a)s \in f(I)$. Thus $f(I)$ is an ideal of S.

Conversely, let J be an ideal of S. We now show that $f^{-1}(J) = \{a \in R : f(a) \in J\}$ is an ideal of R containing $\ker f$. Since $f(0_R) = 0_S \in J$, it follows that $0_R \in f^{-1}(J)$ and thus $f^{-1}(J) \neq \emptyset$. To show $\ker f \subseteq f^{-1}(J)$, let $x \in \ker f$. Then $f(x) = 0_S \in J$ and thus $\ker f \subseteq f^{-1}(J)$. To show $f^{-1}(J)$ is an ideal, let $c, d \in f^{-1}(J)$ and $r \in R$. Then $f(c), f(d) \in J$ and $f(r) \in S$. Since J is an ideal of S, we have $f(c) - f(d), f(r)f(c), f(c)f(r) \in J$. This implies $f(c - d), f(rc), f(cr) \in J$, i.e., $c - d, rc, cr \in f^{-1}(J)$. Hence $f^{-1}(J)$ is an ideal of R containing $\ker f$.

---

[17] If ideals I_1 and I_2 of R correspond to ideals J_1 and J_2 of S respectively, then $I_1 \subseteq I_2$ implies $J_1 \subseteq J_2$.

We define $f^* : \mathcal{I} \longrightarrow \mathcal{J}$ by $f^*(I) = f(I)$, for all $I \in \mathcal{I}$.

Since for every ideal I of R, we have already proved that $f(I)$ is an ideal of S, it follows that f^* is well-defined.

To show f^* is injective, let $I_1, I_2 \in \mathcal{I}$ such that $f^*(I_1) = f^*(I_2)$, i.e., $f(I_1) = f(I_2)$. Let $i_1 \in I_1$. Then $f(i_1) \in f(I_1) = f(I_2)$. This implies $f(i_1) = f(i_2)$ for some $i_2 \in I_2$, i.e., $f(i_1 - i_2) = 0_S$, i.e., $i_1 - i_2 \in \ker f \subseteq I_2$. Again, since $i_2 \in I_2$, it follows that $i_1 = (i_1 - i_2) + i_2 \in I_2$. Thus, $I_1 \subseteq I_2$. Similarly, we can show that $I_2 \subseteq I_1$ and thus $I_1 = I_2$. Hence f^* is injective.

To show f^* is surjective, let $J \in \mathcal{J}$. Then J is an ideal of S and thus $f^{-1}(J)$ is an ideal of R containing $\ker f$. Hence $f^{-1}(J) \in \mathcal{I}$. We now show that $f^*\left(f^{-1}(J)\right) = J$, i.e., $f\left(f^{-1}(J)\right) = J$. For this, let $y \in f\left(f^{-1}(J)\right)$. Then $y = f(z)$ for some $z \in f^{-1}(J)$, i.e., $f(z) \in J$. Therefore, $y = f(z) \in J$. Thus $f\left(f^{-1}(J)\right) \subseteq J$. Again, let $v \in J$. Then $v \in S$. Since f is onto, there exists an element $u \in R$ such that $f(u) = v \in J$. This implies $u \in f^{-1}(J)$, i.e., $v = f(u) \in f\left(f^{-1}(J)\right)$. Therefore, $J \subseteq f\left(f^{-1}(J)\right)$. Hence $f\left(f^{-1}(J)\right) = J$. Thus, f^* is onto and consequently, f^* is bijective.

Finally we prove that f^* is inclusion preserving. For this let $I_1, I_2 \in \mathcal{I}$ such that $I_1 \subseteq I_2$. We show prove $f^*(I_1) \subseteq f^*(I_2)$, i.e., $f(I_1) \subseteq f(I_2)$. For this, let $y \in f(I_1)$. Then there exists $i_1 \in I_1$ such that $y = f(i_1)$. Now, $i_1 \in I_1 \subseteq I_2$ implies $y = f(i_1) \in f(I_2)$. Hence $f(I_1) \subseteq f(I_2)$. Thus f^* is inclusion preserving, as required. $\square$

Corollary 13.2.20. *Let R be a ring and I be an ideal of R. Then there exists an inclusion preserving bijection between the set of all ideals of R containing I and the set of all ideals of R/I.*

Worked-out Exercises

$\Diamond$ **Exercise 13.2.1.** Consider the rings $\mathbb{Z}$ and $\mathbb{Z}_6$. Let $f : \mathbb{Z} \to \mathbb{Z}_6$ be defined by $f(n) = [n]$ for all $n \in \mathbb{Z}$. Show that f is a homomorphism and find $\ker f$.

Solution. Let $n, m \in \mathbb{Z}$. Then $f(n+m) = [n+m] = [n] + [m] = f(n) + f(m)$, and $f(nm) = [nm] = [n][m] = f(n)f(m)$. Hence f is a homomorphism. Now

$$\begin{aligned} \ker f &= \{n \in \mathbb{Z} \mid f(n) = [0]\} \\ &= \{n \in \mathbb{Z} \mid [n] = [0]\} \\ &= \{n \in \mathbb{Z} \mid 6 \text{ divides } n\} \\ &= \{n \in \mathbb{Z} \mid n = 6k \text{ where } k \in \mathbb{Z}\} \\ &= 6\mathbb{Z}. \end{aligned}$$

◇ **Exercise 13.2.2.** Show that the mapping $f : \mathbb{Z}[\sqrt{2}] \to \mathbb{Z}[\sqrt{3}]$ defined by $f(a + b\sqrt{2}) = a + b\sqrt{3}$ is a group homomorphism but not a ring homomorphism.

Solution. Let $a + b\sqrt{2}, c + d\sqrt{2} \in \mathbb{Z}[\sqrt{2}]$. Then

$$
\begin{aligned}
f\big((a + b\sqrt{2}) + (c + d\sqrt{2})\big) &= f\big((a + c) + (b + d)\sqrt{2}\big) \\
&= (a + c) + (b + d)\sqrt{3} \\
&= (a + b\sqrt{3}) + (c + d\sqrt{3}) \\
&= f(a + b\sqrt{2}) + f(c + d\sqrt{2})
\end{aligned}
$$

Hence f is a group homomorphism. Clearly f is surjective. Hence $f(1) = 1$. Then $f(2) = f(1 + 1) = f(1) + f(1) = 2$. But $f(2) = f(\sqrt{2} \cdot \sqrt{2}) = f(\sqrt{2})f(\sqrt{2}) = f(0 + 1\sqrt{2})f(0 + 1\sqrt{2}) = (0 + 1\sqrt{3})(0 + 1\sqrt{3}) = 3$. This shows that f is not a ring homomorphism.

◇ **Exercise 13.2.3.** Show that the ring $2\mathbb{Z}$ is not isomorphic to $5\mathbb{Z}$.

Solution. Suppose, if possible, that there exists a ring isomorphism $f : 2\mathbb{Z} \to 5\mathbb{Z}$. Hence f is a group isomorphism of $(2\mathbb{Z}, +)$ onto $(5\mathbb{Z}, +)$. But $2\mathbb{Z}$ and $5\mathbb{Z}$ are both cyclic groups. 2 is a generator of $2\mathbb{Z}$. Hence $f(2)$ must be a generator of the group $5\mathbb{Z}$. Now we know that 5 and -5 are the only generators of $5\mathbb{Z}$. Consequently, $f(2) = 5$ or -5. Suppose $f(2) = 5$. Then $f(4) = f(2 + 2) = f(2) + f(2) = 5 + 5 = 10$ and $f(4) = f(2 \cdot 2) = f(2)f(2) = 5 \cdot 5 = 25$. This implies that $10 = 25$, which is absurd. If $f(2) = -5$, then proceeding in a similar way as above, we can arrive at another absurd conclusion. Hence there does not exist any ring isomorphism $f : 2\mathbb{Z} \to 5\mathbb{Z}$.

◇ **Exercise 13.2.4.** For any integer $n > 0$, prove that $\mathbb{Z}_n \simeq \mathbb{Z}/n\mathbb{Z}$.

Solution. Define the mapping $f : \mathbb{Z} \longrightarrow \mathbb{Z}_n$ by $f(a) = [a] \in \mathbb{Z}_n$. From the properties of congruence modulo n, it follows that $f(a + b) = [a + b] = [a] + [b] = f(a) + f(b)$ and $f(ab) = [ab] = [a][b] = f(a)f(b)$ for all $a, b \in \mathbb{Z}$. Thus f is a homomorphism. Clearly f is onto, as for each $[i] \in \mathbb{Z}_n$, $[i] = f(i)$. Therefore f is an epimorphism from $\mathbb{Z}$ onto $\mathbb{Z}_n$. Now $\ker f = \{a \in \mathbb{Z} \mid [a] = [0]\} = \{a \in \mathbb{Z} \mid a \equiv 0 \pmod{n}\} = \{a \in \mathbb{Z} \mid n \text{ divides } a\} = n\mathbb{Z}$. Then by the First Isomorphism theorem (Theorem 13.2.16), we have $\mathbb{Z}/n\mathbb{Z} \simeq \mathbb{Z}_n$.

◇ **Exercise 13.2.5.** Find all homomorphisms from the ring $\mathbb{Z}$ onto $\mathbb{Z}$.

Solution. Let $f : \mathbb{Z} \longrightarrow \mathbb{Z}$ be an epimorphism. Now we consider the ideal $\ker f$. If $1 \in \ker f$, then $f(1) = 0$ and thus $f(n) = 0$ for all $n \in \mathbb{Z}$. Hence in this case f is the zero mapping and thus f is not an epimorphism. Therefore, $1 \notin \ker f$. Now $f(1) = f(1 \cdot 1) = f(1)^2$ implies either $f(1) = 0$ or $f(1) = 1$. If $f(1) = 0$, then $1 \in \ker f$

and hence we arrive at a contradiction. Therefore, we must have $f(1) = 1$ and thus $f(n) = n$ for all $n \in \mathbb{Z}$. Hence, there is only one homomorphism from the ring $\mathbb{Z}$ onto itself, which is precisely the identity homomorphism.

◊ **Exercise 13.2.6.** Let R be a commutative ring with identity and $f : R \to S$ be an epimorphism of R onto a ring S. Prove that S is also a commutative ring with identity. If I and J are two ideals of R, then show that $f(I + J) = f(I) + f(J)$ and $f(IJ) = f(I)f(J)$.

Solution. Let $x, y \in S$. Since f is onto, we have $x = f(a)$ and $y = f(b)$ for some $a, b \in R$. Now

$$xy = f(a)f(b) = f(ab) = f(ba) = f(b)f(a) = yx$$

as f is a homomorphism and R is commutative. Thus S is a commutative ring.

Next we show that $f(1_R)$ is the identity of S. Let $x \in S$. Then there exists $a \in R$ such that $f(a) = x$. Now $xf(1_R) = f(a)f(1_R) = f(a1_R) = f(a) = x$. This implies that $f(1_R)$ is the identity of S.

Now let I and J be two ideals of R. Then for any $x \in f(I + J)$, there exists $a \in I + J$ such that $f(a) = x$. Again $a = b + c$ where $b \in I$ and $c \in J$. Thus $x = f(a) = f(b+c) = f(b)+f(c) \in f(I)+f(J)$ which implies that $f(I+J) \subseteq f(I)+f(J)$. Also since $I, J \subseteq I + J$, we have $f(I), f(J) \subseteq f(I+J)$. Then $f(I) + f(J) \subseteq f(I+J)$ as $f(I + J)$ is an ideal of S, by correspondence theorem (Theorem 13.2.19). Therefore $f(I) + f(J) = f(I + J)$.

Again, let $x \in f(I)$ and $y \in f(J)$. Then there exist $a \in I$ and $b \in J$ such that $x = f(a)$ and $y = f(b)$. So $xy = f(a)f(b) = f(ab) \in f(IJ)$. Thus

$$xy \in f(IJ) \text{ for all } x \in f(I) \text{ and for all } y \in f(J). \tag{13.2.1}$$

Now let $u \in f(I)f(J)$. Then $u = \sum_{i=1}^{n} x_i y_i$ where $x_i \in f(I)$, $y_i \in J$ for each $i = 1, 2, \ldots, n$, $(n \in \mathbb{N})$. So by (13.2.1), $u \in f(IJ)$ as $f(IJ)$ is an ideal of S. Thus $f(I)f(J) \subseteq f(IJ)$.

Conversely, let $u \in f(IJ)$. Then there exists $v \in IJ$ so that $f(v) = u$. Now $v = \sum_{i=1}^{n} a_i b_i$ for some $a_i \in I$, $b_i \in J$, $n \in \mathbb{N}$. Thus $u = f(v) = \sum_{i=1}^{n} f(a_i)f(b_i) \in f(I)f(J)$. Therefore $f(IJ) \subseteq f(I)f(J)$. Hence $f(IJ) = f(I)f(J)$.

◊ **Exercise 13.2.7.** Let f be a homomorphism defined on a field F. Show that either f is injective or $f(x) = 0$ for all $x \in F$. Hence conclude that every nontrivial (ring) homomorphic image of a field F is again a field.

Solution. Consider ker f, the kernel of the homomorphism f. Since ker f is an ideal of the field F, we have ker $f = (0)$ or F. If ker $f = F$, then $f(x) = 0$ for all $x \in F$. Otherwise, f is injective by Theorem 13.2.11. Therefore in this case, F is isomorphic to its homomorphic image, $f(F)$ and so $f(F)$ is a field.

◊ **Exercise 13.2.8.** Prove that the fields $\mathbb{R}$ and $\mathbb{C}$ are not isomorphic.

Solution. Suppose, if possible, $f : \mathbb{R} \longrightarrow \mathbb{C}$ is an isomorphism from $\mathbb{R}$ onto $\mathbb{C}$. Then there exists $r \in \mathbb{R}$ such that $f(r) = i$. So $f(r^2) = f(r)^2 = i^2 = -1$. Now since f is a surjective homomorphism, $f(1)$ is the identity of $\mathbb{C}$, i.e., $f(1) = 1$ and hence $f(-1) = -f(1) = -1$ by Theorem 13.2.5(ii). Thus $f(r^2) = f(-1)$ which implies $r^2 = -1$, as f is injective. But there is no such real number satisfying $r^2 = -1$. Therefore there does not exist any isomorphism from $\mathbb{R}$ onto $\mathbb{C}$, i.e., $\mathbb{R}$ and $\mathbb{C}$ are not isomorphic.

◊ **Exercise 13.2.9.** Let I and J be two ideals of a ring R. Show that $R/(I \cap J)$ is isomorphic to a subring of $(R/I) \times (R/J)$.

Solution. Define a mapping $f : R \longrightarrow (R/I) \times (R/J)$ by

$$f(a) = (a + I, a + J), \quad \text{for all} \ \ a \in R.$$

Now $f(a + b) = (a + b + I, a + b + J) = (a + I, a + J) + (b + I, b + J) = f(a) + f(b)$ and $f(ab) = (ab + I, ab + J) = (a + I, a + J)(b + I, b + J) = f(a)f(b)$. Therefore, by First Isomorphism theorem, we have $R/\ker f \cong Imf$.

Now,

$$
\begin{aligned}
\ker f &= \{a \in R : f(a) = (0 + I, 0 + J)\} \\
&= \{a \in R : (a + I, a + J) = (0 + I, 0 + J)\} \\
&= \{a \in R : a \in I, a \in J\} \\
&= I \cap J.
\end{aligned}
$$

Hence $R/(I \cap J) \cong Imf$. Since Imf is a subring of $(R/I) \times (R/J)$, we have $R/(I \cap J)$ is isomorphic to a subring of $(R/I) \times (R/J)$.

◊ **Exercise 13.2.10.** Let p be a prime integer. Show that there are only two nonisomorphic rings with p elements.

Solution. Let $(R, +, \cdot)$ be a ring with p elements. Then $(R, +)$ is a group of prime order p and hence $(R, +) \simeq (\mathbb{Z}_p, +)$.

Case-I: If R is a zero ring, then $(R, +, \cdot) \simeq (\mathbb{Z}_p, +, \odot_1)$, where $[m] \odot_1 [n] = [0]$ for all $[m], [n] \in \mathbb{Z}_p$.

Case-II: Suppose R is not a zero ring. Then there exist elements $a, b \in R$ such that $a \cdot b \neq 0$. Clearly, $a \neq 0 \neq b$. We consider the set $aR = \{ax : x \in R\}$. Then aR contains a non-zero element ab and thus $aR \neq \{0\}$. It is easy to show that aR is a subgroup of $(R, +)$. Since $(R, +)$ is a group of prime order and $aR \neq \{0\}$, we must have $R = aR$. We now define a mapping $f : (R, +) \longrightarrow (R, +)$ by $f(x) = ax$ for all $x \in R$. Since $f(b) = ab \neq 0$, it follows that f is a non-zero group homomorphism from $(R, +)$ onto itself. Now $\ker f$ is a subgroup of $(R, +)$. Since f is a non-zero homomorphism and $(R, +)$ has only two subgroups $\{0\}$ and R itself, we must have $\ker f = \{0\}$, i.e., f is a monomorphism. Now $a \neq 0$ implies $f(a) \neq f(0)$, i.e., $a^2 \neq 0$, i.e., Ra contains a non-zero element a^2. It is easy to show that Ra is a subgroup of $(R, +)$. Since $(R, +)$ is a group of prime order and $Ra \neq \{0\}$, we must have $Ra = R$. Hence $Ra = R = aR$. This implies there exist elements $e, f \in R$ such that $a = ae$ and $a = fa$. Now let y be any element in R. Then $f(ey) = a(ey) = (ae)y = ay = f(y)$. Since f is injective, we must have $ey = y$, i.e., e is a left identity of R (since $y \in R$ is arbitrary). Again, we define a mapping $g : (R, +) \longrightarrow (R, +)$ by $g(x) = xa$ for all $x \in R$. Then one can easily show that g is an isomorphism. Now $g(yf) = (yf)a = y(fa) = ya = g(y)$ implies $yf = y$, i.e., f is a right identity of R. Therefore, $e = ef = f$ and hence e is the identity of the ring R. We denote this identity element of R by 1_R. We now consider the ring $(\mathbb{Z}_p, +, \odot_2)$ where $[m] \odot_2 [n] = [mn]$ for all $[m], [n] \in \mathbb{Z}_p$. We define $\psi : (\mathbb{Z}_p, +, \odot_2) \longrightarrow (R, +, \cdot)$ by $\psi([m]) = m1_R$ for all $[m] \in \mathbb{Z}_p$. Then one can show that ψ is well-defined. Also, it is easy to show that ψ is a monomorphism. Since both $\mathbb{Z}_p$ and R contains exactly p elements and ψ is injective, it follows that ψ is also surjective. Consequently, ψ is an isomorphism and in this case $(R, +, \cdot) \simeq (\mathbb{Z}_p, +, \odot_2)$.

◊ **Exercise 13.2.11.** How many nonisomorphic rings are there of order 105?

Solution. Let $(R, +, \cdot)$ be a ring with 105 elements. Then $(R, +)$ is an Abelian group of order 105 and hence $(R, +) \simeq (\mathbb{Z}_3, +) \oplus (\mathbb{Z}_5, +) \oplus (\mathbb{Z}_7, +)$.

By Worked-out Exercise 13.2.10, it follows that one can define exactly two nonisomorphic multiplication on each of $(\mathbb{Z}_3, +)$, $(\mathbb{Z}_5, +)$ and $(\mathbb{Z}_7, +)$. Hence there are exactly 8 nonisomorphic rings of order 105.

◊ **Exercise 13.2.12.** Let F be a field. For each $p(x) \in F[x]$ (the polynomial ring in x over F) define $\varphi : F[x] \longrightarrow F \times F$ by $\varphi(p(x)) = (p(0), p(1))$.
(i) Prove that φ is a ring homomorphism.
(ii) Prove that the quotient ring $F[x]/\langle x^2 - x \rangle$ is isomorphic to the ring $F \times F$.

Solution. (i) Let $p(x), q(x) \in F[x]$. Now

$$\begin{aligned} \varphi(p(x) + q(x)) &= (p(0) + q(0), p(1) + q(1)) \\ &= (p(0), p(1)) + (q(0), q(1)) \\ &= \varphi(p(x)) + \varphi(q(x)) \end{aligned}$$

and

$$\begin{aligned} \varphi(p(x)q(x)) &= (p(0)q(0), p(1)q(1)) \\ &= (p(0), p(1))(q(0), q(1)) \\ &= \varphi(p(x))\varphi(q(x)) \end{aligned}$$

Hence φ is a ring homomorphism.

(ii) We consider two ideals $I = \langle x \rangle$ and $J = \langle x - 1 \rangle$. Since $1 = x - (x - 1)$, we must have $I + J = F[x]$. Hence by Worked-out Exercise 13.1.14, we have $IJ = I \cap J$. Now $IJ = \langle x \rangle \langle x - 1 \rangle = \langle x^2 - x \rangle$. Moreover, $F[x]/I = F[x]/\langle x \rangle \simeq F$ and $F[x]/J = F[x]/\langle x - 1 \rangle \simeq F$. Hence by Worked-out-Exercise 13.2.9, we have $F[x]/\langle x^2 - x \rangle = F[x]/(IJ) = F[x]/(I \cap J) \simeq (F[x]/I) \times (F[x]/J) = F \times F$.

◊ **Exercise 13.2.13.** Pick the correct option. Let $\mathbb{R}[x]$ be the ring of real polynomial in the variable x. The number of ideals in the quotient ring $\mathbb{R}[x]/\langle x^2 - 5x + 4 \rangle$ is (i) 2 (ii) 3 (iii) 4 (iv) 6.

Solution. Clearly, any ideal of $\mathbb{R}[x]/\langle x^2 - 5x + 4 \rangle$ is of the form $J/\langle x^2 - 5x + 4 \rangle$, where J is an ideal of $\mathbb{R}[x]$ containing $\langle x^2 - 5x + 4 \rangle$. Now the ideals of $\mathbb{R}[x]$ containing $\langle x^2 - 5x + 4 \rangle$ are $\langle x^2 - 5x + 4 \rangle, \langle x - 4 \rangle, \langle x - 1 \rangle$ and $\mathbb{R}[x]$. Hence the ideals of $\mathbb{R}[x]/\langle x^2 - 5x + 4 \rangle$ are $\langle x^2 - 5x + 4 \rangle/\langle x^2 - 5x + 4 \rangle, \langle x - 4 \rangle/\langle x^2 - 5x + 4 \rangle, \langle x - 1 \rangle/\langle x^2 - 5x + 4 \rangle$ and $\mathbb{R}[x]/\langle x^2 - 5x + 4 \rangle$. Consequently, there are exactly 4 ideals of the ring $\mathbb{R}[x]/\langle x^2 - 5x + 4 \rangle$.

◊ **Exercise 13.2.14.** Pick the correct option. The number of non-trivial ring homomorphisms from $\mathbb{Z}_{12}$ to $\mathbb{Z}_{28}$ is (i) 1 (ii) 3 (iii) 4 (iv) 7.

Solution. Let $f : \mathbb{Z}_{12} \longrightarrow \mathbb{Z}_{28}$ be a ring homomorphism. Then $f : (\mathbb{Z}_{12}, +) \longrightarrow (\mathbb{Z}_{28}, +)$ is a group homomorphism. Now $o(f([1]))$ divides 28 as well as divides $o([1]) = 12$. This implies $o(f([1])) = 1$ or 2 or 4. Again since f is a ring homomorphism, we must have $f([1]) = f([1] \cdot [1]) = (f([1]))^2$, i.e., $f([1])$ is an idempotent in $\mathbb{Z}_{28}$. If $o(f([1])) = 1$, then $f([1]) = [0]$ and hence $f([a]) = [0]$ for all $[a] \in \mathbb{Z}_{12}$, i.e., f is a trivial ring homomorphism. So $o(f([1])) \neq 1$. If $o(f([1])) = 2$, then $f([1]) = [14]$. In this case $(f([1]))^2 = [14]^2 = [196] = [0] \neq [14] = f([1])$, a contradiction. Therefore, $o(f([1])) = 4$, i.e., $f([1]) = [7]$ or $[21]$. But $[7]$ is not an idempotent where as $[21]$ is an idempotent. Thus the only ring homomorphism $f : \mathbb{Z}_{12} \longrightarrow \mathbb{Z}_{28}$ is given by $f([a]) = [21a]$ for all $[a] \in \mathbb{Z}_{12}$. Hence option (i) is correct.

Alternative Method : We know that if $m = p_1{}^{\alpha_1} p_2{}^{\alpha_2} \cdots p_r{}^{\alpha_r}$ be the prime factorization of m and $n = p_1{}^{\beta_1} p_2{}^{\beta_2} \cdots p_r{}^{\beta_r} q$ with $\gcd(q, m) = 1$, then the number of ring homomorphism $g : \mathbb{Z}_n \longrightarrow \mathbb{Z}_m$ is 2^l where $l = |\{i : \alpha_i \leq \beta_i\}|$.

Here $28 = 2^2 \cdot 7$ and $12 = 2^2 \cdot 7^0 \cdot 3$ with $\gcd(3, 28) = 1$. Thus $l = |\{i : \alpha_i \leq \beta_i\}| = 1$. Therefore, there are exactly two ring homomorphisms from $\mathbb{Z}_{12}$ to $\mathbb{Z}_{28}$ of which one is trivial ring homomorphism that maps every element of $\mathbb{Z}_{12}$ to $[0] \in \mathbb{Z}_{28}$. Hence there are exactly one non-trivial ring homomorphism from $\mathbb{Z}_{12}$ to $\mathbb{Z}_{28}$. Hence, option (i) is correct.

$\Diamond$ **Exercise 13.2.15.** Let p be a prime. Pick the correct statement from below.
(i) Up to isomorphism, there are exactly four commutative rings of order p^2.
(ii) Every integral domain of order p^2 is a field.
(iii) Up to isomorphism, there are exactly two commutative rings of order p^2.
(iv) Every integral domain of order p^2 is not a field.

Solution. Let R be any ring of order p^2 . Then $(R, +)$ is either isomorphic to $\mathbb{Z}_{p^2}$, (on which one can define at least two different multiplications) or it is isomorphic to $\mathbb{Z}_p \times \mathbb{Z}_p$, on which one can define four different multiplications by Worked-out Exercise 13.2.10. So there are (at least) six non-isomorphic commutative rings of order p^2. Finally, any finite integral domain is a field. Hence option (ii) is correct.

$\Diamond$ **Exercise 13.2.16.** Let $f : \mathbb{Z} \longrightarrow (\mathbb{Z}/4\mathbb{Z}) \times (\mathbb{Z}/6\mathbb{Z})$ be the function defined by $f(n) = (n \bmod 4, n \bmod 6)$ for all $n \in \mathbb{Z}$. Pick the correct statement:
(i) $(0 \bmod 4, 3 \bmod 6)$ is in the image of f.
(ii) $(a \bmod 4, b \bmod 6)$ is in the image of f, for all even integers a and b.
(iii) image of f has exactly 6 elements.
(iv) kernel of $f = 24\mathbb{Z}$.

Solution. Suppose $f(n) = (0 \bmod 4, 3 \bmod 6)$. Then we must have $(n \bmod 4, n \bmod 6) = (0 \bmod 4, 3 \bmod 6)$. But this implies $n = 4k$ as well as $n = 6k' + 3$ for some integers k and k', which is impossible. Therefore, $(0 \bmod 4, 3 \bmod 6)$ is not in the image of f.

Let $a = 2p$ and $b = 2q$ be any two even integers. Then by Chinese Remainder Theorem we have $x = 3p + 4q$ is a common solution of two linear congruences $x \equiv p \bmod 2$ and $x \equiv q \bmod 3$. Now $f(6p + 8q) = (2p \bmod 4, 2q \bmod 6) = (a \bmod 4, b \bmod 6)$. Thus $(a \bmod 4, b \bmod 6)$ is in the image of f, for all even integers a and b.

One can easily check that kernel of $f = 12\mathbb{Z}$ and image of f contains 12 elements. Hence option (ii) is correct.

Exercises

1. A mapping $f : \mathbb{Z}_{12} \to \mathbb{Z}_{20}$ is given by $f([i]_{12}) = 5[i]_{20}$. Prove that f is well-defined and is a homomorphism of the ring $\mathbb{Z}_{12}$ into the ring $\mathbb{Z}_{20}$. Find $ker f$.

2. Show that the mapping $f : \mathbb{Z} \to M_2(\mathbb{Z})$, defined by

$$f(r) = \begin{bmatrix} r & 0 \\ 0 & r \end{bmatrix}$$

   is a homomorphism of rings. Find $ker f$. Is the mapping an isomorphism?

3. Show that the mapping $f : \mathbb{Z}[x] \to \mathbb{Z}$ defined by $f(a_0 + a_1x + \ldots + a_nx^n) = a_0$ is a homomorphism from the ring $\mathbb{Z}[x]$ onto the ring $\mathbb{Z}$. Find $ker f$. Is f an isomorphism?

4. Show that the mapping $f : \mathbb{C} \to M_2(\mathbb{R})$ defined by

$$f(a + ib) = \begin{bmatrix} a & b \\ -b & a \end{bmatrix}$$

   is a homomorphism of rings. Find $ker f$. Is f a monomorphism? Is f an isomorphism of $\mathbb{C}$ onto $M_2(\mathbb{R})$?

5. Show that the mapping $f : \mathbb{Z}[\sqrt{2}] \to M_2(\mathbb{R})$ defined by

$$f(a + b\sqrt{2}) = \begin{bmatrix} a & 2b \\ b & a \end{bmatrix}$$

   is a homomorphism of rings. Find $ker f$.

6. Find the kernel of the homomorphism Φ, described in Example 13.2.3.

7. Let $f : R \to S$ be a nontrivial homomorphism of a ring R with identity into an integral domain S. Then show that $f(1_R)$ is the identity of S.

8. Determine all ring homomorphisms from $\mathbb{Z}_5$ to $\mathbb{Z}_5$.

9. Find all ring homomorphisms from $\mathbb{Z}_6$ to $\mathbb{Z}_6$.

10. Find all ring homomorphisms from (i) $\mathbb{Z}_{12}$ to $\mathbb{Z}_4$ (ii) $\mathbb{Z}_{12}$ to $\mathbb{Z}_{30}$.

11. Determine all ring homomorphisms from $\mathbb{Q}$ to $\mathbb{Q}$.

12. Find all ring homomorphisms from $\mathbb{Z}$ into $\mathbb{Z}$.

13. Consider the rings $\mathbb{Z}[\sqrt{2}]$ and $\mathbb{Z}[\sqrt{5}]$. Show that $\mathbb{Z}[\sqrt{2}]$ and $\mathbb{Z}[\sqrt{5}]$ are isomorphic as groups but not isomorphic as rings.

14. Show that $\mathbb{Z}$ and $2\mathbb{Z}$ are isomorphic as groups but not isomorphic as rings.

15. Show that $7\mathbb{Z}$ and $16\mathbb{Z}$ are isomorphic as groups but not isomorphic as rings.

16. Show that the ring $\mathbb{Z}$ is not isomorphic to any proper subring of itself.

17. Suppose F is a field and there is a ring homomorphism from $\mathbb{Z}$ onto F. Show that $F \simeq \mathbb{Z}_p$ for some prime number p.

18. Prove that the homomorphic image of a principal ideal ring is a principal ideal ring.

19. Prove that the following pairs of rings are not isomorphic:

    (i) $\mathbb{Z}$ and $\mathbb{Z} \times \mathbb{Z}$.

    (ii) $\mathbb{Z}[i]$ and $\mathbb{Z}[\sqrt{2}]$.

    (iii) The fields $\mathbb{Q}$ and $\mathbb{R}$.

20. Consider the field of real numbers, $\mathbb{R}$. Show that identity mapping is the only isomorphism of $\mathbb{R}$ onto itself.

21. Let f, g be two homomorphisms of the field of rational numbers, $\mathbb{Q}$ into a ring R. If f and g agree on $\mathbb{Z}$ (i.e., $f(x) = g(x)$ for all $x \in \mathbb{Z}$), then show that $f = g$.

22. Suppose R is a ring with identity. Prove the following:

    (i) If the characteristic of R is zero, then the ring of integers, $\mathbb{Z}$ is isomorphic to a subring of R.

    (ii) If the characteristic of R is n, then $\mathbb{Z}_n$, the ring of integers modulo n is isomorphic to a subring of R.

23. Find whether the following assertions are true or false. Justify your answer.

    (i) Let R be a commutative ring of characteristic 2. Then the mapping $f : R \to R$ defined by $f(a) = a^2$ is a ring homomorphism.

    (ii) The mapping $f : M_2(\mathbb{R}) \to \mathbb{R}$ defined by $\begin{bmatrix} a & b \\ c & d \end{bmatrix} = a$ is a ring homomorphism.

    (iii) The mapping $f : \mathbb{Z}_4 \to \mathbb{Z}_{12}$ defined by $f([x]) = [3x]$ is a ring homomorphism.

    (iv) The ring $10\mathbb{Z}$ is isomorphic to the ring $20\mathbb{Z}$.

    (v) There exists a ring homomorphism from $\mathbb{Q}$ to some ring R such that $ker\, f = \mathbb{Z}$.

13.3   Maximal Ideals and Prime Ideals

In the following, we shall define two special kinds of ideals which are of great importance in the ring theory.

Definition 13.3.1. Let R be a ring such that $R \neq \{0\}$. A proper ideal I of R is called **maximal** if I is not contained in any other proper ideal of R, i.e., for any ideal J of R, $I \subseteq J \subseteq R$ implies that either $I = J$ or $J = R$.

Example 13.3.2. (i) Consider the ring of integers, $\mathbb{Z}$. $3\mathbb{Z}$ is an ideal of $\mathbb{Z}$ and $3\mathbb{Z} \neq \mathbb{Z}$. Let J be any ideal of $\mathbb{Z}$ such that $3\mathbb{Z} \subset J$. Then there exists $a \in J$ such that $a \notin 3\mathbb{Z}$. Then $3 \nmid a$ and hence $\gcd(a, 3) = 1$. So, we can write $1 = 3n + am$ for some $n, m \in \mathbb{Z}$. Now $3, a \in J$. Hence $3n, am \in J$ and then $1 = 3n + am \in J$. This shows that $J = \mathbb{Z}$ and hence $3\mathbb{Z}$ is a maximal ideal. In fact, proceeding as above we can show that for any prime p, $p\mathbb{Z}$ is a maximal ideal of $\mathbb{Z}$. Now let $I = 6\mathbb{Z}$. I is a proper ideal of $\mathbb{Z}$. Since $6\mathbb{Z} \subset 3\mathbb{Z} \subset \mathbb{Z}$, $6\mathbb{Z}$ is not a maximal ideal of $\mathbb{Z}$.

    (ii) Consider the ring $\mathbb{Z}_6$. In this ring $\{[0]\}$, $\{[0], [2], [4]\}$, $\{[0], [3]\}$ and $\mathbb{Z}_6$ are the only ideals. Here $\{[0], [2], [4]\}$ is a maximal ideal, since it is not contained in any other proper ideal of $\mathbb{Z}_6$. Similarly, $\{[0], [3]\}$ is also a maximal ideal. Notice that $\{[0]\} \subset \{[0], [3]\} \subset \mathbb{Z}_6$ and hence $\{[0]\}$ is not a maximal ideal in $\mathbb{Z}_6$.

(iii) Let F be a field. We know that F has only two ideals, viz. $\{0\}$ and F. Hence $\{0\}$ is a maximal ideal of F.

It appears from the above examples that maximality of the zero ideal in a ring may have something to do with a field structure. Indeed, we have the following theorem:

Theorem 13.3.3. *Let R be a commutative ring with identity, $1 \neq 0$. Then R is a field if and only if $\{0\}$ is a maximal ideal of R.*

Proof. If R is a field, then from Example 13.3.2(iii) we find that $\{0\}$ is a maximal ideal of R. Suppose on the other hand, that $\{0\}$ is a maximal ideal of R. Let $0 \neq a \in R$. Since R is commutative, Ra is an ideal of R and $a = 1a \in Ra$. Hence $\{0\} \subset Ra$. Since $\{0\}$ is a maximal ideal, it follows that $Ra = R$. Now $1 \in R = Ra$. Hence there exists $r \in R$ such that $ra = 1$. This proves that every nonzero element a of R is a unit and hence R is a field. $\square$

We now characterize maximal ideals of a commutative ring by the quotient ring.

Theorem 13.3.4. *Let R be a commutative ring with identity, $1 \neq 0$. Then an ideal M of R is maximal if and only if R/M is a field.*

Proof. Suppose M is a maximal ideal of R. Since R is a commutative ring with identity, it follows that the quotient ring R/M is a commutative ring with identity $1 + M$. If $1 + M = 0 + M$, then $1 \in M$ which implies that $M = R$, so M cannot be a maximal ideal. Hence $1 + M \neq 0 + M$. Now to prove that R/M is a field, we show that every nonzero element of R/M is a unit. Let $a + M$ be a nonzero element of R/M. Then $a + M \neq 0 + M$ implies that $a \notin M$. Let $J = \{ra + m \mid r \in R \text{ and } m \in M\}$. It is easy to see that J is an ideal of R and $m = 0a + m \in J$ for all $m \in M$. Hence J contains M. Now $a = 1a + 0 \in J$ and $a \notin M$ imply that $M \subset J$. Since M is a maximal ideal, it follows that $J = R$. Now $1 \in R = J$. Hence $1 = ra + m$ for some $r \in R$ and $m \in M$. Then $1 + M = (ra + m) + M = (ra + M) + (m + M) = (r + M)(a + M) + (0 + M) = (r + M)(a + M)$. This shows that $a + M$ is a unit in R/M and hence R/M is a field.

Conversely, we now assume that R/M is a field. Since R/M contains at least two elements, $M \subset R$. Let J be an ideal of R such that $M \subset J \subseteq R$. Then there exists $u \in J$ such that $u \notin M$. Hence $u + M \neq 0 + M$ in the field R/M. Then there exists $v + M$ in R/M such that $(v + M)(u + M) = 1 + M$. This shows that $vu + M = 1 + M$, i.e., $1 - vu \in M \subset J$. Now $u \in J$. Hence $vu \in J$. From this, it follows that $1 = (1 - vu) + vu \in J$ and hence $J = R$. So, M is a maximal ideal. $\square$

Alternative Proof. Let R be a commutative ring with identity and M be an ideal of R. Then the quotient ring R/M is also commutative and contains identity (by Theorem 13.1.19). Also by Theorem 13.2.15, there is a canonical epimorphism of R onto R/M. Thus,

M is maximal

$\Longleftrightarrow$ there is no proper ideal (other than M) of R containing M

$\Longleftrightarrow$ R/M is simple   (by Correspondence theorem)

$\Longleftrightarrow$ R/M is a field   (by Theorem13.1.14).   □

Remark 13.3.5. If a commutative ring R *does not contain the identity element*, then Theorem 13.3.4 is not true in general. Indeed, consider the commutative ring $2\mathbb{Z}$. One can check that $4\mathbb{Z}$ is a maximal ideal of $2\mathbb{Z}$, but the quotient ring $2\mathbb{Z}/4\mathbb{Z}$ is not a field, as $2 + 4\mathbb{Z}$ is a non-zero nilpotent element of $2\mathbb{Z}/4\mathbb{Z}$.

Definition 13.3.6. Let R be a ring such that $R \neq \{0\}$. A proper ideal P of R is called *prime*, if for any ideals A, B in R,

$$AB \subseteq P \text{ implies that } A \subseteq P \text{ or } B \subseteq P.$$

Theorem 13.3.7. *Let R be a ring with $R \neq \{0\}$ and P be a proper ideal of R such that for any $a, b \in R$,*

$$ab \in P \text{ implies } a \in P \text{ or } b \in P. \tag{13.3.1}$$

Then P is a prime ideal[18] *of R.*

Moreover, if R is commutative, then a proper ideal P is prime if and only if P satisfies (13.3.1).

Proof. Let P be a proper ideal of R which satisfies (13.3.1). Let A, B be two ideals of R such that $AB \subseteq P$. Suppose $A \nsubseteq P$. Then there exists $a \in A \smallsetminus P$. Now for any $b \in B$, $ab \in AB \subseteq P$. But this implies that $b \in P$ by (13.3.1), as $a \notin P$. Thus $B \subseteq P$. Therefore P is prime.

Now we show that the converse holds in the case of commutative rings. So let R be commutative, P be a prime ideal of R and $a, b \in R$ such that $ab \in P$. Then the (principal) ideal $(ab) \subseteq P$. Now since R is commutative, $(ab) \supseteq (a)(b)$. Thus $(a)(b) \subseteq P$, which implies that $(a) \subseteq P$ or $(b) \subseteq P$. Therefore $a \in P$ or $b \in P$, i.e., P satisfies (13.3.1).   □

Example 13.3.8. Consider the ideal $3\mathbb{Z}$ in the ring $\mathbb{Z}$. Let $a, b \in \mathbb{Z}$ be such that $ab \in 3\mathbb{Z}$. Then $3 \mid ab$. Since 3 is a prime integer then from Theorem 2.3.2, either $3\mid a$ or

---

[18]A prime ideal satisfying (13.3.1) is called a *completely prime* ideal.

$3|b$. Hence, either $a \in 3\mathbb{Z}$ or $b \in 3\mathbb{Z}$. So it follows from Theorem 12.3.6 that $3\mathbb{Z}$ is a prime ideal.

Theorem 13.3.9. *Let R be a commutative ring with identity. Then every maximal ideal of R is prime.*

Proof. Let I be a maximal ideal of R. Then I is a proper ideal of R. Let $a, b \in R$ so that $ab \in I$. Further assume that $a \notin I$. Let $J = \{ra + x \mid r \in R \text{ and } x \in I\}$. It can easily be shown that J is an ideal of R; $a = 1a + 0 \in J$ and if $x \in I$, then $x = 0a + x \in J$. Hence $I \subset J$. Since I is a maximal ideal, it follows that $J = R$. Now $1 \in R$. So, there exist $r \in R$ and $x \in I$ such that $1 = ra + x$. Then $b = r(ab) + xb$. Since $ab \in I$ and $x \in I$, we find that $r(ab) \in I$ and $xb \in I$. Hence $b \in I$. Therefore I is a prime ideal of R. □

One should note that the converse of the above theorem is not true as (0) is a prime ideal of $\mathbb{Z}$, which is not maximal. The following is yet another interesting example.

Example 13.3.10. Let $R = \{(a, b) \mid a, b \in \mathbb{Z}\}$. Then $(R, +, \cdot)$ is a ring where $+$ and $\cdot$ are defined componentwise. Let $I = \{(a, 0) \mid a \in \mathbb{Z}\}$. Then I is a prime ideal of R but it is not maximal, since $I \subset J \subset R$, where $J = \{(a, 2b) \mid a, b \in \mathbb{Z}\}$.

Remark 13.3.11. If a commutative ring R *does not contain the identity element*, then Theorem 13.3.9 is not true in general. Indeed, consider the commutative ring $2\mathbb{Z}$. It is easy to verify that $4\mathbb{Z}$ is a maximal ideal of $2\mathbb{Z}$, but $4\mathbb{Z}$ is not a prime ideal of as $2\mathbb{Z}$, as $2 \cdot 2 \in 4\mathbb{Z}$ but $2 \notin 4\mathbb{Z}$.

We now characterize the prime ideals of a commutative ring by using the quotient ring.

Theorem 13.3.12. *Let R be a commutative ring with identity, $1 \neq 0$. A proper ideal P of R is prime if and only if R/P is an integral domain.*

Proof. Let P be a prime ideal of R. Since R is commutative and R has an identity, we have that R/P is also a commutative ring with identity $1 + P$. Since $P \neq R$, it follows that $1 + P \neq 0 + P$, otherwise $1 + P = P$ implies that $1 \in P$, from which it would follow that $P = R$. Let $a, b \in R$ so that $(a + P)(b + P) = 0 + P = P$. Then $ab + P = P$, i.e., $ab \in P$. Now since P is a prime ideal in a commutative ring R with identity, we have $a \in P$ or $b \in P$, which implies that $a + P = P = 0 + P$ or $b + P = P = 0 + P$. Thus, R/P is an integral domain.

Conversely, suppose R/P is an integral domain. Hence R/P is a commutative ring with identity $1 + P \neq P$. This implies that $1 \notin P$. From this we find that $P \subset R$. Let

$ab \in P$. Then $(a + P)(b + P) = ab + P = P = 0 + P$. Therefore $a + P = 0 + P = P$ or $b + P = 0 + P = P$, which implies that $a \in P$ or $b \in P$. Hence P is prime. $\qquad\square$

Suppose now, R is a commutative ring with identity. Let P be a maximal ideal of R. Then by Theorem 13.3.4, R/P is a field. Since every field is an integral domain, it follows that R/P is an integral domain and hence from Theorem 13.3.12, it follows that P is a prime ideal. So we have the result again, which we proved in Theorem 13.3.9, that in a commutative ring with identity, every maximal ideal is a prime ideal.

We conclude this section by describing all prime ideals and maximal ideals of the ring $\mathbb{Z}$.

It is known to us that the ideals of $\mathbb{Z}$ are $n\mathbb{Z}$, $n = 0, 1, 2, \ldots$ If $n = 0$, then $0\mathbb{Z} = \{0\}$ is a prime ideal of $\mathbb{Z}$. Since $\{0\} \subset n\mathbb{Z}, n \neq 0$, $0\mathbb{Z}$ is not a maximal ideal of $\mathbb{Z}$. If $n = 1$, then $n\mathbb{Z} = \mathbb{Z}$, which is neither prime nor maximal. Let $n \neq 0, 1$. Then we have shown in Theorem 12.2.10 that $\mathbb{Z}/n\mathbb{Z}$, $(n > 1)$, is an integral domain if and only if n is a prime integer. [Also refer to Worked-out Exercise 13.2.4]. Equivalently, we have established in Corollary 12.2.20 that $\mathbb{Z}/n\mathbb{Z}$ is a field if and only if n is a prime integer. Hence from the Theorem 13.3.12, it follows that for $n > 1$, $n\mathbb{Z}$ is a prime ideal if and only if n is a prime integer; equivalently, $n\mathbb{Z}$ is a maximal ideal if and only if n is a prime integer. Hence all the prime ideals of $\mathbb{Z}$ are $0\mathbb{Z}$ and $p\mathbb{Z}$ where p is any prime integer and all the maximal ideals of $\mathbb{Z}$ are $p\mathbb{Z}$, where p is any prime integer. So in $\mathbb{Z}$, every nonzero prime ideal is a maximal ideal.

In Chapter 14, we shall show that this indeed is true in any PID. However there are other classes of rings in which every prime ideal is maximal.

Theorem 13.3.13. *In a Boolean ring B with identity, every prime ideal is a maximal ideal.*

Proof. Let B be a Boolean ring and P be a prime ideal in B. Then $P \neq B$. Suppose J is an ideal of B such that $P \subset J \subseteq B$. Then there exists $b \in J$ such that $b \notin P$. Now $b(1 - b) = b - b^2 = b - b = 0 \in P$. Since B is a commutative ring with identity and P is a prime ideal, it now follows that either $b \in P$ or $1 - b \in P$. But $b \notin P$. Hence $1 - b \in P \subseteq J$. Also $b \in J$. Then $1 = (1 - b) + b \in J$ which implies that $J = B$. Hence P is a maximal ideal of R. $\qquad\square$

We end this section with a result that ensures the existence of a maximal ideal in a ring with identity.

Theorem 13.3.14. *Let R be a ring with identity. Then every proper ideal of R is contained in a maximal ideal of R.*

Proof. Let I be a proper ideal of R and let $\mathcal{A}$ be the collection of all *proper ideals* of R containing I, i.e., $\mathcal{A} = \{J \mid I \subseteq J, J \text{ is a proper ideal of } R\}$. Then $\mathcal{A} \neq \emptyset$, as $I \in \mathcal{A}$. Further, $\mathcal{A}$ is naturally partially ordered with respect to the usual *set inclusion* as the partial order. Let $\mathcal{C} = \{J_\alpha \mid \alpha \in \Lambda\}$, be any linearly ordered subset (cf. Definition 1.2.22) in $\mathcal{A}$. We assert that $\mathcal{C}$ has an upper bound in $\mathcal{A}$. Indeed, it is quite routine to check that $\bigcup_\alpha J_\alpha = K$ (say), serves our purpose. Observe that, since $\mathcal{C}$ is a chain, K becomes an ideal of R (prove it!). Further, since $1 \notin J_\alpha$ for any $\alpha \in \Lambda$, $1 \notin K$, whence K is a proper ideal of R and consequently $K \in \mathcal{A}$. Thus by Zorn's lemma (see Appendix B), $\mathcal{A}$ has a maximal element, say, M. So M contains I and M is a proper ideal of R. It will now be sufficient to show that M is a maximal ideal of R. In fact, if there exists an ideal P of R, such that $M \subset P \subset R$, then $P \in \mathcal{A}$, contradicting the maximality of M in $\mathcal{A}$. Thus no such P exists and hence M is a maximal ideal of R containing I. $\square$

Corollary 13.3.15. *Let R be a ring with identity $1 \neq 0$. Then R has a maximal ideal.*

Proof. Note that $\{0\}$ is a proper ideal of R. Hence the result follows directly from Theorem 13.3.14 above. $\square$

Remark 13.3.16. The ideal J/I is a prime (maximal) ideal of the ring R/I if and only if J is a prime (resp. maximal) ideal of R.

Worked-out Exercises

◇ **Exercise 13.3.1.** Let I denote the set of all polynomials in $\mathbb{Z}[x]$ with constant terms zero. Show that I is a prime ideal.

Solution. Let $f(x)$ and $g(x)$ be two polynomials in I. If a_0 and b_0 are the constant terms of $f(x)$ and $g(x)$ respectively, then $a_0 = b_0 = 0$. Now the constant term of $f(x) - g(x)$ is $a_0 - b_0 = 0 - 0 = 0$. Hence $f(x) - g(x) \in I$. Let $r(x) \in \mathbb{Z}[x]$. Suppose the constant term of $r(x)$ is c_0. Now the constant term of $r(x)f(x)$ is $c_0 a_0 = c_0 \cdot 0 = 0$. Hence $r(x)f(x) \in I$. Since $\mathbb{Z}[x]$ is commutative, $f(x)r(x) \in I$. Hence I is an ideal of $\mathbb{Z}[x]$. Let $p(x) = p_0 + p_1 x + \ldots + p_t x^t$ and $q(x) = q_0 + q_1 x + \ldots + q_m x^m$ be two polynomials in $\mathbb{Z}[x]$ such that $p(x)q(x) \in I$. Now the constant term of $p(x)q(x)$ is $p_0 q_0$ and this must be zero. Then either $p_0 = 0$ or $q_0 = 0$. This implies that either $p(x) \in I$ or $q(x) \in I$. Since $\mathbb{Z}[x]$ is a commutative ring with identity, it now follows that I is a prime ideal.

◊ **Exercise 13.3.2.** Show that the ideal I of the above Worked-out Exercise 13.3.1 is not a maximal ideal.

Solution. Let $J = \{f(x) \in \mathbb{Z}[x] \mid \text{the constant term of } f(x) \text{ is an even integer}\}$. Proceeding as in Worked-out Exercise 13.3.1, we can show that J is an ideal. Clearly J contains I. Now $2 + 3x + 5x^2 \in J$ but $2 + 3x + 5x^2 \notin I$. Hence $I \subset J$. Again $3 + 3x + 5x^2 \in \mathbb{Z}[x]$ but $3 + 3x + 5x^2 \notin J$ so $I \subset J \subset \mathbb{Z}[x]$. Therefore I is not a maximal ideal.

◊ **Exercise 13.3.3.** Find all prime ideals and maximal ideals in the ring $\mathbb{Z}_8$.

Solution. The elements of $\mathbb{Z}_8$ are $[0], [1], [2], \ldots, [7]$. Since $|\mathbb{Z}_8| = 8$, the number of elements in an ideal I of $\mathbb{Z}_8$ is either $1, 2, 4$ or 8. Since $(\mathbb{Z}_8, +)$ is a cyclic group and every ideal is also a subgroup of the group $(\mathbb{Z}_8, +)$, so there exists only one subgroup for each positive divisor of 8. Now the subgroups of $(\mathbb{Z}_8, +)$ are $\{[0]\}, \{[0], [4]\}, \{[0], [2], [4], [6]\}$ and $\mathbb{Z}_8$. Clearly these are also ideals of $\mathbb{Z}_8$. Here $\{[0], [2], [4], [6]\}$ is the only maximal ideal. Now $[4][2] = [8] = [0] \in \{[0]\}$. But $[4] \notin \{[0]\}$ and $[2] \notin \{[0]\}$. Hence $\{[0]\}$ is not a prime ideal. Again $[2][2] = [4] \in \{[0], [4]\}$, but $[2] \notin \{[0], [4]\}$. Hence $\{[0], [4]\}$ is not a prime ideal. Consequently $\{[0], [2], [4], [6]\}$ is the only prime ideal of $\mathbb{Z}_8$.

◊ **Exercise 13.3.4.** In the ring $\mathbb{Z}[i]$, show that the subset $I = \{a + bi \in \mathbb{Z}[i] \mid a \text{ and } b$ are both multiples of $3\}$ is a maximal ideal of $\mathbb{Z}[i]$.

Solution. Since $0 + 0i \in I$, $I \neq \emptyset$. Let $a + bi, c + di \in I$. Then there exist r_1, r_2, r_3, r_4 in $\mathbb{Z}$ such that $a = 3r_1, b = 3r_2, c = 3r_3$ and $d = 3r_4$. Now $(a + bi) - (c + di) = (a - c) + (b - d)i = 3(r_1 - r_3) + 3(r_2 - r_4)i$, shows that $(a + bi) - (c + di) \in \mathbb{Z}[i]$. Let $u + vi \in \mathbb{Z}[i]$. Then $(u + vi)(a + bi) = (ua - vb) + (ub + va)i = (u3r_1 - v3r_2) + (u3r_2 + v3r_1)i = 3(ur_1 - vr_2) + 3(ur_2 + vr_1)i \in I$. Since $\mathbb{Z}[i]$ is a commutative ring, it follows that I is an ideal.

Let J be an ideal of $\mathbb{Z}[i]$ such that $I \subset J \subseteq \mathbb{Z}[i]$. There exists $r + ti \in J$ such that $r + ti \notin I$. We now consider the following cases.

Case I: $3 \nmid r$ and $3 \nmid t$.

We claim that $3 \nmid r^2 + t^2$. Since any integer $m \in \mathbb{Z}$ must be of one of the forms $3k, 3k + 1, 3k + 2$, it follows that $r^2 \equiv 1 \pmod 3$ and $t^2 \equiv 1 \pmod 3$, (since $3 \nmid r$ and $3 \nmid t$). Hence $r^2 + t^2 \equiv 2 \pmod 3$ shows that $3 \nmid r^2 + t^2$. Let $q = r^2 + t^2$, then $\gcd(3, q) = 1$. So there exist integers x, y such that $1 = 3x + qy$. Now $3 \in I \subset J$ and $q = r^2 + t^2 = (r - ti)(r + ti) \in J$. Hence $1 \in J$.

Case II: $3 \mid r$ and $3 \nmid t$.

Since $3 \mid r$, $r = r + i0 \in I \subset J$. Hence $ti = (r + ti) - r \in J$. Then $t^2 = (-ti)(ti) \in J$. Now $3 \nmid t^2$. Therefore $\gcd(3, t^2) = 1$. Now proceeding as in Case I, we can show that $J = \mathbb{Z}[i]$.

Case III: $3 \nmid r$ and $3 \mid t$.

Proceeding as in Case II, we can show that $J = \mathbb{Z}[i]$.

Hence $J = \mathbb{Z}[i]$. Consequently, I is a maximal ideal.

$\Diamond$ **Exercise 13.3.5.** Find the number of elements of the quotient ring $\mathbb{Z}[i]/I$, where I is the ideal of the Worked-out Exercise 13.3.4. Write down all the distinct elements of $\mathbb{Z}[i]/I$.

Solution. Any element of $\mathbb{Z}[i]/I$ is a coset of I, which is of the form $(a + bi) + I$. Now $a = 3k + r$ and $b = 3q + t$ where k, q, r, t are integers and $0 \leq r < 3$, $0 \leq t < 3$. Hence $(a + bi) + I = \left((3k + r) + (3q + t)i\right) + I = \left((3k + 3qi) + (r + ti)\right) + I = (r + ti) + I$ (since $3k + 3qi \in I$), where $0 \leq r < 3$, $0 \leq t < 3$. Suppose, r_1, r_2, t_1, t_2 are integers such that $0 \leq r_i < 3$, $0 \leq t_i < 3$. Then

$$(r_1 + t_1 i) + I = (r_2 + t_2 i) + I$$
$$\Longleftrightarrow \quad (r_1 - r_2) + (t_1 - t_2)i \in I$$
$$\Longleftrightarrow \quad 3 \mid (r_1 - r_2) \text{ and } 3 \mid (t_1 - t_2)$$
$$\Longleftrightarrow \quad r_1 = r_2 \text{ and } t_1 = t_2$$
$$(\text{since } |r_1 - r_2| < 3 \text{ and } |t_1 - t_2| < 3).$$

Hence there are 9 distinct cosets $(r + ti) + I$ which are $(0 + 0i) + I$, $(0 + 1i) + I$, $(0 + 2i) + I$, $(1 + 0i) + I$, $(1 + 1i) + I$, $(1 + 2i) + I$, $(2 + 0i) + I$, $(2 + 1i) + I$ and $(2 + 2i) + I$.

$\Diamond$ **Exercise 13.3.6.** Give an example of a field of 9 elements.

Solution. In Worked-out Exercise 13.3.4, we have proved that I is a maximal ideal of the ring $\mathbb{Z}[i]$. Hence $\mathbb{Z}[i]/I$ is a field. Consequently it is an example of a field with 9 elements.

$\Diamond$ **Exercise 13.3.7.** In the ring $\mathbb{Z}[i]$, show that $I = \{a + bi \in \mathbb{Z}[i] \mid a, b \text{ are both even}\}$ is an ideal of $\mathbb{Z}[i]$, but not a maximal ideal of $\mathbb{Z}[i]$.

Solution. Let $x = a + bi$, $y = c + di \in I$ and $u = r + si \in \mathbb{Z}[i]$. There exist $r_1, r_2, r_3, r_4 \in \mathbb{Z}$ such that $a = 2r_1$, $b = 2r_2$, $c = 2r_3$, $d = 2r_4$. Then $x - y = (a + bi) - (c + di) = (a - c) + (b - d)i = 2(r_1 - r_3) + 2(r_2 - r_4)i \in I$, and $ux = (r + si)(a + bi) = (ra - sb) + (rb + sa)i = 2(rr_1 - sr_2) + 2(rr_2 + sr_1)i \in I$. Since $\mathbb{Z}[i]$ is a commutative ring, it follows that I is an ideal of $\mathbb{Z}[i]$.

Let $J = \{a + bi \in \mathbb{Z}[i] \mid 2 \text{ divides } a^2 + b^2\}$. Since $0 + 0i \in J$, $J \neq \emptyset$. Let $x = a + bi$, $y = c + di \in J$ and $u = r + si \in \mathbb{Z}[i]$. Then $2 \mid a^2 + b^2$ and $2 \mid c^2 + d^2$. Now, $x - y = (a - c) + (b - d)i$. Since $(a - c)^2 + (b - d)^2 = (a^2 + b^2) + (c^2 + d^2) - 2(ac + bd)$, it follows that $2 \mid (a-c)^2 + (b-d)^2$. Again, $ux = (r + si)(a + bi) = (ra - sb) + (rb + sa)i$ and $(ra - sb)^2 + (rb + sa)^2 = r^2(a^2 + b^2) + s^2(a^2 + b^2)$. Hence $2 \mid (ra - sb)^2 + (rb + sa)^2$ implies that $ux = xu \in J$. Consequently, J is an ideal. Now $1 + 2i \in \mathbb{Z}[i]$, but $1 + 2i \notin J$. Hence $J \neq \mathbb{Z}[i]$. Again $1 + 1i \in J$ but $1 + 1i \notin I$, whence we find that $I \subset J \subset \mathbb{Z}[i]$. Consequently, I is not a maximal ideal.

◇ **Exercise 13.3.8.** Show that a proper ideal I of a ring R is a maximal ideal if and only if for any ideal A of R, either $A \subseteq I$ or $A + I = R$.

Solution. Suppose I is a maximal ideal of R and let A be any ideal of R. If $A \not\subseteq I$ then $A + I$ is an ideal of R such that $I \subset A + I$. Since I is maximal, it follows that $A + I = R$.

Conversely, assume that the proper ideal I satisfies the given condition. Let J be an ideal of R such that $I \subset J$. Now $J \not\subseteq I$. Therefore, $I + J = R$. But $I + J = J$. Thus $J = R$. Hence I is a maximal ideal of R.

◇ **Exercise 13.3.9.** Let R be a commutative ring with identity. Let A and B be two distinct maximal ideals of R. Show that $AB = A \cap B$.

Solution. Since $AB \subseteq A$ and $AB \subseteq B$, $AB \subseteq A \cap B$. Since A and B are distinct maximal ideals, there exists $b \in B$ such that $b \notin A$. Then $(A, b) = \{a + br \mid a \in A, r \in R\}$ is an ideal of R such that $A \subset (A, b)$. Since A is maximal, $(A, b) = R$. This implies that $1 = a + br$ for some $a \in A$ and $r \in R$. Let $x \in A \cap B$. Then $x = x1 = xa + xbr = xa + (xb)r \in AB$. Hence $A \cap B \subseteq AB$. Thus $AB = A \cap B$.

◇ **Exercise 13.3.10.** Consider the ring $C[a, b]$ of all real valued continuous functions defined on $[a, b]$. Let $c \in [a, b]$ and $M_c = \{f \in C[a, b] : f(c) = 0\}$. Then prove that M_c is a maximal ideal of $C[a, b]$.

Solution. We define a mapping $\varphi : C[a, b] \longrightarrow \mathbb{R}$ by $\varphi(f) = f(c)$ for all $f \in C[a, b]$. Then one can easily check that φ is a ring epimorphism. Hence by First Isomorphism theorem we have $C[a, b] / \ker \varphi \simeq \mathbb{R}$.

Now $\ker \varphi = \{f \in C[a, b] : \varphi(f) = 0\} = \{f \in C[a, b] : f(c) = 0\} = M_c$. Therefore, $C[a, b] / M_c \simeq \mathbb{R}$ and consequently M_c is a maximal ideal of $C[a, b]$.

◇ **Exercise 13.3.11.** Let M be a maximal ideal of $C[a, b]$. Prove that there exists a unique element $z \in [a, b]$ such that $M = M_z = \{f \in C[a, b] : f(z) = 0\}$.

Solution. First we prove that for any proper ideal I of the ring $C[a,b]$ there exists $x \in [a,b]$ such that $f(x) = 0$ for all $f \in I$. Assume that for each point of $x \in [a,b]$, there exists a function $f \in I$ such that $f(x) \neq 0$. Then there exists a neighborhood N_x of x in $[a,b]$ such that $f \neq 0$ on N_x. Since $[a,b]$ is compact and $\{N_x : x \in [a,b]\}$ is an open cover of $[a,b]$, there exists a finite subcover $\{N_{x_1}, N_{x_2}, \ldots, N_{x_m}\}$ of $\{N_x : x \in [a,b]\}$. This implies there exist functions $f_1, f_2, \ldots, f_m \in I$ such that for each $x \in [a,b]$, we have $f_i(x) \neq 0$ for some i (depending on x). Then the function $f = f_1^2 + f_2^2 + \cdots + f_m^2 \in I$ such that $f > 0$ on I. Therefore $1 = \frac{f}{f} \in I$ and $I = C[a,b]$, a contradiction. Thus if M is maximal, then the set $Z = \{z \in [a,b] : f(z) = 0 \text{ for all } f \in M\}$ is non-empty. But for each $z \in Z$, we have $M \subseteq M_z$. Thus by maximality of M, we must have Z is a singleton set $\{z\}$ for some $z \in [a,b]$ and thus $M = M_z$.

◇ **Exercise 13.3.12.** Is the ideal $I = \{f \in C[0,1] : f(0) = f(1) = 0\}$ a maximal ideal in the ring $C[0,1]$?

Solution. Here the given ideal I is not a maximal ideal of $C[0,1]$. Infact I is not a prime ideal of $C[0,1]$. We consider two functions f and g in $C[0,1]$ defined by $f(x) = x$ and $g(x) = x - 1$ for all $x \in [0,1]$. Then the product function $fg \in I$ but neither $f \in I$ nor $g \in I$.

◇ **Exercise 13.3.13.** Pick the correct statement. Let p, q be distinct primes. Then
(i) $\mathbb{Z}/p^2 q\mathbb{Z}$ has exactly 3 distinct ideals.
(ii) $\mathbb{Z}/p^2 q\mathbb{Z}$ has exactly 3 distinct prime ideals.
(iii) $\mathbb{Z}/p^2 q\mathbb{Z}$ has exactly 2 distinct prime ideals.
(iv) $\mathbb{Z}/p^2 q\mathbb{Z}$ has unique maximal ideal.

Solution. The ideals of the ring $\mathbb{Z}/p^2 q\mathbb{Z}$ are $\{[0]\}, \langle [p] \rangle, \langle [p^2] \rangle, \langle [q] \rangle, \langle [pq] \rangle$ and $\mathbb{Z}/p^2 q\mathbb{Z}$. Now the ideals $\langle [p^2] \rangle$ and $\langle [pq] \rangle$ are only two prime ideals as well as maximal ideals of the ring $\mathbb{Z}/p^2 q\mathbb{Z}$. Hence option (iii) is correct.

◆ **Exercise 13.3.14.** Pick the correct statement(s). For a positive integer m, let a_m denote the number of distinct prime ideals of the ring $\frac{\mathbb{Q}[x]}{\langle x^m - 1 \rangle}$. Then
(i) $a_4 = 2$ (ii) $a_4 = 3$ (iii) $a_5 = 2$ (iv) $a_5 = 3$.

Solution. Consider the ring $\frac{\mathbb{Q}[x]}{\langle x^4 - 1 \rangle}$. The prime ideals of $\frac{\mathbb{Q}[x]}{\langle x^4 - 1 \rangle}$ are $\frac{\langle x - 1 \rangle}{\langle x^4 - 1 \rangle}, \frac{\langle x + 1 \rangle}{\langle x^4 - 1 \rangle}$ and $\frac{\langle x^2 + 1 \rangle}{\langle x^4 - 1 \rangle}$. Again, if we consider the ring $\frac{\mathbb{Q}[x]}{\langle x^5 - 1 \rangle}$, then its prime ideals are $\frac{\langle x - 1 \rangle}{\langle x^5 - 1 \rangle}$ and $\frac{\langle x^4 + x^3 + x^2 + x + 1 \rangle}{\langle x^5 - 1 \rangle}$. Hence options (ii) and (iii) are correct.

Exercises

1. Find all prime ideals and maximal ideals in the following rings.

   (i) $\mathbb{Z}_6$, (ii) $\mathbb{Z}_9$, (iii) $\mathbb{Z}_7$, (iv) $\mathbb{Z}_{10}$, (v) $\mathbb{Z}_{12}$, (vi) $\mathbb{R}$, (vii) $\mathbb{R} \times \mathbb{R}$.

2. Let $I = \{a_0 + a_1 x + a_2 x^2 + \ldots + a_n x^n \in \mathbb{Z}[x] \mid 5 \text{ divides } a_0\}$. Show that I is a prime ideal of $\mathbb{Z}[x]$. Is I a maximal ideal?

3. Let $I = \{f(x) \in \mathbb{Z}[x] \mid 6 \text{ divides the constant term of } f(x)\}$. Show that I is an ideal of $\mathbb{Z}[x]$, but not a prime ideal.

4. Let $I = \{(n, m) \in \mathbb{Z} \times \mathbb{Z} \mid 3 \text{ divides } n\}$. Show that I is a maximal ideal of $\mathbb{Z} \times \mathbb{Z}$.

5. Let R be a commutative ring with identity, $1 \neq 0$. Prove that R is an integral domain if and only if (0) is a prime ideal of R.

6. Let n be a positive integer. Prove that the following conditions are equivalent.

   (i) n is a prime integer.

   (ii) $\mathbb{Z}/n\mathbb{Z}$ is an integral domain.

   (iii) $\mathbb{Z}/n\mathbb{Z}$ is a field.

7. Let R be a finite commutative ring with identity $1 \neq 0$. Prove that an ideal I of R is a prime ideal if and only if I is a maximal ideal.

8. (a) Let $I \neq \{0\}$ be a proper ideal of a PID R such that the quotient ring R/I has no zero divisors. Prove that R/I is a field.

   (b) Let R be an integral domain. Prove that if every proper ideal of R is a prime ideal, then R is a field.

9. Let $r \in \mathbb{R}$. Show that $I_r = \{f(x) \in \mathbb{R}[x] \mid f(r) = 0\}$ is a maximal ideal of $\mathbb{R}[x]$. Prove that $\mathbb{R}[x]/I_r \simeq \mathbb{R}$.

10. Let $I = \{a + bi \in \mathbb{Z}[i] \mid a \text{ and } b \text{ are both multiples of } 5\}$. Show that I is an ideal of $\mathbb{Z}[i]$. Is I a maximal ideal? Find the number of elements of the quotient ring $\mathbb{Z}[i]/I$.

11. Let $I = \{a + bi \in \mathbb{Z}[i] \mid a \text{ and } b \text{ are both multiples of } 7\}$. Show that I is an ideal of $\mathbb{Z}[i]$. Is I a maximal ideal? Find the number of elements of the quotient ring $\mathbb{Z}[i]/I$.

12. Let $I = \{a + b\sqrt{2} \in \mathbb{Z}[\sqrt{2}] \mid a \text{ and } b \text{ are both multiples of } 5\}$. Show that I is an ideal of $\mathbb{Z}[\sqrt{2}]$. Also show that I is a maximal ideal of $\mathbb{Z}[\sqrt{2}]$. Find the number of elements of the field $\mathbb{Z}[\sqrt{2}]/I$.

13. Let $I = \{a + bi \in \mathbb{Z}[i] \mid 2 \text{ divides } a - b\}$. Show that I is a maximal ideal of $\mathbb{Z}[i]$. Find the number of elements of the field $\mathbb{Z}[i]/I$.

14. Let R be the ring of all continuous functions from $\mathbb{R}$ to $\mathbb{R}$ (cf. Worked-out Exercise 12.1.1). Then show that the set $I = \{f \in R \mid f(0) = 0\}$ is a maximal ideal of R.

15. Find whether the following assertions are true or false. Justify your answer.

    (a) Let $I = \{(n, m) \in \mathbb{Z} \times \mathbb{Z} \mid n \text{ and } m \text{ are even integers}\}$. Then I is a maximal ideal of $\mathbb{Z} \times \mathbb{Z}$.

    (b) The intersection of all maximal ideals of the ring $\mathbb{Z}$ is the ideal (0).

    (c) In $\mathbb{Z}[\sqrt{2}]$, $(\sqrt{2})$ is a maximal ideal.

    (d) In $\mathbb{Z}[i]$, (0) is a prime ideal.

16. Let R be a commutative ring with identity. Find which of the following statements about R are correct:
    (a) Every ideal is a prime ideal.
    (b) Every ideal is a principal ideal.
    (c) Every ideal is a maximal ideal.
    (d) Every maximal ideal is a prime ideal.

17. Let R be a finite non-zero commutative ring with unity. Then which of the following statements are necessarily true?
    (a) Any non-zero element of R is either a unit or a zero divisor.
    (b) A non-zero element of R may exist which is neither a unit nor a zero divisor.
    (c) Every prime ideal of R is maximal.
    (d) Every zero divisor of R is nilpotent.

13.4 Regular Rings

In the section, we define a special kind of rings and study its properties.

Definition 13.4.1. An element a in a ring R is said to be *regular* if there exists an element $x \in R$ such that $a = axa$. If every element in the ring is regular, then the ring is said to be a *regular ring* .

Example 13.4.2. (i) Consider any field F. Let $a \in F$ be any element. If $a = 0$, then $a = 0 = 0 \cdot 0 \cdot 0 = a \cdot a \cdot a$. If $a \neq 0$, then $a = aa^{-1}a$. Hence every field is regular.

(ii) Consider the ring $\mathbb{Z}_6$. In this ring $[0] = [0][0][0], [1] = [1][1][1], [2] = [2][2][2], [3] = [3][3][3], [4] = [4][4][4], [5] = [5][5][5]$. Hence $\mathbb{Z}_6$ is a regular ring which is not a field.

(iii) Consider the ring $(\mathbb{Z}, +, \cdot)$. Here no element other than $0, \pm 1$ is regular. Thus $(\mathbb{Z}, +, \cdot)$ is not a regular ring.

(iv) Consider the set R of all real sequences. Then $(R, +, \cdot)$ is a ring where '+' and '·' is defined by

$$\{a_n\}_{n=1}^{\infty} + \{b_n\}_{n=1}^{\infty} = \{a_n + b_n\}_{n=1}^{\infty},$$
$$\{a_n\}_{n=1}^{\infty} \cdot \{b_n\}_{n=1}^{\infty} = \{a_n b_n\}_{n=1}^{\infty}.$$

Let $a = \{a_n\}_{n=1}^{\infty} \in R$ be any element. We consider a sequence $x = \{x_n\}_{n=1}^{\infty} \in R$, where $x_n = 0$ if $a_n = 0$ and $x_n = a_n^{-1}$ if $a_n \neq 0$. Then it is easy to show that $axa = a$. Therefore R is a regular ring.

Theorem 13.4.3. *Let R be a commutative ring with identity. Then R is regular if and only if $\langle a \rangle = \langle a^2 \rangle$ for all $a \in R$.*

Proof. First suppose that R is regular and $a \in R$. Clearly $\langle a^2 \rangle \subseteq \langle a \rangle$. Since R is regular, there exists an element $x \in R$ such that $a = axa = a^2x$. Now $\langle a \rangle = aR = a^2xR \subseteq a^2R = \langle a^2 \rangle$. Hence $\langle a \rangle = \langle a^2 \rangle$.

Conversely, let R be commutative ring with identity such that $\langle a \rangle = \langle a^2 \rangle$ for all $a \in R$. To show R is regular, let $x \in R$ be an arbitrary element. Then $\langle x \rangle = \langle x^2 \rangle$. Now $x \in \langle x \rangle = \langle x^2 \rangle = x^2 R$ implies $x = x^2 y$ for some $y \in R$, i.e., $x = xyx$. Consequently, R is regular. $\square$

Theorem 13.4.4. *A ring R with identity is a regular ring if and only if for any $a \in R$ there exists an idempotent $e \in R$ such that $Ra = Re$.*

Proof. First suppose that R is a regular ring and $a \in R$. So there exists an element $x \in R$ such that $a = axa$. Let $e = xa$. Then $e^2 = (xa)(xa) = x(axa) = xa = e$ and thus e is an idempotent. Now $Ra = Raxa = Rae \subseteq Re = Rxa \subseteq Ra$. Hence $Ra = Re$.

Conversely, suppose that for each $a \in R$ there exists an idempotent $e \in R$ such that $Ra = Re$. Let $x \in R$. Then $Rx = Rf$ for some idempotent $f \in R$. Now $x \in Rx = Rf$ implies $x = yf$ for some $y \in R$. This implies $xf = yf^2 = yf = x$. Now $f \in Rf = Rx$ implies $f = zx$ for some $z \in R$. Therefore, $x = xf = xzx$ and thus x is regular. Consequently, R is a regular ring. $\square$

Corollary 13.4.5. *In a regular ring with identity every principal left ideal is generated by some idempotent element.*

Theorem 13.4.6. *In a regular ring with identity the sum of two principal left ideals is a principal left ideal.*

Proof. Let Ra and Rb be two principal left ideals of a regular ring R. Now by Theorem 13.4.4 there exists an idempotent $e \in R$ such that $Ra = Re$. Then
$$
\begin{aligned}
Ra + Rb &= Re + Rb \\
&= \{re + tb : r, t \in R\} \\
&= \{re + tbe - tbe + tb : r, t \in R\} \\
&= \{(r + tb)e + tb(1 - e) : r, t \in R\} \\
&= Re + Rb(1 - e).
\end{aligned}
$$

Let $c = b(1 - e)$. Then $ce = 0$. Again, by Theorem 13.4.4 there exists an idempotent $f \in R$ such that $Rc = Rf$. Here $f \in Rf = Rc$ implies $f = yc$ for some $y \in R$. Thus $fe = (yc)e = y(ce) = 0$. Hence $Ra + Rb = Re + Rc = Re + Rf$, where e and f are idempotents satisfying $fe = 0$.

Let $g = (1 - e)f$. Then $eg = 0 = ge$. Also $g^2 = g(1 - e)f = gf - gef = gf = g$. Now $Rg = R(1 - e)f \subseteq Rf$ and $Rf = Rff = Rcf = Rb(1 - e)f = Rbg \subseteq Rg$. Hence $Rf = Rg$. Therefore, $Ra + Rb = Rc + Rg$ where e and g are idempotents satisfying $eg = 0 = ge$.

Clearly, $R(e + g) \subseteq Re + Rg$. Now $e = e^2 + eg = e(e + g) \in R(e + g)$ implies $Re \subseteq R(e + g)$. Similarly, $g = ge + g^2 = g(e + g) \in R(e + g)$ implies $Rg \subseteq R(e + g)$. Hence $Re + Rg \subseteq R(e + g)$. Therefore, $Re + Rg = R(e + g)$. Consequently, $Ra + Rb = R(e + g)$. $\square$

Corollary 13.4.7. *In a regular ring with identity, every finitely generated left ideal is a principal left ideal.*

Theorem 13.4.8. *A ring R with identity is regular ring if and only for any left ideal A and any right ideal B of R, $BA = A \cap B$.*

Proof. First suppose that R is a regular ring. Let A be any left ideal and B be any right ideal of R. Clearly $BA \subseteq A \cap B$. For the reverse inclusion, let $a \in A \cap B$. Since R is regular, there exists an element $x \in R$ such that $a = axa \in BA$. Therefore, $A \cap B \subseteq BA$ and hence $BA = A \cap B$.

Conversely, let R be a ring such that $BA = A \cap B$ for any left ideal A and any right ideal B of R. To show R is regular, let $a \in R$ be an arbitrary element. Then we consider the left ideal Ra and the right ideal aR. By the given condition we have $(Ra) \cap (aR) = (aR)(Ra) \subseteq aRa$. Now $a \in (Ra) \cap (aR) \subseteq aRa$ implies $a = aba$ for some $b \in R$. Hence R is regular. $\square$

Worked Out Exercises

$\Diamond$ **Exercise 13.4.1.** Let $M_2(\mathbb{R})$ denote the ring of all 2×2 matrices over $\mathbb{R}$ with respect to usual addition and usual multiplication of matrices. Show that $M_2(\mathbb{R})$ is a regular ring.

Solution. Let $A = \begin{pmatrix} a & b \\ c & d \end{pmatrix} \in M_2(\mathbb{R})$.

Case-I : Suppose $\det A - ad - bc \neq 0$. Then A^{-1} exists and $A - AA^{-1}A$. Hence A is regular.

Case-II : Suppose $\det A = ad - bc = 0$.

Case-II(a) : If A is the zero matrix, i.e., $A = \begin{pmatrix} 0 & 0 \\ 0 & 0 \end{pmatrix}$, then for any $B \in M_2(\mathbb{R})$ we have $A = ABA$ and hence A is regular.

Case-II(b) : Suppose A is a non-zero matrix. Then one of a, b, c and d is non-zero. Suppose $a \neq 0$. Then we take $B = \begin{pmatrix} \frac{1}{a} & 0 \\ 0 & 0 \end{pmatrix}$. Then

$$ABA = \begin{pmatrix} a & b \\ c & d \end{pmatrix} \begin{pmatrix} \frac{1}{a} & 0 \\ 0 & 0 \end{pmatrix} \begin{pmatrix} a & b \\ c & d \end{pmatrix} = \begin{pmatrix} a & b \\ c & \frac{bc}{a} \end{pmatrix} = \begin{pmatrix} a & b \\ c & d \end{pmatrix}$$

since $ad - bc = 0$.

If $c \neq 0$, then we take $B = \begin{pmatrix} 0 & \frac{1}{c} \\ 0 & 0 \end{pmatrix}$. Then

$$ABA = \begin{pmatrix} a & b \\ c & d \end{pmatrix} \begin{pmatrix} 0 & \frac{1}{c} \\ 0 & 0 \end{pmatrix} \begin{pmatrix} a & b \\ c & d \end{pmatrix} = \begin{pmatrix} a & \frac{ad}{c} \\ c & d \end{pmatrix} = \begin{pmatrix} a & b \\ c & d \end{pmatrix} = A.$$

Similarly, if $b \neq 0$ or $d \neq 0$, then we can find B such that $ABA = A$. Consequently, $M_2(\mathbb{R})$ is a regular ring.

◇ **Exercise 13.4.2.** Let R be a commutative ring with identity. If R is regular, then every proper prime ideal of R is maximal.

Solution. Let P be any proper prime ideal of R. To show P is maximal, let I be any ideal of R such that $P \subset I$. Then there exists an element $a \in I$ such that $a \notin P$. Since R is regular, there exists an element $x \in R$ such that $a = axa$. This implies $a(1 - xa) = 0 \in P$. Since P is prime and $a \notin P$, we must have $1 - xa \in P \subset I$. Again, $a \in I$ implies $xa \in I$. Hence $1 = (1 - xa) + xa \in I$ and thus $I = R$. Consequently, P is maximal.

◇ **Exercise 13.4.3.** The centre of a regular ring is again regular.

Solution. Let $a \in Z(R)$, where $Z(R)$ denotes the centre of the ring R. Since R is regular, there exists an element $x \in R$ such that $a = axa = a^2x = xa^2$. Let $z \in R$. Then $x(a^2z) = (xa^2)z = az = za = za^2x = (a^2z)x$ implies a^2z commutes with x and so it commutes with x^3. Therefore, $(a^2z)x^3 = x^3(a^2z)$, i.e., $z(a^2x^3) = (a^2x^3)z$. Since $z \in R$ is arbitrary, it follows that $a^2x^3 \in Z(R)$. Let $y = a^2x^3$. Then $y \in Z(R)$ and $y = a^2x^3 = x(ax)(ax) = xax = ax^2$. Moreover, $aya = a(ax^2)a = a(ax)(ax) = axa = a$. Consequently, $Z(R)$ is regular.

Exercises

1. In each of the following cases test whether R is a regular ring. Justify your answer.

   (a) $R = \mathbb{Z} \times \mathbb{Z}$ (b) $R = \mathbb{Z} \times \mathbb{Q}$ (c) $R = \mathbb{Z}_4$ (d) $R = \mathbb{Z}_8$ (e) $R = \mathbb{Z}_{11}$
   (f) $R = \mathbb{Z}_7 \times \mathbb{Z}_5$ (g) $R = F_1 \times F_2$, where F_1 and F_2 are two fields   (h) $R = \mathbb{Z}_9$ (i) $R = \mathbb{Z}_{10}$ (j) $R = \mathbb{Z}_6 \times \mathbb{Z}_{14}$.

2. Let R be a regular ring. Prove that every ideal of R is again regular.

3. Let I be an ideal of a ring R. If both I and R/I are regular, prove that R is also regular.

4. In a ring R, let T denote the intersection of all maximal ideals of a ring R. If $a \in T$ is regular, then prove that $a = 0$.

5. For each nonzero element x of a ring R with unity 1, if there exists a unique element $y \in R$ such that $xyx = x$, prove that $xy = 1 = yx$.

6. If R is a regular ring with 1_R, show that every nonzero element is either an unit or a zero divisor.

7. Find which of the following statements are true.

   (a) Every finite ring is regular.

   (b) Every Boolean ring is regular.

   (c) Every finite integral domain is regular.

   (d) Every element of a regular ring is idempotent.

13.5 Embedding of Rings

Does 2 divide 2? Don't be tempted to answer in the affirmative! The answer is *yes* if you consider the problem over the ring of integers $\mathbb{Z}$, but the answer is *no*, if you are dealing with $2\mathbb{Z}$, the ring of even integers. Observe that $1 \notin 2\mathbb{Z}$. Indeed, a ring without identity lacks some important properties. Fortunately however, we shall find that any ring is isomorphic to a subring of a ring with identity. In fact, we shall see shortly that any integral domain is isomorphic to a subring of a field.

Definition 13.5.1. A ring R is said to be *embedded* in a ring S if there exists a monomorphism $f : R \to S$.

From the above definition, we find that a ring R can be embedded in a ring S if there exists a subring T of S such that R is isomorphic to T.

In the following theorem, we show that any ring R can be embedded in a ring with identity.

Theorem 13.5.2. *Any ring R can be embedded in a ring S with identity such that R can be considered as an ideal of S. Moreover, if R is commutative, then S is also a commutative ring.*

Proof. The proof is a constructive one, where we construct a ring S. Let $S = \mathbb{Z} \times R$. Define binary operations, addition and multiplication on S by

$$(n, a) + (m, b) = (n + m, a + b) \quad \text{and} \quad (n, a)(m, b) = (nm, ma + nb + ab)$$

for all $n, m \in \mathbb{Z}$ and $a, b \in R$. Now it is just a routine matter to show that S is a ring under these two operations where $(0, 0)$ is the additive identity element. Now $(1, 0) \in \mathbb{Z} \times R$ where 1 is the integer one and 0 is the zero element of R.

For any $(n, a) \in \mathbb{Z} \times R$, we find that

$$(1, 0)(n, a) = (1.n, n0 + 1a + 0 \cdot a) = (n, a) = (n.1, 1a + n0 + a \cdot 0) = (n, a)(1, 0).$$

Hence $(1, 0)$ is the identity element of this ring.

Define $f : R \to \mathbb{Z} \times R$ by $f(a) = (0, a)$ for all $a \in R$. Obviously, f is injective. Now for all $a, b \in R$,

$$f(a + b) = (0, a + b) = (0, a) + (0, b) = f(a) + f(b)$$

and

$$f(ab) = (0, ab) = (00, 0a + 0b + ab) = (0, a)(0, b) = f(a)f(b).$$

Hence $f : R \to \mathbb{Z} \times R$ is a monomorphism. This implies that R is embedded in a ring S with identity.

Now $f(R) = \{(0, a) \,|\, a \in R\}$ is a subring of S and R is isomorphic to $f(R)$. We now show that $f(R)$ is an ideal of S. Let $(n, b) \in S$ and $(0, a) \in f(R)$. Then,

$$(n, b)(0, a) = (n0, 0b + na + ba) = (0, na + ba)$$

Since $na \in R$ and $ba \in R$ we find that $na + ba \in R$ and hence $(0, na + ba) = f(na + ba) \in f(R)$.

Similarly, we can show that $(0, a)(n, b) \in R$. Hence $f(R)$ is an ideal of S. Since $R \simeq f(R)$, we can consider that R is an ideal of S.

Finally, suppose R is commutative. Let $(n, a), (m, b) \in S$. Then

$$\begin{aligned} (n, a)(m, b) &= (nm, ma + nb + ab) \\ &= (mn, nb + ma + ba) \text{ (since R is a commutative ring)} \\ &= (m, b)(n, a). \end{aligned}$$

Hence S is a commutative ring.   □

In the above construction, one should note that the characteristic of the ring S is always zero. This does not depend on the characteristic of the ring R. Clearly, if the characteristic of R is zero, then R can be embedded in a ring S such that characteristic of S is the same as that of R. In the Worked-out Exercise 13.5.7, we will show that a ring R of finite characteristic, (say m) can be embedded in a ring S with identity such that characteristic of S is m.

It is already known to us that every field is an integral domain and every finite integral domain is a field. Now is there any further relation between these structures? Consider the ring of integers, $\mathbb{Z}$. $\mathbb{Z}$ is a subring of the field of rational numbers, $\mathbb{Q}$. Is it true for any integral domain that it is contained in some field? In fact, it is. In order to construct such a field, in the following let us follow (i.e., generalize) the construction of rational numbers from the integral domain of integers.

Definition 13.5.3. Let D be an integral domain. Let

$$R = D \times (D \setminus \{0\}) = \{(a, b) \mid a, b \in D, \ b \neq 0\}.$$

Define a binary relation $\sim$ on R by

$$(a, b) \sim (c, d) \ \text{ if and only if } \ ad = bc.$$

Proposition 13.5.4. *The binary relation $\sim$ defined on R is an equivalence relation.*

Proof. Let $(a, b) \in R$. Then $a, b \in D$ and $ab = ba$ since D is commutative. But this implies $(a, b) \sim (a, b)$ for each $(a, b) \in R$. So $\sim$ is reflexive. Now assume that there are $(a, b), (c, d) \in R$ such that $(a, b) \sim (c, d)$. Then $ad = bc$ which implies that $cb = da$, again by commutative property of D. Thus $(c, d) \sim (a, b)$ which proves that $\sim$ is symmetric. Finally, suppose that $(a, b), (c, d), (e, f) \in R$ with $(a, b) \sim (c, d)$ and $(c, d) \sim (e, f)$. So $ad = bc$ and $cf = de$. Now $afd = adf = bcf = bde = bed$. Since $d \neq 0$ and D is an integral domain, by Theorem 12.2.11, we have $af = be$. Then $(a, b) \sim (e, f)$. Therefore $\sim$ is transitive and hence an equivalence relation. $\square$

Remark 13.5.5. Note that for any $(a, b) \in R$, $(a, b) \sim (ac, bc)$ for all $c \in D \setminus \{0\}$. Thus in particular, $(0, 1) \sim (0, c)$ and $(1, 1) \sim (c, c)$ for all $c \in D \setminus \{0\}$.

Definition 13.5.6. For each $(a, b) \in R$, let us denote the equivalence class of (a, b) under the relation $\sim$ on R by $[a, b]$. Also, let F be the set of all equivalence classes of $\sim$, i.e., $F = R/\sim = \{[a, b] \mid (a, b) \in R\}$. Define[19]

$$[a, b] + [c, d] = [ad + bc, bd] \ \text{ and } \ [a, b] \cdot [c, d] = [ac, bd] \tag{13.5.1}$$

for all $[a, b], [c, d] \in F$.

Proposition 13.5.7. *The set F along with the operations defined by (13.5.1) forms a field.*

Proof. Firstly, it is required to show that the operations defined by (13.5.1) are well-defined. Let $a, c, p, r \in D$ and $b, d, q, s \in D \setminus \{0\}$ be such that $[a, b] = [p, q]$ and $[c, d] = [r, s]$. Then $aq = bp$ and $cs = dr$. Now $(ad + bc)(qs) = aqds + bcqs =$

---

[19]These definitions are exactly the same as the addition and multiplication of two rational numbers, $\frac{a}{b}$ and $\frac{c}{d}$.

$bpds + bqcs = bdps + bdqr = bdps + bdqr = (bd)(ps + qr)$. Thus $[a, b] + [c, d] = [ad + bc, bd] = [ps + qr, qs] = [p, q] + [r, s]$ and so the addition is well-defined. Again, $(ac)(qs) = aqcs = bpdr = (bd)(pr)$ which implies that $[a, b][c, d] = [ac, bd] = [pr, qs] = [p, q][r, s]$, proving that the multiplication is also well-defined.

Now in the following, we show that F along with the binary operations defined in (13.5.1) satisfies all the axioms required to be a field.[20] Let $[a, b], [c, d], [e, f] \in F$. Then,

Associativity for addition:
$$[a, b] + ([c, d] + [e, f]) = [a, b] + [cf + de, df] = [a(df) + b(cf + de), b(df)]$$
$$= [adf + bcf + bde, bdf] = [(ad + bc)f + (bd)e, (bd)f] = ([a, b] + [c, d]) + [e, f].$$

Associativity for multiplication:
$$[a, b]([c, d][e, f]) = [a, b][ce, df] = [ace, bdf] = [ac, bd][e, f] = ([a, c][b, d])[e, f].$$

Commutativity for addition:
$$[a, b] + [c, d] = [ad + bc, bd] = [cb + da, db] = [c, d] + [a, b].$$

Commutativity for multiplication:
$$[a, b][c, d] = [ac, bd] = [ca, db] = [c, d][a, b].$$

Distributive laws:

We first note that for any $x, y \in D$ and $z \in D \setminus \{0\}$, $[x, z] + [y, z] = [xz + zy, z^2] = [x + y, z]$, since $(xz + zy, z^2) = ((x + y)z, z^2) \sim (x + y, z)$ by Remark 13.5.5. Thus, $[a, b]([c, d] + [e, f]) = [a, b][cf + de, df] = [acf + ade, bdf] = [acf, bdf] + [ade, bdf] = [ac, bd] + [ae, bf] = [a, b][c, d] + [a, b][e, f]$.

Also, $([a, b] + [c, d])[e, f] = [ad + bc, bd][e, f] = [ade + bce, bdf] = [ade, bdf] + [bce, bdf] = [ae, bf] + [ce, df] = [a, b][e, f] + [c, d][e, f]$.

Existence of additive identity:
$$[a, b] + [0, 1] = [a \cdot 1 + b \cdot 0, b \cdot 1] = [a, b].$$

Existence of multiplicative identity:
$$[a, b][1, 1] = [a \cdot 1, b \cdot 1] = [a, b].$$

Existence of additive inverse:
$$[a, b] + [-a, b] = [ab - ba, b^2] = [0, b^2] = [0, 1] \text{ by Remark 13.5.5.}$$

Existence of multiplicative inverse (for nonzero elements):

Let $[a, b] \neq [0, 1]$. Then $(a, b) \not\sim (0, 1)$ which, by Remark 13.5.5, implies that $a \neq 0$. Therefore, $(b, a) \in R$ and so we have $[a, b][b, a] = [ab, ba] = [1, 1]$.

---

[20]Readers are advised to do this on their own. The calculations are exactly the same as one does for proving the field axioms for the set of rational numbers.

Thus summarizing all the above facts, we get that F is a field. □

Theorem 13.5.8. *Every integral domain is embedded in a field.*

Proof. Let D be an integral domain. Then by Proposition 13.5.7,

$$F = (D \times (D \setminus \{0\}))/ \sim = \{[a,b] \mid a,b \in D, \ b \neq 0\}$$

is a field under the binary operations defined by (13.5.1), where $\sim$ is an equivalence relation on $D \times (D \setminus \{0\})$, as described in Definition 13.5.3. We show that D is embedded in the field F.

Define the mapping

$$\phi : D \longrightarrow F \ \text{ by } \ \phi(a) = [a,1].$$

We prove that ϕ is our required monomorphism. Let $a,b \in D$. Then $\phi(a+b) = [a+b,1] = [a,1] + [b,1] = \phi(a) + \phi(b)$. Also $\phi(ab) = [ab,1] = [a,1][b,1] = \phi(a)\phi(b)$. Thus ϕ is a homomorphism of D into F. Finally, if $a,b \in D$ be such that $\phi(a) = \phi(b)$, then $[a,1] = [b,1]$. This implies that $(a,1) \sim (b,1)$ and hence $a = b$. Therefore ϕ is injective and so D is isomorphic to the subring $\{[a,1] \in F \mid a \in D\}$ of F. □

Definition 13.5.9. For an integral domain D, the field F described above (cf. Definition 13.5.6) is called the **quotient field** (or the **field of quotients**) of D.

Example 13.5.10. The field of rational numbers $\mathbb{Q}$ is the quotient field of the ring of integers, $\mathbb{Z}$.

Now let D be an integral domain and F be its quotient field. Since D is embedded in F, we may identify elements of D with their images (under the monomorphism, ϕ) in F and hence we may consider D as a *subring* of F. In this sense, F may also be called the **quotient field extension** of D. Moreover with this consideration, for any $a \in D \setminus \{0\}$, a^{-1} denotes the multiplicative inverse of $\phi(a)$, i.e., $a^{-1} = [a,1]^{-1} = [1,a]$ and any element $[a,b]$ in F is denoted by ab^{-1}, as $[a,b] = [a,1][1,b]$. Thus the quotient field F of an integral domain D can be described as

$$F = \{ab^{-1} \mid a,b \in D, \ b \neq 0\}.$$

We may formalize the above discussion in the following theorem:

Theorem 13.5.11. *Let D be an integral domain and K be a field containing D. Let $Q = \{ab^{-1} \in K \mid a,b \in D, \ b \neq 0\}$. Then Q is a subfield of K and it is isomorphic to the quotient field of D.*

Proof. Let F be the quotient field of D. Define the mapping

$$\psi : F \longrightarrow Q \text{ by } \psi([a,b]) = ab^{-1}.$$

We first need to show that ψ is well-defined. Let $[a,b] = [c,d]$ in F for some $a,b,c,d \in D \subseteq K$ with $b,d \neq 0$. Then $(a,b) \sim (c,d)$ and so $ad = bc$. This implies that $ab^{-1} = cd^{-1}$. Thus ψ is well-defined. Conversely, $ab^{-1} = cd^{-1}$ (for some $a,b,c,d \in D$ with $b,d \neq 0$) implies that $ad = bc$ and hence we have $[a,b] = [c,d]$. This shows that ψ is one-to-one. Also ψ is onto by definition.

Finally, we show that ψ is a homomorphism. Let $a,b,c,d \in D$ with $b,d \neq 0$. Then $\psi([a,b] + [c,d]) = \psi([ad+bc,bd]) = (ad+bc)(bd)^{-1} = (ad+bc)d^{-1}b^{-1} = ab^{-1} + cd^{-1} = \psi([a,b]) + \psi([c,d])$ and $\psi([a,b][c,d]) = \psi([ac,bd]) = (ac)(bd)^{-1} = acd^{-1}b^{-1} = (ab^{-1})(cd^{-1}) = \psi([a,b]) \cdot \psi([c,d])$. Thus, ψ is a homomorphism and hence an isomorphism, i.e., $F \simeq Q$. This, in turn, implies that Q is a field and so a subfield of K (cf. Worked-out Exercise 13.2.7). $\square$

Remark 13.5.12. It follows from the above theorem that given an integral domain, its quotient field is unique up to isomorphism, i.e., any two quotient fields of an integral domain are isomorphic and henceforth whenever we say that F is the quotient field of an integral domain D, we mean that F is isomorphic to the quotient field of D.

We know that any field is an integral domain. So what is the quotient field of a field? Clearly, it is nothing but the field itself[21] (verify!). Now by the above Theorem, we have come to know that every integral domain is, in fact, a subring of a field. But it is not true that whenever an integral domain is a subring of a field, then the field is the quotient field of it. For example, $\mathbb{Z} \subseteq \mathbb{Q} \subseteq \mathbb{R} \subseteq \mathbb{C}$, where $\mathbb{Z}$ is a subring of all of the three fields. But in this chain, $\mathbb{Q}$ is the quotient field of $\mathbb{Z}$. Also, it is not very difficult to understand that $\mathbb{Q}$ is the smallest field containing $\mathbb{Z}$. Indeed we have the following theorem:

Theorem 13.5.13. *Let D be an integral domain and F be its quotient field. Then F is the smallest field containing D.*

Proof. Let K be a field containing D. Let $x \in F$. Then by Theorem 13.5.11, we may write $x = ab^{-1}$ for some $a,b \in D$ with $b \neq 0$. Now since $a,b \in D \subseteq K$, we have $a,b \in K$ and since $b \neq 0$, we also have $b^{-1} \in K$ (as K is a field). Thus $x = ab^{-1} \in K$ which implies that $F \subseteq K$, as required. $\square$

---

[21]More precisely, isomorphic to the given field.

Worked-out Exercises

◇ **Exercise 13.5.1.** Find the quotient field of the integral domain

$$\mathbb{Z}[i] = \{a + bi \mid a, b \in \mathbb{Z}\}.$$

Solution. The integral domain $\mathbb{Z}[i]$ is contained in the field $\mathbb{C}$ of complex numbers. Thus by Theorem 13.5.11, $Q = \{uv^{-1} \in \mathbb{C} \mid u, v \in \mathbb{Z}[i], \ v \neq 0\}$ is the quotient field of $\mathbb{Z}[i]$. Let $u, v \in \mathbb{Z}$ such that $v \neq 0$. Then $u = a + bi$ and $v = c + di \neq 0$ for some $a, b, c, d \in \mathbb{Z}$. Now,

$$uv^{-1} = \frac{a + bi}{c + di} = \frac{(a + bi)(c - di)}{(c + di)(c - di)} = \frac{(ac + bd) + (bc - ad)i}{c^2 + d^2}$$
$$= \frac{ac + bd}{c^2 + d^2} + \frac{bc - ad}{c^2 + d^2} i \in \mathbb{Q}[i],$$

as $a, b, c, d \in \mathbb{Z}$. Thus $Q \subseteq \mathbb{Q}[i]$.

Conversely, let $x + yi \in \mathbb{Q}[i]$. Then $x = \frac{a}{b}$ and $y = \frac{c}{d}$, where $a, b, c, d \in \mathbb{Z}$ with $b, d \neq 0$. Since $\mathbb{Z} \subseteq \mathbb{Z}[i]$, we have $a, b, c, d \in \mathbb{Z}[i]$. So $x = ab^{-1}, y = cd^{-1} \in Q$. Also since $i \in \mathbb{Z}[i] \subseteq Q$, we have $x + yi \in Q$. Therefore $\mathbb{Q}[i] \subseteq Q$ and hence $Q = \mathbb{Q}[i]$, i.e., the quotient field of $\mathbb{Z}[i]$ is $\mathbb{Q}[i]$.

◇ **Exercise 13.5.2.** Find the quotient field of the integral domain $\mathbb{R}[x]$, the ring of polynomials with real coefficients.

Solution. Consider the set $\mathbb{R}(x) = \left\{ \frac{f(x)}{g(x)} \mid f(x), g(x) \in \mathbb{R}[x], \ g(x) \neq 0 \right\}$. Define addition and multiplication in $\mathbb{R}(x)$ as follows:

$$\frac{f_1(x)}{g_1(x)} + \frac{f_2(x)}{g_2(x)} = \frac{f_1(x)g_2(x) + f_2(x)g_1(x)}{g_1(x)g_2(x)}$$

$$\frac{f_1(x)}{g_1(x)} \cdot \frac{f_2(x)}{g_2(x)} = \frac{f_1(x)f_2(x)}{g_1(x)g_2(x)}.$$

Verify that $\mathbb{R}(x)$ is a field under the operations defined above. Now for any $f(x) \in \mathbb{R}[x]$, $f(x) = \frac{f(x)}{1} \in \mathbb{R}(x)$. So $\mathbb{R}[x] \subseteq \mathbb{R}(x)$. Then it is clear from Theorem 13.5.11 that $\mathbb{R}(x)$ is the quotient field of $\mathbb{R}[x]$.

◇ **Exercise 13.5.3.** Let D be an integral domain with the quotient field F. Let R be another integral domain such that $D \subseteq R \subseteq F$. Prove that the quotient field of R is isomorphic to F.

Solution. We have that the integral domain R is contained in the field F. So by Theorem 13.5.11, the quotient field of R is given by

$$Q = \{ab^{-1} \in F \mid a, b \in R, \ b \neq 0\}.$$

Thus $Q \subseteq F$. Also since F is the quotient field of D, for any $x \in F$, $x = ab^{-1}$ where $a, b \in D$ with $b \neq 0$. Since $D \subseteq R$, we have $x \in Q$, i.e., $F \subseteq Q$. So $Q = F$. Hence, the quotient field of R is F.

◇ **Exercise 13.5.4.** Let D and D' be two isomorphic integral domains through an isomorphism f. Show that f can be uniquely extended to an isomorphism of F onto F', where F and F' are quotient fields of D and D' respectively.

Solution. We have $F = \left\{ ab^{-1} \in F \mid a, b \in D,\ b \neq 0 \right\}$ and

$$F' = \left\{ uv^{-1} \in F' \mid u, v \in D',\ v \neq 0 \right\}.$$

Define the map $\bar{f} : F \longrightarrow F'$ by $\bar{f}(ab^{-1}) = f(a)f(b)^{-1}$. Now for any $a, b, c, d \in D$ with $b, d \neq 0$ we have

$$ab^{-1} = cd^{-1} \Longleftrightarrow ad = bc \Longleftrightarrow f(ad) = f(bc) \Longleftrightarrow f(a)f(d) = f(b)f(c)$$
$$\Longleftrightarrow f(a)f(b)^{-1} = f(c)f(d)^{-1} \Longleftrightarrow \bar{f}(ab^{-1}) = \bar{f}(cd^{-1})$$

as $f : D \longrightarrow D'$ is an isomorphism. Thus $\bar{f}$ is well-defined as well as injective. Now,

$$\bar{f}(ab^{-1} + cd^{-1}) = \bar{f}((ad + bc)(bd)^{-1}) = f(ad + bc)f(bd)^{-1}$$
$$= \ (f(a)f(d) + f(b)f(c))f(d)^{-1}f(b)^{-1} = f(a)f(b)^{-1} + f(c)f(d)^{-1}$$

and

$$\bar{f}(ab^{-1} \cdot cd^{-1}) = \bar{f}((ac)(bd)^{-1}) = f(ac)f(bd)^{-1}$$
$$= \ f(a)f(c)f(d)^{-1}f(b)^{-1} = f(a)f(b)^{-1} \cdot f(c)f(d)^{-1}$$

as f is a homomorphism. Finally, let $uv^{-1} \in F'$ where $u, v \in D'$ with $v \neq 0$. Since f is surjective, there exist $a, b \in D$ such that $f(a) = u$ and $f(b) = v$. Also since $v \neq 0$, we have $b \neq 0$ as f is a homomorphism. Then $\bar{f}(ab^{-1}) = f(a)f(b)^{-1} = uv^{-1}$, proving that $\bar{f}$ is surjective. Therefore, $\bar{f}$ is an isomorphism, i.e., $F \cong F'$.

◇ **Exercise 13.5.5.** A field F is said to be a ***prime field*** if F has no subfield other than itself. Show that any prime field F is isomorphic to either $\mathbb{Q}$, the field of rational numbers or the field $\mathbb{Z}_p$ of integers modulo a prime p.

Solution. Let F be a prime field. By Theorem 12.2.24, we know that the characteristic of F is either prime or zero. First suppose the characteristic of F is zero. Then $n1 \neq 0$ for all $n \in \mathbb{Z} \setminus \{0\}$. Let

$$R = \{n1 \in F \mid n \in \mathbb{Z}\}.^{22}$$

---

[22] Recall that we follow the convention that $n1 = 0$ for $n = 0$ and $n1 = (-n)(-1)$ for $n < 0$.

Clearly $0, 1 \in R$ (for $n = 0$ and $n = 1$ respectively). Thus R is nonempty. Now let $m1, n1 \in R$ for some $m, n \in \mathbb{Z}$. Then $m1 - n1 = (m - n)1 \in R$ and $(m1)(n1) = (mn)1 \in R$. Thus R is a subring of F which contains the identity and hence R is an integral domain, as F is so.

Now it is easy to verify that the mapping $f : R \longrightarrow \mathbb{Z}$ defined by $f(n1) = n$ is a ring isomorphism, i.e., $R \simeq \mathbb{Z}$. Hence by the above problem, the quotient field of R is isomorphic to the quotient field of $\mathbb{Z}$ which is $\mathbb{Q}$, the field of rational numbers. Now since $R \subseteq F$, the quotient field of R is a subfield of F. But F is a prime field. Therefore, F is equal to the quotient field of R and so F is isomorphic to $\mathbb{Q}$.

Next suppose the characteristic of F is prime, say, p. Then $pa = 0$ for all $a \in F$. In particular, $p1 = 0$. Thus in this case, one may show that the subset $S = \{n1 \in F \mid n = 0, 1, 2, 3, \ldots, p - 1\}$ is a subring of F containing identity and it is isomorphic to the field $\mathbb{Z}_p$ through an isomorphism which sends $n1 \in S$ to $[n] \in \mathbb{Z}_p$. Again since F is a prime field, we have $F = S$, i.e., F is isomorphic to $\mathbb{Z}_p$.

$\lozenge$ **Exercise 13.5.6.** Let D be an integral domain and E be its quotient field. Show that D and E have the same characteristic.

Solution. Since D is isomorphic to a subring of E, consider D as a subring of E (identifying elements of D with their isomorphic images) with the same identity element, say 1. Now by Worked-out Exercise 12.2.9, we have that the characteristic of a ring with identity 1, is n if and only if n is the least positive integer such that $n1 = 0$. Thus characteristic of D is n (say), if and only if n is the least positive integer such that $n1 = 0$, which is again true if and only if the characteristic of E is n. Therefore the characteristic of D and E are the same.

$\blacklozenge$ **Exercise 13.5.7.** Let R be a ring of characteristic n. Prove that R can be extended to a ring with identity which is also of characteristic n.

Solution. Define the set

$$S = \mathbb{Z}_n \times R = \{([m], r) \mid [m] \in \mathbb{Z}_n, r \in R\}.$$

Also, define the operations of addition and multiplication[23] on S by

$$([m], a) + ([p], b) = ([m + p], a + b)$$
$$([m], a) \cdot ([p], b) = ([mp], ab + pa + mb).$$

---

[23]As usual, here pa denotes p times addition of a and mb denotes m times addition of b.

We show that $(S, +, \cdot)$ is a ring. Since the addition is defined component wise, $(S, +)$ becomes a direct product of abelian groups $(R, +)$ and $(\mathbb{Z}_n, +)$. Thus $(S, +)$ is also an abelian group.

We now show that the multiplication is well-defined. For this, suppose $[m] = [m_1]$ and $[p] = [p_1]$. Then $m_1 = m + t_1 n$ and $p_1 = p + t_2 n$ for some $t_1, t_2 \in \mathbb{Z}$. Then $m_1 p_1 = mp + (t_2 m + t_1 p + t_1 t_2 n)n$ implies that $[m_1 p_1] = [mp]$. Also $p_1 a = pa + (t_2 n)a = pa + t_2(na) = pa + t_2 0 = pa$, since characteristic of R is n and $m_1 b = mb + (t_1 n)b = mb + t_1(nb) = mb + t_1 0 = mb$. Hence,

$$
\begin{aligned}
([m_1], a)([p_1], b) &= ([m_1 p_1], ab + p_1 a + m_1 b) \\
&= ([mp], ab + pa + mb) \\
&= ([m], a)([p], b).
\end{aligned}
$$

Consequently, the multiplication is well-defined.

Now let $([m], a), ([p], b), ([q], c) \in S$. Then,

$$
\begin{aligned}
&\Big(([m], a)([p], b)\Big)([q], c) \\
=\; &([mp], ab + pa + mb)\,([q], c) \\
=\; &\Big([(mp)q], (ab + pa + mb)c + q(ab + pa + mb) + (mp)c\Big) \\
=\; &\Big([mpq], abc + pac + mbc + qab + (qp)a + (qm)b + (mp)c\Big) \\
=\; &\Big([m(pq)], a(bc + qb + pc) + (pq)a + m(bc + qb + pc)\Big) \\
=\; &([m], a)([pq], bc + qb + pc) \\
=\; &([m], a)\Big(([p], b)([q], c)\Big)
\end{aligned}
$$

which implies that the multiplication in S is associative. Next we verify the distributive law:

$$
\begin{aligned}
&([m], a)\Big(([p], b) + ([q], c)\Big) \\
=\; &([m], a)([p + q], b + c) \\
=\; &\Big([m(p + q)], a(b + c) + (p + q)a + m(b + c)\Big) \\
=\; &([mp + mq], ab + ac + pa + qa + mb + mc) \\
=\; &([mp], ab + pa + mb) + ([mq], ac + qa + mc) \\
=\; &([m], a)([p], b) + ([m], a)([q], c).
\end{aligned}
$$

Similarly, one can check the other distributive law. All these verifications show that $(S, +, \cdot)$ is a ring. Clearly, $([0], 0)$ is the zero element of S. Now we note that

$$([m], a)([1], 0) = ([m \cdot 1], a \cdot 0 + 1a + m0) = ([m], a) = ([1], 0)([m], a)$$

for all $([m], a) \in S$. Thus $([1], 0)$ is the identity of the ring S. Also for any $([m], a) \in S$, we have $n([m], a) = (n[m], na) = ([0], 0)$ since $[m] \in \mathbb{Z}_n$ and characteristic of R is n.

Further, if t is a positive integer such that $t < n$, then $t([1], 0) = ([t], 0) \neq ([0], 0)$. Therefore S is a ring with identity which is of characteristic n.

Finally, we show that R is embedded in S, i.e., there is an injective homomorphism from R into S. Define the mapping $f : R \longrightarrow S$ by $f(a) = ([0], a)$. The map is clearly one-to-one as $f(a) = f(b) \Longrightarrow ([0], a) = ([0], b) \Longrightarrow a = b$. Now, $f(a + b) = ([0], a + b) = ([0], a) + ([0], b) = f(a) + f(b)$ and $f(ab) = ([0], ab) = ([0], a)([0], b) = f(a)f(b)$. Thus f is a homomorphism, as required.

Therefore, R is isomorphic to a subring of a ring with identity, which is also of characteristic n. In other words, R can be extended to a ring with identity which is also of characteristic n.

Exercises

1. Find the quotient field of the integral domain
$$\mathbb{Z}[\sqrt{5}] = \left\{ a + b\sqrt{5} \mid a, b \in \mathbb{Z} \right\}.$$

2. Let $R = \left\{ \frac{a}{b} \in \mathbb{Q} \mid 7 \text{ does not divide } b \right\}$. Show that R is an integral domain and find the quotient field of R.

3. Find the quotient field of the integral domain $\mathbb{Z}[x]$, the ring of polynomials with integer coefficients.

4. Let D be an integral domain. Show that the polynomial ring $D[x]$ is an integral domain and find its quotient field. Suppose E is the field of quotient of D. What is the relation between the quotient fields of $D[x]$ and $E[x]$?

5. Prove that the quotient field of a field is the field itself.

6. Prove that every field contains a subfield which is isomorphic either to $\mathbb{Q}$ or $\mathbb{Z}_p$. This subfield is called the **prime subfield** of that field.

7. Let K be a field with its prime subfield F. Show that every automorphism f on K fixes the elements of F, i.e., $f(a) = a$ for all $a \in F$.

8. Prove that every automorphism of an integral domain can be uniquely extended to an automorphism of its quotient field.

9. Let R be a commutative ring with no zero divisors. Then show that R can be embedded in an integral domain.

Chapter 14

Factorization in Integral Domains

14.1 Factorization Domain

In this section, we begin by introducing the concept of divisibility in an arbitrary commutative ring and then concentrate mainly on integral domains. As usual our natural inspiration is the ring of integers, $\mathbb{Z}$. For any two integers $a \neq 0$ and b (say), a is said to divide b if and only if there exists an integer c such that $ac = b$. An abstraction of this idea leads us to define the following:

Definition 14.1.1. Let R be a commutative ring with identity. Let $a, b \in R$ such that $a \neq 0$. Then a is said to **divide** b if there exists $c \in R$ such that $ac = b$. We write $a \mid b$. In this case, a is called a **divisor** of b. If $a \mid b$ and $b \mid a$, then a and b are called **associates**. We write $a \sim b$.

Note that 1 is a divisor of any element $a \in R$ and every nonzero element of R divides 0. If u is a unit in R, then $u \mid 1$ and hence $u \mid a$ for all $a \in R$. In the ring $\mathbb{Z}$, $2 \sim -2$. In general, $n \sim -n$ for all $n \in \mathbb{Z} \setminus \{0\}$. Recall that the principal ideal generated by an element $a \in R$ is denoted by (a). Then the following theorem is obvious.

Theorem 14.1.2. *Let R be a commutative ring with identity and $a, b, u \in R \setminus \{0\}$. Then*

(i) $a \mid b \iff b \in (a) \iff (b) \subseteq (a)$;

(ii) $a \sim b \iff (a) = (b)$;

(iii) the binary relation $\sim$ on $R \setminus \{0\}$ is an equivalence relation;

(iv) u is a unit in $R \iff u \sim 1 \iff (u) = R$.

(v) If R is an integral domain, then $a \sim b$ if and only if $a = bu$ for some unit u in R.

Proof. The proof for other parts being obvious, we only prove (v).

Let R be an integral domain. If $a \sim b$, then $a \mid b$ and $b \mid a$. These imply $a = bu$ and $b = av$ for some $u, v \in R$. Then $a = bu = (av)u$ and so $a(1 - vu) = 0$. Since R is an integral domain and $a \neq 0$, we have $1 - vu = 0$. Thus $vu = 1$. Since R is commutative, we have $v = u^{-1}$, i.e., u is a unit.

Conversely, let $a = bu$ where u is a unit in R. Then by definition, $b \mid a$. Also since u is a unit, $b = au^{-1}$, which implies $a \mid b$. Therefore $a \sim b$. $\qquad\square$

The concept of *prime numbers* is very much associated with divisibility of integers. In the following, we define analogous concepts in the case of an arbitrary commutative ring with identity.

Definition 14.1.3. Let R be a commutative ring with identity. Then a *nonzero nonunit* element $p \in R$ is called ***irreducible*** in R, if $p = ab$ for some $a, b \in R$ implies, either a is a unit in R or b is a unit in R. On the other hand, a *nonzero nonunit element* p is called ***prime*** in R, if $p \mid ab$ for some $a, b \in R$ implies, either $p \mid a$ or $p \mid b$.

Example 14.1.4. (i) In the ring $\mathbb{Z}$, any prime number is *prime as well as irreducible.*

(ii) In the ring $\mathbb{Z}_6$, $[2]$ is *prime but not irreducible*, as $[2] = [2] \cdot [4]$ but neither $[2]$ nor $[4]$ is a unit in $\mathbb{Z}_6$.

(iii) The field $\mathbb{Q}$ of all rational numbers has neither any irreducible element nor any prime element, as every nonzero element of $\mathbb{Q}$ is a unit. Indeed, such an assertion is true for any field.

Remark 14.1.5. Note that in an integral domain R, associates of an irreducible element of R are irreducible and associates of a prime element of R are prime (prove!).

Theorem 14.1.6. *Let p be a nonzero nonunit element in an integral domain R. Then*
(i) p is irreducible if and only if $d \mid p$, $d \in R$ implies that either d is a unit or $d \sim p$;[1]
(ii) p is prime if and only if (p) is a nonzero prime ideal of R;
(iii) If p is prime, then p is irreducible.

Proof. (i) Follows immediately from the definition of irreducible elements.

(ii) Suppose p is prime. Then $(p) \neq (0)$ as $p \neq 0$. Also since p is not a unit, (p) is a proper ideal of R. Now let $b, c \in R$ be such that $bc \in (p)$. Then $bc = px$ for some $x \in R$. So $p \mid bc$ which implies that $p \mid b$ or $p \mid c$, as p is prime. Therefore $b \in (p)$ or $c \in (p)$ and hence (p) is a prime ideal of R.

---

[1]That is, p has no *proper* divisor. For $a, b \in R$ with $b \mid a$, b is called a ***proper divisor*** of a if b is neither an associate of a nor a unit.

Conversely, let (p) be a nonzero prime ideal of R. Then $p \neq 0$ and since $(p) \neq R$, we find p is a nonunit element of R. Let $p \mid bc$ for some $b, c \in R$. Then $bc \in (p)$, which implies that $b \in (p)$ or $c \in (p)$, as (p) is a prime ideal of R. Thus $p \mid b$ or $p \mid c$, proving that p is prime.

(iii) Let p be a prime element of R and $p = bc$ for some $b, c \in R$. Since p is prime, we have $p \mid b$ or $p \mid c$. Suppose $p \mid b$. Then $b = px$ for some $x \in R$. This implies that $p = pxc$, i.e., $p(1 - xc) = 0$. Since R is an integral domain and $p \neq 0$, we have $xc = 1$ and so c is a unit in R. Similarly, one can show that if $p \mid c$, then b is a unit. Therefore p is irreducible. $\square$

Before proceeding further, let us concentrate our discussion on the ring $\mathbb{Z}[\sqrt{-5}] = \{a + b\sqrt{-5} \mid a, b \in \mathbb{Z}\}$, where addition and multiplication are respectively defined by

$$(a + b\sqrt{-5}) + (c + d\sqrt{-5}) = (a + c) + (b + d)\sqrt{-5}$$
$$(a + b\sqrt{-5}) \cdot (c + d\sqrt{-5}) = (ac - 5bd) + (ad + bc)\sqrt{-5}.$$

It is a subring (with identity) of the field of complex numbers. Hence $\mathbb{Z}[\sqrt{-5}]$ is an integral domain. In the following, we show some interesting properties of elements of $\mathbb{Z}[\sqrt{-5}]$:

(i) **1 and -1 are the only units of $\mathbb{Z}[\sqrt{-5}]$**: We show that an element $a + b\sqrt{-5} \in \mathbb{Z}[\sqrt{-5}]$ is a unit if and only if $a^2 + 5b^2 = 1$. Suppose $a + b\sqrt{-5}$ is a unit. Then there exists an element $c + d\sqrt{-5} \in \mathbb{Z}[\sqrt{-5}]$ such that $(a + b\sqrt{-5})(c + d\sqrt{-5}) = 1$. Then $\overline{(a + b\sqrt{-5})(c + d\sqrt{-5})} = \bar{1}$, where $\bar{\alpha}$ denotes the conjugate of α in $\mathbb{C}$. Hence $(a - b\sqrt{-5})(c - d\sqrt{-5}) = 1$, whence we have

$$1 = (a + b\sqrt{-5})(c + d\sqrt{-5})(a - b\sqrt{-5})(c - d\sqrt{-5}) = (a^2 + 5b^2)(c^2 + 5d^2).$$

Since $a, b, c, d \in \mathbb{Z}$, we find that $a^2 + 5b^2 = 1$.

Conversely, suppose that $a^2 + 5b^2 = 1$. Then $(a + b\sqrt{-5})(a - b\sqrt{-5}) = 1$. Hence $(a + b\sqrt{-5})$ is a unit. Now if $a^2 + 5b^2 = 1$, then $a = \pm 1$ and $b = 0$ as $a, b \in \mathbb{Z}$. Hence it follows that 1 and -1 are the only units of $\mathbb{Z}[\sqrt{-5}]$.

(ii) **$1 + \sqrt{-5}, 1 - \sqrt{-5}, 3, 2$ are irreducible elements in $\mathbb{Z}[\sqrt{-5}]$**: We show that 3 is an irreducible element. Let $3 = (a + b\sqrt{-5})(c + d\sqrt{-5})$, where $(a + b\sqrt{-5}), (c + d\sqrt{-5}) \in \mathbb{Z}[\sqrt{-5}]$. Then proceeding as above, we have $3 = (a - b\sqrt{-5})(c - d\sqrt{-5})$, whence

$$9 = 3 \cdot 3 = (a^2 + 5b^2)(c^2 + 5d^2) \tag{14.1.1}$$

Now there are no $a, b, c, d \in \mathbb{Z}$, for which $a^2 + 5b^2 = 3$ and $c^2 + 5d^2 = 3$. Hence (14.1.1) implies that either $a^2 + 5b^2 = 1$ or $c^2 + 5d^2 = 1$, i.e., either $a + b\sqrt{-5}$ is a unit or

$c + d\sqrt{-5}$ is a unit. So, we see that 3 is an irreducible element in $\mathbb{Z}[\sqrt{-5}]$. Similarly, one can show that $2, 1 + \sqrt{-5}, 1 - \sqrt{-5}$ are irreducible elements in $\mathbb{Z}[\sqrt{-5}]$.

(iii) $1 + \sqrt{-5}, 1 - \sqrt{-5}, 3, 2$ are not prime elements in $\mathbb{Z}[\sqrt{-5}]$: We prove it for 3, and leave the rest of the similar verifications for the reader. Since $3 \cdot 2 = 6$, we find that $3 \mid 6$. But $6 = (1 + \sqrt{-5})(1 - \sqrt{-5})$. Hence $3 \mid (1 + \sqrt{-5})(1 - \sqrt{-5})$. Suppose $3 \mid 1 + \sqrt{-5}$ in $\mathbb{Z}[\sqrt{-5}]$. Then there exists $u + v\sqrt{-5} \in \mathbb{Z}[\sqrt{-5}]$ such that $3(u + v\sqrt{-5}) = 1 + \sqrt{-5}$. This implies that $3u = 1$ and $3v = 1$. But there are no integers u, v for which $3u = 1$ or $3v = 1$. Hence $3 \nmid 1 + \sqrt{-5}$. Similarly, we can show that $3 \nmid 1 - \sqrt{-5}$. Consequently, 3 is not a prime element.

In part (iii) of Theorem 14.1.6, we have seen that in any integral domain, every prime element is irreducible. But we have shown in the domain $\mathbb{Z}[\sqrt{-5}]$ that 3 is an irreducible element which is not a prime. An interesting point to note is that, there are some special integral domains where the distinction between these two concepts disappears. Now we are going to consider one such class of integral domains.

Recall that an integral domain R is said to be a **principal ideal domain** (in short, **PID**), if every ideal of R is a principal ideal.

Example 14.1.7. (i) Consider the ring of integers, $\mathbb{Z}$. It is an integral domain. Also by Worked-out Exercise 13.1.2 , we know that every ideal of $\mathbb{Z}$ is of the form $n\mathbb{Z} = (n)$ for some nonnegative integer n. Thus $\mathbb{Z}$ is an example of PID.

(ii) In the next chapter, we shall see that the polynomial ring $\mathbb{R}[x]$ over the field of real numbers is a PID . But the polynomial ring $\mathbb{Z}[x]$ is not a PID.

Theorem 14.1.8. *In a PID R, a nonzero nonunit element p is irreducible if and only if p is prime.*

Proof. Let p be an irreducible element. Suppose $a, b \in R$ be such that $p \mid ab$. Then $ab = pv$ for some $v \in R$. Let $I = \{rb + tp \mid r, t \in R\}$. It can be easily shown that I is an ideal. Since R is a PID, there exists $d \in R$ such that $I = (d)$. Now $p = 0b + 1p \in (d)$. Hence $p = du$ for some $u \in R$. Since p is irreducible, either d is a unit or u is a unit. If d is unit, $1 \in (d) = I$. Hence $1 = rb + tp$ for some $r, t \in R$. Then $a = rab + tap = rpv + tap = p(rv + ta)$ implies that $p \mid a$.

If u is a unit, then $d = pu^{-1} \in (p)$. Thus $I = (d) \subseteq (p) \subseteq I$, so that $I = (p)$. Now $b = 1b + 0p \in I$. Hence $b \in (p)$, which implies that $p \mid b$. Thus we find that either $p \mid a$ or $p \mid b$. Hence p is a prime element.

The converse follows from part (iii) of Theorem 14.1.6. $\qquad \square$

The following theorem describes the relation among maximal ideals, prime ideals, irreducible elements and prime elements in a PID.

Theorem 14.1.9. *Let p be an element of a PID R. Then the following are equivalent:*

   (i)   *p is irreducible.*

  (ii)   *(p) is a nonzero maximal ideal.*

 (iii)   *(p) is a nonzero prime ideal.*

 (iv)   *p is prime.*

Proof. $(i) \Rightarrow (ii)$: Let p be an irreducible element in a PID R. Then by definition, p is nonzero and nonunit. Hence $(p) \neq R$ and also $(p) \neq (0)$. Let J be an ideal of R such that $(p) \subset J$. Since R is a PID, there exists $d \in R$ such that $J = (d)$. Then $(p) \subset (d)$. Now $p \in (d)$. Hence $p = du$ for some $u \in R$. Since p is irreducible, either d is a unit or u is a unit. If d is a unit, then $1 \in (d) = J$ which implies that $J = R$. If u is a unit, then $d = pu^{-1}$ shows that $J = (d) \subseteq (p)$, which contradicts our assumption that $(p) \subset J$. Hence if $(p) \subset J$, then $J = R$. Consequently, (p) is a maximal ideal.

$(ii) \Rightarrow (iii)$: Follows from Theorem 13.3.9.

$(iii) \Rightarrow (iv)$: Follows from Theorem 14.1.6(ii).

$(iv) \Rightarrow (i)$: Follows from Theorem 14.1.6(iii).   □

Let us now exploit another nice property of the ring of integers. Let $n > 1$ be a positive integer. Then n can be expressed uniquely as a product of prime numbers. Since $\mathbb{Z}$ is a PID, prime numbers and irreducible elements of $\mathbb{Z}$ are indistinguishable. We now define a class of integral domains in which every nonzero nonunit element can be factorized in terms of irreducible elements.

Definition 14.1.10. Let a be a nonzero nonunit element in an integral domain R. If $a = p_1 p_2 \ldots p_r$ where $p_1, p_2, \ldots, p_r$ are irreducible elements in R, then $p_1 p_2 \ldots p_r$ is called a ***factorization*** of a in R. An integral domain R is called a ***factorization domain*** (in short, ***FD***), if every nonzero nonunit element in R has a factorization in terms of irreducible elements of R.

Clearly, the ring of integers is a FD. To give some other examples of FD, we prove the following theorem.

Theorem 14.1.11. *Let R be an integral domain. Suppose there exists a function $\delta : R \smallsetminus \{0\} \to \mathbb{N}_0$ such that, for all $a, b \in R \smallsetminus \{0\}$, $\delta(ab) \geq \delta(b)$, where equality holds if and only if a is a unit. Then R is a FD.*

Proof. Suppose R is not a FD. Hence there exists a nonzero nonunit element a such that a is not factorizable. Let $T = \{b \in R \,|\, b \text{ is a nonzero nonunit but not factorizable}\}$. Hence $T \neq \emptyset$. Let $T_1 = \{\delta(b) \,|\, b \in T\}$. Now T_1 is a nonempty subset of $\mathbb{N}_0$. Hence by the well-ordering principle, T_1 has a least element. So, we can find an element $b \in T$ such that $\delta(b) \leq \delta(a)$ for all $a \in T$. Since $b \in T$, b is a nonzero nonunit and also not irreducible. Note that, every irreducible element gives a factorization of itself. Hence there exist nonzero nonunit elements $c, d \in R$ such that $b = cd$. Now at least one of c, d does not have a factorization; otherwise, the factorizations of c and d put together produce a factorization of b. Suppose c is not factorizable. Then $c \in T$ and hence $\delta(c) \in T_1$. Since d is not a unit, we find that $\delta(b) > \delta(c)$. This contradicts the fact that $\delta(b)$ is the least element in T_1. Hence R is a FD. $\qquad\qquad\square$

By virtue of this theorem, we can find different examples of factorizable domains.

Example 14.1.12. (i) $\mathbb{Z}$ is a FD, because we have a function $\delta(a) = |a|$ which satisfies the conditions of the above theorem.

(ii) $\mathbb{Z}[i]$ is a FD, since $\delta(a+ib) = a^2+b^2$ is a function satisfying the given conditions.

(iii)   Consider the domain $\mathbb{Z}[\sqrt{-5}]$. Define $\delta : \mathbb{Z}[\sqrt{-5}] \longrightarrow \mathbb{N}_0$ by $\delta(a + b\sqrt{-5}) = a^2 + 5b^2$. We have already shown that $a + b\sqrt{-5}$ is a unit in $\mathbb{Z}[\sqrt{-5}]$ if and only if $a^2 + 5b^2 = 1$, i.e., if and only if $\delta(a+b\sqrt{-5}) = 1$. Let $a+b\sqrt{-5}, c+d\sqrt{-5} \in \mathbb{Z}[\sqrt{-5}] \setminus \{0\}$. Then,

$$
\begin{aligned}
&\delta\big((a + b\sqrt{-5})(c + d\sqrt{-5})\big) \\
={}& \delta\big((ac - 5bd) + (ad + bc)\sqrt{-5}\big) \\
={}& (ac - 5bd)^2 + 5(ad + bc)^2 \\
={}& (a^2 + 5b^2)(c^2 + 5d^2) \\
\geq{}& a^2 + 5b^2 \quad \text{(equality holds if and only if } c^2 + 5d^2 = 1)
\end{aligned}
$$

Hence $\mathbb{Z}[\sqrt{-5}]$ is a FD.

Definition 14.1.13. An integral domain R is called a ***unique factorization domain*** (in short ***UFD***),[2] if the following conditions are satisfied:

(i) for every nonzero nonunit element $a \in R$, $a = a_1 a_2 \cdots a_n$ for some positive integer n, where each a_i is irreducible;

(ii) if $a = a_1 a_2 \cdots a_n = b_1 b_2 \cdots b_m$ where a_i and b_i are irreducible, then $m = n$ and each $a_i \sim b_{\sigma(i)}$ for some permutation σ on the set $\{1, 2, \ldots, n\}$.

---

[2] Also called ***Gaussian domain***.

Example 14.1.14. Certainly $\mathbb{Z}$ is an example of a UFD. In the sequel, we shall show that any PID is a UFD. Also the famous Gauss' theorem, that we shall discuss in the next chapter (cf. Theorem 15.1.27), will assure us that a polynomial ring over a UFD is again a UFD. In particular, $\mathbb{Z}[x]$ is a UFD.

Theorem 14.1.15. *Every irreducible element in a UFD is prime.*

Proof. Let $a \in R$ be irreducible and $a \mid bc$ for some $b, c \in R$. If either b or c is zero, then a divides one of b, c. So suppose $b \neq 0$, $c \neq 0$. If one of b or c is a unit, then $bc \sim c$ or $bc \sim b$ which implies that $a \mid c$ or $a \mid b$, i.e., a is prime. Hence, assume neither b nor c is a unit.

Now since $a \mid bc$, there exists $x \in R$ so that $ax = bc$. It follows that x must be a nonzero nonunit (prove it!) element. Since R is a UFD, we have the unique (up to associates) factorization in terms of irreducible elements on both sides of the above equality, namely,

$$au_1u_2\cdots u_r = b_1b_2\cdots b_s \cdot c_1c_2\cdots c_t \text{ (say).}$$

Then by uniqueness of the factorization, we have $a \sim b_i$ for some i or $a \sim c_j$ for some j. If $a \sim b_i$, then $a \mid b_i$ and hence $a \mid b$. On the other hand, if $a \sim c_j$, then $a \mid c_j$, which implies that $a \mid c$. Thus $a \mid b$ or $a \mid c$. Hence a is prime. $\square$

Corollary 14.1.16. *Let R be a UFD and p be a nonzero nonunit element of R. Then p is irreducible if and only if p is prime.*

Proof. Follows from the above theorem and Theorem 14.1.6(iii). $\square$

Theorem 14.1.17. *A factorization domain R is a UFD if and only if every irreducible element of R is prime.*

Proof. One side follows from Theorem 14.1.15. Let R be a factorization domain in which every irreducible element is prime. We show that R is a UFD. Since R is a FD, it is sufficient to show that factorization of a nonzero nonunit element a of R in terms of irreducible (hence prime) elements is unique.

Now to show the uniqueness of the representation of a as a product of primes, we assume that a can be expressed as a product of primes in two ways; say,

$$a = p_1p_2\ldots p_t = q_1q_2\ldots q_r, \tag{14.1.2}$$

where p_i and q_j are primes. Suppose $t > r$. Now $p_1 \mid a$. Hence $p_1 \mid q_1q_2\ldots q_r$. Then by Problem 9 of Exercises 14.1, p_1 divides one of $q_1, q_2, \ldots, q_r$. By relabeling, if necessary, we may assume $p_1 \mid q_1$. Since q_1 is irreducible, p_1 is an associate of q_1. Hence $q_1 = p_1 u_1$ for some unit $u_1 \in R$. Thus,

$$p_1 p_2 \ldots p_t = p_1 u_1 q_2 \ldots q_r \qquad \ldots (*)$$

and by cancellation (since R is a domain), $p_2 p_3 \ldots p_t = u_1 q_2 \ldots q_r$.

Again $p_2 \mid u_1 q_2 \ldots q_r$. Since u_1 is a unit, $p_2 \nmid u_1$. Hence p_2 divides one of $q_2, q_3, \ldots, q_r$. Assume as above, $p_2 \mid q_2$. Then $q_2 = p_2 u_2$ where u_2 is a unit and

$$p_2 p_3 \ldots p_t = p_2 u_2 u_1 q_3 \ldots q_r.$$

Again by cancellation,

$$p_3 p_4 \ldots p_t = u_1 u_2 q_3 \ldots q_r.$$

Repeating this process we obtain,

$$p_{r+1} p_{r+2} \ldots p_t = u_1 u_2 \ldots u_r.$$

This implies that p_{r+1} divides a unit, which is a contradiction. Hence $t \not> r$. Similarly, we can show that $r \not> t$. Consequently, $r = t$ and also we find that p_i and q_i are associates for $i = 1, 2, \ldots, r$. This proves the uniqueness. $\qquad\square$

Let us now consider the domain $\mathbb{Z}[\sqrt{-5}]$ once again. We have shown that it is a FD. In this domain, 3 is *irreducible but not a prime element*. Hence from Theorem 14.1.17, it follows that $\mathbb{Z}[\sqrt{-5}]$ is not a UFD.

Thus we see that, like PID, in the case of UFD also, there is no difference between prime and irreducible elements. In fact, we show that any PID is a UFD. We proceed through some preliminary lemmas.

Lemma 14.1.18. *Let R be a PID. If (a_n), $n \in \mathbb{N}$ be any infinite sequence of principal ideals of R such that*

$$(a_1) \subseteq (a_2) \subseteq \cdots \subseteq (a_n) \subseteq \cdots,$$

then there exists $m \in \mathbb{N}$ so that $(a_n) = (a_m)$ for all $n \geq m$.

Proof. We have $I = \bigcup_{n \in \mathbb{N}} (a_n)$ is an ideal of R. Now since R is a PID, $I = (a)$ for some $a \in R$. Since $a \in I$, $a \in (a_m)$ for some $m \in \mathbb{N}$. Therefore, $I = (a) \subseteq (a_m) \subseteq (a_n) \subseteq I$ for all $n \geq m$. This implies $(a_n) = (a_m)$ for all $n \geq m$. $\qquad\square$

Lemma 14.1.19. *Let a be a nonzero nonunit element of a PID R. Then there exists a prime element $p \in R$ such that $p \mid a$.*

Proof. Since a is not a unit, we have $(a) \neq R$. Observe that either (a) is itself a maximal ideal of R or else there exists $a_1 \in R$ such that $(a) \subset (a_1)$. If (a_1) is a maximal ideal, then call it M. Otherwise, there exists $a_2 \in R$ such that $(a_1) \subset (a_2)$. Proceeding in this way, we get a strictly ascending chain of principal ideals in the PID R. Then by the above lemma, this chain must terminate after finite steps and we find a maximal ideal[3] M of R such that $(a) \subseteq M$. Now since R is a PID, $M = (p)$ for some prime $p \in R$, by Theorem 14.1.9. Then $(a) \subseteq (p)$ which implies that $p \mid a$, as required.   □

Lemma 14.1.20. *If R is a PID, then every nonzero nonunit element of R has a factorization into a finite product of prime elements.*

Proof. Let a be a nonzero nonunit element of R. By Lemma 14.1.19, there exists a prime element p_1 in R such that $p_1 \mid a$. Then $a = p_1 a_1$ for some $0 \neq a_1 \in R$. Thus $(a) \subseteq (a_1)$. If $(a) = (a_1)$, then we have $a_1 = ra$ for some $r \in R$. Then $a = p_1 a_1 = p_1 ra$ which implies that $p_1 r = 1$, as R is an integral domain. But then p_1 becomes a unit, which is a contradiction. Therefore $(a) \subset (a_1)$. If $(a_1) \neq R$, then a_1 is not a unit. Also $a_1 \neq 0$. So we can repeat the process on a_1, whereby we get an increasing chain of principal ideals:

$$(a) \subset (a_1) \subset (a_2) \subset \cdots \subset (a_n) \subset \cdots$$

with $a_{i-1} = p_i a_i$ for some prime $p_i \in R$. We continue the process until a_n becomes a unit for some n. The sequence must terminate because of Lemma 14.1.18. Therefore,

$$(a) \subset (a_1) \subset \cdots \subset (a_n) = R,$$

as a_n is a unit. So we have

$$a = p_1 a_1 = p_1 p_2 a_2 \cdots = p_1 p_2 \cdots p_{n-1} a_{n-1},$$

where $a_{n-1} = p_n a_n$. Now since p_n is a prime and a_n is a unit, a_{n-1} is an associate of prime and so it is itself a prime. This completes the proof.   □

Theorem 14.1.21. *Every PID is a UFD.*

Proof. By Lemma 14.1.20, each nonzero nonunit element has a factorization. Hence it follows that every PID is a FD. Again in a PID, every irreducible element is a prime element. Hence from Theorem 14.1.17, it follows that every PID is a UFD.   □

Interestingly, the converse of the above theorem is not true. Indeed, we have already mentioned that $\mathbb{Z}[x]$ is a UFD but later on we shall prove that $\mathbb{Z}[x]$ is not a PID (cf. Worked-out Exercise 14.1.5).

---

[3]One may also refer to Theorem 13.3.14 in this regard.

Worked-out Exercises

$\Diamond$ **Exercise 14.1.1.** Determine all the associates of $1 + i\sqrt{5}$ in $\mathbb{Z}[i\sqrt{5}]$.

Solution. We know that the only units of $\mathbb{Z}[i\sqrt{5}]$ are 1 and -1. This implies that the associates of $1 + i\sqrt{5}$ are $1 + i\sqrt{5}$ itself and $-1 - i\sqrt{5}$.

$\Diamond$ **Exercise 14.1.2.** Find a prime element in $\mathbb{Z}_{10}$ which is not irreducible.

Solution. Consider the element $[2] \in \mathbb{Z}_{10}$. We show that $[2]$ is prime but not irreducible. Let $[a], [b] \in \mathbb{Z}_{10}$ be such that $[2] \mid [a][b]$. Then we have $2k \equiv ab \pmod{10}$ for some integer k which implies that $ab = 2k + 10n$ for some integer n. Therefore ab is even and so at least one of a and b is even which proves that $[2]$ divides $[a]$ or $[b]$. Hence $[2]$ is prime in $\mathbb{Z}_{10}$.

The prime element $[2]$ is not irreducible as $[2] = [32] = [4][8]$ but none of $[4]$ and $[8]$ are units in $\mathbb{Z}_{10}$. [4]

$\Diamond$ **Exercise 14.1.3.** Show that the integral domain $\mathbb{Z}[\sqrt{3}] = \{a + b\sqrt{3} \mid a, b \in \mathbb{Z}\}$ is a FD.

Solution. Define $\delta : \mathbb{Z}[\sqrt{3}] \smallsetminus \{0\} \to \mathbb{N}_0$ as follows: for all $a + b\sqrt{3} \in \mathbb{Z}[\sqrt{3}], \delta(a + b\sqrt{3}) = |a^2 - 3b^2|$. Now $\delta(a + b\sqrt{3}) = 1$ if and only if $|a^2 - 3b^2| = 1$ if and only if $(a + b\sqrt{3})(a - b\sqrt{3}) = \pm 1$ if and only if $a + b\sqrt{3}$ is a unit. Let $a + b\sqrt{3}, c + d\sqrt{3}$ be two nonzero elements of $\mathbb{Z}[\sqrt{3}]$. Then $\delta((a + b\sqrt{3})(c + d\sqrt{3})) = |a^2 - 3b^2||c^2 - 3d^2| \geq |c^2 - 3d^2| = \delta(c + d\sqrt{3})$, where equality holds if and only if $\delta(a + b\sqrt{3}) = 1$, i.e., if and only if $a + b\sqrt{3}$ is a unit. Hence $\mathbb{Z}[\sqrt{3}]$ is a FD.

$\Diamond$ **Exercise 14.1.4.** Let N_1 be the set of all natural numbers greater than 1. Call an integer $n \in N_1$ *square free* if n is not divisible by the square of any integer that belongs to N_1. Consider the domain $\mathbb{Z}[\sqrt{n}] = \{a + b\sqrt{n} \mid a, b \in \mathbb{Z}\}$ for some square free integer $n \in N_1$. Prove that $a + b\sqrt{n}$ is irreducible in $\mathbb{Z}[\sqrt{n}]$ if $|a^2 - nb^2|$ is prime in $\mathbb{Z}$.

Solution. Let $a + b\sqrt{n} \in \mathbb{Z}[\sqrt{n}]$ be such that $|a^2 - nb^2|$ is a prime number, say p. Now if $a + b\sqrt{n} = (c + d\sqrt{n})(e + f\sqrt{n})$, then $a = ce + ndf$ and $b = cf + de$. Thus $p = |a^2 - nb^2| = |(ce + ndf)^2 - n(cf + de)^2| = |c^2e^2 + 2ncdef + n^2d^2f^2 - n(c^2f^2 + 2cdef + d^2e^2| = |(c^2 - nd^2)(e^2 - nf^2)| = |c^2 - nd^2||e^2 - nf^2|$. Since p is prime, we have either $|c^2 - nd^2| = 1$ or $|e^2 - nf^2| = 1$. If $|c^2 - nd^2| = 1$, then we have $|(c + d\sqrt{n})(c - d\sqrt{n})| = 1$ which implies $c + d\sqrt{n}$ is a unit in $\mathbb{Z}[\sqrt{n}]$ with $(c + d\sqrt{n})^{-1} = c - d\sqrt{n}$ or $-(c - d\sqrt{n})$. Similarly if $|e^2 - nf^2| = 1$, then we have that $e + f\sqrt{n}$ is a unit in $\mathbb{Z}[\sqrt{n}]$. Thus $a + b\sqrt{n}$ is irreducible in $\mathbb{Z}[\sqrt{n}]$.

---

[4]Recall that $[r]$ is a unit in $\mathbb{Z}_n$ if and only if $\gcd(n, r) = 1$.

◇ **Exercise 14.1.5.** Find an ideal in the polynomial ring $\mathbb{Z}[x]$ which is not a principal ideal. Hence justify that $\mathbb{Z}[x]$ is not a PID.

Solution. Let $I = (\{2, x\})$, i.e., I be the ideal in $\mathbb{Z}[x]$ generated by elements 2 and x. We show that I is not a principal ideal. Suppose, if possible, $I = (f(x))$ for some polynomial $f(x)$ in $\mathbb{Z}[x]$. Now, $2 \in I = (f(x))$ implies that there exists $g_1(x) \in \mathbb{Z}[x]$ such that $2 = f(x)g_1(x)$. But this shows $\deg f(x) = 0$, i.e., $f(x)$ is a constant, say a. So $x \in I = (f(x)) = (a)$. Then there is a polynomial $g_2(x) \in \mathbb{Z}[x]$ so that $x = ag_2(x)$ which implies that $a = 1$ or -1.

In either case, $I = \mathbb{Z}[x]$. Therefore $1 \in I = (\{2, x\})$. Then there are $g(x), h(x) \in \mathbb{Z}[x]$ such that $1 = 2g(x) + xh(x)$ which is a contradiction as the constant term on the right hand side is an even integer, whereas that on the left hand side is 1. Therefore I cannot be a principal ideal in $\mathbb{Z}[x]$. Hence $\mathbb{Z}[x]$ is not a PID.

◇ **Exercise 14.1.6.** Consider the ring $R = \mathbb{Z}[\sqrt{-5}] = \{a + b\sqrt{-5} : a, b \in \mathbb{Z}\}$ and the element $\alpha = 1 + \sqrt{-5}$ of R. Now pick the correct statement(s) from the following.
(i) α is prime.
(ii) α is irreducible.
(iii) R is not a unique factorization domain.
(iv) R is not an integral domain.

Solution. Let $a + b\sqrt{-5}, c + d\sqrt{-5} \in R$ such that $1 + \sqrt{-5} = (a + b\sqrt{-5})(c + d\sqrt{-5})$. Then $6 = (a^2 + 5b^2)(c^2 + 5d^2)$. So possibilities are either $a^2 + 5b^2 = 1$ and $c^2 + 5d^2 = 6$ or $a^2 + 5b^2 = 6$ and $c^2 + 5d^2 = 1$ or $a^2 + 5b^2 = 2$ and $c^2 + 5d^2 = 3$ or $a^2 + 5b^2 = 3$ and $c^2 + 5d^2 = 2$. But there is no set of integers a, b, c and d for which $a^2 + 5b^2 = 2$ or 3 and $c^2 + 5d^2 = 3$ or 2. Hence either $a^2 + 5b^2 = 1$ or $c^2 + 5d^2 = 1$, i.e., either $a + b\sqrt{-5} = 1$ or $c + d\sqrt{-5} = 1$. Therefore, $1 + \sqrt{-5}$ is irreducible. But $1 + \sqrt{-5}$ is not prime, as $(1 + \sqrt{-5}) \mid (2 \cdot 3)$ but neither $(1 + \sqrt{-5}) \mid 2$ nor $(1 + \sqrt{-5}) \mid 3$. Now R is an integral domain all the irreducible elements are not prime. Thus R is not a unique factorization domain. Hence options (ii) and (iii) are correct.

◇ **Exercise 14.1.7.** Which of the following statement is true?
(i) $\mathbb{Z}[\sqrt{5}]$ is a unique factorization domain.
(ii) $\mathbb{Z}[\sqrt{5}]$ is not a unique factorization domain.
(iii) $\mathbb{Z}_6$ is an integral domain.
(iv) $\mathbb{Z}[i\sqrt{5}]$ is a unique factorization domain.

Solution. We first show that $2 \in \mathbb{Z}[\sqrt{5}]$ is irreducible but not prime. For this let $2 = (a + b\sqrt{5})(c + d\sqrt{5})$ for some $a + b\sqrt{5}, c + d\sqrt{5} \in \mathbb{Z}[\sqrt{5}]$. Then it can be shown that

$4 = (a^2 - 5b^2)(c^2 - 5d^2)$. So possibilities are either $a^2 - 5b^2 = 1$ and $c^2 - 5d^2 = 4$ or $a^2 - 5b^2 = 4$ and $c^2 - 5d^2 = 1$ or $a^2 - 5b^2 = 2$ and $c^2 - 5d^2 = 2$. But there is no set of integers a, b, c and d for which $a^2 - 5b^2 = 2$ and $c^2 - 5d^2 = 2$. Hence either $a + b\sqrt{5} = \pm 1$ or $c + d\sqrt{5} = \pm 1$. Thus 2 is irreducible in $\mathbb{Z}[\sqrt{5}]$. But $2 \mid (2 \cdot 2) = 4 = (3 + \sqrt{5})(3 - \sqrt{5})$, but neither $2 \mid (3 + \sqrt{5})$ nor $2 \mid (3 - \sqrt{5})$. Therefore, $\mathbb{Z}[\sqrt{5}]$ is not a unique factorization domain. Also we know that $\mathbb{Z}_6$ is not an integral domain and by Exercise 14.1.6 $\mathbb{Z}[i\sqrt{5}]$ is not a unique factorization domain. Hence option (ii) is correct.

◊ **Exercise 14.1.8.** Which of the following statement is true?
(i) 5 is prime but 7 is not prime in the ring $\mathbb{Z}[\sqrt{2}]$.
(ii) 5 and 7 are both primes in the ring $\mathbb{Z}[\sqrt{2}]$.
(iii) 7 is prime but 5 is not prime in the ring $\mathbb{Z}[\sqrt{2}]$.
(iv) Neither 5 nor 7 is prime in the ring $\mathbb{Z}[\sqrt{2}]$.

Solution. Now $7 \mid (3 + \sqrt{2})(3 - \sqrt{2})$, but neither $7 \mid (3 + \sqrt{2})$ nor $7 \mid (3 - \sqrt{2})$. Therefore, 7 is not prime in $\mathbb{Z}[\sqrt{2}]$.

We now show that $5 \in \mathbb{Z}[\sqrt{2}]$ is prime. For this let $5 \mid (a + b\sqrt{2})(c + d\sqrt{2})$ for some $a + b\sqrt{2}, c + d\sqrt{2} \in \mathbb{Z}[\sqrt{2}]$. Then $25 = (a^2 - 2b^2)(c^2 - 2d^2)$. Now $5 \mid 25 = (a^2 - 2b^2)(c^2 - 2d^2)$ implies either $5 \mid (a^2 - 2b^2)$ or $5 \mid (c^2 - 2d^2)$. Suppose $5 \mid (a^2 - 2b^2)$, i.e., $a^2 - 2b^2 \equiv 0 \pmod{5}$. Now we consider the following table :

a, b	a^2, b^2 (mod 5)	$2b^2$ (mod 5)
0	0	0
1	1	2
2	4	3
3	4	3
4	1	2

From this table, we see that $a^2 - 2b^2 \equiv 0 \pmod{5}$ if and only if a, b are both divisible by 5. Therefore $5 \mid (a + b\sqrt{2})$. Similarly we can show that if $5 \mid c^2 - 2d^2$ then $5 \mid (c + d\sqrt{2})$. Thus 5 is a prime element in $\mathbb{Z}[\sqrt{2}]$. Hence option (i) is correct.

Exercises

1. Determine all the associates of $[8]$ in $\mathbb{Z}_{10}$.

2. In $\mathbb{Z}[\sqrt{3}]$, show that $2 + \sqrt{3}$ is a unit and $3 + 2\sqrt{3}$ is an associate of $\sqrt{3}$.

3. Determine all the units of $\mathbb{Z}[i]$.

4. Determine all the associates of $8 + 3i$ in $\mathbb{Z}[i]$.

5. Determine all units of $\mathbb{Z}[i\sqrt{3}]$. Show that 2, $1 + i\sqrt{3}$ are irreducible in $\mathbb{Z}[i\sqrt{3}]$ but not prime.

6. Find all the units of $\mathbb{Z}_7[x]$. Also determine all the associates of $x^2 + [2]$ in $\mathbb{Z}_7[x]$.

7. Find all associates of $1 + i$ in $\mathbb{Z}[i]$.

8. Determine whether the following elements are prime or irreducible or none of them, in respect of the rings associated with them:

   (i) $[2], [3], [4], [7], [9], [10]$ in $\mathbb{Z}_{12}$.

   (ii) $2, 4 + \sqrt{10}$ in $\mathbb{Z}[\sqrt{10}]$.

   (iii) $3, 5, 11, 2 + i, 3 + i, 2 - i, 1 - i$ in $\mathbb{Z}[i]$.

   (iv) $23, 1 + i3\sqrt{5}, 3 + i\sqrt{5}, 2 + i\sqrt{5}, 7 + i3\sqrt{5}$ in $\mathbb{Z}[i\sqrt{5}]$.

9. Let D be a commutative ring with identity. If p be a prime element of D such that $p \mid a_1 a_2 \ldots a_n$ $(n \geq 2)$, $a_i \in D$. Then prove that $p \mid a_i$ for some $i \in \{1, 2, \ldots, n\}$.

10. Prove that $a + ib$ is prime in $\mathbb{Z}[i]$, if $a^2 + b^2$ is prime in $\mathbb{Z}$.

11. Prove that $a + ib\sqrt{3}$ is irreducible in $\mathbb{Z}[i\sqrt{3}]$, if $a^2 + 3b^2$ is prime in $\mathbb{Z}$.

12. In $\mathbb{Z}[\sqrt{5}]$, show that 2 and $1 + \sqrt{5}$ are irreducible but not prime.

13. In $\mathbb{Z}[\sqrt{-5}]$, show that the factorization of 21 as a product of irreducible elements is not unique.

14. Let p be a prime number of the form $4n + 1$. Prove that $p = a^2 + b^2$ for some $a, b \in \mathbb{Z}$ and p is not prime in $\mathbb{Z}[i]$. Also show that an integer m is a prime element in $\mathbb{Z}[i]$ if m is a prime number of the form $4n + 3$.

15. Let $I \neq (0)$ be an ideal of $\mathbb{Z}[i]$. Prove that the quotient ring $\mathbb{Z}[i]/I$ is finite.

16. Let $I \neq \{0\}$ be a proper ideal of a PID R such that the quotient ring R/I has no nonzero zero divisors. Prove that R/I is a field.

17. Prove that the integral domains $\mathbb{Z}[i\sqrt{n}]$ for $n = 6, 7, 10$ are FD but not UFD.

18. Let R be a UFD and $d \in R \setminus \{0\}$. Show that the number of principal ideals containing d is finite.

19. Determine whether the following statements are true or false. Justify your answer.

    (i) 3 is an irreducible element in $\mathbb{Z}[i]$.

    (ii) 5 is an irreducible element in $\mathbb{Z}[i]$.

    (iii) 13 is an irreducible element in $\mathbb{Z}[i]$.

    (iv) $1 + i$ is irreducible element in $\mathbb{Z}[i]$.

    (v) Every prime element of $\mathbb{Z}$ is also a prime element in $\mathbb{Z}[i]$.

    (vi) In $\mathbb{Z}[\sqrt{2}]$, $2 + \sqrt{2}$ and $\sqrt{2}$ are associates.

    (vii) 3 is a prime in $\mathbb{Q}$.

    (viii) $\sqrt{3}$ is irreducible in $\mathbb{R}$.

    (ix) In $\mathbb{Z}_4$, $[2]$ is an irreducible element.

20. Let R be a subring of $\mathbb{Q}$ containing 1. Then which of the following statement is necessarily true?

    (i) R is a principal ideal domain (PID).

    (ii) R contains infinitely many prime ideals.

    (iii) R contains a prime ideal which is not a maximal ideal.

    (iv) For every maximal ideal M in R, the quotient structure R/M is finite.

14.2 Euclidean Domain

In this section, we define another important class of integral domains. Euclidean division algorithm is very much well-known to us from the beginning of learning the method of division in our school days, which states: dividend = divisor × quotient + remainder. Apart from the ring of integers, there are many integral domains in which the division algorithm holds. They are called Euclidean domains.

Definition 14.2.1. An integral domain R is called a **Euclidean domain** (in short, **ED**), if there exists a function $\delta : R \smallsetminus \{0\} \longrightarrow \mathbb{N}_0$ satisfying the following conditions:

(i) $\delta(a) \leq \delta(ab)$ for all $a, b \in R \smallsetminus \{0\}$;

(ii) for any $a, b \in R$ with $b \neq 0$, there exist $q, r \in R$ (called respectively, **quotient** and **remainder**) such that

$$a = bq + r, \quad \text{where either } r = 0 \text{ or } \delta(r) < \delta(b).$$

The function δ is called a **Euclidean norm function** (or **Euclidean valuation**) on R.

Remark 14.2.2. First note that, for any $a \in R \smallsetminus \{0\}$, $\delta(a) \leq \delta((-1)a) = \delta(-a)$ which in turn implies that $\delta(-a) \leq \delta(-(-a)) = \delta(a)$ and so we have $\delta(a) = \delta(-a)$ for all $a \in R \smallsetminus \{0\}$.

Secondly, for any $a \in R \smallsetminus \{0\}$, $\delta(1) \leq \delta(1 \cdot a) = \delta(a)$. Thus $\delta(1)$ is the least element in the subset $\delta(R \smallsetminus \{0\})$ of the well-ordered set, $\mathbb{N}_0$.

Finally, the group of units of R is precisely the set

$$\{u \in R \mid \delta(u) = \delta(1)\} \quad \text{(cf. Worked-out Exercise 14.2.1)}.$$

Example 14.2.3. Any field F is a Euclidean domain with $\delta(a) = 1$ for all $a \in F \smallsetminus \{0\}$. Note that, for all $a, b \in F \smallsetminus \{0\}$, $ab \neq 0$ and then $\delta(a) = 1 = \delta(ab)$ and for any $c \in F$, $c = (ca^{-1})a + 0$.

Example 14.2.4. The ring of integers, $\mathbb{Z}$ is a Euclidean domain with $\delta(a) = |a|$ for all $a \in \mathbb{Z} \smallsetminus \{0\}$. Note that for any $a, b \in \mathbb{Z} \smallsetminus \{0\}$, $|a| \leq |ab|$ and for any $a \in \mathbb{Z}$, $b \in \mathbb{Z} \smallsetminus \{0\}$, there exist $q, r \in \mathbb{Z}$ such that $a = bq + r$ where either $r = 0$ or $|r| < |b|$.

Example 14.2.5. (Ring of Gaussian integers):
The ring $\mathbb{Z}[i] = \{a + ib \mid a, b \in \mathbb{Z}\}$ is called the ring of Gaussian integers (cf. Example 12.1.5). Define $\delta(a + ib) = |a + ib|^2 = a^2 + b^2$ for all $a + ib \in \mathbb{Z}[i] \smallsetminus \{0\}$. Clearly,

$\delta(u) > 0$ for all $u \neq 0$ in $\mathbb{Z}[i]$. Further for any $u, v \in \mathbb{Z}[i] \smallsetminus \{0\}$, $\delta(uv) = |uv|^2 = |u|^2 |v|^2 \geq |u|^2 = \delta(u)$ since $|v|^2$ is sum of squares of two integers (both of which are not simultaneously zero).

Next let $u, v \in \mathbb{Z}[i]$ with $v \neq 0$. Then $u = a + ib$ and $v = c + id$ for some $a, b, c, d \in \mathbb{Z}$ such that $(c, d) \neq (0, 0)$. Now,

$$\frac{u}{v} = \frac{(a + ib)(c - id)}{c^2 + d^2} = \alpha + i\beta \ \ \text{(say)},$$

where α, β are rational numbers. Then there exist integers m and n such that $|m - \alpha| \leq \frac{1}{2}$ and $|n - \beta| \leq \frac{1}{2}$. So $u = (\alpha + i\beta)v = (m + in)v + [(\alpha - m) + i(\beta - n)]v$. Now $[(\alpha - m) + i(\beta - n)]v = u - (m + in)v \in \mathbb{Z}[i]$, as $\mathbb{Z}[i]$ is a ring and $u, v, m + in \in \mathbb{Z}[i]$. Let $r = [(\alpha - m) + i(\beta - n)]v$. Then $r = [c(\alpha - m) - d(\beta - n)] + i[c(\beta - n) + d(\alpha - m)]$ and

$$
\begin{aligned}
\delta(r) &= [c(\alpha - m) - d(\beta - n)]^2 + [c(\beta - n) + d(\alpha - m)]^2 \\
&= (\alpha - m)^2(c^2 + d^2) + (\beta - n)^2(c^2 + d^2) \\
&= [(\alpha - m)^2 + (\beta - n)^2](c^2 + d^2) \\
&= [(\alpha - m)^2 + (\beta - n)^2]|v|^2 \\
&\leq (\tfrac{1}{4} + \tfrac{1}{4})|v|^2 \\
&= \tfrac{1}{2}|v|^2 \\
&< |v|^2 \\
&= \delta(v).
\end{aligned}
$$

Thus taking $q = m + in$, we have $u = vq + r$ where either $r = 0$ or $\delta(r) < \delta(v)$. Hence $\mathbb{Z}[i]$ is a Euclidean domain.

Theorem 14.2.6. *Every Euclidean domain is a PID.*

Proof. Let R be a Euclidean domain with a Euclidean valuation δ. Suppose I is a nonzero ideal of R. Let

$$T = \{\delta(x) \in \mathbb{N}_0 \mid x \neq 0, \ x \in I\}.$$

Clearly, T is a nonempty subset of $\mathbb{N}_0$. Then by the well-ordering principle, T has a least element. So, there exists a nonzero element $a \in I$ such that $\delta(a)$ is the least element in T. If $b \in I$, then $b = aq + r$ for some $q, r \in R$ where either $r = 0$ or $\delta(r) < \delta(a)$.

Now $r = b - aq \in I$, as $a, b \in I$. If $r \neq 0$, then $\delta(r) \geq \delta(a)$ by the choice of the element a in I. So $r = 0$ and hence $b = aq \in (a)$. Thus $I \subseteq (a)$. Also since $a \in I$, we have $I = (a)$. Therefore R is a PID. $\square$

The following example shows that the converse is not true.

Example 14.2.7. Let R be the ring defined by

$$R = \left\{ a + b(1 + i\sqrt{19})/2 \mid a, b \in \mathbb{Z} \right\}.$$

Then R is a PID but not a Euclidean domain.[5]

Thus we have the following:

$$\text{Euclidean domain} \implies \text{PID} \implies \text{UFD}$$

But the converse implications do not hold.

Now we shall define the greatest common divisor and the least common multiple in an arbitrary commutative ring with identity.

Definition 14.2.8. Let R be a commutative ring with identity. Let $a, b \in R$ such that a and b are not both zero. A nonzero element $d \in R$ is called a **greatest common divisor** (in short, **gcd**) or **highest common factor** (in short, **hcf**) of a and b if

(i) $d \mid a$ and $d \mid b$;

(ii) $x \mid a$, $x \mid b$, $x \in R \implies x \mid d$.

We write $d = \gcd(a, b)$ or sometimes simply (a, b). The elements a and b are called **relatively prime** or **prime to each other** if $\gcd(a, b)$ is a unit (i.e., $\gcd(a, b) \sim 1$).

Similarly, let $a, b \in R$ such that $a, b \neq 0$. Then an element $c \in R$ is called a **least common multiple** (in short, **lcm**) of a and b if

(i) $a \mid c$ and $b \mid c$;

(ii) $a \mid y$, $b \mid y$, $y \in R \implies c \mid y$.

We write $c = \text{lcm}\,(a, b)$ or simply $[a, b]$.

It is important to understand that in general, $\gcd(a, b)$ may or may not exist. But if a gcd exists, then it is unique up to associates, i.e., if x and y both are greatest common divisors of a and b, then $x \sim y$. The same is true for lcm also. For example, we consider the following:

---

[5]The proof is beyond the scope of the book. However one may find a proof in *J. C. Wilson, A principal ideal ring that is not a Euclidean ring, Mathematics Magazine* **46** *(1973), 34-38.*

Example 14.2.9. In $\mathbb{Z}$, both 3 and -3 are the greatest common divisors of 6 and 9. Similarly 18 and -18 are the least common multiples of them. Clearly, $3 \sim -3$ and $18 \sim -18$.

Theorem 14.2.10. *If R is a UFD, then there exists a gcd for any $a, b \in R \smallsetminus \{0\}$.*

Proof. If a or b is a unit, then $\gcd(a, b) = 1$. Suppose a and b are non-units. Then both of them can be uniquely (up to associates) expressed as finite products of irreducible elements. Moreover we can express each of these products in terms of the same set of irreducible elements as

$$a \sim p_1{}^{r_1} p_2{}^{r_2} \cdots p_n{}^{r_n} \quad \text{and} \quad b \sim p_1{}^{s_1} p_2{}^{s_2} \cdots p_n{}^{s_n},$$

where p_i's are "distinct" irreducible elements (in the sense that $p_i \nsim p_j$ if and only if $i \neq j$) and r_i, s_i are nonnegative integers such that $r_i = 0$ $[s_i = 0]$ if and only if p_i was not associated with any of the irreducible factors in the original expression of a [resp. b].

Now it is an easy exercise to verify that

$$\gcd(a, b) = p_1{}^{t_1} p_2{}^{t_2} \cdots p_n{}^{t_n},$$

where $t_i = \min(r_i, s_i)$ for each $i = 1, 2, \ldots, n$. We leave this simple verification to the reader. □

Now since every Euclidean domain is a PID and every PID is a UFD, the above theorem is also true for these classes of domains. But in the case of a PID (and hence also for a Euclidean domain) we have something more.

Theorem 14.2.11. *Let R be a PID and $a, b \in R \smallsetminus \{0\}$. Then there exists $\gcd(a, b)$. Also if $d = \gcd(a, b)$, then there exist $x, y \in R$ such that $d = ax + by$.*

Proof. Let I be the ideal generated by $\{a, b\}$. Then $I = Ra + Rb$. Now since R is a PID, $I = (d)$ for some $d \in R$. Thus there exist $x, y \in R$ such that $d = ax + by$. Since $a, b \in I = (d)$, we have $d \mid a$ and $d \mid b$. Also, if there is some $c \in R$ so that $c \mid a$ and $c \mid b$, then $c \mid (ax + by) = d$. Therefore $d = \gcd(a, b)$. Hence there exists $\gcd(a, b) = d$ and $d = ax + by$ for some $x, y \in R$. □

Corollary 14.2.12. *Let R be a Euclidean domain and $a, b \in R \smallsetminus \{0\}$. Then there exists $\gcd(a, b)$. Also if $d = \gcd(a, b)$, then there exist $x, y \in R$ such that $d = ax + by$.*

Proof. Since every Euclidean domain is a PID, the result follows from the above theorem. □

Remark 14.2.13. Consider the polynomial ring $\mathbb{Z}[x]$ and two elements $x, 2 \in \mathbb{Z}[x]$. Then $gcd(2, x)$ exists and $gcd(2, x) = 1$. But $gcd(2, x)$ cannot be expressed as $2f(x) + xg(x)$ for any two polynomials $f(x), g(x) \in \mathbb{Z}[x]$. Supppose $1 = gcd(2, x) = 2(a_0 + a_1 x + a_2 x^2 + \cdots + a_n x^n) + x(b_0 + b_1 x + b_2 x^2 + \cdots + b_n x^n)$ for some $a_0 + a_1 x + a_2 x^2 + \cdots + a_n x^n, b_0 + b_1 x + b_2 x^2 + \cdots + b_n x^n \in \mathbb{Z}[x]$. Then comparing coefficients we must have $1 = 2a_0$, a contradiction. This contradiction ensures that $gcd(2, x)$ cannot be expressed as $2f(x) + xg(x)$ for any two polynomials $f(x), g(x) \in \mathbb{Z}[x]$.

Furthermore, in an arbitrary ring, gcd of finite number of elements, not all zero, may not exist. Following example justifies our claim.

Example 14.2.14. Let us consider the ring $\mathbb{Z}[i\sqrt{5}] = \{a + ib\sqrt{5} : a, b \in \mathbb{Z}\}$ discussed immediately after Theorem 14.1.6. In this ring $gcd(2, 1 + i\sqrt{5}) = 1$, while *gcd* of $6(1 - i\sqrt{5})$ and $3(1 + i\sqrt{5})(1 - i\sqrt{5})$ does not exist.

Indeed, it is known that the units in the ring $\mathbb{Z}[i\sqrt{5}]$ are ± 1. Let $a + ib\sqrt{5} = gcd(2, 1 + i\sqrt{5})$. Then $(a + ib\sqrt{5})|2$ and thus $2 = (a + ib\sqrt{5})(c + id\sqrt{5})$ for some $c + id\sqrt{5} \in \mathbb{Z}[i\sqrt{5}]$. This implies $4 = (a^2 + 5b^2)(c^2 + 5d^2)$.

Hence
$$a^2 + 5b^2 = 2, \quad c^2 + 5d^2 = 2 \qquad (i)$$
or,
$$a^2 + 5b^2 = 4, \quad c^2 + 5d^2 = 1 \qquad (ii)$$
or,
$$a^2 + 5b^2 = 1, \quad c^2 + 5d^2 = 4. \qquad (iii)$$

Now equation (I) cannot hold for any $a, b, c, d \in \mathbb{Z}$. The only integral solutions of $a^2 + 5b^2 = 4$ are $a = \pm 2$ and $b = 0$ and similarly the only integral solutions of $a^2 + 5b^2 = 1$ are $a = \pm 1$ and $b = 0$. Thus from equation (ii) and equation (iii), we find that $gcd(2, 1 + i\sqrt{5}) = 1$ or 2. If $gcd(2, 1 + i\sqrt{5}) = 2$, then $2|(1 + i\sqrt{5})$. This implies $1 + i\sqrt{5} = 2(p + iq\sqrt{5})$ for some $p + iq\sqrt{5} \in \mathbb{Z}[i\sqrt{5}]$. Thus, $2p = 1 = 2q$. But there do not exist integers p and q for which $2p = 1 = 2q$. Hence $gcd(2, 1 + i\sqrt{5}) = 1$.

Suppose $gcd(6(1 - i\sqrt{5}), 3(1 + i\sqrt{5})(1 - i\sqrt{5}))$ exists. Then $gcd(6(1 - i\sqrt{5}), 3(1 + i\sqrt{5})(1 - i\sqrt{5})) = 3(1 - i\sqrt{5})gcd(2, 1 + i\sqrt{5}) = 3(1 - i\sqrt{5})$. Now $(1 + i\sqrt{5})(1 - i\sqrt{5}) = 6$. Hence 6 is a common divisor of $6(1 - i\sqrt{5})$ and $3(1 + i\sqrt{5})(1 - i\sqrt{5})$. Consequently, $6|3(1 - i\sqrt{5})$. This implies $2|(1 - i\sqrt{5})$, which is not true in $\mathbb{Z}[i\sqrt{5}]$. Therefore, $gcd(6(1 - i\sqrt{5}), 3(1 + i\sqrt{5})(1 - i\sqrt{5}))$ does not exist.

A natural generalization of the definition of *lcm* (cf. 14.2.8) of two nonzero elements in a commutative ring is given below.

Definition 14.2.15. Let $a_1, a_2, \ldots, a_n$ be nonzero elements of a commutative ring R. An element $m \in R$ is said to be a **least common multiple** (in short lcm) of $a_1, a_2, \ldots, a_n$; denoted by $lcm(a_1, a_2, \ldots, a_n)$ if

1) $a_i | m$ for $i = 1, 2, \ldots, n$ (m is a common multiple)
2) if $a_i | c$ for $i = 1, 2, \ldots, n$; then $m | c$.

Theorem 14.2.16. *Let $a_1, a_2, \ldots, a_n$ be nonzero elements of a commutative ring R with identity. Then $a_1, a_2, \ldots, a_n$ have a least common multiple if and only if the ideal $\bigcap_{i=1}^{n} \langle a_i \rangle$ is a principal ideal.*

Proof. First suppose that $m = lcm(a_1, a_2, \ldots, a_n)$ exists. Then the element m lies in each of the principal ideals $\langle a_i \rangle$, for $i = 1, 2, \ldots, n$, whence in the intersection $\bigcap_{i=1}^{n} \langle a_i \rangle$. This means $\langle m \rangle \subseteq \bigcap_{i=1}^{n} \langle a_i \rangle$. On the other hand any element $r \in \bigcap_{i=1}^{n} \langle a_i \rangle$ is a common multiple of each of the a_i. But m is a lcm, so that $m | r$, or, equivalently, $r \in \langle m \rangle$. This leads to the inclusion $\bigcap_{i=1}^{n} \langle a_i \rangle \subseteq \langle m \rangle$ and hence $\bigcap_{i=1}^{n} \langle a_i \rangle = \langle m \rangle$.

Conversely, we assume that $\bigcap_{i=1}^{n} \langle a_i \rangle$ is a principal ideal of R, say $\bigcap_{i=1}^{n} \langle a_i \rangle = \langle a \rangle$. Since $\langle a \rangle \subseteq \langle a_i \rangle$, it follows that $a_i | a$ for every i. This implies a is a common multiple of $a_1, a_2, \ldots, a_n$. Let b be any other common multiple of $a_1, a_2, \ldots, a_n$. Then $a_i | b$ implies that $\langle b \rangle \subseteq \langle a_i \rangle$ for each $i = 1, 2, \ldots, n$. This implies $\langle b \rangle \subseteq \bigcap_{i=1}^{n} \langle a_i \rangle = \langle a \rangle$ and hence $a | b$. Consequently a is lcm of $a_1, a_2, \ldots, a_n$. $\square$

The method of finding the *gcd* in a Euclidean domain is known as **Euclidean algorithm**. In the following, we shall describe it[6]:

Let R be a Euclidean domain and $a, b \in R$ such that a, b are not both zero. If $b = 0$, then $a = \gcd(a, b)$. Suppose $b \neq 0$. Then we have $q, r \in R$ such that $a = bq + r$ where either $r = 0$ or $\delta(r) < \delta(b)$. If $r = 0$, then clearly $b = \gcd(a, b)$. If $r \neq 0$, let $d = \gcd(b, r)$. Then $d | b$ and $d | r$, which implies that $d | (bq + r) = a$. Also if $x \in R$ be such that $x | a$ and $x | b$, then $x | (a - bq) = r$. This implies that $x | d$ as $d = \gcd(b, r)$. Hence $d = \gcd(a, b)$.

---

[6]One can easily recognize the method. It is exactly the same as what we did in our school days, in the case of positive integers.

Now consider the elements b and r and by applying the division algorithm for them we get $q_1, r_1 \in R$ so that $b = rq_1 + r_1$ where either $r_1 = 0$ or $\delta(r_1) < \delta(r)$. If $r_1 = 0$, then $r \mid b$ and hence $r = \gcd(b, r) = \gcd(a, b)$. Otherwise, $r_1 \neq 0$ and we continue the process to obtain

$$
\begin{aligned}
a &= bq + r, & \text{where} \quad \delta(r) &< \delta(b) \\
b &= rq_1 + r_1, & \text{where} \quad \delta(r_1) &< \delta(r) \\
r &= r_1 q_2 + r_2, & \text{where} \quad \delta(r_2) &< \delta(r_1) \\
&\;\;\vdots & \vdots &
\end{aligned}
$$

The above process must terminate after a finite number of steps, since $\delta(b)$ is a positive integer and there exist finite number of distinct positive integers less than $\delta(b)$. Thus, finally we have

$$ r_{n-1} = r_n \, q_{n+1} $$

for some n, i.e., at some stage the remainder $r_{n+1} = 0$, for otherwise the values of $\delta(r_i)$ go on decreasing indefinitely. So we have

$$ \gcd(a, b) = \gcd(b, r_1) = \gcd(r_1, r_2) = \ldots = \gcd(r_{n-1}, r_n) = r_n. $$

Also using the equalities obtained above, one can easily compute $x, y \in R$ so that $\gcd(a, b) = ax + by$. This is illustrated in Worked-out Exercise 14.2.5. For a better understanding, the reader is asked to go through Example 2.1.12 again.

Worked-out Exercises

$\Diamond$ **Exercise 14.2.1.** Let R be a Euclidean domain with the Euclidean norm δ. Let $u \in R \smallsetminus \{0\}$. Prove that u is a unit in R if and only if $\delta(u) = \delta(1)$.

Solution. If u is a unit, then there exists $v \in R$ so that $uv = 1$. Then $\delta(u) \leqslant \delta(uv) = \delta(1)$. But $\delta(1) \leqslant \delta(u)$. This implies that $\delta(u) = \delta(1)$.

Conversely, let $\delta(u) = \delta(1)$. Now since R is a Euclidean domain, we have $q, r \in R$ such that $1 = qu + r$ where $r = 0$ or $\delta(r) < \delta(u)$. Since $\delta(u) = \delta(1) \leqslant \delta(r)$, we have $r = 0$. Thus, $1 = qu$ which implies that u is a unit in R.

$\Diamond$ **Exercise 14.2.2.** Let R be a Euclidean domain with the Euclidean norm δ. Let $a, b \in R \smallsetminus \{0\}$. Prove that b is a unit in R if and only if $\delta(a) = \delta(ab)$ (i.e., b is not a unit in R if and only if $\delta(a) < \delta(ab)$ for all $a \in R \smallsetminus \{0\}$).

Solution. Suppose b is a unit in R. Then $\delta(ab) \leqslant \delta(abb^{-1}) = \delta(a)$. Also $\delta(a) \leqslant \delta(ab)$. Therefore $\delta(a) = \delta(ab)$.

Conversely, suppose $\delta(a) = \delta(ab)$. Now by the Euclidean property of R, we have $q, r \in R$ such that $a = qab + r$ where $r = 0$ or $\delta(r) < \delta(ab)$. If $r \neq 0$, then $r = a(1 - qb) \neq 0$. This implies that $\delta(ab) = \delta(a) \leqslant \delta(a(1 - qb)) = \delta(a - qab) = \delta(r)$. Thus $r = 0$. So $a(1 - qb) = a - aqb = 0$ which implies that $1 - qb = 0$ as $a \neq 0$ and R is an integral domain. Therefore $qb = 1$ and hence b is a unit in R.

$\Diamond$ **Exercise 14.2.3.** Prove that $\mathbb{Z}[\sqrt{2}] = \{a + b\sqrt{2} \mid a, b \in \mathbb{Z}\}$ is a Euclidean domain.

Solution. Define $\delta(a+b\sqrt{2}) = |a^2 - 2b^2|$ for all $a+b\sqrt{2} \in \mathbb{Z}[\sqrt{2}] \setminus \{0\}$. Clearly, $\delta(u) \geqslant 0$ for all $u \neq 0$ in $\mathbb{Z}[\sqrt{2}]$. Also verify that $a^2 - 2b^2 = 0$ if and only if $a = b = 0$ as $a, b \in \mathbb{Z}$. Thus $\delta(u) \geqslant 1$ for all $u \in \mathbb{Z}[\sqrt{2}] \setminus \{0\}$. Further, for any $u = a + b\sqrt{2}, v = c + d\sqrt{2} \in \mathbb{Z}[\sqrt{2}] \setminus \{0\}$, $\delta(uv) = \delta((ac + 2bd) + (bc + ad)\sqrt{2}) = |(ac + 2bd)^2 - 2(bc + ad)^2| = |a^2c^2 + 4abcd + 4b^2d^2 - 2(b^2c^2 + 2abcd + a^2d^2)| = |a^2c^2 + 4b^2d^2 - 2b^2c^2 - 2a^2d^2| = |(a^2 - 2b^2)(c^2 - 2d^2)| = \delta(u)\delta(v) \geqslant \delta(u)$ as $\delta(v) \geqslant 1$.

Next let $u, v \in \mathbb{Z}[\sqrt{2}]$ with $v \neq 0$. Then $u = a + b\sqrt{2}$ and $v = c + d\sqrt{2}$ for some $a, b, c, d \in \mathbb{Z}$ such that $(c, d) \neq (0, 0)$. Now,

$$\frac{u}{v} = \frac{(a + b\sqrt{2})(c - d\sqrt{2})}{c^2 - 2d^2} = \alpha + \beta\sqrt{2} \quad \text{(say)},$$

where α, β are rational numbers. Then there exist integers m and n such that $|m - \alpha| \leq \frac{1}{2}$ and $|n - \beta| \leq \frac{1}{2}$. So

$$u = (\alpha + \beta\sqrt{2})v = (m + n\sqrt{2})v + [(\alpha - m) + (\beta - n)\sqrt{2}]v.$$

Now $[(\alpha - m) + (\beta - n)\sqrt{2}]v = u - (m + n\sqrt{2})v \in \mathbb{Z}[\sqrt{2}]$, as $\mathbb{Z}[\sqrt{2}]$ is a ring and $u, v, m+n\sqrt{2} \in \mathbb{Z}[\sqrt{2}]$. Let $r = [(\alpha - m) + (\beta - n)\sqrt{2}]v$. Then following Example 14.2.5, $\delta(r) = |(\alpha - m)^2 - 2(\beta - n)^2||c^2 - 2d^2| \leq (\frac{1}{4} + \frac{2}{4})|c^2 - 2d^2| = \frac{3}{4}|c^2 - 2d^2| < |c^2 - 2d^2| = \delta(v)$. Thus taking $q = m + n\sqrt{2}$, we have $u = vq + r$ where either $r = 0$ or $\delta(r) < \delta(v)$. Hence $\mathbb{Z}[\sqrt{2}]$ is a Euclidean domain.

$\blacklozenge$ **Exercise 14.2.4.** Determine all the prime elements of $\mathbb{Z}[i]$.

Solution. We first note that since $\mathbb{Z}[i]$ is a Euclidean domain (cf. Example 14.2.5), prime and irreducible elements of $\mathbb{Z}[i]$ are the same. Also, the only units of $\mathbb{Z}[i]$ are $\pm 1, \pm i$ (cf. Problem 3 of Exercise 14.1). Let $z = a + ib$ be an irreducible (or prime) element in $\mathbb{Z}[i]$. Then, associates of z are $\pm z$ and $\pm iz$ which are also primes in $\mathbb{Z}[i]$.

Now if $b = 0$, i.e., $z = a \in \mathbb{Z}$. Then z must be a prime number, for otherwise z has a nontrivial factorization in $\mathbb{Z}$ and hence in $\mathbb{Z}[i]$. But not all prime numbers are prime elements in $\mathbb{Z}[i]$. For example, $5 = (2+i)(2-i)$. In fact, by Problem 14 of Exercise 14.1, we know that $z \in \mathbb{Z}$ is a prime element of $\mathbb{Z}[i]$ if and only if z is of the form $4n+3$. Therefore, in this case, $z = \pm p$ where p is a prime number of the form $4n+3$.

Let $b \neq 0$. If $a = 0$, then $z = ib$ and so $b \in \mathbb{Z}$ is an associate of z. So we have $z = \pm ip$ where p is a prime number of the form $4n+3$.

Let $a, b \neq 0$. Then $\bar{z} = a - ib$ is also irreducible. For if $\bar{z} = z_1 z_2$ be a nontrivial factorization of $\bar{z}$, then $z = \overline{z_1}\,\overline{z_2}$ is also a nontrivial factorization of z. Therefore, $a^2 + b^2 = z\bar{z}$ is a factorization of $a^2 + b^2$ in $\mathbb{Z}[i]$ in terms of irreducible factors which is unique up to associates as $\mathbb{Z}[i]$, being an Euclidean domain, certainly a UFD. This at once follows that $a^2 + b^2$ is a prime integer because any nontrivial factorization of $a^2 + b^2$ in terms of prime integers would be a different from the one that we already have.

Conversely, arguing as in Worked-out Exercise 14.1.4, one can show that, if $a^2 + b^2$ is a prime integer, then $a + ib$ is prime in $\mathbb{Z}[i]$. Hence, in this case, $z = a + ib$, $(a, b \neq 0)$ is prime in $\mathbb{Z}[i]$ if and only if $a^2 + b^2$ is a prime number.

$\Diamond$ **Exercise 14.2.5.** Find the gcd of $-3 + 11i$ and $8 - i$ in $\mathbb{Z}[i]$. Also find $x, y \in \mathbb{Z}[i]$ such that $\gcd(-3 + 11i, 8 - i) = (-3 + 11i)x + (8 - i)y$.

Solution. We shall follow the Euclidean algorithm. We have $\frac{-3+11i}{8-i} = \frac{(-3+11i)(8+i)}{65} = \frac{-35+85i}{65} = -\frac{7}{13} + \frac{17}{13}i = (-1+i) + \left(\frac{6}{13} + \frac{4}{13}i\right) = (-1+i) + \frac{2}{13}(3+2i)$. Thus $-3+11i = (-1+i)(8-i) + \frac{2}{13}(3+2i)(8-i) = (-1+i)(8-i) + \frac{2}{13}(26+13i)$. Therefore,

$$-3 + 11i = (-1+i)(8-i) + (4+2i). \tag{14.2.1}$$

Again, $\frac{8-i}{4+2i} = \frac{(8-i)(4-2i)}{20} = \frac{30-20i}{20} = \frac{3}{2} - i = (1-i) + \frac{1}{2}$. Then we have

$$8 - i = (1-i)(4+2i) + (2+i). \tag{14.2.2}$$

Finally, $\frac{4+2i}{2+i} = 2$ and so $4 + 2i = 2(2+i)$. Therefore, $\gcd(-3+11i, 8-i) = 2+i$.

Now to find the desired values of x and y, we use the above equations and proceed as follows:

$$
\begin{aligned}
2+i &= (8-i) - (1-i)(4+2i) \quad \text{by (14.2.2)} \\
&= (8-i) - (1-i)\{(-3+11i) - (-1+i)(8-i)\} \quad \text{by (14.2.1)} \\
&= (-1+i)(-3+11i) + \{1 + (1-i)(-1+i)\}(8-i) \\
&= (-1+i)(-3+11i) + (1+2i)(8-i)
\end{aligned}
$$

Thus $x = -1 + i$ and $y = 1 + 2i$. [7]

◊ **Exercise 14.2.6.** Prove that 2 and $1 + i\sqrt{5}$ are relatively prime in the integral domain $\mathbb{Z}[i\sqrt{5}]$.

Solution. We know that only units of $\mathbb{Z}[i\sqrt{5}]$ are 1 and -1. Suppose $a + ib\sqrt{5}$ is a common divisor of 2 and $1 + i\sqrt{5}$. Then $2 = (a + ib\sqrt{5})(c + id\sqrt{5})$ for some $c + id\sqrt{5} \in \mathbb{Z}[i\sqrt{5}]$. So we have

$$4 = (a^2 + 5b^2)(c^2 + 5d^2).$$

Now since $a, b, c, d \in \mathbb{Z}$, we have $a^2 + 5b^2 = 1, 2$ or 4. Also note that since $a, b \in \mathbb{Z}$, $a^2 + 5b^2 \neq 2$ and $a^2 + 5b^2 = 4$ implies that $a = \pm 2$ and $b = 0$. Therefore in this case, $a + ib\sqrt{5} = 2$ divides $1 + i\sqrt{5}$. Then there exists $u + iv\sqrt{5} \in \mathbb{Z}[i\sqrt{5}]$ such that $(1 + i\sqrt{5}) = 2(u + iv\sqrt{5})$. But this implies that $2u = 1$ which is a contradiction as $u \in \mathbb{Z}$.

Therefore $a^2 + 5b^2 = 1$, which implies that $a = \pm 1$ and $b = 0$. Thus the only common divisors of 2 and $1 + i\sqrt{5}$ are 1 and -1. Hence 2 and $1 + i\sqrt{5}$ are relatively prime in $\mathbb{Z}[i\sqrt{5}]$.

◊ **Exercise 14.2.7.** In a UFD R, for any $a, b \neq 0$ prove that $ab \sim \gcd(a, b) \operatorname{lcm}(a, b)$.

Solution. Let d be a gcd of a and b respectively. Let $a = dx$ and $b = dy$. We show that $c = dxy$ is the lcm of a and b. Clearly $a \mid c$ and $b \mid c$. Let $u \in R$ such that $a \mid u$ and $b \mid u$. Then $dx \mid u$ and since $y \mid b$, we also have $y \mid u$. Thus $c = dxy \mid u$. Therefore c is a lcm of a and b.

Now $ab = dx \cdot dy = d^2xy = dc$. Also since any two gcds are associates and the same is true for lcms, we have $ab \sim \gcd(a, b) \operatorname{lcm}(a, b)$ as required.

◊ **Exercise 14.2.8.** Prove that in a PID, every nonzero proper ideal can be expressed uniquely (up to order) as a finite product of prime ideals.

Solution. Let R be a PID and I be a nonzero proper ideal of R. Then $I = (a)$ for some nonzero nonunit element $a \in R$. Since any PID is a UFD by Theorem 14.1.21, we have

$$a = a_1 a_2 \ldots a_n, \tag{14.2.3}$$

where each $a_i \in R$ is irreducible and hence prime. Let $M_i = (a_i)$ for each i. Also by Theorem 14.1.9, each M_i is a prime ideal of R. We show that $I = M_1 M_2 \ldots M_n$. Clearly, it follows from (14.2.3) that $a \in M_1 M_2 \ldots M_n$ and hence $I = (a) \subseteq M_1 M_2 \ldots M_n$.

---

[7]Note that the values of x and y are not unique.

Conversely, let $x \in M_1 M_2 \ldots M_n$. Then,

$$x = \sum_{k=1}^{m} b_{1k} b_{2k} \ldots b_{nk},$$

where $b_{ik} \in M_i$ for all $i = 1, 2, \ldots, n$. Now since $M_i = (a_i)$, we have for each i and for each k, $b_{ik} = a_i x_{ik}$ for some $x_{ik} \in R$. Thus for each k, $b_{1k} b_{2k} \ldots b_{nk} = a_1 a_2 \ldots a_n x_{1k} x_{2k} \ldots x_{nk} = a x_{1k} x_{2k} \ldots x_{nk} \in I$. This implies that

$$x = \sum_{k=1}^{m} b_{1k} b_{2k} \ldots b_{nk} \in I.$$

Therefore $I = M_1 M_2 \ldots M_n$ as required.

◊ **Exercise 14.2.9.** Which of the following statement is true?
(i) $\mathbb{Z}[i]$ is not a Euclidean domain.
(ii) $\mathbb{Z}[i]$ is not a principal ideal domain.
(iii) For every nonzero ideal I of $\mathbb{Z}[i]$, the quotient ring $\mathbb{Z}[i]/I$ is finite.
(iv) There is a nonzero ideal I of $\mathbb{Z}[i]$ for which the quotient ring $\mathbb{Z}[i]/I$ is infinite.

Solution. We know that $\mathbb{Z}[i]$ is a Euclidean domain and hence a principal ideal domain.

We now show that for every nonzero ideal I of $\mathbb{Z}[i]$, the quotient ring $\mathbb{Z}[i]/I$ is finite. We know that $\mathbb{Z}[i]$ is a Euclidean domain with Euclidean valuation $\delta : \mathbb{Z}[i] \setminus \{0\} \longrightarrow \mathbb{N}_0$, defined by $\delta(a + ib) = a^2 + b^2$ for all $a + ib \in \mathbb{Z}[i] \setminus \{0\}$. Then $\mathbb{Z}[i]$ is a principal ideal domain and hence $I = \langle \alpha \rangle$ for some $\alpha (\neq 0) \in I$. Let $(x + iy) + I \in \mathbb{Z}[i]/I$ be any element. Then there exist elements $q, r \in \mathbb{Z}[i]$ such that $x + iy = q\alpha + r$ where either $r = 0$ or $\delta(r) < \delta(\alpha)$. Therefore, $(x + iy) + I = r + I$ where either $r = 0$ or $\delta(r) < \delta(\alpha)$. But there are only finitely many elements in $\mathbb{Z}[i]$ whose valuation is less than $\delta(\alpha)$. Thus $\mathbb{Z}[i]/I$ is a finite ring. Hence option (iii) is correct.

◊ **Exercise 14.2.10.** Which of the following statement is true?
(i) $\mathbb{Z}[\sqrt{2}]$ is not a Euclidean domain.
(ii) $\mathbb{Z}[\sqrt{2}]$ is a Euclidean domain.
(iii) $\mathbb{Z}[\sqrt{5}]$ is a principal ideal domain.
(iv) $\mathbb{Z}[\sqrt{5}]$ is a Euclidean domain.

Solution. By Worked-out Exercise 14.1.7, it follows that $\mathbb{Z}[\sqrt{5}]$ is not a unique factorization domain. Therefore, $\mathbb{Z}[\sqrt{5}]$ is neither a Euclidean domain nor a principal ideal domain. Again we have proved in Worked-out Exercise 14.2.3 that $\mathbb{Z}[\sqrt{2}]$ is a Euclidean domain. Hence option (ii) is correct.

Exercises

1. Let R be a Euclidean domain with a Euclidean norm δ. Prove that $\delta(a) = \delta(-a)$ for all nonzero elements a in R.

2. Let R be a Euclidean domain with a Euclidean norm δ and $a, b \in R \smallsetminus \{0\}$ such that $a \sim b$. Show that $\delta(a) = \delta(b)$. Conversely, if $\delta(a) = \delta(b)$ for some $a, b \in R \smallsetminus \{0\}$ so that either $a \mid b$ or $b \mid a$, then show that $a \sim b$.

3. Show that for each positive integer n, $\delta(a) = |a|^n$ is a Euclidean norm on $\mathbb{Z}$.

4. Prove that $\mathbb{Z}[\sqrt{3}] = \{a + b\sqrt{3} \mid a, b \in \mathbb{Z}\}$ is a Euclidean domain.

5. Prove that $\mathbb{Z}[\sqrt{n}]$ is a Euclidean domain for $n = -1$ and $n = -2$.

6. Let $a, b \in \mathbb{Z}[\sqrt{3}]$ where $a = -102 + 10\sqrt{3}$ and $b = 1 + 7\sqrt{3}$. Find $q, r \in \mathbb{Z}[\sqrt{3}]$ so that $a = bq + r$, where either $r = 0$ or $r = \alpha + \beta\sqrt{3}$ with $|\alpha^2 - 3\beta^2| < 146$.

7. In a UFD R, let $a, b \in R \smallsetminus \{0\}$, prove that any two greatest common divisors of a and b are associates.

8. In a UFD R, let $a, b, c \in R \smallsetminus \{0\}$. If $a \mid bc$ and $\gcd(a, b) \sim 1$, then show that $a \mid c$.

9. Let R be a UFD and $a, b, c \in R \smallsetminus \{0\}$. Show that $\gcd(ca, cb) \sim c \gcd(a, b)$.

10. Let R be a UFD and $a, b \in R \smallsetminus \{0\}$. Prove that there exists a lcm of a and b in R.

11. Let R be a commutative ring with identity and $a_1, a_2, \ldots, a_n \in R \smallsetminus \{0\}$. Define (inductively) gcd and lcm of $a_1, a_2, \ldots, a_n$. Prove that they exist if R is a UFD.

12. Let R be a Euclidean domain. Without using Theorem 14.2.10, prove that any two nonzero elements $a, b \in R$ have a gcd and $\gcd(a, b) = ax + by$ for some $x, y \in R$.

13. Find the gcd of $3 + i$ and $-5 + 10i$ in $\mathbb{Z}[i]$.

14. Find $x, y \in \mathbb{Z}[i]$ such that $\gcd(3 + i, -5 + 10i) = (3 + i)x + (-5 + 10i)y$.

15. Show that $2 + 11i$ and $2 - 7i$ are relatively prime in the integral domain $\mathbb{Z}[i]$.

16. Let R be a PID and $a, b, c \in R \smallsetminus \{0\}$ such that $c = ax + by$ for some $x, y \in R$. Prove that $\gcd(a, b) \mid c$.

17. Let R be a Euclidean domain and $a, b \in R$ with $b \neq 0$. Let $q, r \in R$ so that $a = bq + r$ where $r \neq 0$. Prove that $\gcd(a, b) = \gcd(b, r)$.

Chapter 15

Polynomial Rings

15.1 Ring of Polynomials

This section deals with a very important class of rings, namely, the ring of polynomials. Already we have seen that these rings provide examples and counter examples on a number of occasions. Now it is time to give a special attention to them, as this class of rings play a major role in the study of advanced ring theory, field theory and especially in the area of commutative algebra and algebraic geometry.

In Example 12.1.9, we have described the polynomial ring over a commutative ring with identity. Now we shall define it again in a more formal way and with some more rigor in order to establish the existence of it as an algebraic structure.

Throughout the chapter we assume that if a ring R contains 1, then $1 \neq 0$.

Definition 15.1.1. Let R be a commutative ring with identity. Let S be the set of all infinite sequences of elements of R, i.e.,

$$S = \{(a_0, a_1, a_2, a_3, \ldots, a_n, \ldots) \mid a_i \in R, \ i = 0, 1, 2, 3, \ldots\}.$$

Let T be the subset of S defined by

$$T = \big\{(a_0, a_1, a_2, a_3, \ldots, a_n, \ldots) \in S \mid a_i = 0 \ \text{ for all } \ i \geq n$$
$$\text{for some nonnegative integer } \ n \big\}.$$

Define addition and multiplication on T as follows:

$$(a_0, a_1, a_2, a_3, \ldots) + (b_0, b_1, b_2, b_3, \ldots)$$
$$= (a_0 + b_0, a_1 + b_1, a_2 + b_2, a_3 + b_3, \ldots), \tag{15.1.1}$$

$$(a_0, a_1, a_2, a_3, \ldots) \cdot (b_0, b_1, b_2, b_3, \ldots) = (c_0, c_1, c_2, c_3, \ldots), \tag{15.1.2}$$

where

$$c_k = \sum_{i=0}^{k} a_i b_{k-i} = \sum_{\substack{i,j=0 \\ i+j=k}}^{k} a_i b_j, \quad k = 0,1,2,3,\dots.$$

In the following theorem, we shall prove that T becomes a ring with the binary operations defined above and in fact, it is again a commutative ring with identity. Now for convenience, we shall use the following notation with the help of a formal symbol x which will provide us a better (as well as more natural) description of the elements of T:

$$\begin{aligned}
\text{Denote} \quad (a,0,0,0,\dots) \quad &\text{by} \quad a = ax^0 \\
(0,a,0,0,\dots) \quad &\text{by} \quad ax = ax^1 \\
(0,0,a,0,\dots) \quad &\text{by} \quad ax^2 \\
(0,0,0,a,0,\dots) \quad &\text{by} \quad ax^3 \\
&\text{and so on,}
\end{aligned}$$

for all $a \in R$. Thus in this notation ax^n (n being a nonnegative integer) represents the sequence $(a_0, a_1, a_2, a_3, \dots)$ where $a_i = 0$ for all $i \neq n$ and $a_n = a$. Note that we are identifying x^0 with $1 \in R$ and x^1 with x. With this notation, a general element $(a_0, a_1, a_2, a_3, \dots, a_n, 0, 0, \dots) \in T$ can be written as $a_0 + a_1 x + a_2 x^2 + a_3 x^3 + \cdots + a_n x^n$, as

$$\begin{aligned}
&(a_0, a_1, a_2, a_3, \dots, a_n, 0, 0, \dots) \\
&= (a_0, 0, 0, \dots) + (0, a_1, 0, 0, \dots) + (0, 0, a_2, 0, \dots) \\
&\quad + (0, 0, 0, a_3, 0, \dots) + (0, 0, \dots, 0, a_n, 0, \dots).
\end{aligned}$$

This symbol x is called **indeterminate** over R, the general expression $a_0 + a_1 x + a_2 x^2 + a_3 x^3 + \cdots + a_n x^n$ is called a **polynomial** over R in the indeterminate x and the elements a_i, $i = 0, 1, 2, \dots, n$ are called **coefficients** of the above polynomial. Finally, the ring T is denoted by $R[x]$ and is called the **ring of polynomials** or the **polynomial ring** over R in the indeterminate x. Once this polynomial ring (of a single variable) is defined, one can easily extend it inductively for several indeterminates. Define $R[x, y] = (R[x])[y]$, where the later one is the polynomial ring over $R[x]$ in the indeterminate y. Similarly, we can define $R[x_1, x_2, x_3, \dots, x_n]$ inductively by considering

$$R[x_1, x_2, \dots, x_i] = (R[x_1, x_2, \dots, x_{i-1}])[x_i]$$

for each $i = 2, 3, 4, \dots, n$.

Remark 15.1.2. Note that in the above representation of elements of T in terms of polynomials, the element $(0, 1, 0, 0, \dots)$ is denoted by $1x$ which we shall identify with x. Also, for any $a \in R$, $ax = (a, 0, 0, \dots)(0, 1, 0, 0, \dots) = (0, a, 0, 0, \dots) = (0, 1, 0, 0, \dots)(a, 0, 0, \dots) = xa$ by (15.1.2).

Again, since we have identified $ax^0 \in R[x]$ with $a \in R$, it is very important to understand that R is considered as a subring of $R[x]$. Finally, observe that two polynomials $a_0 + a_1 x + a_2 x^2 + a_3 x^3 + \cdots + a_n x^n$ and $b_0 + b_1 x + b_2 x^2 + b_3 x^3 + \cdots + b_m x^m$ in $R[x]$ are equal if and only if $m = n$ and $a_i = b_i$ for all $i = 0, 1, 2, 3, \ldots, n$, which is evident from their equality as elements of T.

Theorem 15.1.3. *Let R be a commutative ring with identity. Then $R[x]$ (as defined above) is a commutative ring with identity and R is a subring of $R[x]$.*

Proof. We must prove the set T along with the binary operations defined by (15.1.1) and (15.1.2), forms a ring. Since addition is defined component wise, it is easy to verify that this addition is associative, commutative, that there is an additive identity, namely, the zero sequence, $\theta = (0, 0, 0, \ldots)$ (where all the entries are zero) and for each sequence $\sigma = (a_0, a_1, a_2, \ldots) \in T$, there exists a sequence $\sigma' = (-a_0, -a_1, -a_2, \ldots) \in T$ such that $\sigma + \sigma' = \theta$. All these verifications prove that $(T, +)$ is an Abelian group.

Thus it remains to prove that the multiplication is associative, commutative, distributive over addition and there is a multiplicative identity. So let us choose any three elements σ, τ, η of T, where $\sigma = (a_0, a_1, a_2, \ldots)$, $\tau = (b_0, b_1, b_2, \ldots)$, $\eta = (c_0, c_1, c_2, \ldots)$. Then $\sigma\tau = (d_0, d_1, d_2, \ldots)$, where $d_l = \sum\limits_{\substack{i,j=0 \\ i+j=l}}^{l} a_i b_j$, $l = 0, 1, 2, 3, \ldots$. Since R is commutative, we have $d_l = \sum\limits_{\substack{j,i=0 \\ j+i=l}}^{l} b_j a_i$, for all $l = 0, 1, 2, 3, \ldots$. This implies that $\sigma\tau = \tau\sigma$ for all $\sigma, \tau \in T$ and so the multiplication defined in (15.1.2) is commutative.

Again $(\sigma\tau)\eta = (e_0, e_1, e_2, \ldots)$, where $e_r = \sum\limits_{\substack{l,k=0 \\ l+k=r}}^{r} d_l c_k$, $r = 0, 1, 2, 3, \ldots$. Thus $e_r = \sum\limits_{\substack{i,j,k=0 \\ i+j+k=r}}^{r} a_i b_j c_k$. Similarly $\sigma(\tau\eta) = (f_1, f_2, f_3, \ldots)$, where $f_r = \sum\limits_{\substack{i,s=0 \\ i+s=r}}^{r} a_i \left(\sum\limits_{\substack{j,k=0 \\ j+k=s}}^{s} b_j c_k \right)$ $= \sum\limits_{\substack{i,j,k=0 \\ i+j+k=r}}^{r} a_i b_j c_k, r = 0, 1, 2, 3, \ldots$. Therefore $e_r = f_r$ for all $r = 0, 1, 2, 3, \ldots$. This implies that $(\sigma\tau)\eta = \sigma(\tau\eta)$ for all $\sigma, \tau, \eta \in T$ and hence the multiplication is associative.

Now let $\sigma(\tau + \eta) = (g_0, g_1, g_2, \ldots)$ and $\sigma\tau + \sigma\eta = (h_0, h_1, h_2, \ldots)$. Then $g_k = \sum\limits_{\substack{i,j=0 \\ i+j=k}}^{k} a_i(b_j + c_j)$ and $h_k = \left(\sum\limits_{\substack{i,j=0 \\ i+j=k}}^{k} a_i b_j \right) + \left(\sum\limits_{\substack{i,j=0 \\ i+j=k}}^{k} a_i c_j \right) = \sum\limits_{\substack{i,j=0 \\ i+j=k}}^{k} a_i(b_j + c_j)$ for $k = 0, 1, 2, 3, \ldots$. Thus $\sigma(\tau + \eta) = \sigma\tau + \sigma\eta$ for all $\sigma, \tau, \eta \in T$, which proves the distributive law.

Finally, it is easy to see that the sequence $(1, 0, 0, 0, \ldots)$ acts as an identity for the product (15.1.2). Therefore, T is a commutative ring with identity and identifying any element $a \in R$ with the sequence $(a, 0, 0, 0, \ldots) \in T$, we may consider R as a subring of T, which is denoted by $R[x]$. This completes the proof.   □

Now let us explore some elementary properties of a polynomial ring over a commutative ring with identity.

Definition 15.1.4. Let R be a commutative ring with identity. Let $f(x) = a_0 + a_1 x + a_2 x^2 + a_3 x^3 + \cdots + a_n x^n \in R[x]$ with $a_n \neq 0$. Then a_n is called the **leading coefficient** and n is called the **degree** of $f(x)$. In other words, degree of a polynomial $f(x)$ in $R[x]$ is the highest power of x in $f(x)$ and the leading coefficient[1] is the coefficient of the highest power of x in $f(x)$. We write $n = \deg f(x)$. If $a_n = 1$, then $f(x)$ is called **monic**. An element of R is also called a **constant polynomial**.

Proposition 15.1.5. *Let R be a commutative ring with identity and $f(x), g(x) \in R[x]$. Then,*

(i) $\deg\big(f(x)\,g(x)\big) \leq \deg f(x) + \deg g(x)$. *The equality holds if R is an integral domain;*

(ii) $\deg\big(f(x) + g(x)\big) \leq \max\big\{\deg f(x),\ \deg g(x)\big\}$.

Proof. (i) Let $m = \deg f(x)$, $n = \deg g(x)$ and a_m, b_n be the leading coefficients of $f(x)$ and $g(x)$ respectively. Then $a_m, b_n \neq 0$. Now the expression of $f(x)g(x)$ terminates [2] with the term $a_m b_n x^{m+n}$. Thus the first part of (i) follows. Also if R is an integral domain, then $a_m b_n \neq 0$ and so in this case, $\deg\big(f(x)g(x)\big) = m + n = \deg f(x) + \deg g(x)$.

(ii) Obvious and left as an exercise.   □

Theorem 15.1.6. (Division algorithm) *Let R be a commutative ring with identity. Let $f(x)$ and $g(x)$ be two polynomials in $R[x]$ such that the leading coefficient of $g(x)$ is a unit in R. Then there exist unique polynomials $q(x)$ and $r(x)$ in $R[x]$ (called **quotient** and **remainder** respectively) such that*

$$f(x) = q(x)g(x) + r(x),$$

where either $r(x) = 0$ or $\deg r(x) < \deg g(x)$.

Proof. If $f(x) = 0$, then $f(x) = 0 \cdot g(x) + 0$ proves the theorem. Let $f(x) = a_0 + a_1 x + a_2 x^2 + \cdots + a_n x^n$, $a_n \neq 0$ and $g(x) = b_0 + b_1 x + b_2 x^2 + \cdots + b_m x^m$, where

---

[1] Note that the leading coefficient is *always* nonzero, for otherwise the degree of the polynomial would be diminished.

[2] Considering as an element of T, all the entries after $(m + n + 1)$th place are zero.

b_m is a unit in R. If $n = m = 0$, then $f(x) = a_0$ and $g(x) = b_0$, which must then be a unit in R. So $f(x) = a_0 = (a_0 b_0^{-1})b_0 = (a_0 b_0^{-1})g(x) + 0$. Also if $n < m$, then $f(x) = 0 \cdot g(x) + f(x)$ with $\deg f(x) = n < m = \deg g(x)$. We proceed by induction on $\deg f(x) = n$. Assume that $n \geq m > 0$ and the division algorithm holds for all $f(x) \in R[x] \setminus \{0\}$ with $\deg f(x) < n$.

Let $f(x) \in R[x]$ such that $\deg f(x) = n$. Let $h(x) = f(x) - a_n b_m^{-1} x^{n-m} g(x)$. If $h(x) = 0$, then $f(x) = (a_n b_m^{-1} x^{n-m})g(x) + 0$. If $h(x) \neq 0$, then $\deg h(x) < n$ and so by induction hypothesis, $h(x) = q(x)g(x) + r(x)$ for some $q(x), r(x) \in R[x]$ where either $r(x) = 0$ or $\deg r(x) < \deg g(x)$. This implies that $f(x) = \big(q(x) + a_n b_m^{-1} x^{n-m}\big)g(x) + r(x)$, where $r(x)$ has the same property as above. This completes the induction and proves the division algorithm in $R[x]$.

Now suppose $f(x) = q_1(x)g(x) + r_1(x) = q_2(x)g(x) + r_2(x)$, for some $q_i(x), r_i(x) \in R[x]$, where either $r_i(x) = 0$ or $\deg r_i(x) < \deg g(x)$, $(i = 1, 2)$. This implies that $\big(q_1(x) - q_2(x)\big)g(x) = r_2(x) - r_1(x)$. Now if $r_1(x) \neq r_2(x)$, then $0 \leq \deg\big(r_2(x) - r_1(x)\big) < \deg g(x)$. But since b_m is a unit, we have $\deg\big(r_2(x) - r_1(x)\big) = \deg\big((q_1(x) - q_2(x))g(x)\big) = \deg\big(q_1(x) - q_2(x)\big) + \deg g(x) \geq \deg g(x)$, which is a contradiction. Therefore $r_1(x) = r_2(x)$ and so $\big(q_1(x) - q_2(x)\big)g(x) = 0$. Again since b_m is a unit, the product cannot be identically zero unless $q_1(x) = q_2(x)$. Thus in this case, the quotient and the remainder of the division algorithm are unique. $\square$

Definition 15.1.7. Let R be a commutative ring with identity and $f(x) = a_0 + a_1 x + a_2 x^2 + \cdots + a_n x^n \in R[x]$. For any $r \in R$, define

$$f(r) = a_0 + a_1 r + a_2 r^2 + \cdots + a_n r^n.$$

If $f(r) = 0$, then an element $r \in R$ is called a **root** [3] of $f(x)$.

Corollary 15.1.8. (Remainder Theorem) *Let R be a commutative ring with identity, $f(x) \in R[x]$ and $a \in R$. Then there exists $q(x) \in R[x]$ such that*

$$f(x) = (x - a)q(x) + f(a).$$

Proof. Since the leading coefficient of the polynomial $(x - a)$ is 1, by Theorem 15.1.6, there exist $q(x), r(x) \in R[x]$ such that $f(x) = (x - a)q(x) + r(x)$, where either $r(x) = 0$ or $\deg r(x) < \deg(x - a) = 1$. Then $r(x)$ is a constant polynomial, i.e., $r(x) = r \in R$. Thus $f(x) = (x - a)q(x) + r$ which implies that $f(a) = (a - a)q(a) + r = r$. This completes the proof. $\square$

---

[3] Also called a **zero** of $f(x)$.

Corollary 15.1.9. (Factorization Theorem) *Let R be a commutative ring with identity, $f(x) \in R[x]$ and $a \in R$. Then $(x - a)$ divides $f(x)$ if and only if a is a root of $f(x)$ (i.e., $f(a) = 0$).* [4]

Proof. Follows immediately from the remainder theorem (Corollary 15.1.8).   □

Now, we shall study polynomial rings over some special classes of commutative rings with identity and the first one is an integral domain.

Theorem 15.1.10. *If R is an integral domain, then $R[x]$ is also an integral domain. In particular, if K is a field, then $K[x]$ is an integral domain.*

Proof. By Theorem 15.1.3, $R[x]$ is a commutative ring with 1_R. Let $f(x), g(x) \in R[x] \setminus \{0\}$ with the respective leading coefficients a_m and b_n. Then $a_m, b_n \neq 0$. As R is an ID, $a_m b_n \neq 0$ and it is the leading coefficient of the polynomial $f(x)g(x)$. Hence $f(x)g(x) \neq 0$. Thus $R[x]$ is also an integral domain. Rest is obvious.   □

The converse of the above theorem is also true, since R is a subring of $R[x]$, which contains the identity. One can easily generalize the result as follows:

Corollary 15.1.11. *Let R be a commutative ring with identity. Then $R[x_1, x_2, x_3, \ldots, x_n]$ is an integral domain if and only if R is an integral domain.*

Proof. Follows from the repeated application of the above theorem.   □

Next, it is natural to ask that: is there any special property for the polynomial ring over a field? The following theorem answers the question.

Theorem 15.1.12. *If K is a field, then $K[x]$ is a Euclidean domain.*

Proof. By Theorem 15.1.10, $K[x]$ is an integral domain. Define $\delta : K[x] \setminus \{0\} \longrightarrow \mathbb{N}_0$ by $\delta(f(x)) = \deg f(x)$. Let $f(x), g(x) \in K[x] \setminus \{0\}$. Then $f(x)g(x) \neq 0$ and $\delta(f(x)g(x)) = \deg(f(x)g(x)) = \deg f(x) + \deg g(x) \geq \deg f(x) = \delta(f(x))$.

Let $f(x)$ and $g(x)$ be two polynomials in $K[x]$ such that $g(x) \neq 0$. Then the leading coefficient of $g(x)$ is nonzero and hence a unit in K. Then by Theorem 15.1.6, there exist $q(x), r(x) \in K[x]$ such that $f(x) = q(x)g(x) + r(x)$, where either $r(x) = 0$ or $\deg r(x) < \deg g(x)$. Therefore, $K[x]$ is a Euclidean domain.   □

Remark 15.1.13. Note that the quotient and the remainder of the division algorithm in the case of polynomial ring $K[x]$ over a field K are unique, by Theorem 15.1.6.

---

[4]The root $a \in R$ of $f(x) \in R[x]$ is said to be of ***multiplicity*** m if $(x-a)^m \mid f(x)$ but $(x-a)^{m+1} \nmid f(x)$.

Corollary 15.1.14. *For a field K, $K[x]$ is a PID (and hence a UFD also).*

Proof. Follows from Theorems 15.1.12, 14.2.6 (and 14.1.21). $\square$

Corollary 15.1.15. *Let K be a field and $f(x)$ be a polynomial in $K[x]$ with $\deg f(x) > 0$. Let $I = (f(x))$ be the principal ideal generated by $f(x)$. Then the following conditions are equivalent:*

(i) $f(x)$ is an irreducible element in $K[x]$;

(ii) I is a maximal ideal of $K[x]$;

(iii) $K[x]/I$ is a field;

(iv) $K[x]/I$ is an integral domain;

(v) I is a prime ideal of $K[x]$;

(vi) $f(x)$ is a prime element in $K[x]$.

Proof. Follows from Theorems 14.1.9, 13.3.12 and the Corollary 15.1.14 above. $\square$

The following theorem is of great importance, as it proves that the converse[5] of Corollary 15.1.14 also holds.

Theorem 15.1.16. *Let R be a commutative ring with identity such that $R[x]$ is a PID. Then R is a field.*

Proof. Let $a \in R \smallsetminus \{0\}$ and let $I = (\{a, x\})$ be the ideal generated by a and x. Then $I = aR[x] + xR[x]$ as $R[x]$ is a commutative ring with identity. Since $R[x]$ is a PID, there exists $u(x) \in R[x]$ such that $I = u(x)R[x]$. Then $a = u(x)v(x)$ for some $v(x) \in R[x]$. Now as $\deg a = 0$, we have $\deg u(x) = \deg v(x) = 0$. So $u(x) = u$ (say) for some $u \in R$. Also, $x \in I$ implies that $x = uf(x)$ for some $f(x) \in R[x]$. Again, as $\deg x = 1$ and $\deg u = 0$, it follows that $\deg f(x) = 1$. Thus $f(x) = b + cx$ for some $b, c \in R$. Then $x = u(b + cx)$, which implies that u is invertible (as $uc = 1$), i.e., a unit of R. Therefore $I = R[x]$ and hence $1 = ap(x) + xq(x)$ for some $p(x), q(x) \in R[x]$. Let $p(x) = c_0 + c_1 x + c_2 x^2 + \ldots + c_n x^n$. Then $1 = ac_0 + ac_1 x + ac_2 x^2 + \ldots + ac_n x^n + xq(x)$. Hence $1 = ac_0$. This implies that a^{-1} exists in R. Therefore R is a field, as every nonzero element of R is a unit. $\square$

---

[5]Only for the assertion outside parenthesis.

Example 15.1.17. The above theorem shows at once that $\mathbb{Z}[x]$ is not a PID as $\mathbb{Z}$ is not a field. Similarly, we have for a field K, $K[x, y]$ (in general, $K[x_1, x_2, \ldots x_n]$ for $n > 1$) is not a PID. But we shall prove afterwards, using Gauss' theorem (cf. Theorem 15.1.27) that all these domains are UFD.

We shall now proceed to prove the Gauss' theorem which states that the polynomial ring over a UFD is also a UFD. We begin with the following definition:

Definition 15.1.18. Let R be a UFD and $f(x) = a_0 + a_1 x + a_2 x^2 + a_3 x^3 + \cdots + a_n x^n \in R[x]$ be a polynomial with $a_n \neq 0$. Define the **content** of $f(x)$ by

$$c(f) = \gcd(a_0, a_1, a_2, \ldots, a_n).$$

A polynomial $f(x) \in R[x] \smallsetminus \{0\}$ is said to be **primitive** if $c(f) \sim 1$ (i.e., $c(f)$ is a unit).

In the polynomial ring $\mathbb{Z}[x]$, we know that 1 and -1 are the only units. Now $c(4 + 8x + 2x^2) = \gcd(4, 8, 2) = 2$ shows that $4 + 8x + 2x^2$ is not a primitive polynomial in $\mathbb{Z}[x]$, but $3 + 2x + 7x^2 + 8x^3$ is a polynomial in $\mathbb{Z}[x]$ such that $c(3 + 2x + 7x^2 + 8x^3) = \gcd(3, 2, 7, 8) = 1$, whence $3 + 2x + 7x^2 + 8x^3$ is a primitive polynomial in $\mathbb{Z}[x]$. However, we know that all the nonzero elements of $\mathbb{Q}$ are the units of $\mathbb{Q}[x]$, whence $4 + 8x + 2x^2$ is a primitive polynomial in $\mathbb{Q}[x]$.

Lemma 15.1.19. Let R be a UFD. If $f(x) \in R[x]$, $f(x) \neq 0$, then $f(x) = c(f)g(x)$, where $g(x) \in R[x]$ is primitive.

Proof. Follows immediately from the above definition. $\qquad\square$

Now consider the polynomials $f(x) = 3 + 4x + 7x^2$ and $g(x) = 8 + 7x^2 + 9x^3$ in $\mathbb{Z}[x]$. Observe that $c(f) = \gcd(3, 4, 7) = 1$ and $c(g) = 1$. Hence both these polynomials are primitive. Now, $f(x)g(x) = (3 + 4x + 7x^2)(8 + 7x^2 + 9x^3) = 24 + 32x + 77x^2 + 55x^3 + 85x^4 + 63x^5$. It can be easily seen that $c(fg) = 1$. Hence $f(x)g(x)$ is also a primitive polynomial.

We prove this result in any polynomial ring $R[x]$, when R is a UFD.

Theorem 15.1.20. Let R be a UFD and $f(x), g(x)$ be two primitive polynomials in $R[x]$. Then $f(x)g(x)$ is also a primitive polynomial. Moreover, for any $f(x), g(x) \in R[x] \smallsetminus \{0\}$, $c(fg) \sim c(f)c(g)$.

Proof. Let $f(x) = a_0 + a_1 x + a_2 x^2 + \cdots + a_n x_n$, $a_n \neq 0$ and $g(x) = b_0 + b_1 x + b_2 x^2 + \cdots + b_m x_m$, $b_m \neq 0$ be two primitive polynomials in $R[x]$. If $n = 0$, then $f(x) = a_0$ is a unit of R and $c(fg) \sim c(g) \sim 1$, as both $f(x)$ and $g(x)$ are primitive. So $f(x)g(x)$ is primitive. Similarly, the result holds for $m = 0$. Thus assume that $m, n \geq 1$.

Suppose, if possible, p is a prime factor of $c(fg)$. Now since $f(x)$ is primitive, p does not divide some coefficient a_i, $i \in \{0, 1, 2, \ldots, n\}$. Let a_j be the first coefficient of $f(x)$ (i.e., j is the least value of i), which is not divisible by p. Similarly, let b_k be the first coefficient of $g(x)$, which is not divisible by p. In $f(x)g(x)$, the coefficient of x^{j+k} (say, c_{j+k}) is given by $c_{j+k} = (a_0 b_{j+k} + a_1 b_{j+k-1} + \cdots + a_{j-1} b_{k+1}) + a_j b_k + (a_{j+1} b_{k-1} + a_{j+2} b_{k-2} + \cdots + a_{j+k} b_0)$. Now, by our choice $p \mid b_r$ for all $r < k$ and $p \mid a_s$ for all $s < j$. Therefore, $p \mid (a_{j+1} b_{k-1} + a_{j+2} b_{k-2} + \cdots + a_{j+k} b_0)$ and $p \mid (a_0 b_{j+k} + a_1 b_{j+k-1} + \cdots + a_{j-2} b_{k+2} + a_{j-1} b_{k+1})$. Also since $p \mid c(fg)$, we have $p \mid c_{j+k}$. Thus $p \mid a_j b_k$. But this implies that $p \mid a_j$ or $p \mid b_k$, as p is prime, which is a contradiction. Hence there is no prime factor of $c(fg)$. In other words, $c(fg) \sim 1$, i.e., $f(x)g(x)$ is primitive.

The last part of the theorem follows from the above lemma. Let $f(x), g(x) \in R[x] \smallsetminus \{0\}$. Then $f(x) = c(f)f_1(x)$ and $g(x) = c(g)g_1(x)$, where $f_1(x)$ and $g_1(x)$ are primitive. Thus $f(x)g(x) = c(f)c(g)f_1(x)g_1(x)$. By the above result, $f_1(x)g_1(x)$ is primitive and hence $c(fg) \sim c(f)c(g)$ $\hfill\square$

Definition 15.1.21. Let R be a commutative ring with identity. Then a polynomial $f(x) \in R[x]$ is called ***irreducible over*** R, if $f(x)$ is an irreducible element in $R[x]$ (cf. Definition 14.1.3). A polynomial, which is neither zero nor a unit and which is not irreducible over R, is called ***reducible over*** R.

Example 15.1.22. $f(x) = 6 + 8x = 2(3 + 4x)$ shows that neither 2 nor $3 + 4x$ is a unit in $\mathbb{Z}[x]$. Hence $f(x)$ is not irreducible. Since $f(x)$ is a nonzero nonunit element in $\mathbb{Z}[x]$, it follows that, $f(x)$ is a reducible polynomial in $\mathbb{Z}[x]$. But the polynomial $3 + 4x$ is an irreducible polynomial in $\mathbb{Z}[x]$.

Remark 15.1.23. Note that every irreducible polynomial over a UFD R is primitive in $R[x]$, by Lemma 15.1.19.

Theorem 15.1.24. (Gauss' Lemma) *Let D be a UFD and E be the quotient field of D. Let $f(x) \in D[x]$ be a primitive polynomial of positive degree. Then $f(x)$ is irreducible in $D[x]$ if and only if $f(x)$ is irreducible in $E[x]$.*

Proof. Let $f(x)$ be an irreducible polynomial in $E[x]$. If $f(x) = g(x)h(x)$ in $D[x]$, then $g(x)$ and $h(x)$ cannot be both of positive degree, for then $f(x)$ would be reducible in $E[x]$ also. So let $\deg(g(x)) = 0$. Thus $g(x) \in D$. Since $f(x)$ is primitive in $D[x]$, it follows that $g(x)$ is a unit in D. Similarly, if $\deg(h(x)) = 0$, then $h(x)$ is a unit in D. So $f(x)$ is irreducible in $D[x]$.

Conversely, let $f(x)$ be irreducible in $D[x]$. Let if possible, $f(x)$ be reducible in $E[x]$. Then there exists nonzero nonunit elements $g(x)$ and $h(x)$ in $E[x]$ such that $f(x) = g(x)h(x)$

$$= (\alpha_0 + \alpha_1 x + \alpha_2 x^2 + \cdots + \alpha_n x^n)(\beta_0 + \beta_1 x + \beta_2 x^2 + \cdots + \beta_m x^m). \quad (15.1.3)$$

Since E is a field, an element $r(x) \in E[x] \setminus \{0\}$ is a unit if and only if $r(x)$ is of degree zero. Hence $g(x)$ and $h(x)$ are polynomials of positive degree in $E[x]$. Now for each $i = 0, 1, 2, \ldots, n$, $\alpha_i = a_i b_i^{-1}$ and for each $j = 0, 1, 2, \ldots, m$, $\beta_j = \bar{a}_j \bar{b}_j^{-1}$ for some $a_i, b_i, \bar{a}_i, \bar{b}_j \in D$.

Let $d = b_0 b_1 \ldots b_n \bar{b}_0 \bar{b}_1 \ldots \bar{b}_m \in D$. Multiplying both sides of (15.1.3) by d, we get

$$df(x) = \Big(\sum_{i=0}^{n} c_i x^i \Big) \Big(\sum_{j=0}^{m} \bar{c}_j x^j \Big) = u(x)v(x), \text{ (say),}$$

where $c_i = a_i b_0 b_1 \ldots b_{i-1} b_{i+1} \ldots b_n \in D$ and $\bar{c}_j = \bar{a}_j \bar{b}_0 \bar{b}_1 \ldots \bar{b}_{j-1} \bar{b}_{j+1} \ldots \bar{b}_m \in D$. Thus $u(x), v(x) \in D[x]$. So

$$df(x) = c(u)c(v)u_1(x)v_1(x),$$

where $u_1(x)$ and $v_1(x)$ are primitive polynomials in $D[x]$. Therefore, $d \sim c(u)c(v)$ as $f(x)$ is primitive. So $f(x) = \alpha u_1(x)v_1(x)$ where $\alpha \in D$ is a unit. But then $f(x)$ is reducible in $D[x]$ which is a contradiction. This completes the proof. $\square$

Remark 15.1.25. Note that for each $f(x) \in E[x]$, there exist $a, b \in D$, $b \neq 0$ such that $f(x) = (ab^{-1})h(x)$, where $h(x) \in D[x]$ and $h(x)$ is primitive.

Lemma 15.1.26. *Let D be a UFD and E be the quotient field of D. If $f(x), g(x)$ be primitive polynomials in $D[x]$, then $f(x) \sim g(x)$ in $D[x]$ if and only if $f(x) \sim g(x)$ in $E[x]$.*

Proof. Suppose $f(x) \sim g(x)$ in $E[x]$. Then $g(x) = (ab^{-1})f(x)$ for some $a, b \in D$, $b \neq 0$. Then $bg(x) = af(x)$. Taking the contents of both sides we get $b \sim a$ (as $f(x)$ and $g(x)$ are primitive), i.e., $g(x) \sim f(x)$ in $D[x]$. The proof of the converse part is obvious. $\square$

Theorem 15.1.27. (Gauss) *Let D be a UFD, then $D[x]$ is also a UFD.*

Proof. Let $f(x) \neq 0$ in $D[x]$. If $\deg(f(x)) = 0$, then $f(x) \in D$. Since D is a UFD, $f(x)$ has a unique factorization in D and hence in $D[x]$. So, let $\deg(f(x)) \geq 1$. Let E be the quotient field of D and we have $D \subseteq E$. Now $f(x) = c(f)g(x)$, where $g(x)$ is a primitive polynomial in $D[x] \subseteq E[x]$.

Since $g(x) \in E[x]$, $\deg(g(x)) \geq 1$ and $E[x]$ is a Euclidean domain by Theorem 15.1.12 and hence a UFD, it follows that

$$g(x) = q_1(x)q_2(x)\dots q_m(x), \tag{15.1.4}$$

where each $q_i(x)$ is irreducible in $E[x]$ and is of a positive degree. Let $a_i, b_i \in D$, $(i = 1, 2, \dots, m)$ be such that $q_i(x) = (a_i b_i^{-1})g_i(x)$, where $g_i(x) \in D[x]$ is a primitive polynomial. Then by (15.1.4),

$$b_1 b_2 \dots b_m g(x) = a_1 a_2 \dots a_m g_1(x)g_2(x)\dots g_m(x).$$

Since the product of primitive polynomials is primitive by Theorem 15.1.20, it follows by taking contents of both sides that, $b_1 b_2 \dots b_m \sim a_1 a_2 \dots a_m$ in D, so that

$$g(x) = ug_1(x)g_2(x)\dots g_m(x),$$

where u is a unit in D. Also since each $g_i(x)$ is irreducible in $E[x]$ and primitive in $D[x]$, it follows that $g_i(x), i = 1, 2, \dots, n$, are irreducible in $D[x]$, by Gauss' Lemma (Theorem 15.1.24). Thus,

$$f(x) = uc(f)g_1(x)g_2(x)\dots g_m(x). \tag{15.1.5}$$

Now, if $c(f)$ is a unit in D, then $uc(f)g_1(x)$ is an irreducible element in $D[x]$. If $c(f)$ is not a unit, then by unique factorization property of D, there exist irreducible elements $d_1, d_2, \dots, d_n$ in D such that $c(f) = d_1 d_2 \dots d_n$ and hence $f(x) = \bar{d_1} d_2 \dots d_n g_1(x)g_2(x)\dots g_m(x)$, where $\bar{d_1} = d_1 u$. Now $\bar{d_1}, d_2, \dots, d_n$ are also irreducible elements in $D[x]$. Hence it follows that $f(x)$ can be expressed as a product of irreducible elements in $D[x]$.

We now show that any factorization of $f(x)$ in $D[x]$ is unique. To prove this, we first note that

$$f(x) = c(f)g_1(x)g_2(x)\dots g_m(x),$$

where $g_i(x), i = 1, 2, \dots, m$ are irreducible in $D[x]$. Now, any factorization of $f(x)$ in $D[x]$ must be of the form

$$f(x) = d_1 d_2 \dots d_r g_1(x)g_2(x)\dots g_m(x),$$

where either $c(f) = d_1 d_2 \ldots d_r = d$ is a unit or $d_1, d_2, \ldots, d_r$ are irreducible elements of D and $g_1(x), g_2(x), \ldots, g_m(x)$ are irreducible elements of $D[x]$.

Let

$$f(x) = c(f)g_1(x)g_2(x) \ldots g_m(x) = d_1 d_2 \ldots d_r g_1(x)g_2(x) \ldots g_m(x)$$

and

$$f(x) = c(f)h_1(x)h_2(x) \ldots h_s(x) = e_1 e_2 \ldots e_t h_1(x)h_2(x) \ldots h_s(x)$$

be two factorizations of $f(x)$ in $D[x]$. Then,

$$
\begin{aligned}
& g_1(x)g_2(x) \ldots g_m(x) \\
= \ & u h_1(x)h_2(x) \ldots h_s(x) \quad \text{where } u \text{ is a unit in } D \\
= \ & \bar{h}_1(x)\,\bar{h}_2(x) \ldots \bar{h}_s(x) \quad \text{where } \bar{h}_1(x) = u h_1(x) \text{ and } \bar{h}_j(x) = h_j(x) \ldots (*)
\end{aligned}
$$

Since $g_i(x), i = 1, 2, \ldots, m$, $\bar{h}_1(x), h_j(x), j = 2, \ldots, s$ are irreducible and primitive in $D[x]$, therefore these polynomials are irreducible in $E[x]$. Now $E[x]$ is a UFD, hence from $(*)$, it follows that $m = t$ and there exists a permutation σ on $\{1, 2, \ldots, m\}$ such that $g_i(x) \sim h_{\sigma(i)}(x)$. Again, $c(f) \in D$ and D is a UFD, hence if $c(f)$ is not a unit, its factorization in D and hence in $D[x]$, is unique. Therefore the factorization of $f(x)$ in $D[x]$ is unique. Hence $D[x]$ is a UFD. $\qquad\square$

Corollary 15.1.28. *Let D be a UFD, then $D[x_1, x_2, \ldots, x_n]$ is also a UFD. In particular, if K is a field, then $K[x_1, x_2, \ldots, x_n]$ is a UFD.*

Proof. Since $D[x_1, x_2, \ldots x_n] \simeq D_{n-1}[x_n]$, where $D_{n-1} = D[x_1, x_2, \ldots x_{n-1}]$, the result follows by induction on n from Gauss' theorem. $\qquad\square$

The following diagram (Fig. 28) depicts the inter-relation among the various domains discussed so far.

$$ED \longrightarrow PID \longrightarrow UFD \longrightarrow FD \longrightarrow ID$$

Fig. 28

Till now we have discussed and established the inter-relationships as shown above, giving supporting examples in terms of various well-known structures. To put the state of affairs in a nutshell, we bring an end to this section with the following compact tabular representation, which substantiates the above diagram in terms of various examples.

ID	FD	UFD	PID	ED	Field
$\mathbb{Q}$	✓	✓	✓	✓	✓
$\mathbb{R}$	✓	✓	✓	✓	✓
$\mathbb{Z}$	✓	✓	✓	✓	✗
$\mathbb{Q}[x]$	✓	✓	✓	✓	✗
$\mathbb{R}[x]$	✓	✓	✓	✓	✗
$\mathbb{Z}[\frac{1+i\sqrt{19}}{2}]$	✓	✓	✓	✗	✗
$\mathbb{Z}[x]$	✓	✓	✗	✗	✗
$\mathbb{Z}[i\sqrt{5}]$	✓	✗	✗	✗	✗
R	✗	✗	✗	✗	✗

where $R = \{a_0 + a_1 x + \ldots + a_n x^n \in \mathbb{Q}[x] : a_0 \in \mathbb{Z}, n \in \mathbb{N}_0\}$ which is a subring of $\mathbb{Q}[x]$ with identity and hence an integral domain. But we have $x = 2\left(\frac{1}{2}x\right) = 2 \cdot 2\left(\frac{1}{4}x\right) = 2 \cdot 2 \cdot 2\left(\frac{1}{8}x\right)$ and so on. In general, one may verify that, x has no factorization interms of finite number of irreducible elements. Indeed, if $x = p(x)q(x)$ where $p(x), q(x)$ are nonzero nonunit elements of R then either $\deg p(x) = 0$ and $\deg q(x) = 1$ or the other way round. So, $x = a(bx + c)$, for some $a, c \in \mathbb{Z}, b \in \mathbb{Q}, a, b \neq 0$. Then $ac = 0$ and since R is an integral domain we have $c = 0$ i.e., $x = a(bx)$. Thus $ab = 1$. Since $a \in \mathbb{Z}$, let $a = n, b = \frac{1}{n}$. Then $x = n\left(\frac{1}{n}x\right) = n \cdot 2\left(\frac{1}{2n}x\right) = n \cdot 2 \cdot 2\left(\frac{1}{4n}x\right) = \ldots\ldots$ where none of the terms within brackets is irreducible. Thus, x has no factorization, as claimed above. Hence R is an ID but not a FD.

Worked-out Exercises

───

◇ **Exercise 15.1.1.** If R is a commutative ring with identity, then show that $R[x]$ and R have the same characteristic.

Solution. We first note that R is a subring of $R[x]$ such that both have the same identity, 1. Now if R is of characteristic zero, then there is no such positive integer n so that $n1 = 0$. Then $R[x]$ is also of characteristic zero. Similarly, if $R[x]$ is of characteristic zero, then R also has the characteristic zero.

Again if R is of finite characteristic, then characteristic of R is a positive integer n, where n is the least positive integer such that $n1 = 0$. This implies that the characteristic of $R[x]$ is n, since 1 is also the identity of $R[x]$. Similar arguments prove the converse that if the characteristic of $R[x]$ is n, then R has the same characteristic.

◇ **Exercise 15.1.2.** Find the gcd of the polynomials $f(x)$ and $g(x)$ in the polynomial ring $R[x]$, where $f(x) = [2](x^5 - x^4 + x^3 - x - [1])$, $g(x) = x^4 - [2]x^2 + [2]$ and $R = \mathbb{Z}_5$.

Solution. We have

$$
x^4 - [2]x^2 + [2] \enspace \Big|\; \begin{array}{l} [2]x-[2] \\ \hline [2]x^5 - [2]x^4 + [2]x^3 \qquad -[2]x-[2] \end{array}
$$

$$
\begin{array}{rrrr}
 & [2]x^5 & -[4]x^3 & +[4]x \\
 & - & + & - \\
\hline
 & -[2]x^4+ & x^3 & -x-[2] \\
 & -[2]x^4 & +[4]x^2 & -[4] \\
 & + & - & + \\
\hline
 & x^3-[4]x^2- & x+[2] \\
 & = \; x^3+ & x^2- & x+[2]
\end{array}
$$

$$
x^3 + x^2 - x + [2] \enspace \Big|\; \begin{array}{l} x-[1] \\ \hline x^4 \quad -[2]x^2 \qquad + [2] \end{array}
$$

$$
\begin{array}{rrr}
x^4+x^3- & x^2+ [2]x \\
- & - & + & - \\
\hline
-x^3- & x^2- [2]x+ [2] \\
-x^3- & x^2+ & x- [2] \\
+ & + & - & + \\
\hline
 & -[3]x+[4] \\
 & = [2]x+ [4] \\
 & =[2](x+[2])
\end{array}
$$

$$
x + [2] \enspace \Big|\; \begin{array}{l} x^2- \quad x+ [1] \\ \hline x^3+ \quad x^2- \quad x+[2] \end{array}
$$

$$
\begin{array}{rrr}
x^3+[2]x^2 \\
- & - \\
\hline
- & x^2- & x+[2] \\
- & x^2-[2]x \\
+ & + \\
\hline
 & x+[2] \\
 & x+[2] \\
 & - & - \\
\hline
 & [0]
\end{array}
$$

Therefore,

$$
\begin{aligned}
f(x) &= [2](x^5 - x^4 + x^3 - x - [1]) \\
&= (x^4 - [2]x^2 + [2])([2]x - [2]) + x^3 + x^2 - x + [2],
\end{aligned}
$$

$$
x^4 - [2]x^2 + [2] = (x^3 + x^2 - x + [2])(x - [1]) + [2](x + [2])
$$

$$
x^3 + x^2 - x + [2] = (x + [2])(x^2 - x + [1]).
$$

Hence $\gcd(f(x), g(x)) = \gcd\Big([2](x^5 - x^4 + x^3 - x - [1]), x^4 - [2]x^2 + [2]\Big) = x + [2]$.

◇ **Exercise 15.1.3.** Let R be a commutative ring with identity and S be a subring of R which contains the identity. For $t \in R$, define $S[t] = \{f(t) \in R \mid f(x) \in S[x]\}$. Prove that $S[t]$ is a subring of R and there exists a unique homomorphism $\phi : S[x] \longrightarrow S[t]$ such that $\phi(x) = t$ and $\phi(a) = a$ for all $a \in S$.

Solution. Certainly $0 \in S[t]$, as the zero-polynomial belongs to $S[x]$. Let $a, b \in S[t]$. Then there exist $f(x), g(x) \in S[x]$ such that $a = f(t)$ and $b = g(t)$. Let $h(x) = f(x) - g(x)$ and $k(x) = f(x)g(x)$. Then $h(x), k(x) \in S[x]$ and $h(t) = f(t) - g(t) = a - b$ and $k(t) = f(t)g(t) = ab$. So $a - b, ab \in S[t]$. This implies that $S[t]$ is a subring of R. Define $\phi : S[x] \longrightarrow S[t]$ by $\phi(f(x)) = f(t)$. Clearly, $\phi(x) = t$ and $\phi(a) = a$ for all $a \in S$.

Let $f(x), g(x) \in S[x]$. Let $p(x) = f(x) + g(x)$ and $q(x) = f(x)g(x)$. Then $\phi(p(x)) = p(t) = f(t) + g(t) = \phi(f(x)) + \phi(g(x))$ and $\phi(q(x)) = q(t) = f(t)g(t) = \phi(f(x))\phi(g(x))$. These imply that ϕ is a homomorphism such that $\phi(x) = t$ and $\phi(a) = a$ for all $a \in S$.

To show that ϕ is unique with this property, let $\psi : S[x] \longrightarrow S[t]$ a homomorphism with $\psi(x) = t$ and $\psi(a) = a$ for all $a \in S$. Let $f(x) = a_0 + a_1 x + a_2 x^2 + \ldots + a_n x^n \in S[x]$. Then $\psi(f(x)) = \psi(a_0 + a_1 x + a_2 x^2 + \ldots + a_n x^n) = \psi(a_0) + \psi(a_1)\psi(x) + \psi(a_2)\{\psi(x)\}^2 + \ldots + \psi(a_n)\{\psi(x)\}^n = a_0 + a_1 t + a_2 t^2 + \ldots + a_n t^n = f(t) = \phi(f(x))$ since ψ is a homomorphism, $\psi(x) = t$ and $\psi(a) = a$ for all $a \in S$. Thus $\psi = \phi$ which proves the uniqueness of ϕ as required.

◇ **Exercise 15.1.4.** Let R be an integral domain and $f(x)$ be a nonzero polynomial in $R[x]$ of degree n. Then show that $f(x)$ has at most n roots in R (counted according to multiplicity).

Solution. We prove this result by induction on the degree n of $f(x)$. If $n = 0$, then $f(x)$ is a constant polynomial and so $f(x)$ has no roots in R. Therefore the result is true for $n = 0$. Suppose now the result is true for all polynomials of degree $k < n$, where $n \geq 1$. Let $f(x) \in R[x]$ and $\deg f(x) = n$. If $f(x)$ has no root in R, then we are done. Suppose $f(x)$ has a root a in R. Then by Corollary 15.1.9, $(x - a) \mid f(x)$. Let $f(x) = (x - a)^r g(x)$ where $g(x) \in R[x]$ and degree of $g(x) = n - r$. Then by induction hypothesis, $g(x)$ has at most $n - r$ roots in R. Let b be a root of $f(x)$ such that $b \neq a$. Then $0 = f(b) = (b - a)^r g(b)$ in R. Since R is an ID and $b - a \neq 0$, we find that $g(b) = 0$. Hence any root of $f(x)$ in R, different from a, is a root of $g(x)$. Therefore, $f(x)$ has at most $(n - r) + r = n$ roots. This completes the induction.

◇ **Exercise 15.1.5.** Prove that the ideal $\langle x, 2 \rangle$ is a maximal ideal of $\mathbb{Z}[x]$.

Solution. Let R be a ring and $a \in R$. Let $\langle a \rangle_R$ denote the principal ideal of R generated by the element a. Now,

$$\langle x, 2 \rangle_{\mathbb{Z}[x]}$$
$$= \{xf(x) + 2g(x) : f(x), g(x) \in \mathbb{Z}[x]\}$$
$$= \{xf(x) + 2(a_0 + a_1x + \cdots + a_nx^n) : f(x), g(x) = a_0 + a_1x + \cdots + a_nx^n \in \mathbb{Z}[x]\}$$
$$= \{xh(x) + 2a_0 : h(x) = f(x) + 2a_1 + a_2x + \cdots + a_nx^{n-1} \in \mathbb{Z}[x], a_0 \in \mathbb{Z}\}$$
$$= \langle x \rangle_{\mathbb{Z}[x]} + \langle 2 \rangle_{\mathbb{Z}}.$$

Hence $\dfrac{\mathbb{Z}[x]}{\langle x, 2 \rangle_{\mathbb{Z}[x]}} = \dfrac{\frac{\mathbb{Z}[x]}{\langle x \rangle_{\mathbb{Z}[x]}}}{\frac{\langle x, 2 \rangle_{\mathbb{Z}[x]}}{\langle x \rangle_{\mathbb{Z}[x]}}} = \dfrac{\frac{\mathbb{Z}[x]}{\langle x \rangle_{\mathbb{Z}[x]}}}{\frac{\langle x \rangle_{\mathbb{Z}[x]} + \langle 2 \rangle_{\mathbb{Z}}}{\langle x \rangle_{\mathbb{Z}[x]}}} \simeq \dfrac{\mathbb{Z}}{\langle 2 \rangle_{\mathbb{Z}}} = \mathbb{Z}/2\mathbb{Z} \simeq \mathbb{Z}_2.$

Since $\mathbb{Z}_2$ is a field, it follows that $\dfrac{\mathbb{Z}[x]}{\langle x, 2 \rangle_{\mathbb{Z}[x]}}$ is a field. Consequently, $\langle x, 2 \rangle_{\mathbb{Z}[x]}$ is a maximal ideal of $\mathbb{Z}[x]$.

Alternative solution : To show $\langle x, 2 \rangle$ is a maximal ideal of $\mathbb{Z}[x]$, let I be any ideal of $\mathbb{Z}[x]$ such that $\langle x, 2 \rangle \subset I$. Then there exists an element $f(x) = a_0 + a_1x + a_2x^2 + \cdots + a_nx^n \in I$ such that $f(x) \notin \langle x, 2 \rangle$. Now, $x \in \langle x, 2 \rangle$ implies $a_1x + a_2x^2 + \cdots + a_nx^n = x(a_1 + a_2x + \cdots + a_nx^{n-1}) \in \langle x, 2 \rangle \subset I$. Hence $a_0 \in I$ but $a_0 \notin \langle x, 2 \rangle$. If a_0 is even, then $a_0 = 2k$ for some $k \in \mathbb{Z}$. Since $2 \in \langle x, 2 \rangle$, it follows that $a_0 = 2k \in \langle x, 2 \rangle$, a contradiction. Hence a_0 must be odd and therefore, $a_0 = 2r + 1$ for some $r \in \mathbb{Z}$. Then $1 = a_0 - 2r \in I$ and thus $I = \mathbb{Z}[x]$. Consequently, $\langle x, 2 \rangle$ is a maximal ideal of $\mathbb{Z}[x]$.

◊ **Exercise 15.1.6.** Which of the following ring is a PID ?
(i) $\mathbb{Q}[x, y]/\langle y \rangle$ (ii) $\mathbb{Z} \oplus \mathbb{Z}$
(iii) $\mathbb{Z}[x]$ (iv) $M_2(\mathbb{Z})$, the ring of 2×2 matrices with entries in $\mathbb{Z}$.

Solution. Any element $f(x, y) \in \mathbb{Q}[x, y]$ can be expressed as $f(x, y) = g(x) + yh(x, y)$ where $g(x) \in \mathbb{Q}[x]$ and $h(x, y) \in \mathbb{Q}[x, y]$. Then the mapping $\varphi : \mathbb{Q}[x, y] \longrightarrow \mathbb{Q}[x]$ defined by $\varphi(f(x, y)) = g(x)$, where $f(x, y) = g(x) + yh(x, y)$, is a ring epimorphism. So by First Isomorphism Theorem of rings, it follows that $\mathbb{Q}[x, y]/\ker \varphi \simeq \mathbb{Q}[x]$. One can easily check that $\ker \varphi = \langle y \rangle$. Therefore, $\mathbb{Q}[x, y]/\langle y \rangle \simeq \mathbb{Q}[x]$. Since $\mathbb{Q}[x]$ is a PID, it follows that $\mathbb{Q}[x, y]/\langle y \rangle$ is also a PID.

We know $\mathbb{Z}[x]$ is not a PID. Also none of $\mathbb{Z} \oplus \mathbb{Z}$ and $M_2(\mathbb{Z})$ are integral domain. Hence the ring in option (i) is a PID.

◊ **Exercise 15.1.7.** Which of the following rings are principal ideal domains (PID)?
(i) $\mathbb{Q}[x]$ (ii) $\mathbb{Z}[x]$ (iii) $\mathbb{Z}_8[x]$ (iv) $\mathbb{Z}_{11}[x]$.

Solution. For a ring R, $R[x]$ is a PID if and only if R is a field. Here $\mathbb{Q}$ and $\mathbb{Z}_{11}$ are two fields. Therefore, $\mathbb{Q}[x]$ and $\mathbb{Z}_{11}[x]$ are principal ideal domains. Hence rings given in options (i) and (iv) are PID.

◊ **Exercise 15.1.8.** Let R be the ring obtained by taking the quotient of $(\mathbb{Z}/6\mathbb{Z})[x]$ by the principal ideal $\langle 2x + 4 \rangle$. Pick the correct statement(s).

(i) R has infinitely many elements.   (ii) R is a field.

(iii) 5 is unit in R.   (iv) 4 is unit in R.

Solution. For any positive integer n, $x^n \notin \langle 2x + 4 \rangle$. Hence $x^n + \langle 2x + 4 \rangle \neq 0 + \langle 2x + 4 \rangle \in \frac{(\mathbb{Z}/6\mathbb{Z})[x]}{\langle 2x+4 \rangle} = R$. Moreover, for any two distinct positive integers m and n, $x^n - x^m \notin \langle 2x + 4 \rangle$, i.e., $x^n + \langle 2x+4 \rangle \neq x^m + \langle 2x+4 \rangle$ in R. Hence R contains infinite number of elements.

Again, the element $4 \in R$ is a nonzero and non-identity idempotent element. Therefore, 4 is nonunit element in R and consequently, R is not a field. Also, $5 = -1$ in R and -1 is unit in R. Thus 5 is unit in R. Hence options (i) and (iii) are correct.

◊ **Exercise 15.1.9.** Which of the following quotient rings are fields?

(i) $\mathbb{F}_3[x]/\langle x^2 + x + 1 \rangle$, where $\mathbb{F}_3$ is the finite field with 3 elements.

(ii) $\mathbb{Z}[x]/\langle x - 3 \rangle$.

(iii) $\mathbb{Q}[x]/\langle x^2 + x + 1 \rangle$.

(iv) $\mathbb{F}_2[x]/\langle x^2 + x + 1 \rangle$, where $\mathbb{F}_2$ is the finite field with 2 elements.

Solution. In $\mathbb{F}_3[x]$, $x^2 + x + 1 = x^2 - 2x + 1 = (x - 1)^2$. This implies $x^2 + x + 1$ is not irreducible in $\mathbb{F}_3[x]$. Consequently, $\mathbb{F}_3[x]/\langle x^2 + x + 1 \rangle$ is not a field. Now since $\mathbb{Z}[x]/\langle x - 3 \rangle \simeq \mathbb{Z}$, we have $\mathbb{Z}[x]/\langle x - 3 \rangle$ is not a field. Again, $x^2 + x + 1$ is an irreducible polynomial in $\mathbb{Q}[x]$. Hence $\mathbb{Q}[x]/\langle x^2+x+1 \rangle$ is a field. Finally, x^2+x+1 is an irreducible polynomial in $\mathbb{F}_2[x]$. Hence $\mathbb{F}_2[x]/\langle x^2 + x + 1 \rangle$ is a field. Therefore, quotient rings in options (iii) and (iv) are fields.

◊ **Exercise 15.1.10.** Let A denote the quotient ring $\mathbb{Q}[x]/\langle x^3 \rangle$. Pick the right option(s).

(i) There are exactly three distinct proper ideals in A.

(ii) There is only one prime ideal in A.

(iii) A is an integral domain.

(iv) Let f, g be in $\mathbb{Q}[x]$ such that $\overline{f} \cdot \overline{g} = 0$ in A. Then $f(0) \cdot g(0) = 0$. [Here $\overline{f}$ and $\overline{g}$ denote the image of f and g respectively in A.]

Solution. Ideals of $A(= \mathbb{Q}[x]/\langle x^3 \rangle)$ are $\{0 + \langle x^3 \rangle\}$, $\langle x^2 \rangle/\langle x^3 \rangle$, $\langle x \rangle/\langle x^3 \rangle$ and $\mathbb{Q}[x]/\langle x^3 \rangle = A$. One can easily check that $\langle x \rangle/\langle x^3 \rangle$ is the only one prime ideal of $\mathbb{Q}[x]/\langle x^3 \rangle$. Now

$x + \langle x^3 \rangle$ and $x^2 + \langle x^3 \rangle$ are two non-zero elements of A such that $(x + \langle x^3 \rangle)(x^2 + \langle x^3 \rangle) = x^3 + \langle x^3 \rangle = 0 + \langle x^3 \rangle$. Thus A is not an integral domain.

Finally, $\overline{f} \cdot \overline{g} = 0$ in A implies $(f(x) + \langle x^3 \rangle)(g(x) + \langle x^3 \rangle) = 0 + \langle x^3 \rangle$, i.e., $f(x) \cdot g(x) \in \langle x^3 \rangle$, i.e., $f(x) \cdot g(x) = x^3 h(x)$ for some $h(x) \in \mathbb{Q}[x]$. Therefore, $f(0) \cdot g(0) = 0$. Therefore, options (i), (ii) and (iv) are correct.

Exercises

1. In $\mathbb{Z}_6[x]$, find $f(x) + g(x), f(x)g(x), \deg f(x), \deg g(x), \deg(f(x) + g(x))$ and $\deg(f(x)g(x))$ where $f(x) = [2] + [3]x + x^2 + [2]x^5$, $g(x) = [1] + [2]x^2 + [5]x^3 + [3]x^4$.

2. In $\mathbb{Z}_7[x]$, let $f(x) = [2] + [3]x + x^2 + [2]x^5$, $g(x) = [1] + [2]x^2 + [5]x^3 + [3]x^4$. Find $f(x) + g(x), f(x)g(x), \deg f(x), \deg g(x), \deg(f(x) + g(x))$ and $\deg(f(x)g(x))$.

3. Let $f(x) = x^2 + x + [4] \in \mathbb{Z}_{10}[x]$. Show that $[7]$ is a root of $f(x)$.

4. In $\mathbb{Z}_5[x]$, express the polynomial $x^4 + [4]$ as a product of linear factors.

5. In $\mathbb{Z}_7[x]$, factorize $f(x) = x^3 + [1]$ into linear factors.

6. Find all the roots of the polynomial $x^5 - [3]x^3 + [4]x^2 + x + [2] \in \mathbb{Z}_7[x]$ which lie in $\mathbb{Z}_7$.

7. Let R be the ring $\mathbb{Z} \times \mathbb{Z}$. Solve the polynomial equation: $(1,1)x^2 - (5,14)x + (6,33) = (0,0)$ over R. Show that the linear equation, $(5,0)x + (20,0) = (0,0)$ has infinitely many roots in R.

8. † Let R be a commutative ring with identity. Show that $f(x) = a_0 + a_1 x + a_2 x^2 + \cdots + a_n x^n$ is a unit in $R[x]$ if and only if a_0 is a unit and $a_1, a_2, \ldots, a_n$ are nilpotent elements of R.

9. † Let D be a Euclidean domain in which the Euclidean norm δ satisfies an additional condition that for any $a, b \in D$, $\delta(a + b) \leq \max\{\delta(a), \delta(b)\}$. Then prove that either D is a field or $D \simeq K[x]$ where K is a field.

10. Let $f(x) = [2]x^6 - x^5 + [3]x^4 + [3]x^3 - [5]x^2 + [4]$ and $g(x) = [2]x^4 - [3]x^2 + [5]x + [1]$ be two polynomials in $\mathbb{Z}_7[x]$. Find the polynomials $q(x), r(x) \in \mathbb{Z}_7[x]$ so that $f(x) = q(x)g(x) + r(x)$ where either $r(x) = 0$ or $\deg r(x) < \deg g(x)$.

11. Find the gcd of the polynomials $f(x)$ and $g(x)$ in the polynomial ring $R[x]$, where

    (i) $f(x) = 2x^5 + 3x^4 + 9x^3 + x^2 + 13x + 20$, $g(x) = 3x^4 - x^3 + 12x^2 - 13x + 55$ and $R = \mathbb{Q}$.

    (ii) $f(x) = x^3 + x + [1]$, $g(x) = x^3 - x^2 - [1]$ and $R = \mathbb{Z}_3$.

    (iii) $f(x) = x^5 - x^4 + [3]x^3 - [3]x^2 + [3]x + [6]$, $g(x) = [3]x^4 - [3]x^2 - [5]x + [8]$ and $R = \mathbb{Z}_{13}$.

12. Find all polynomials of degree 2 in $\mathbb{Z}_2[x]$.

13. Let K be an infinite field and $f(x) \in K[x]$. If $f(x)$ has infinite roots in K, then prove that $f(x)$ is the zero polynomial.

14. Let R be an integral domain. Show that an element u is a unit in $R[x]$ if and only if u is a unit in R.

15. Let K be a field and $p(x) \in K[x]$. Let P be the principal ideal generated by $p(x)$. Prove that $K[x]/P$ is an integral domain if and only if $K[x]/P$ is a field.

16. Let K be a field. Suppose $\phi : K[x] \longrightarrow K[x]$ be an automorphism such that $\phi(u) = u$ for all $u \in K$. Prove that $\phi(x) = ax + b$ for some $a, b \in K$.

17. Let R be a UFD and $f(x) \in R[x]$ be a primitive polynomial of degree ≥ 1. Prove that every positive degree factor of $f(x)$ is also primitive.

18. Let K be a field and $f(x) \in K[x]$ with $\deg f(x) = n > 0$. Let $I = (f(x))$, the principal ideal generated by $f(x)$. Show that

$$K[x]/I = \{g(x) + I \mid g(x) \in K[x], \text{ either } g(x) = 0 \text{ or } \deg g(x) < n\}.$$

19. Let R be a commutative ring with identity. Prove that $R[x]/(x) \simeq R$, where (x) is the principal ideal generated by x.

20. Construct a polynomial ring $R[x]$ for any commutative ring R (possibly without identity). Show that R is a subring of $R[x]$ and if I is any ideal of R, then $I[x]$ is also an ideal of $R[x]$.

21. Prove that $\mathbb{Z}_4[x]$ has infinitely many units and infinitely many nilpotent elements.

22. Factorize $x^3 - 1$ as a product of irreducible polynomials in $\mathbb{Z}[x], \mathbb{Q}[x], \mathbb{R}[x], \mathbb{C}[x]$ and in $\mathbb{Z}_3[x], \mathbb{Z}_5[x]$.

23. Give an example of a ring R with identity and a maximal ideal I of R such that $I[x]$ is not a maximal ideal in $R[x]$.

24. (a) Let R be a commutative ring with identity. If I is a prime ideal of R, show that $I[x]$ is a prime ideal of $R[x]$.
    (b) Prove that the ideal $\langle x, 3 \rangle$ is a maximal ideal of $\mathbb{Z}[x]$.

25. Is it true that $\mathbb{Z}[x] \simeq \mathbb{Z}$? Does there exist a commutative ring R such that $R[x] \simeq \mathbb{Z}$?

26. Find the correct answer for the following:
    (a) The number of zeros of $[2]x + [1]$ in $\mathbb{Z}_4[x]$ is
         (i) 1 (ii) 2 (iii) 0 (iv) 4
    (b) The number of zeros of $x^2 + [3]x + [2]$ in $\mathbb{Z}_6[x]$ is
         (i) 4 (ii) 2 (iii) 0 (iv) 1
    (c) The number of idempotent elements in $\mathbb{Z}_4[x]$ is
         (i) 1 (ii) 2 (iii) Infinite (iv) 4
    (d) The number of units in $\mathbb{Z}_5[x]$ is
         (i) 1 (ii) 2 (iii) 4 (iv) Infinite
    (e) If $f(x) = x^3 + [3]x + [2] \in \mathbb{Z}_5[x]$ then the number of roots of $f(x)$ in $\mathbb{Z}_5$ is
         (i) 0 (ii) 1 (iii) 3 (iv) 2

27. Find whether the following statements are true or false. Justify your answer giving counter examples whenever necessary.
    (a) The characteristic of $\mathbb{Z}_2[x]$ is 2.
    (b) $\mathbb{Z}_2[x]$ is a finite field.
    (c) $K[x]$ may be a field for some field K.

    (d)　$x^2 - 2$ is irreducible in $\mathbb{Z}[x]$.

    (e)　The ideal (x) in $\mathbb{Q}[x]$ is maximal.

    (f)　$x^2 - 2$ is irreducible in $\mathbb{Q}[x]$ but not so in $\mathbb{R}[x]$.

    (g)　In $\mathbb{Z}_5[x]$, $[2]x + [3]$ is an associate of $[3]x + [2]$.

    (h)　In $\mathbb{Z}_5[x]$, $[3]x^2 + [4]x + [3] = ([4]x + 1)([2]x + [3])$.

    (i)　$6 + 2x + 8x^2 + 12x^3$ is a primitive polynomial in $\mathbb{Q}[x]$.

    (j)　$x^2 + 2x + 1$ is primitive but not irreducible in $\mathbb{Z}[x]$.

    (k)　$2x + 4$ is irreducible in both $\mathbb{Z}[x]$ and $\mathbb{Q}[x]$.

28. †　Find two polynomials $f, g \in \mathbb{Z}[x]$ such that $\gcd(f, g) = 1$ but there exist no pair of polynomials $h, k \in \mathbb{Z}[x]$ so that $fh + gk = 1$.

29. Which of the following is an irreducible factor of $x^{12} - 1$ over $\mathbb{Q}$?
(i) $x^8 + x^4 + 1$.
(ii) $x^4 + 1$.
(iii) $x^4 - x^2 + 1$.
(iv) $x^5 - x^4 + x^3 - x^2 + x - 1$.

30. Let R be a commutative ring with unity, such that $R[x]$ is a UFD. Denote the ideal $\langle x \rangle$ of $R[x]$ by I. Pick the correct statement(s) from below:
(i) I is prime.
(ii) If I is maximal, then $R[x]$ is a PID.
(iii) If $R[x]$ is a Euclidean domain, then I is maximal.
(iv) If $R[x]$ is a PID, then it is a Euclidean domain.

31. Let R be a Euclidean domain such that R is not a field. Then the polynomial ring $R[x]$ is always
(i) a Euclidean domain.
(ii) a principal ideal domain, but not a Euclidean domain.
(iii) a unique factorization domain, but not a principal ideal domain.
(iv) not a unique factorization domain.

15.2　Irreducibility of Polynomials

It is clear from Gauss' theorem discussed in the last section that every polynomial ring over a unique factorization domain is again a unique factorization domain. This implies that every polynomial over a UFD R has a unique factorization in $R[x]$ in terms of its irreducible elements,i.e., irreducible polynomials. Though the existence of such a factorization is ensured by Gauss' Theorem, obtaining that explicitly, often becomes a very hard problem. There is no general method known for obtaining this factorization, not even for deciding whether a polynomial is irreducible or not. *It is still an open problem to get a (general) necessary and sufficient criterion for irreducibility of a polynomial (even over the field of rational numbers).* However we have some sufficient conditions for this. The Eisenstein's criterion, given below, is the most famous one.

Theorem 15.2.1. (Eisenstein's criterion) *Let D be a UFD and E be the quotient field of D. Let $f(x) = a_0 + a_1 x + \ldots + a_n x^n$ be a nonconstant polynomial in $D[x]$. Suppose there exists a prime $p \in D$ such that*

   (i) $p \mid a_i, \ i = 0, 1, 2, \ldots, n-1$

   (ii) $p \nmid a_n$

   (iii) $p^2 \nmid a_0$.

Then $f(x)$ is irreducible in $E[x]$. Moreover, if $f(x)$ is primitive, then $f(x)$ is irreducible in $D[x]$.

Proof. First, we note that there exists a primitive polynomial $g(x) \in D[x]$ such that $f(x) = c(f)g(x)$. Now, either $c(f) \sim 1$ or $c(f) \nsim 1$. Suppose $c(f) \sim 1$. Then $f(x) \sim g(x)$. Hence $f(x)$ is a primitive polynomial. In this case, we show that $f(x)$ is irreducible in $D[x]$. Suppose $f(x)$ is not irreducible. Now $f(x)$ is a nonconstant polynomial. Hence there exist two nonzero nonunit polynomials $h_1(x) = c_0 + c_1 x + \ldots + c_m x^m$ and $h_2(x) = d_0 + d_1 x + \ldots + d_r x^r$ in $D[x]$ such that $f(x) = h_1(x)h_2(x)$. Then $n = r + m$. If $h_1(x) = c_0$ then $c_0 \neq 0$, nonunit and $f(x) = c_0 h_2(x)$ implies that $f(x)$ is not primitive. Hence $m > 0$. Similarly $r > 0$. Hence $0 < r < n$ and $0 < m < n$. Now $f(x) = h_1(x)h_2(x)$ implies that $a_0 = c_0 d_0$. Since $p \mid a_0$, $p \mid c_0 d_0$. Hence either $p \mid c_0$ or $p \mid d_0$. Again, $p^2 \nmid a_0$. Hence p cannot divide both of c_0 and d_0. So (without any loss of generality), assume that p divides c_0 and p does not divide d_0. Again $a_n = c_m d_r$ and $p \nmid a_n$. Hence $p \nmid c_m$ and $p \nmid d_r$. So, we find that $p \mid c_0$ and $p \nmid c_m$. Hence, there exists a positive integer $i \leq m$ such that $p \mid c_0, \ldots, p \mid c_{i-1}$ but $p \nmid c_i$. Considering the coefficient of x^i in $f(x)$ and in $h_1(x)h_2(x)$, we find that

$$a_i = c_i d_0 + c_{i-1} d_1 + \ldots + c_0 d_i \qquad (15.2.1)$$

where $c_{m+1} = c_{m+2} = \ldots = 0$ and $d_{r+1} = d_{r+2} = \ldots = 0$ in (15.2.1). Now as $p \mid c_0, p \mid c_1, \ldots, p \mid c_{i-1}$, we find that $p \mid a_i - c_i d_0$. Since $i \leq m < n$, it follows from assumption (i) that $p \mid a_i$. Hence $p \mid c_i d_0$. But $p \nmid c_i$ and $p \nmid d_0$ which is not possible as p is a prime integer. Hence $f(x)$ is irreducible in $D[x]$. Since $f(x)$ is also primitive, so from Gauss' lemma, $f(x)$ is irreducible in $E[x]$.

We now consider the case when $c(f)$ is not a unit in $D[x]$. Let $c(f) = d$. Then $f(x) = dg(x)$ where $g(x)$ is a primitive polynomial in $D[x]$. Let $g(x) = t_0 + t_1 x + \ldots + t_n x^n$. Then $a_i = d t_i, \ i = 0, 1, \ldots, n$. Since $p \nmid a_n, \ p \nmid d$. Hence for the polynomial $g(x)$, we find $p \mid t_i, \ i = 0, 1, \ldots, n-1, \ p \nmid t_n$ and $p^2 \nmid t_0$. Hence from the above case, it follows that $g(x)$ is irreducible in $E[x]$. Since d is a unit in $E[x]$, we find that $f(x) \sim g(x)$ in $E[x]$. Therefore $f(x)$ is irreducible in $E[x]$. $\qquad \square$

Corollary 15.2.2. *Let* $f(x) = a_0 + a_1 x + \ldots + a_n x^n$ *be a nonconstant polynomial in* $\mathbb{Z}[x]$. *Suppose there exists a prime* p *such that*

(i) $p \mid a_i, \ i = 0, 1, 2, \ldots, n - 1$,

(ii) $p \nmid a_n$

(iii) $p^2 \nmid a_0$.

Then $f(x)$ *is irreducible over* $\mathbb{Q}$. *Moreover, if* $f(x)$ *is primitive, then* $f(x)$ *is irreducible over* $\mathbb{Z}$.

Proof. Follows from the above theorem and fact that $\mathbb{Z}$ is a UFD and $\mathbb{Q}$ is the quotient field of $\mathbb{Z}$.   □

Example 15.2.3. Let $f(x) = 5x^4 + 4x^3 - 6x^2 - 14x + 2 \in \mathbb{Z}[x]$. Then $2 \nmid 5$, $2 \mid 4$, $2 \mid (-6)$, $2 \mid (-14)$, $2 \mid 2$ but $2^2 \nmid 2$. Thus $f(x)$ is an irreducible polynomial over $\mathbb{Q}$, by Eisenstein's criterion. Also since $f(x)$ is primitive, it is irreducible over $\mathbb{Z}$.

Example 15.2.4. Let us consider the polynomial $f(x) = 1 + x + x^2 + x^3 + \cdots + x^{p-1} \in \mathbb{Z}[x]$, where p is a prime number. This polynomial is called a ***cyclotomic polynomial***. Clearly f is primitive. Now consider the polynomial $f(x + 1)$. Since $f(x) = \frac{x^p - 1}{x - 1}$, we have

$$
\begin{aligned}
f(x + 1) &= \frac{(x + 1)^p - 1}{(x + 1) - 1} \\[2mm]
&= \frac{x^p + px^{p-1} + \binom{p}{2} x^{p-2} + \cdots + \binom{p}{i} x^{p-i} + \cdots + px}{x} \\[2mm]
&= x^{p-1} + px^{p-2} + \binom{p}{2} x^{p-3} + \cdots + \binom{p}{i} x^{p-i-1} + \cdots + p
\end{aligned}
$$

which is clearly irreducible over $\mathbb{Q}$ by Eisenstein's criterion. Now it is easy to understand that if there is a nontrivial factorization of $f(x)$, say, $f(x) = g(x)h(x)$, then there is also a nontrivial factorization of $f(x + 1)$, namely, $f(x + 1) = g(x + 1)h(x + 1)$. Therefore $f(x)$ is irreducible over $\mathbb{Q}$ and hence over $\mathbb{Z}$, as $f(x)$ is primitive in $\mathbb{Z}[x]$.

In the following, we shall describe some other conditions for irreducibility of polynomials.

Theorem 15.2.5. *Let* F *be a field and* $f(x) \in F[x]$ *with* $\deg f(x) = 2$ *or* 3. *Then* $f(x)$ *is irreducible over* F *if and only if* $f(x)$ *has no root in* F.

Proof. Suppose $\deg f(x) = 3$ and $f(x)$ is irreducible. If $f(x)$ has a root in F, say a, then $x - a$ divides $f(x)$ in $F[x]$ and so $f(x)$ is reducible over F.

Conversely, suppose $f(x)$ has no roots in F. Assume that $f(x)$ is reducible. Then $f(x) = g(x)h(x)$ for some $g(x), h(x) \in F[x]$, $\deg g(x) \geq 1$ and degree $h(x) \geq 1$. Now if

$\deg f(x) = \deg(g(x)h(x)) = 3$, either $\deg g(x) = 1$ and $\deg h(x) = 2$ or the other way round. To be specific, let $\deg g(x) = 1$ and $\deg h(x) = 2$. Then $g(x) = ax + b$ for some $a, b \in F$, $a \neq 0$. Now $-a^{-1}b \in F$ and $g(-a^{-1}b) = 0$. Thus, $-a^{-1}b$ is a root of $g(x)$ and hence $-a^{-1}b$ is a root of $f(x)$ in F. This is a contradiction to our assumption that $f(x)$ has no roots in F. Hence, $f(x)$ is irreducible over F. A similar argument can be used for the case when $\deg f(x) = 2$. □

By virtue of the above theorem, we can find some irreducible polynomials. For example, $x^2 + 1, x^2 + 5$ have no roots in $\mathbb{R}$. Hence these are irreducible polynomials, whereas $x^3 + 1$ has a root -1 in $\mathbb{R}$, whence it is not an irreducible polynomial; rather $x^3 + 1 = (x + 1)(x^2 - x + 1)$ shows that $x^3 + 1$ is reducible in $\mathbb{R}[x]$. Again consider the field $\mathbb{Z}_3$. $x^3 + [2]x + [2]$ is a polynomial in $\mathbb{Z}_3[x]$. Now none of the elements $[0], [1]$ and $[2]$ are roots of this polynomial. Hence $x^3 + [2]x + [2]$ is an irreducible polynomial in $\mathbb{Z}_3[x]$.

The following theorem provides a very useful criterion to determine rational roots of a polynomial in $\mathbb{Z}[x]$.

Theorem 15.2.6. Let $f(x) = a_0 + a_1 x + a_2 x^2 + \cdots + a_n x^n \in \mathbb{Z}[x]$ with $a_0, a_n \neq 0$. If $\frac{p}{q} \in \mathbb{Q}$ is a root of $f(x)$ (where p and q are relatively prime integers and $q > 0$), then $p \mid a_0$ and $q \mid a_n$.

Proof. We have $f(\frac{p}{q}) = 0$ and so $a_0 + a_1(\frac{p}{q}) + a_2(\frac{p}{q})^2 + \cdots + a_n(\frac{p}{q})^n = 0$ which implies that

$$a_0 q^n + a_1 p q^{n-1} + a_2 p^2 q^{n-2} + \cdots + a_{n-1} p^{n-1} q + a_n p^n = 0.$$

Thus we have $p \mid a_0 q^n$ and $q \mid a_n p^n$, since all other terms are divisible by p and q. But p and q are relatively prime. So $p \mid a_0$ and $q \mid a_n$, as required. □

Example 15.2.7. (i) Consider the polynomial $f(x) = 9x^3 - 7x^2 + 11x + 5$ over $\mathbb{Z}$. Here $a_0 = 5$ and $a_3 = 9$. Now the only factors of 5 are ± 1 and ± 5, whereas factors of 9 are $\pm 1, \pm 3, \pm 9$. Thus by the above theorem, possible rational roots of $f(x)$ are $\pm 1, \pm 5, \pm \frac{1}{3}, \pm \frac{5}{3}, \pm \frac{1}{9}, \pm \frac{5}{9}$. But one may easily verify that none of them is a root of $f(x)$ and hence by Theorem 15.2.5, $f(x)$ is irreducible over $\mathbb{Q}$ as well as over $\mathbb{Z}$, since $f(x)$ is primitive.

(ii) Next consider the polynomial $g(x) = x^3 - 9x^2 + 15x - 2$. According to the previous theorem, the only possible rational roots of $g(x)$ are ± 2 and we see that $g(2) = 0$. Therefore $g(x)$ is not irreducible over $\mathbb{Q}$.

Finally, we note that, in order to determine the irreducibility of a polynomial in $\mathbb{Z}[x]$, it is sometimes useful to consider the corresponding polynomial in $\mathbb{Z}_p[x]$ for prime number p.

Theorem 15.2.8. *Let $f(x) = a_0 + a_1 x + a_2 x^2 + \cdots + a_n x^n \in \mathbb{Z}[x]$ with $a_n \neq 0$ and $n > 1$. If there exists a prime number p such that*

   (i) $p \nmid a_n$ and

   (ii) $\bar{f}(x) = [a_0] + [a_1]x + \ldots + [a_n]x^n$ is irreducible in $\mathbb{Z}_p[x]$,

then $f(x)$ is irreducible in $\mathbb{Q}[x]$.

Proof. If possible, let $f(x)$ be reducible in $\mathbb{Q}[x]$. Now if $f(x)$ is irreducible in $\mathbb{Z}[x]$, then it is primitive by Remark 15.1.23 and hence it is also irreducible in $\mathbb{Q}[x]$ by Gauss' lemma (cf. Theorem 15.1.24). Thus, $f(x)$ is reducible in $\mathbb{Z}[x]$ and $f(x) = g(x)h(x)$ where $g(x) = b_0 + b_1 x + \ldots + b_m x^m$ and $h(x) = c_0 + c_1 x + \ldots + c_t x^t$ belong to $\mathbb{Z}[x]$ such that $\deg g(x) = m, \deg h(x) = t$ and $1 < m < n$, $1 < t < n$.

Now in $\mathbb{Z}_p[x]$, $[a_0] + [a_1]x + \ldots + [a_n]x^n = ([b_0] + [b_1]x + \ldots + [b_m]x^m)([c_0] + [c_1]x + \ldots + [c_t]x^t)$. Hence $[a_n] = [b_m][c_t]$. Now $p \nmid a_n$. Hence $[a_n] \neq [0]$. Then $[b_m] \neq [0]$ and $[c_t] \neq [0]$. Therefore, $\bar{f}(x)$ is reducible in $\mathbb{Z}_p[x]$, which is a contradiction. Hence $f(x)$ is irreducible in $\mathbb{Q}[x]$. $\square$

Example 15.2.9. Let $f(x) = 13x^3 - 8x^2 + 11x - 3$. As a polynomial of $\mathbb{Z}_2[x]$, $\bar{f}(x) = x^3 + x + [1]$ which is irreducible over $\mathbb{Z}_2$ as $\bar{f}([0]) = \bar{f}([1]) = [1] \neq [0]$ (by Theorem 15.2.5). Also $2 \nmid 13$. Thus by the above theorem, $f(x)$ is irreducible over $\mathbb{Q}$.

Worked-out Exercises

$\Diamond$ **Exercise 15.2.1.** Let F be a field. Show that every polynomial of degree 1 is an irreducible polynomial in $F[x]$.

Solution. Since $\deg f(x) = 1$, $f(x)$ is nonzero and nonunit. Suppose $f(x) = g(x)h(x)$, where $g(x), h(x) \in K[x]$. Clearly, $g(x), h(x)$ are nonzero polynomials. Now $1 = \deg f(x) = \deg g(x) + \deg h(x)$. Hence either $\deg g(x) = 1$ and $\deg h(x) = 0$ or, $\deg g(x) = 0$ and $\deg h(x) = 1$. Hence either $g(x) \in F \smallsetminus \{0\}$ or $h(x) \in F \smallsetminus \{0\}$. This implies that either $g(x)$ is a unit or $h(x)$ is a unit. Hence $f(x)$ is irreducible.

$\Diamond$ **Exercise 15.2.2.** Let F be a field and $f(x) \in F[x]$ with $\deg f(x) \geq 2$. If $f(x)$ is irreducible in $F[x]$, then show that $f(x)$ has no root in F. Show that the converse of this result is not always true.

Solution. Let a be a root of $f(x)$ in F. Then by Remainder Theorem, $f(x) = (x - a)g(x)$ for some $g(x) \in F[x]$. Now $\deg f(x) \geq 2$. Hence $\deg g(x) \geq 1$. Therefore $f(x)$ is not irreducible in $F[x]$. Hence if $f(x)$ is irreducible in $F[x]$, then $f(x)$ has no root in F.

Now consider the polynomial $f(x) = (x^2 + 1)(x^2 + 2)$ in $\mathbb{Q}[x]$. This polynomial has no root in $\mathbb{Q}$. But $f(x)$ is reducible in $\mathbb{Q}[x]$.

◇ **Exercise 15.2.3.** Show that $f(x) = x^3 + [2]x + [4]$ is irreducible in $\mathbb{Z}_5[x]$.

Solution. $f([0]) = [4], f([1]) = [7] = [2], f([2]) = [3] + [4] + [4] = [1], f([3]) = [2] + [1] + [4] = [2], f([4]) = [4] + [3] + [4] = [1]$. Hence $f(x)$ has no roots in $\mathbb{Z}_5$. Thus, $f(x)$ is irreducible in $\mathbb{Z}_5[x]$.

◇ **Exercise 15.2.4.** Let R be a UFD and $f(x) \in R[x]$. Show that $f(x)$ is irreducible over R if and only if $f(x + a)$ is irreducible over R for any $a \in R$.

Solution. Let $f(x)$ be irreducible over R. If $f(x + a)$ is not irreducible, then $f(x + a) = g(x)h(x)$, where $g(x)$ and $h(x)$ are nonzero and nonunit elements in $R[x]$. Thus $f(x) = g(x - a)h(x - a)$. Clearly, $g(x - a)$ and $h(x - a)$ are not zero (i.e., not the zero polynomial as $g(x), h(x)$ are not so). Also, only units of $R[x]$ are units of R, as R is an integral domain. Now if $g(x - a)$ is a unit, then it is a constant polynomial and hence it is equal to $g(x)$ which implies that $g(x)$ is also a unit. Therefore $g(x - a)$ is not a unit. Similarly, $h(x - a)$ is not a unit. But then $f(x)$ is not irreducible, which is a contradiction. Thus $f(x + a)$ is also irreducible. In an exactly similar way, one can prove the converse that if $f(x + a)$ is irreducible, then $f(x)$ is also so.

◇ **Exercise 15.2.5.** Show that the following polynomials are irreducible:

(i) $2x^4 + 6x^3 - 9x^2 + 15$ over $\mathbb{Z}$;

(ii) $x^3 + 2x^2 + 3$ over $\mathbb{Q}$;

(iii) $x^5 + x^2 + [1]$ over $\mathbb{Z}_2$;

(iv) $x^3 - [9]$ over $\mathbb{Z}_{31}$.

Solution. (i) Let $f(x) = 2x^4 + 6x^3 - 9x^2 + 15$. Now 3 is prime in $\mathbb{Z}$ and $3 \nmid 2$, $3 \mid 6$, $3 \mid 9$, $3 \mid 15$ but $3^2 = 9 \nmid 15$. Thus following Eisenstein's criterion, we have $f(x)$ is irreducible over $\mathbb{Q}$, the quotient field of $\mathbb{Z}$. Moreover $f(x)$ is primitive, as $\gcd\{2, 6, 9, 15\} = 1$. Therefore $f(x)$ is irreducible over $\mathbb{Z}$.

(ii) Let $f(x) = x^3 + 2x^2 + 3$. Since $\deg f(x) = 3$, we have if $f(x)$ is not irreducible (over $\mathbb{Q}$), then $f(x)$ must have a linear factor, i.e., $f(x)$ has a root over $\mathbb{Q}$. Now by

Theorem 15.2.6, the possible roots of $f(x)$ are $\frac{p}{q}$, $(p, q \in \mathbb{Z}, \ q \neq 0)$, where $p \mid 3$ and $q \mid 1$. The only possibilities are ± 3. But $f(3) = 48 \neq 0$ and $f(-3) = -6 \neq 0$. Therefore $f(x)$ has no linear factor and hence $f(x)$ is irreducible over $\mathbb{Q}$.

(iii)   Let $f(x) = x^5 + x^2 + [1] \in \mathbb{Z}_2[x]$. First we note that $f(x)$ has no linear factor as $f([0]) = [1] = f([1])$. Thus if $f(x)$ is not irreducible, then $f(x)$ must have an irreducible quadratic factor. Now there are four quadratic polynomials in $\mathbb{Z}_2[x]$, namely x^2, $x^2 + [1]$, $x^2 + x$, $x^2 + x + [1]$ and among them, the only [6] irreducible one is $x^2 + x + [1]$.

Let $f(x) = (x^2 + x + [1])(x^3 + ax^2 + bx + c)$ where $a, b, c \in \mathbb{Z}_2$. Then we have $[1] + a = [0]$, $[1] + a + b = [0]$, $a + b + c = [1]$, $b + c = [0]$, $c = [1]$. The first two equalities imply that $b = [0]$ and the last one says $c = [1]$. But then $[1] = b + c = [0]$, which is a contradiction. Therefore $f(x)$ is irreducible over $\mathbb{Z}_2$.

(iv)   Let $f(x) = x^3 - [9] \in \mathbb{Z}_{31}$. As in (ii), if $f(x)$ is not irreducible, then $f(x)$ must have a linear factor, i.e., $f(x)$ has a root in $\mathbb{Z}_{31}$. But one may verify that there is no element $\alpha \in \mathbb{Z}_{31}$ such that $\alpha^3 = [9]$. Therefore, $f(x)$ is irreducible over $\mathbb{Z}_{31}$.

$\Diamond$ **Exercise 15.2.6.** Let $f(x)$ be an irreducible polynomial over a field F. Show that the quotient ring $F[x]/\big(f(x)\big)$ is a field in which F is *embedded*,[7] where $\big(f(x)\big)$ is the principal ideal generated by $f(x)$.

Solution. By Corollary 15.1.15, we have that $F[x]/\big(f(x)\big)$ is a field. Now define the mapping $\phi : F \longrightarrow F[x]/\big(f(x)\big)$ by $\phi(a) = a + I$, where $I = \big(f(x)\big)$. We show that ϕ is a monomorphism.

Let $a, b \in F$. Then $\phi(a + b) = (a + b) + I = (a + I) + (b + I)$ and $\phi(ab) = ab + I = (a + I)(b + I)$. Thus ϕ is a homomorphism. Suppose $\phi(a) = \phi(b)$ for some $a, b \in F$. Then $a + I = b + I$ which implies that $a - b \in I = \big(f(x)\big)$. Now since $f(x)$ is irreducible in $F[x]$ and $a, b \in F$, I has no constant polynomial other than the zero polynomial. Thus we have $a - b = 0$. So $a = b$. Therefore, ϕ is injective and hence a monomorphism as required.

$\blacklozenge$ **Exercise 15.2.7.** Let $f(x)$ be an irreducible polynomial over $\mathbb{Z}_p$, where p is a prime number and $\deg f(x) = n$. Show that $\mathbb{Z}_p[x]/\big(f(x)\big)$ is a field containing p^n elements.

---

[6]Note that $x^2 + [1] = (x + [1])^2$ over $\mathbb{Z}_2$.

[7]Recall that a ring R is said to be **embedded** in another ring S if R is isomorphic to a subring of S. In particular, if R and S are fields, then S is called an **extension** of R. The given result is very much important in field theory as it provides a construction of an extension field from a given field.

Solution. Since $f(x)$ is an irreducible polynomial, the ideal $I = (f(x))$ is a maximal ideal. Hence $\mathbb{Z}_p[x]/I$ is a field. The field $\mathbb{Z}_p[x]/I$ consists of all cosets $g(x) + I$, where $g(x) \in \mathbb{Z}_p[x]$. Now by division algorithm there exist polynomials $q(x)$ and $r(x)$ in $\mathbb{Z}_p[x]$ such that $g(x) = q(x)f(x) + r(x)$ where either $r(x) = 0$ or, $\deg r(x) < n$. Hence,

$$\mathbb{Z}_p[x]/I = \{r(x) + I \mid \text{either } r(x) = 0 \text{ or } \deg r(x) < n\}.$$

Let
$$T = \{a_0 + a_1 x + \ldots + a_{n-1}x^{n-1} \in \mathbb{Z}_p[x] \mid a_i \in \mathbb{Z}_p\}.$$

Since $\mathbb{Z}_p$ has p elements, the number of such polynomials of the form $a_0 + a_1 x + \ldots + a_{n-1}x^{n-1}$ is p^n. Let $t_1(x), t_2(x) \in T$ such that $t_1(x) + I = t_2(x) + I$. Then $f(x) \mid (t_1(x) - t_2(x))$. Now $\deg f(x) = n$ and if $t_1(x) - t_2(x) \neq 0$, then $\deg(t_1(x) - t_2(x)) < n$. Hence $f(x) \mid t_1(x) - t_2(x)$ if and only if $t_1(x) - t_2(x) = 0$, i.e., $t_1(x) = t_2(x)$. Hence $\mathbb{Z}_p[x]/I = \{t(x) + I \mid t(x) \in T\}$ contains exactly p^n elements. Therefore, $\mathbb{Z}_p[x]/I$ is a field containing p^n elements.

◊ **Exercise 15.2.8.** Using the Worked-out Exercise 15.2.7 above, construct a field containing 27 elements.

Solution. By virtue of the above problem, we have to produce only an irreducible polynomial of degree 3 over $\mathbb{Z}_3$. We show that

$$f(x) = x^3 + x^2 + [2] \in \mathbb{Z}_3[x]$$

is such a choice. Since $\deg f(x) = 3$, as before, $f(x)$ fails to be irreducible only if $f(x)$ has a root in $\mathbb{Z}_3$. But $f([0]) = [2]$, $f([1]) = [4] = [1]$ and $f([2]) = [14] = [2]$. Therefore, $f(x)$ is irreducible over $\mathbb{Z}_3$. Hence the field $\mathbb{Z}_3[x]/(f(x))$ contains $3^3 = 27$ elements.

◊ **Exercise 15.2.9.** Prove that $x^2 + 1$ is irreducible over $\mathbb{R}$. Hence prove that $\mathbb{R}[x]/(x^2 + 1)$ is a field which is isomorphic to $\mathbb{C}$, the field of complex numbers.

Solution. There is no real number satisfying the polynomial $p(x) = x^2 + 1$. Thus $p(x)$ has no linear factor and hence no nontrivial factor over $\mathbb{R}$. Therefore $p(x)$ is irreducible over $\mathbb{R}$.

Then by Worked-out Exercise 15.2.6, we have that $\mathbb{R}[x]/(p(x))$ is a field, say K. We show that K is isomorphic to $\mathbb{C}$, the field of complex numbers. Define $\phi : \mathbb{R}[x] \to \mathbb{C}$ by $\phi(f(x)) = f(i)$ for all $f(x) \in \mathbb{R}[x]$. Let $f(x), g(x) \in \mathbb{R}[x]$. Let $h(x) = f(x) + g(x)$ and $t(x) = f(x)g(x)$. Now $h(x), t(x) \in \mathbb{R}[x]$ and

$$\phi(f(x) + g(x)) = \phi(h(x)) = h(i) = f(i) + g(i) = \phi(f(x)) + \phi(g(x));$$

$$\phi\big(f(x)g(x)\big) = \phi\big(t(x)\big) = t(i) = f(i)g(i) = \phi\big(f(x)\big)\phi\big(g(x)\big).$$

Hence ϕ is a homomorphism. Let $a + bi \in \mathbb{C}$. Then $f(x) = a + bx \in \mathbb{R}[x]$ and $\phi\big(f(x)\big) = a + bi$. Therefore, ϕ is a homomorphism from $\mathbb{R}[x]$ onto $\mathbb{C}$. Hence by First Isomorphism theorem, $\mathbb{R}[x]/ker\,\phi \simeq \mathbb{C}$.

Since $\phi(x^2 + 1) = i^2 + 1 = -1 + 1 = 0$, it follows that $x^2 + 1 \in ker\,\phi$. Let $f(x) \in ker\,\phi$. By division algorithm, there exist $q(x)$ and $r(x)$ in $\mathbb{R}[x]$ such that $f(x) = q(x)(x^2 + 1) + r(x)$, where either $r(x) = 0$ or $\deg r(x) < 2$. Then $r(x) = a + bx$ for some $a, b \in \mathbb{R}$. Now $r(x) = f(x) - q(x)(x^2 + 1) \in ker\,\phi$. Hence $\phi\big(r(x)\big) = 0$. Then $a + bi = 0$. Hence $a = 0$, $b = 0$. This shows that $r(x) = 0$. Hence $f(x) = q(x)(x^2 + 1)$. Thus we find that $ker\,\phi = (x^2 + 1)$. This completes the proof.

$\Diamond$ **Exercise 15.2.10.** Find all irreducible polynomials of degree 2 in $\mathbb{Z}_2[x]$.

Solution. Any polynomial of degree 2 in $\mathbb{Z}_2[x]$ is of the form $ax^2 + bx + c$, where $a, b, c \in \mathbb{Z}_2 = \{[0], [1]\}$. Now $a \neq [0]$. Therefore, $a = [1]$. Then $x^2, x^2 + x, x^2 + [1]$ and $x^2 + x + [1]$ are the only polynomials of degree 2 in $\mathbb{Z}_2[x]$. Now $x^2 = xx$, $x^2 + x = x(x + [1])$ and $x^2 + [1] = (x + [1])(x + [1])$, whence we conclude that all these three polynomials are reducible. Let $f(x) = x^2 + x + [1]$. Then $f([0]) = [1] \neq 0$ and $f([1]) = [3] = [1] \neq 0$. Therefore, $f(x)$ has no root in $\mathbb{Z}_2$. Thus, $x^2 + x + [1]$ is irreducible over $\mathbb{Z}_2$.

$\Diamond$ **Exercise 15.2.11.** For a prime number p, how many irreducible monic polynomials of degree 2 are there in $\mathbb{Z}_p[x]$?

Solution. Let $f(x) = x^2 + ax + b \in \mathbb{Z}_p[x]$ where $a, b \in \mathbb{Z}_p$. Since $|\mathbb{Z}_p| = p$, there are p^2 such polynomials in $\mathbb{Z}_p[x]$. Now if $f(x)$ is not irreducible, then $f(x) = (x - \alpha)(x - \beta)$ for some $\alpha, \beta \in \mathbb{Z}_p$. Now, how many such distinct products of factors occur? [8] If α, β are distinct, then the number is $\binom{p}{2} = \frac{p(p-1)}{2}$ and if $\alpha = \beta$, then the number is p. Thus the total number of distinct products is

$$\frac{p(p-1)}{2} + p = \frac{p(p+1)}{2}.$$

Therefore the required number of irreducible monic polynomials over $\mathbb{Z}_p$ of degree 2 is

$$p^2 - \frac{p(p+1)}{2} = \frac{p(p-1)}{2}.$$

$\Diamond$ **Exercise 15.2.12.** Prove that the ideal $\langle x^2 + 1, y \rangle$ is a maximal ideal of $\mathbb{R}[x, y]$.

Solution. Let R be a ring and $a \in R$. Let $\langle a \rangle_R$ denote the principal ideal of R generated by the element a.

---

[8] Certainly $(x - \alpha)(x - \beta)$ and $(x - \beta)(x - \alpha)$ are the same products of the factors.

Now,

$$\langle x^2 + 1, y\rangle_{\mathbb{R}[x,y]} = \{(x^2+1)f(x,y) + yg(x,y) : f(x,y), g(x,y) \in \mathbb{R}[x,y]\}$$
$$= \langle x^2+1\rangle_{\mathbb{R}[x]} + \langle y\rangle_{\mathbb{R}[x,y]}.$$

Hence $\dfrac{\mathbb{R}[x,y]}{\langle x^2+1,y\rangle_{\mathbb{R}[x,y]}} \simeq \dfrac{\frac{\mathbb{R}[x,y]}{\langle y\rangle_{\mathbb{R}[x,y]}}}{\frac{\langle x^2+1,y\rangle_{\mathbb{R}[x,y]}}{\langle y\rangle_{\mathbb{R}[x,y]}}} = \dfrac{\frac{(\mathbb{R}[x])[y]}{\langle y\rangle}}{\frac{\langle x^2+1\rangle_{\mathbb{R}[x]}+\langle y\rangle_{\mathbb{R}[x,y]}}{\langle y\rangle_{\mathbb{R}[x,y]}}} \simeq \dfrac{\mathbb{R}[x]}{\langle x^2+1\rangle_{\mathbb{R}[x]}} \simeq \mathbb{C}.$

Since $\mathbb{C}$ is a field, it follows that $\dfrac{\mathbb{R}[x,y]}{\langle x^2+1,y\rangle_{\mathbb{R}[x,y]}}$ is a field. Consequently, the ideal $\langle x^2+1, y\rangle_{\mathbb{R}[x,y]}$ is a maximal ideal of $\mathbb{R}[x,y]$.

◊ **Exercise 15.2.13.** Let I_1 be the ideal generated by $x^4 + 6x^2 + 5$ and I_2 be the ideal generated by $x^3 + 1$ in $\mathbb{Q}[x]$. If $F_1 = \mathbb{Q}[x]/I_1$ and $F_2 = \mathbb{Q}[x]/I_2$, then pick the right option(s) from below.

(i) F_1 and F_2 are fields.

(ii) F_1 is a field, but F_2 is not a field.

(iii) F_1 is not a field while F_2 is a field.

(iv) neither F_1 nor F_2 is a field.

Solution. Now $x^4 + 6x^2 + 5 = (x^2 + 5)(x^2 + 1)$ and $x^3 + 1 = (x+1)(x^2 - x + 1)$. Thus neither $x^4 + 3x^2 + 2$ nor $x^3 + 1$ is an irreducible polynomial in $\mathbb{Q}[x]$. Hence neither F_1 nor F_2 is a field. Hence option (iv) is correct.

◊ **Exercise 15.2.14.** Let I_1 be the ideal generated by $x^2 + 5$ and I_2 be the ideal generated by $x^4 + 3x^2 + 2$ in $\mathbb{Q}[x]$. If $R_1 = \mathbb{Q}[x]/I_1$ and $R_2 = \mathbb{Q}[x]/I_2$, then pick the right option(s) from below.

(i) R_1 and R_2 are fields.

(ii) R_1 is a field, but R_2 is not a field.

(iii) R_1 is an integral domain, but R_2 is not an integral domain.

(iv) R_1 and R_2 are not integral domains.

Solution. Now $x^4 + 3x^2 + 2 = (x^2 + 2)(x^2 + 1)$ is not an irreducible polynomial in $\mathbb{Q}[x]$, where as $x^2 + 5$ is irreducible in $\mathbb{Q}[x]$. Thus R_1 is a field, where as R_2 is not an integral domain. Hence options (ii) and (iii) are correct.

◊ **Exercise 15.2.15.** Let $R = \mathbb{Q}[x]/I$ where I is the ideal generated by $1 + x^2$. Let y be the coset of x in R. Then pick the right option(s) from below.

(i) $y^2 + 1$ is irreducible over R.

(ii) $y^2 + y + 1$ is irreducible over R.

(iii) $y^2 - y + 1$ is irreducible over R.

(iv) $y^3 + y^2 + y + 1$ is irreducible over R.

Solution. Here $x^2 + 1$ is irreducible in $\mathbb{Q}[x]$ and thus $R = \mathbb{Q}[x]/I$ is a field. Now $y^2 + 1 = x^2 + 1 + I = 0 + I$, the zero element of $\mathbb{Q}[x]/I$. Thus $y^2 + y + 1 = x + I$ and $y^2 - y + 1 = -x + I$ are two one degree polynomials over a field and hence they are irreducible. Finally, $y^3 + y^2 + y + 1 = (y^2 + 1)(y + 1)$ implies $y^3 + y^2 + y + 1$ is not irreducible. Hence options (ii) and (iii) are correct.

$\diamond$ **Exercise 15.2.16.** Let $f(x) = x^3 + x^2 + x + 1$ and $g(x) = x^3 + 1$. Then pick the correct option(s) in $\mathbb{Q}[x]$.
(i) g.c.d.$(f(x), g(x)) = x + 1$.
(ii) g.c.d.$(f(x), g(x)) = x^2 - 1$.
(iii) l.c.m.$(f(x), g(x)) = x^5 + x^3 + x^2 + 1$.
(iv) l.c.m.$(f(x), g(x)) = x^5 + x^4 + x^3 + x^2 + 1$.

Solution. Now $f(x) = (x + 1)(x^2 + 1)$ and $g(x) = (x + 1)(x^2 - x + 1)$ implies g.c.d.$(f(x), g(x)) = x + 1$. Also l.c.m.$(f(x), g(x)) = (x + 1)(x^2 + 1)(x^2 - x + 1) = x^5 + x^3 + x^2 + 1$. Hence options (i) and (iii) are correct.

$\diamond$ **Exercise 15.2.17.** Let $f(x) = x^4 + 3x^3 - 9x^2 + 27x + 3$ and let p be a prime. Let $f_p(x)$ be the corresponding polynomial with coefficients in $\mathbb{Z}/p\mathbb{Z}$. Then find the correct statement from the following.
(i) $f_2(x)$ is irreducible over $\mathbb{Z}/2\mathbb{Z}$.
(ii) $f(x)$ is irreducible over $\mathbb{Q}$.
(iii) $f_3(x)$ is irreducible over $\mathbb{Z}/3\mathbb{Z}$.
(iv) $f(x)$ is irreducible over $\mathbb{Z}$.

Solution. Over $\mathbb{Z}/2\mathbb{Z}$, $f_2(x) = x^4 + x^3 + x^2 + x + 1$ and none of $[0]$ and $[1]$ is a root of $f(x)$. Let $f_2(x) = (x^2 + ax + b)(x^2 + cx + d)$ then $a + c = [1], ac + b + d = [1], ad + bc = [1]$ and $bd = [1]$. This implies $b = [1] = d$ and $a = [1] = c$. Then $[1] = a + c = [1] + [1] = [0]$, a contradiction. Hence $f_2(x)$ is irreducible over $\mathbb{Z}/2\mathbb{Z}$.

By Eisensten's criterion, it follows that $f(x)$ is irreducible over $\mathbb{Q}$. Since $f(x)$ is a primitive polynomial, we must have $f(x)$ is irreducible over $\mathbb{Z}$.

Now $f_3(x) = x^4$ and hence $f_3(x)$ is not irreducible over $\mathbb{Z}/3\mathbb{Z}$. Hence options (i), (ii) and (iv) are correct.

$\diamond$ **Exercise 15.2.18.** Let $f(x) \in \mathbb{Z}[x]$ be a primitive polynomial of degree ≥ 2. Pick the correct statement(s) from below.
(i) If $f(x)$ is irreducible in $\mathbb{Z}[x]$, then it is irreducible in $\mathbb{Q}[x]$.
(ii) If $f(x)$ is irreducible in $\mathbb{Q}[x]$, then it is irreducible in $\mathbb{Z}[x]$.
(iii) If $f(x)$ is irreducible in $\mathbb{Z}[x]$, then for all primes p the reduction $\overline{f(x)}$ of $f(x)$ modulo

p is irreducible in $\mathbb{F}_p[x]$.

(iv) If $f(x)$ is irreducible in $\mathbb{Z}[x]$, then it is irreducible in $\mathbb{R}[x]$.

Solution. Statement (i) is true, as it follows from a well known result.

Statement (ii) is not true in general. But since $f(x)$ is a primitive polynomial, so it is true.

Statement (iii) is false, as $x^2 + 1$ is irreducible in $\mathbb{Z}[x]$, but $\overline{x^2 + 1}$ modulo 2 is not irreducible in $\mathbb{F}_2[x]$.

Statement (iv) is false, as $x^2 - 2$ is irreducible in $\mathbb{Z}[x]$, but $x^2 - 2$ is not irreducible in $\mathbb{R}[x]$.

Hence options (i) and (ii) are correct.

◇ **Exercise 15.2.19.** Consider the ideal $I = \langle x^2 + 1, y \rangle$ in the polynomial ring $\mathbb{C}[x, y]$. Which of the following statement is true?

(i) I is a prime ideal.

(ii) I is a prime ideal but not a maximal ideal.

(iii) I is a maximal ideal but not a prime ideal.

(iv) I is neither a prime ideal nor a maximal ideal.

Solution. Similar to Worked-out Exercise 15.2.12, one can prove that $\mathbb{C}[x, y]/\langle x^2 + 1, y \rangle \simeq \mathbb{C}[x]/\langle x^2 + 1 \rangle$. Now we show that $\langle x^2 + 1 \rangle$ is not a prime ideal of $\mathbb{C}[x]$. For this we observe that $(x + i)(x - i) = x^2 + 1 \in \langle x^2 + 1 \rangle$, but neither $x + i \in \langle x^2 + 1 \rangle$ nor $x - i \in \langle x^2 + 1 \rangle$. Therefore, $\langle x^2 + 1 \rangle$ is not a prime ideal of $\mathbb{C}[x]$. Consequently, $\langle x^2 + 1, y \rangle$ is neither a prime ideal nor a maximal ideal of $\mathbb{C}[x, y]$. Hence option (iv) is correct.

◇ **Exercise 15.2.20.** In which of the following fields F, the polynomial $x^3 - 231231x + 312312$ is irreducible in $F[x]$?

(i) the field $\mathbb{F}_3$ with 3 elements.

(ii) the field $\mathbb{F}_7$ with 7 elements.

(iii) the field $\mathbb{F}_{13}$ with 13 elements.

(iv) the field $\mathbb{Q}$ of rational numbers.

Solution. Over $\mathbb{F}_3, \mathbb{F}_7, \mathbb{F}_{13}$; the given polynomial $x^3 - 231231x + 312312 = x^3$. Therefore, $x^3 - 231231x + 312312$ is not irreducible over $\mathbb{F}_3, \mathbb{F}_7$ and $\mathbb{F}_{13}$. Now $3 \in \mathbb{Z}$ is prime such that $3 \mid 231231, 312312$ but $3^2 = 9 \nmid 312312$. Therefore, by Eisenstein's criterion, it follows that $x^3 - 231231x + 312312$ is irreducible in $\mathbb{Q}[x]$. Hence option (iv) is correct.

◇ **Exercise 15.2.21.** Consider the polynomial $f(x) = x^4 - x^3 + 14x^2 + 5x + 15$. Also for a prime number p, let $\mathbb{F}_p$ denote the field with p elements. Which of the following are always true?

(i) Considering f as a polynomial with coefficients in $\mathbb{F}_3$, it has no roots in $\mathbb{F}_3$.

(ii) Considering f as a polynomial with coefficients in $\mathbb{F}_3$, it is product of two irreducible
factors of degree 2 over $\mathbb{F}_3$.

(iii) Considering f as a polynomial with coefficients in $\mathbb{F}_7$, it has an irreducible factor
of degree 3 over $\mathbb{F}_7$.

(iv) f is a product of two polynomials of degree 2 over $\mathbb{Z}$.

Solution. Now in $\mathbb{F}_3[x]$, $f(x) = x^4 - x^3 + 2x^2 + 2x = x(x^3 - x^2 + 2x + 2)$ and we see
that $x^3 - x^2 + 2x + 2$ is irreducible over $\mathbb{F}_3$. So 0 is a root of $f(x)$ in $\mathbb{F}_3$ and $f(x)$ is
product of two irreducible polynomials x and $x^3 - x^2 + 2x + 2$ over $\mathbb{F}_3$ of degree 1 and
3 respectively.

Again in $\mathbb{F}_7[x]$, $f(x) = x^4 - x^3 + 5x + 1 = (x - 3)(x^3 + 2x^2 + 6x + 4)$ and we see
that $x^3 + 2x^2 + 6x + 4$ is irreducible over $\mathbb{F}_7$. Hence $f(x)$ has an irreducible factor of
degree 3 over $\mathbb{F}_7$.

Suppose $f(x) = x^4 - x^3 + 14x^2 + 5x + 15 = (x^2 + ax + b)(x^2 + cx + d)$ over $\mathbb{Z}$,
where a, b, c and d are integers. Then we have $a + c = -1, b + d + ac = 14, ad + bc = 5$
and $bd = 15$. Now $bd = 15$ implies either $b = 1$ and $d = 15$ or $b = -1$ and $d = -15$
or $b = 15$ and $d = 1$ or $b = -15$ and $d = -1$ or $b = 3$ and $d = 5$ or $b = -3$ and
$d = -5$ or $b = 5$ and $d = 3$ or $b = -5$ and $d = -3$. Suppose $b = 1$ and $d = 15$. Then
$15a + c = 5$. Also $a + c = -1$. These two imply that $a = \frac{3}{7} \notin \mathbb{Z}$, a contradiction.
Similarly, we arrive at a contradiction when $b = -1$ and $d = -15$ or $b = 15$ and $d = 1$
or $b = -15$ and $d = -1$. Next suppose that $b = 3$ and $d = 5$. Then $5a + 3c = 5$. Also
$a + c = -1$. These two imply that $a = 4$ and $c = -5$. Thus $b + d + ac = -12 \neq 14$, a
contradiction. Similarly, we arrive at a contradiction when $b = -3$ and $d = -5$ or $b = 5$
and $d = 3$ or $b = -5$ and $d = -3$. Therefore, there are no integers a, b, c and d such
that $f(x) = (x^2 + ax + b)(x^2 + cx + d)$, i.e., $f(x)$ is not a product of two polynomials
of degree 2 over $\mathbb{Z}$. Hence option (iii) is correct.

$\lozenge$ **Exercise 15.2.22.** Let $\mathbb{R}[x]$ be the polynomial ring over $\mathbb{R}$ in one variable. Let
$I \subseteq \mathbb{R}[x]$ be an ideal. Pick the correct option(s) from statements below.

(i) I is a maximal ideal if and only if I is a non-zero prime ideal.

(ii) I is a maximal ideal if and only if the quotient ring $\mathbb{R}[x]/I$ is isomorphic to $\mathbb{R}$.

(iii) I is a maximal ideal if and only if $I = \langle f(x) \rangle$, where $f(x)$ is a non-constant
irreducible polynomial over $\mathbb{R}$.

(iv) I is a maximal ideal if and only if there exists a nonconstant polynomial $f(x) \in I$
of degree ≤ 2.

Solution. If I ia a maximal ideal of $\mathbb{R}[x]$, then clearly I is a non-zero prime ideal of $\mathbb{R}[x]$. On the other hand let I be a non-zero prime ideal of $\mathbb{R}[x]$. Since $\mathbb{R}[x]$ is a PID, it follows that $I = \langle f(x) \rangle$ for some prime element $f(x) \in \mathbb{R}[x]$. Since $f(x)$ is prime in a PID, it follows that $f(x)$ must be irreducible. Thus $I = \langle f(x) \rangle$ is a maximal ideal of $\mathbb{R}[x]$.

Consider the maximal ideal $\langle x^2 + 1 \rangle$ of $\mathbb{R}[x]$. Here the corresponding quotient ring $\mathbb{R}[x]/\langle x^2 + 1 \rangle \simeq \mathbb{C} \not\simeq \mathbb{R}$.

Since $\mathbb{R}[x]$ is a PID, so definitely any maximal ideal I must be generated by some non-constant irreducible polynomial. On the other hand any ideal generated by irreducible element in a PID must be a maximal ideal.

Consider the ideal $I = \langle x^2 - 2 \rangle$ of $\mathbb{R}[x]$. Then I contains a non-constant polynomial $x^2 - 2$ of degree 2, but $I = \langle x^2 - 2 \rangle$ is not a maximal ideal of $\mathbb{R}[x]$, as $x^2 - 2$ is not an irreducible element in $\mathbb{R}[x]$. Hence options (i) and (iii) are correct.

◇ **Exercise 15.2.23.** Which of the following statements are true?
(i) $\mathbb{Z}[x]$ is a principal ideal domain.
(ii) $\mathbb{Z}[x, y]/\langle y + 1 \rangle$ is a unique factorization domain.
(iii) If R is a principal ideal domain and I is a non-zero prime ideal, then R/I has finitely many prime ideals.
(iv) If R is a principal ideal domain, then any subring of R containing 1 is again a principal ideal domain.

Solution. We know $\mathbb{Z}[x]$ is not a PID. Now $\mathbb{Z}[x, y]/\langle y + 1 \rangle \simeq \mathbb{Z}[x]$ is a unique factorization domain.

Since $I \neq R$, then I is a non-zero proper prime ideal of a principal ideal domain and hence I is maximal. Consequently, R/I is a field. We know a field has (0) as its only prime ideal. Finally, consider the PID $\mathbb{Q}[x]$ and its subring $\mathbb{Z}[x]$ which contains the identity element. But here $\mathbb{Z}[x]$ is not a PID. Hence options (ii) and (iii) are correct.

◇ **Exercise 15.2.24.** Which of the following rings are principal ideal domains?
(i) $\mathbb{Z}[x]/\langle x^2 + 1 \rangle$ (ii) $\mathbb{Z}[x]$
(iii) $\mathbb{C}[x, y]$ (iv) $\mathbb{R}[x, y]/\langle x^2 + 1, y \rangle$.

Solution. Similar to Worked-out Exercise 15.2.9, one can prove that $\mathbb{Z}[x]/\langle x^2 + 1 \rangle \simeq \mathbb{Z}[i]$ and we know that $\mathbb{Z}[i]$ is a principal ideal domain. Moreover $\mathbb{Z}[x]$ and $\mathbb{C}[x, y]$ are not a principal ideal domains. By Worked-out Exercise 15.2.13, we have $\mathbb{R}[x, y]/\langle x^2 + 1, y \rangle \simeq \mathbb{C}$, which is a principal ideal domain. Therefore, options (i) and (iv) is correct.

Exercises

1. Show that the following polynomials are irreducible:

    (i) $2x^5 + 15x^3 + 10x + 5$ over $\mathbb{Z}$;

    (ii) $x^2 + x + [1]$ over $\mathbb{Z}_2$;

    (iii) $x^6 + x^3 + 1$ over $\mathbb{Q}$;

    (iv) $10x^3 - 7x + 14$ over $\mathbb{Q}$;

    (v) $2x^3 - 7x + 1$ over $\mathbb{Q}$;

    (vi) $x^4 - 5x^2 + x + 1$ over $\mathbb{Z}$;

    (vii) $x^4 + 2x + 2$ over $\mathbb{Q}$;

    (viii) $x^3 + [2]x - [1]$ over $\mathbb{Z}_5$;

    (ix) $x^2 + [1]$ over $\mathbb{Z}_7$;

    (x) $x^3 - [9]$ over $\mathbb{Z}_{11}$.

2. Let $f(x)$ be an irreducible polynomial over $\mathbb{R}$. Show that $0 < \deg f(x) \leq 2$.

3. For every prime number p and every positive integer n, show that $x^n - p$ is irreducible over $\mathbb{Q}$.

4. Find all irreducible polynomials of degree ≤ 2 in $\mathbb{Z}_p[x]$ for $p = 3$ and 5.

5. $x^4 + 1$ is irreducible over $\mathbb{Q}$ but reducible over all $\mathbb{Z}_p$ for any prime p.

6. Let $f(x) = x^3 + [6] \in \mathbb{Z}_7[x]$. Express $f(x)$ as a product of irreducible factors in $\mathbb{Z}_7[x]$.

7. Factorize $f(x) = x^3 + x^2 + x + [1]$ in $\mathbb{Z}_2[x]$.

8. For any prime number p, show that the polynomial $f(x) = 1 - x + x^2 - x^3 + \cdots + (-1)^{p-1}x^{p-1}$ is irreducible over $\mathbb{Z}$.

9. Show that the polynomial $x^7 + x^5 + [1]$ is irreducible over $\mathbb{Z}_2$ and hence prove that $x^7 - 9x^5 + 11$ is so over $\mathbb{Z}$.

10. Give an example of a polynomial which is irreducible over $\mathbb{Z}$ but not so over $\mathbb{Z}_2$.

11. † Show that $x^2 + x + [4]$ is irreducible over $\mathbb{Z}_{11}$. Hence show that $\mathbb{Z}_{11}[x]/(x^2 + x + [4])$ is a field containing 121 elements.

12. † Construct a finite field containing $n = 9$ elements. Do the same for $n = 8$.

13. † Generalize Theorem 15.2.6 for an arbitrary UFD instead of $\mathbb{Z}$ and prove it.

14. Find whether the following statements are true or false. Justify your answer and give counter examples whenever necessary.
    (a) $\mathbb{Z}_2[x]/(x^2 + x + [1])$ is a field.
    (b) $\mathbb{Z}_3[x]/(x^2 + x + [1])$ is a field.
    (c) The ideal $(x^2 + [1])$ is prime in $\mathbb{Z}_2[x]$.
    (d) $\mathbb{Q}[x]/(x^2 + 1)$ is a field.

15. Let $\langle p(x) \rangle$ denote the ideal generated by the polynomial $p(x) \in \mathbb{Q}[x]$. If $f(x) = x^3 + x^2 + x + 1$ and $g(x) = x^3 - x^2 + x - 1$, then find the correct option from statements below.
    (i) $\langle f(x) \rangle + \langle g(x) \rangle = \langle x^3 + x \rangle$.
    (ii) $\langle f(x) \rangle + \langle g(x) \rangle = \langle f(x) \cdot g(x) \rangle$.
    (iii) $\langle f(x) \rangle + \langle g(x) \rangle = \langle x^2 + 1 \rangle$.
    (iv) $\langle f(x) \rangle + \langle g(x) \rangle = \langle x^4 - 1 \rangle$.

16. Which of the following polynomials are irreducible over the indicated rings?
    (i) $x^5 - 3x^4 + 2x^2 - 5x + 8$ over $\mathbb{R}$.
    (ii) $x^3 + 2x^2 + x + 1$ over $\mathbb{Q}$.
    (iii) $x^3 + 3x^2 - 6x + 3$ over $\mathbb{Z}$.
    (iv) $x^4 + x^2 + 1$ over $\mathbb{Z}/2\mathbb{Z}$.

17. Which of the following polynomials are irreducible in $\mathbb{Z}[x]$?
    (i) $x^4 + 10x + 5$.
    (ii) $x^3 - 2x + 1$.
    (iii) $x^4 + x^2 + 1$.
    (iv) $x^3 + x + 1$.

18. Let R be the ring $\mathbb{Z}[x]/\langle (x^2 + x + 1)(x^3 + x + 1) \rangle$. The cardinality of the ring R is
    (i) 27   (ii) 32   (iii) 64   (iv) infinite.

19. For a positive integer n, let $f_n(x) = x^{n-1} + x^{n-2} + \cdots + x + 1$. Pick the correct statement from below.
    (i) $f_n(x)$ is an irreducible polynomial in $\mathbb{Q}[x]$ for every positive integer n.
    (ii) $f_p(x)$ is an irreducible polynomial in $\mathbb{Q}[x]$ for every prime number p.
    (iii) $f_{p^e}(x)$ is an irreducible polynomial in $\mathbb{Q}[x]$ for every prime number p and every positive integer e.
    (iv) $f_{p^2}(x)$ is an irreducible polynomial in $\mathbb{Q}[x]$ for every prime number p.

20. Let $f(x) = x^3 + 2x^2 + x - 1$. Determine in which of the following cases $f(x)$ is irreducible over the corresponding field K.
    (i) $K = \mathbb{Q}$, the field of rational numbers.
    (ii) $K = \mathbb{R}$, the field of real numbers.
    (iii) $K = \mathbb{F}_2$, the finite field with 2 elements.
    (iv) $K = \mathbb{F}_3$, the finite field with 3 elements.

Appendices

Appendix A

Russell's Paradox

Before trying to give the *definition* of a set, let us examine the nature of the statements called *definition*; that is to say, let us try to understand, *what is the definition of a* DEFINITION? To find an answer to such a question is anything but simple. The path towards the answer goes down to the bottomless depth of logic behind mathematical reasoning, formally known as *foundations of mathematics*. In the limited scope of discussion here, we only focus our attention on certain aspects of a *definition* in mathematics. Every definition must be understood to be an *if and only if* type of statement, though it is conventional to drop the *only if* part. Also, a definition of a new concept is always dependent on some other concepts, supposed to be defined previously. For example, if *circle* be defined as *the locus of such a moving point in a plane, which is always at a fixed distance from a fixed point in the plane*— observe that the knowledge of so many concepts like *locus, point, plane, distance* etc., are required to appreciate this definition. Try, if you like, to *define point* in geometry to observe similar features. All these said and done, how then, can one *define* the very first concept of a new branch of knowledge (like that of a *set* in the theory of Sets)? Let us examine the so-called definition of a set in this light. If we consider a set as a *well-defined collection of distinct objects*, the natural question that pops up is '*what is a collection*'? If you retort with, '*a collection is an aggregate of things*', you run the danger of being asked, '*what is an aggregate then*'? By now, you are surely beginning to understand that this will lead to a futile search of synonyms to the word *collection*, which will surely end sometime, as our language is finite, though the corresponding question may still remain unanswered. This shows the circularity of this definition proving it to be worthless. The immense importance of definition attached to the classical representations of mathematical science was thus recognized as a structural weakness and a serious threat to the theory of sets arose at the beginning of the previous century, when outright logical paradoxes became apparent. In 1902, in a letter to Frége (1848-1925), Bertrand Russell (1872-1970) pointed out the danger of unrestricted freedom in using the concept of *set*, which then inevitably would lead to contradictions. This is famous as **Russell's paradox** in the literature of mathematics. To explain it in brief, we begin with the observation that a set can easily have elements which are themselves sets e.g., $\left\{a, b, \{c, d\}\right\}$. This leads to the possibility that a set might well contain itself as one of its elements, though most sets do not contain themselves as elements. For example, the set of all integers, which itself is certainly not an integer and hence this set does not contain itself as an element. Let us call such a set *ordinary*. On the other hand, the sets which contain themselves as their elements may be called *extraordinary*. For example, *the set of all those sets that can be defined by an English phrase of less than thirty words* is such a set, as the English phrase required to describe it takes less than thirty words! Don't you find these extraordinary sets a bit too much, as if cooked up to create logical trouble? Come, let us shun them and concentrate on *the set of all ordinary sets*. Call this set A. Observe that every element of the set A is an ordinary set. The question is, what about the set A itself ? Is it ordinary or extraordinary? If A is ordinary, then it must be a member of itself, as A is the set of *all* ordinary sets— and thereby A becomes extraordinary; on the other hand if A is extraordinary, and so a member of itself, then it indicates that A must be ordinary, as A is the set of all *ordinary* sets. This simple but elegant logical derivation by Russell shows that the mere existence of the set A (which was formed in accordance with the so-called definition of a set) leads us to a contradiction, where we have a set A, which is not a member of itself if and only if it is a member of itself!

In the year 1918, Russell proposed a popular version of it, known as **Barber paradox**. A barber has a signboard stating : *I shave all those men in town and only those men, who do not shave themselves.* We leave this little bit of mental gymnastics to the reader to find *who shaves the barber?*

This, among other factors led mathematicians to realize with a stronger conviction that, not every concept used can be defined, and there must be some undefined or primitive concepts to begin with— concepts which we understand sufficiently enough to make communication about them possible. These should be followed by some axioms, (the so-called self-evident truths), that are statements regarding the primitive concepts without proof— which can be looked upon as pillars to hold the entire edifice of the theory and the rest of the assertions must be logically deducible from them. Such a systematic representation, aptly known as a *formal system* (or, *axiomatic system*), was looked upon by many mathematicians in the first quarter of the last century, as the most formidable and rigorously precise way of presenting mathematical thought. But Kurt Gödel (1906-1976) in 1931 conclusively proved that every consistent formal system is *incomplete* in the sense that, there must evolve some statement from within the formal system that can neither be proved nor disproved within the system. Alfred Tarski (1902-1983) investigated the notion of *truth* of a statement in the formal system and his findings put together with Gödel leads us to a somewhat puzzling philosophical conclusion— *truth may not necessarily be subject to proof!*

Appendix B

Axiom of Choice

Let $\{A_\alpha : \alpha \in \Lambda\}$ be any nonempty family of nonempty sets where each A_α is a subset of a nonempty set X. Then the function $f : \{A_\alpha : \alpha \in \Lambda\} \to X$ is called **choice function** if $f(A_\alpha) = a_\alpha \in A_\alpha$ for every $\alpha \in \Lambda$, i.e., in a sense, the function f chooses a single point $a_\alpha \in A_\alpha$ for each set A_α of the family.

Note that the choice function may also be defined on any nonempty family of nonempty sets $\{A_\alpha : \alpha \in \Lambda\}$, by considering $X = \bigcup_{\alpha \in \Lambda} A_\alpha$.

The **axiom of choice** states that, *there exists a choice function for any nonempty family of nonempty sets.*

An equivalent form is given in the following statement, known as **Zermelo's postulate**, which is as follows:

Let $\{A_\alpha : \alpha \in \Lambda\}$ *be any nonempty family of disjoint nonempty sets. Then there exists a subset B of the union $\bigcup_{\alpha \in \Lambda} A_\alpha$ such that the intersection of B and each set A_α is precisely singleton.*

However natural and obvious these statements may look, it is fascinating to know that these axioms have far-reaching consequences and are instrumental in deriving some of the most elegant and powerful theorems in the entire body of mathematics.

We now take the liberty to discuss yet another equivalent form of these axioms, known as the **Zorn's lemma**. Before stating it, we have to discuss the relevant vocabularies first. Let $(X, \leq)$ be a partially ordered set and A be any subset of X. An element $x \in X$ is said to be an **upper bound** of A, if for every $a \in A$, we have $a \leq x$. Further, an element $y \in X$ is said to be a **maximal element** of X, if for any $z \in X$, $y \leq z$ implies that $y = z$. Now Zorn's lemma goes as follows: *Let X be a nonempty partially ordered set, in which every linearly ordered subset has an upper bound in X. Then X contains at least one maximal element.*

Another famous proposition by Zermelo tells us that *every set can be well-ordered*, in the sense that each of its nonempty subset contains a *first element*. Note that, an element $a \in X$ is said to be a **first element** of X if $a \leq x$ for all $x \in X$.

These three statements, viz., Axiom of choice, Zorn's lemma and Zermelo's theorem are like three main pillars of set theory. These are equivalent in the sense that, assuming the validity of any one of them, the two others can be *proved*. However, it is highly significant that all of them cannot be proved independently. The proof of their equivalence is out of scope here.

Appendix C

Prime Problems

More than two millenniums ago, Euclid proved that there exist infinitely many primes; also it was known to the Greeks that these numbers are irregularly spaced among the natural numbers, in the sense that there can be arbitrary large gaps between successive primes, but till date no one has been able to find an exact pattern of their appearance among natural numbers[9] nor some formula that produces *all the primes*! However some prime producing polynomials are now known. In 1976, Jones and others produced a polynomial in 26 variables, whose *positive* values for the integer values of the variables, are only primes. In the late 19th century, it was shown by Hadamard that the number of primes, less than or equal to n approaches $\frac{n}{\ln n}$ as n gets very large[10]. In September 1985, the supercomputer Cray X-MP identified the then largest prime number known to man, after more than three hours of doing 400 million calculations per second. It was a 65,050-digit number equal to $2^{216,091} - 1$. Numbers of such form are referred to as ***Mersenne numbers***, after a 17th century French monk, Marin Mersenne (1558-1648), who had a passion for numbers besides his monastic duties. Found in 1999, a Mersenne prime, $2^{6,972,593} - 1$ of 2,098,960 digits is credited to Nayan Hajratwala (It has earned him USD 50,000 prize money!) This number was a result of three years of searching jointly by harnessing the efforts of 21,000 computers through a program known as GIMPS (The Great Internet Mersenne Prime Search). GIMPS currently offers a USD 3000 research discovery award for participants who download and run their free software and whose computer discovers a new Mersenne prime having fewer than 100 million digits. There are several prizes, including a USD 150,000 prize, offered by the Electronic Frontier Foundation for record large primes of 100 million digits and larger. In 2008 the record passed ten million digits, earning a USD 100,000 prize. Additional prizes are being offered for the first prime number found with at least one hundred million digits and the first with at least one billion digits. As of September 2021, the largest known prime number, found in 2018 is $2^{82,589,933} - 1$, a number with 24,862,048 digits. You may log on to http://primes.utm.edu/largest.html for upgraded results.

---

[9]Around August 2002, in a major breakthrough, Prof. Manindra Agrawal(1966 -), a faculty of IIT, Kanpur, India, working together with two of his Ph.D. students, Neeraj Kayal and Nitin Saxena, has produced, to the great surprise of the experts, a polynomial time deterministic algorithm (now known as AKS theorem) to test whether a given number is prime or not. The proof is only 9 pages long! An interested reader can find the details about this result in the web site http://www.cse.iitk.ac.in

[10]It is fascinating to know that Gauss suggested this result, purely empirically, in 1791, when he was a boy of mere fourteen.

Pythagoras and his school called a natural number **perfect**, if it equals the sum of all its divisors (except the number itself). The first perfect number is 6, followed by 28, 496 and 8, 128. Believe it or not, the ancient Greeks were aware of these numbers, and not only that, Euclid recognized—hats off to his genius— that these four numbers are generated by the formula $2^{n-1}(2^n - 1)$ for $n = 2, 3, 5$ and 7. Note that in all of these four cases, $2^n - 1$ happens to be a prime. Indeed, it can be proved that the formula $2^{n-1}(2^n - 1)$ generates an even perfect number whenever $2^n - 1$ is a prime. But unfortunately, though n must be a prime for $2^n - 1$ to be a prime, the converse is not true, as can be easily seen with $n = 11$. In fact, $2^{11} - 1 = 2047 = 23 \times 89$. It took seventeen centuries after Euclid before the fifth perfect number was discovered, which is 33, 550, 336. Till date, we know about thirty-eight of these numbers. Whether there are infinitely many perfect numbers, is still an open problem. Also it is queer to observe that all these thirty-eight perfect numbers are even, i.e., divisible by 2. Using computers, it has been shown that there are no *odd perfect numbers* $< 10^{300}$. The crown of the oldest unsolved problem in mathematics goes to a problem that confounded the ancient Greeks and everyone since : *Does there exist an odd perfect number?*

The beauty of this problem and many other problems in number theory lies in their simple look. These problems may well be appreciated by a high school student, but the solutions to quite a few of them still elude the finest of mathematicians. We now discuss in brief two such open problems. **Goldbach conjecture**(1742):*any even number (except 2) can be expressed as a sum of two prime numbers* [e.g., $4 = 2 + 2$, $6 = 3 + 3$, $8 = 3 + 5$ etc.]. This was suggested by Christian Goldbach, in a letter dated June 7, 1742 to Leonard Euler. It has been shown by T.O. Silva in 2012 that Goldbach conjecture is true for all numbers up to $4 \cdot 10^{18}$. But the general statement still awaits a proof or a counter example. For a complete solution to this conjecture within March 2004, there was a prize of USD 1,000,000 offered by Faber and Faber in U.K. and Bloomsbury Publishing, USA, which went unclaimed. The best known *effort* till date towards solving this problem is due to a Chinese mathematician Chen Jingrun, who proved in 1973 using Sieve theory, a weaker version of Goldbach conjecture, that every sufficiently large even number is the sum of a prime and an *almost prime* (i.e., product of two prime integers), where the term *sufficiently large* is a mathematical jargon that means larger than some given large number.

A *twin prime* refers to a pair of prime numbers of the form $(p, p + 2)$. The **twin prime conjecture** claims that *there are infinitely many twin primes*. It is known that there are 808,675,888,577,436 twin prime pairs below 10^{18}. Discovered in September 2016, the largest known twin prime pair till January 2018 is $2996863034895 \cdot 2^{1290000} \pm 1$.

On April 17, 2013, Yitang Zhang announced a surprising proof that for some integer N less than 70 million, there are infinitely many pairs of primes that differ by N. Fields medalist Terence Tao subsequently proposed a *Polymath Project* collaborative effort to optimize Zhangs bound. Assuming the Elliott - Halberstam conjecture and its generalized form, the Polymath project wiki states that the bound has been reduced to 12 and 6, respectively, independently by James Maynard and Terence Tao. It is believed that further up-gradation of these results may not be possible with existing techniques of mathematics.

No wonder that Gauss once remarked, "Mathematics is the queen of science and number theory is the queen of Mathematics"!

Appendix D

Laurels in Mathematics

The **Fields Medal**, named after a Canadian mathematician John C. Fields (1863-1932), widely rated as the *Nobel Prize for Mathematics*, is awarded by International Mathematical Union (IMU), the apex international body of mathematicians. The International Congress of Mathematicians (ICM) at Zurich 1932, accepted the proposal for such an award, made by Fields in his will and it was first awarded in the following congress at Oslo in 1936. Among the first recipients was **L.V. Ahlfors**, for his contribution to the theory of functions of complex variables. Due to the outbreak of World War II, the next Fields medal was not awarded until 1950, and since then this prestigious award is being presented every four years at the ICM. The award constitutes of a gold medal and a prize worth 15,000 Canadian Dollars. The medal on one side shows an inscription of the head of Archimedes (287-212 BC), together with a quotation "`Transire suum pectus mundoque potiri`," that can be translated as *Rise above oneself and grasp the world*. On the other side ,the inscription reads "`Congregati ex toto orbe mathematici ob scripta insignia tribuere`," which means, *The mathematicians assembled here from all over the world pay tribute for outstanding work*.

Though it was never formally mentioned in the will of Fields, the award is traditionally restricted to young researchers, not older than 40 years. A recent omission, it is believed, was **Andrew J. Wiles** of Princeton University, who played the final lead role in the masterly solution of the age old problem, known as Fermat'sLast Theorem. However, a special tribute, the *IMU Silver Plaque*, was awarded to him during ICM, Berlin, 1998. For the first time in its history, ICM was held in India during August

2010 at Hyderabad. A copy of Fields' will and a complete list of the luminaries of the mathematical world who were awarded the Fields Medal till date, can be found in the websites **http://elib.zib.de/IMU/medals** and **www.fields.toronto.edu**

In Seoul ICM, South Korea, August 2014, Fields medals were awarded to

1. **Artur Avila** (*Centre National de la Recherche Scientifique*) for his profound contributions to dynamical systems theory, which have changed the face of the field, using the powerful idea of renormalization as a unifying principle.

2. **Manjul Bhargava** (*Princeton University*) for developing powerful new methods in the geometry of numbers, which he applied to count rings of small rank and to bound the average rank of elliptic curves.

3. **Martin Hairer** (*University of Warwick*) for his outstanding contributions to the theory of stochastic partial differential equations, and in particular for the creation of a theory of regularity structures for such equations.

4. **Maryam Mirzakhani** (*Stanford University*) for her outstanding contributions to the dynamics and geometry of Riemann surfaces and their moduli spaces.

Incidentally, Maryam Mirzakhani became the first woman as well as the first Iranian; Artur Avila, the first South American; and Manjul Bhargava, the first person of Indian origins to win the Fields Medal. Unfortunately on 14th July 2017 Maryam Mirzakhani passed away prematurely at an age of only 40 years.

At the 2018 International Congress of Mathematicians, held in Rio de Janeiro, Brazil, from 1st August to 9th August, the four winners of the coveted Fields Medal were **Caucher Birkar** of University of Cambridge, UK, **Alessio Figalli** of Swiss Federal Institute of Technology, Zurich, Switzerland, **Peter Scholze** of University of Bonn, Germany and **Akshay Venkatesh** of Stanford University, US. Professor Venkatesh, currently a Professor of Mathematics at the Institute for Advanced Study, US, was born on 21st November 1981, in New Delhi, India. His parents moved to Perth in Western Australia when he was two years old. He was awarded the Fields Medal "for his synthesis of Analytic number theory, homogeneous dynamics, topology and representation theory, which has resolved long-standing problems in areas such as the equidistribution of arithmetic objects."

For outstanding research in algebra and algebraic number theory, **Cole Prize**, in memory of Frank Nelson Cole, is awarded by American Mathematical Society, since 1928. Presently it is awarded every three years, and the prize money amounts to USD 5000. Among others, **Feit** and **Thompson** in 1965 and **Aschbacher** in 1980 received this prize for their contribution to the *theory of simple groups*. In the year 2003, Cole prize was awarded to **Hiraku Nakajima** of Japan, for his work in representation theory and geometry. We would like to mention here that, the fifth Cole prize (1954) was awarded to the famous Indian mathematician **Harish-Chandra** (1923-1983) for his outstanding research publication on representations of semisimple Lie Algebra, published in *Transactions of the American Mathematical Society*, in 1951. Born on October 11, 1923 at Kanpur, India, a student of Allahabad University, Harish-Chandra was initially interested in Theoretical Physics, Quantum Mechanics in particular. He went to Cambridge University and did his Ph.D. under the supervision of Nobel Laureate physicist P. Dirac(1902-1984). Later Harish-Chandra became more interested in mathematics, and in 1947 switched over to Princeton, USA. He was elected a Fellow of the Royal Society in 1973. He received the **Ramanujan Medal** from Indian National Science Academy, in 1974.

Another prestigious International Award since 1983, also given at the ICM, is the **Nevanlinna Prize**, donated by University of Helsinki, in commemoration of the Finnish mathematician Rolf Nevanlinna. This award also constitutes of a gold medal and cash prize of 15,000 Canadian Dollars, to be awarded to a person below 40 years, for *outstanding contributions to theoretical computer science*. The 2002 award went to **Madhu Sudan** of Massachusetts Institute of Technology. An Indian by birth, Madhu Sudan was a student of IIT Delhi till 1987 and later obtained his Ph.D. from University of California, Berkeley in 1992. His award winning work was on *probabilistically checkable proofs, non-approximability of optimization problem and on error-correcting codes*. In 2014 it was awarded to **Subhash Khot** FRS, for his original contributions that provide critical insight into unresolved problems in the field of computational complexity. He is best known for his unique games conjecture. Born on June 10, 1978, in Ichalkaranji of Maharastra, he is an Indian-American mathematician and theoretical computer scientist who is the Julius Silver Professor of Computer Science in the Courant Institute of Mathematical Sciences at New York University.

Another prize of high international repute, given annually for lifetime achievements, was launched in 2003 by the Norwegian Academy of Science and Letters. Named after the great Norwegian mathematician Neils Heinrich Abel(1802-1829), who died a tragic death of tuberculosis at the early age of 26, the prize money amounts to 6 million Croner (about 9.2 Lakhs USD). **Jean-Pierre Serre** (15th September, 1926-) of Collège de France, Paris, the youngest ever recipient of the Fields Medal (1954, at the age of 27) was awarded the first **Abel Prize**, on 3rd June 2003. In 2007, the prize went to **Srinivasa S. R. Varadhan** of Courant Institute of Mathematical Sciences,

New York, for his fundamental contributions to probability theory and in particular, for creating a unified theory of large deviations. Born in Chennai on January 2, 1940, Varadhan did his Ph.D. from ISI, Kolkata. In 2008, it was awarded to **John G. Thompson** and **Jacques Tits** for 'shaping modern group theory', one in the direction of finite groups and the other, in the direction of linear groups. Thompson revolutionized the theory of finite groups by proving extraordinarily deep theorems that laid the foundation for the complete classification of finite simple groups, one of the greatest achievements of twentieth century mathematics. In 2016, the recipient was **Andrew Wiles** for his stunning proof of Fermat's Last Theorem by way of the modularity conjecture for semistable elliptic curves, opening a new era in number theory. 2019 saw the first ever woman recipient as **Karen Uhlenbeck** of University of Texas at Austin, for her pioneering achievements in geometric partial differential equations, gauge theory and integrable systems, and for the fundamental impact of her work on analysis, geometry and mathematical physics. In 2021, the winners were **Avi Wigderson** of the Institute for Advanced Study, Princeton and **László Lovász** of Eőtvős Loránd University, Hungary.

From 2010, **Chern Medal** for lifetime achievements have been instituted at the ICM. Along with the medal in the name of Shiing-Shen Chern there is a cash prize of USD 250,000 and a scope to donate an equal amount to some organization for the cause of supporting research in mathematics. The first recipient was **Louis Nirenberg** for his work on non-linear elliptic PDE. The 2018 Medal went to **Masaki Kashiwara** "For his outstanding and foundational contributions to algebraic analysis and representation theory sustained over a period of almost 50 years".

The **SASTRA Ramanujan Prize** of worth USD10,000 was founded in 2005 by the Shanmugha Arts, Science, Technology & Research Academy (SASTRA) in Kumbakonam, Srinivasa Ramanujan's hometown. It is awarded every year on Ramanujan's birthday to a young mathematician of age below 32 years (the age at which Ramanujan died), who is judged to have done outstanding work in Ramanujan's fields of interest. The first recipients in 2005 were **Manjul Bhargava** of Princeton University and **Kannan Soundararajan** of Michigan University, followed by **Terrence Tao** of UCLA in 2006. In 2021 the winner was **Will Sawin** of Columbia University, USA.

The 2021 **DST-ICTP-IMU Ramanujan Prize** (*for young mathematicians from developing countries*) went to **Neena Gupta** of ISI, Kolkata who had received S S Bhatnagar prize earlier in 2019 for solving a sixty year old open problem known as Zariski cancellation. **Sujatha Ramdorai** in 2006, **Amalendu Krishna** in 2015 and **Ritabrata Munshi** in 2018 are other Indian recipients of this prestigious award.

Appendix E

From the days of Pythagoras, it was known to the Greeks, and everyone since then, that if the lengths of three sides of a triangle be 3, 4 and 5 units then it must be a right-angled triangle. The search towards finding all the right-angled triangles with integral side-lengths, then amounts to the search for finding all positive integer solutions (a, b, c), [usually called a *Pythagorean triple*] to the Pythagorean equation $a^2 + b^2 = c^2$. From any such Pythagorean triple, one can, with a little bit of calculation, derive infinitely many other Pythagorean triples. This naturally encourages an inquisitive mind to think about the possibility of finding such number triplets for a similar equation with positive integral exponent greater than 2. The most general problem of this type was addressed around 1637 by a French scholar Pierre de Fermat (1601-1665). Undoubtedly, one of the most celebrated statement in mathematics, popularly known as the **Fermat's Last Theorem** (FLT in short), says that *the equation* $x^n + y^n = z^n$ *has no solution in positive integers* x, y *and* z *when* $n > 2$. In spite of Fermat's emphatic claim to have found "an admirable proof" of this result, the general proof was never found in his works. However, he later gave an explicit proof of the case $n = 4$. It is a debatable point that if he could deal with the general case successfully, he probably would not have bothered with the particular case $n = 4$ later. The case $n = 3$ was dealt with initially in the 18th century by Leonhard Euler, and finally Gauss gave the correct proof of this case. In view of these results, it was soon realized that, to prove Fermat's theorem, it would be sufficient to prove it for odd prime exponents only. The case $n = 5$ was initiated by Dirichlet and settled by Legendre around 1825, while the French engineer cum mathematician Gabriel Lamé proved it for $n = 7$ in 1939. Sophie Germain proved that if n is an odd prime < 100, FLT is unsolvable in integers not divisible by n. In the middle of 19th century, E. Kummer greatly enhanced this pursuit by proving this theorem for *regular primes*[11]. Interestingly, all primes less than 37 happen to be regular, and though there is a probabilistic argument suggesting that the class of such numbers should be very large, nonetheless it is now known that there are infinitely many irregular prime numbers as well.

After the introduction of computers, the scenario changed rapidly with the tremen-

---

[11]To define a **regular prime** in the light of Kummer's discussion, consider $\frac{x}{e^x - 1} = 1 - \frac{x}{2} + \frac{x^2}{12} - \frac{x^4}{720} + \frac{x^6}{30240} - \frac{x^8}{1209600} + \ldots$ and define the ith **Bernoulli number** B_i to be the coefficient of $\frac{x^i}{i!}$ in the above expression. For example, B_8 is $-\frac{1}{30}$. A prime number $p \geq 7$ is called regular, if p does not divide the numerator of any even-indexed Bernoulli number up to B_{p-3}.

dous pace of improvement in calculating power of these machines, and in 1993 it was proved by J. Buhler, R. Crandall et al., that FLT is true for all prime exponents below 4,000,000. But the mathematical community worldwide was awaiting a general proof. In June 1993, after almost 360 years of the inception of this *theorem*, Andrew Wiles (1953-) of Princeton University, finally came forward with an abstract proof. A fatal logical gap in the argument was pointed out by N. Katz within a short period. However, in October 1994, Richard Taylor (1962-) and Wiles released a corrected version of the previous proof, dividing it into two articles, that appeared in the *Annals of Mathematics* in 1995 and together it was more than 130 pages long, really a little too long to be contained in the margin of any book! The proof is highly technical and to be able to appreciate the proof, it requires extensive knowledge of *elliptic curves* [12] and *modular forms*, detailed treatment of which are out of scope here. The curious connection between the FLT and elliptic curves, apparently two completely distinct disciplines, was first pointed out by Yves Hellegouarch around 1975. Jean-Pierre Serre attacked the problem from the elliptic curves and tried to tackle the FLT. In 1985, G. Frey, going further in the direction of Serre, tried an *indirect method* of proof and introduced a special class of elliptic curves, now called *Frey elliptic curves*[13], that *exists if and only if FLT is false*. In 1986, K. Ribet proved that elliptic curves associated to the solution of Fermat's equation, if such a solution exists, must be *non-modular*. It shows that FLT is equivalent to *Shimura-Taniyama conjecture*, that says, *elliptic curves are modular*, by virtue of which problems about elliptic curves can be replaced by problems about modular functions. Thus if the conjecture is true, so has to be FLT. Here came the master stroke from Wiles, who explored Frey's approach further and interlinked Ribet's result on Shimura-Taniyama conjecture with a particular class of elliptic curves, the *semistable* elliptic curves. He then argued that the semistable case of Shimura-Taniyama conjecture[14] suffices to justify FLT and proved this case to establish Fermat's Last Theorem in the end.

---

[12]These are cubic Diophantine equations of the form $y^2 = ax^3 + bx^2 + cx + d$, with rational coefficients. The name refers to elliptic functions and has got nothing to do with the curve's shape.

[13]If a nontrivial solution to FLT, $A^n + B^n = C^n$ exists, than Frey elliptic curve associated with it is $y^2 = x(x + A^n)(x - B^n)$, in which x and y are new variables.

[14]However, in 1999, a general proof of the Shimura-Taniyama conjecture, for all the elliptic curves with integer coefficients, has been announced by C. Breuil, B. Conrad, F. Diamond and R. Taylor.

Appendix F

"I have never done anything useful. No discovery of mine has made, or is likely to make, directly or indirectly, for good or ill, the least difference to the amenity of the world." These boasting words, this complacent pride about the pristine *uselessness* of his vocation, are found in the penultimate paragraph of the marvelous book *A Mathematician's Apology* by G.H. Hardy, a number theorist, who is often referred to as the *Purest of the Pure Mathematicians*. Imagine what would have been his reaction today, to know that, the security of exchange of sensitive private data through public channels that controls many a facets of today's modern urban life governed by Information Technology, from personal Net-banking to the use of debit or credit cards at POS, from safe transmission of secret business policy of MNC giants, to the safe custody of state or military secrets of a nation, all such things are heavily dependent on the *usefulness* of mathematics, amazingly number theory in particular. For about the last quarter of a century, Cryptology, the science of ciphering and deciphering of data has undergone a boom to become one of the most upcoming areas of mathematical research and a gateway to a lucrative career too. One such famous protocol, known as RSA cryptosystem[15], works on the mathematical principles, that are not an iota more than what is discussed in the Chapter on Integers of this book. Hence we find it instructive to present it here in a naive way as an immediate and beautiful application of this otherwise abstract mathematics[16].

The Problem : *Suppose you are A, and B is your friend. You two want to exchange freely your private or sensitive data through public channel, say internet, in such a way that no third party who may receive the transmission can make any sense out of it in finite time.*

RSA Protocol : Three fundamental steps:

I. Key generation [*Public* Key, known to everyone; *Private* Key, kept secret]
II. Encryption [made by public key]
III. Decryption [made by private key]

---

[15]It is named after the three inventors R. Rivest, A.Shamir and L. Adleman of MIT.

[16]Of course at the actual implementation level, there are many other complex concerns for the safety of the data, to protect it from the possible attacks from the adversaries, that make the body of the modern subject of Cryptanalysis and Cryptosynthesis.

Key Generation by A :   [*Here comes (large) Prime Numbers*]

(a) Randomly choose two distinct **large primes**, p and q and keep them secret.

        [Typically at least 512 bits each, or, about 155 decimal digits.]

(b) Compute the **modulus**, $n = pq$.

(c) Compute the **Euler totient** $\phi(n) = \phi(pq) = \phi(p)\phi(q) = (p-1)(q-1)$.

(d) Choose an integer e (**public exponent**)[17] such that,

$$e > 1 \text{ and } \gcd(e, \phi(n)) = 1.$$

(e) Determine d (**private exponent**) so that, $de \equiv 1 (\mathrm{mod}\, \phi(n))$.

(f) **Public** key of A (*to be disclosed*) is (n, e);

(g) **Private** key of A (*to be kept secret*) is (n, d).

Encryption by B:Plaintext to Ciphertext   [*Here comes Modular Arithmetic*]

(a) B, who knows the Public key of A, wants to send message (**plaintext**) **M** to A.

(b) First B converts **M** into an integer m such that $0 < m < n$ by a scheme[18].

(c) Then B computes the **ciphertext** c, as $c \equiv m^e (\mathrm{mod}\, n)$.

(d) B transmits c to A.

Decryption by A:Ciphertext to plaintext   [*Modular Arithmetic again*]

(a) A recovers m from c by $m \equiv c^d (\mathrm{mod}\, n)$.

(b) Indeed, $c^d \equiv (m^e)^d \equiv m^{ed} \equiv m^{1+k\phi(n)} \equiv m(m^k)^{\phi(n)} \equiv m(\mathrm{mod}\, n)$.[19]

(c) From m, now A can recover **M** by reversing the *Padding scheme*.

AN EASY ILLUSTRATION OF PRINCIPLES   [RSA Cryptosystem at work]

(a) Let us take $p = 7$, $q = 11$; then the **modulus** $n = pq = 77$.

(b) Totient $\phi(n) = \phi(77) = \phi(7)\phi(11) = 6 \cdot 10 = 60$.

(c) Choose **public exponent**, say $e = 13$ ($e > 1$, co-prime to 60.)

(d) Find **private exponent** d from $13d \equiv 1 (\mathrm{mod}\, 60)$. Check[20] that $d = 37$.

---

[17] From further security reasons at the actual implementation level e is chosen as an odd integer between 1 and $n - 1$.

[18] This is done by some previously agreed upon reversible protocol, technically called a *Padding scheme* which may be known to all. For example, one may use $a = 01, b = 02, \ldots, z = 26$ and *space*$=00$. If the converted message is numerically larger than n, it can be broken up into several number blocks of necessary size before applying the next step.

[19] Follows from Euler's generalization of Fermat's Little Theorem, when m and n are mutually prime. The other case can be proved by Chinese Remainder theorem, as we shall shortly see.

[20] See Worked-out Exercise 2.6.2

(e) Public key $(n = 77, e = 13)$; Private key $(n = 77, d = 37)$.

(f) Suppose the plaintext message is: **b**; so the converted number is $m = 02$.

(g) Encryption: $c = 2^{13}(\mathrm{mod}\, 77) = 30(\mathrm{mod}\, 77)$.

(h) Message (**ciphertext**) sent through public channel : 30.

(i) For Decryption[21]: Calculate $30^{37}(\mathrm{mod}\, 77) = 2(\mathrm{mod}\, 77)$.

(j) From the decrypted message 2, we get back the original plaintext : **b**.

| **Security of the System** | [Why does it work?]

Given only n, e and c but *not the (large) prime factors* of n, it is *practically impossible* to recover m. Why? Because, factoring is '**hard**'.[22]

Contrary to the theoretical claim of the Fundamental theorem of Arithmetic (Theorem 2.3.9), till date there is no time-efficient computer algorithm known for factorization of arbitrary large[23] integers. This is a blessing in disguise, as this '*inability*' provides us the theoretical certainty about the unbreakability of RSA.[24] For such an integer m, of course a factor can be found by an exhaustive search via division through primes less than first $\sqrt{m}$ integers (Theorem 2.3.7). However, from prime number theorem of Hadamard (Appendix C), it can be seen that there are about $2\sqrt{m}(\log m)^{-1}$ primes in this interval and so for a number m of 100 decimal digits this procedure will require at least $4 \cdot 10^{42}$ operations of division by primes. If a computer can execute one million divisions per second, then it will take about 10^{35} years for it to complete the calculation. Of course there are other algorithms as well, but none of them is efficient enough. So RSA is secure as long as *large* primes are used, and when a threat of breach may occur due to advancement of hardware power, only larger primes will have to be used to begin with; well, at least till *quantum computer*[25] becomes a reality.

Next Problem : *Since my public key is known to everyone, anyone may use it to forge a false message to misguide me! How to ensure that the message is really sent by the person it claims to be sent from?*

---

[21]Large calculations involving modular exponentiation and modular inversion are actually done by suitable mathematical software. However, for small values they can be manually calculated, at least in principle.

[22]To recover the prime factors of a 1024-bit number it would take a current machine a year, costing USD 10 million.

[23]'Large' is a technical jargon, which refers to integers having at least 300 decimal digits or more.

[24]Indeed, anything in the realm of mathematics that is computationally *hard*, is a potential area for possible development of some cryptographic protocol.

[25]A quantum computer will be able to break RSA (2048 bit) easily. But we are yet to build one!

Here comes the idea of **digital signature**. At the end of the message one may put his/her digital signature by *reversing the RSA protocol*, so that the intended recipient of the message may decipher the signature and be certain that it is really sent by the right person.

| Digital Signature | [*The reverse role of RSA*]

- Suppose P wants to send a signed message to Q.
- P knows his Public key (n_1, e_1), Private key (n_1, d_1) and Q's Public key (n_2, e_2).
- P will convert his name[26] to a string of numbers [say k] as before and **decode** it by his *private key* (to make it k_1, say) and put it at the end of the real message m and then encrypt both parts of (m, k_1) separately, using Q's public key to get (c, s).
- So P computes k_1, as $k_1 \equiv k^{d_1} \pmod{n_1}$ and sends the encoded message c with his **digital signature** s using $s = k_1^{e_2} \pmod{n_2}$ to Q as (c, s).
- When Q decrypts the whole signed message (in two parts) as usual by his private key, after decryption he will find the last part (i.e. s) giving a meaningless junk k_1.
- So Q will then **encode** that junk k_1 using P's *public key* as $k_1^{e_1} \pmod{n_1}$ to get back k, which authenticates the message.

| An Example of Digital Signature | [27]

	Private Key	Public Key
P :	$(n_1 = 637501, d_1 = 343481)$	$(n_1 = 637501, e_1 = 137)$
Q :	$(n_2 = 551051, d_2 = 157015)$	$(n_2 = 551051, e_2 = 7)$

- Suppose P wants to send a signed message **GO** to Q.
- According our padding scheme G is 07 and O is 15, so **m = 0715**.
- Suppose P's signature is TUA which gives **k = 202101**.
- Now first P computes $k_1 = 202101^{343481} \pmod{637501} = 554957$.
- Since this is larger than n_2, she will break it in two parts 554 and 957 and calculate $554^7 \pmod{551051} = 491120$ and $957^7 \pmod{551051} = 311427$ to make her digital signature $s = 491120, 311427$.
- Finally P computes $c = 715^7 \pmod{551051} = 492800$; and sends her signed message to Q as

[492800; my decoding of TUA is 491120, 311427]

---

[26]It may as well be just any string, like AGFJK, say; and P may declare with the ciphered message that his signature is derived out of this string.

[27]All the modular arithmetic involved in this example are done by computer.

To Decipher:

- Q computes $492800^{157015} \pmod{551051}$=715 i.e., **0715** which stands for **GO**.
- Q computes $491120^{157015} \pmod{551051}$=**554** and $311427^{157015} \pmod{551051}$=**957**, which when put together gives 554957– a junk as per the padding scheme.
- So he calculates $554957^{137} \pmod{637501}$=**202101**, and gets the matching signature **TUA**.

Mathematical Justification of the RSA Decryption

Our claim was that if $c = m^e \pmod{n}$ then $m = c^d \pmod{n}$. Note that, by construction, $ed \equiv 1 \pmod{\phi(n)}$ and thus $ed = 1 + k\phi(n)$ for some integer k. The proof now proceeds by considering two different cases. In the first case, m **is co-prime to** n. By Euler's generalization to Fermat's Little Theorem, it follows that, $m^{k\phi(n)} = 1 \pmod{n}$ and thus $c^d (\bmod\ n) = m^{ed} (\bmod\ n) = m^{1+k\phi(n)} (\bmod\ n) = m \cdot (m^k)^{\phi(n)} (\bmod\ n) = m (\bmod\ n)$, which establishes that the decryption is successful when m is co-prime to n. Suppose next that, m **is not co-prime to** n, so that one or both of p and q divide m. To be specific we consider the case where $p|m$ and $q \nmid m$; the other possible cases require only minor modifications. Because $p|m$, we have $m = 0 \pmod{p}$ and thus $m^{ed} = 0 = m (\bmod\ p)$. Because $q \nmid m$, we have, $m^{q-1} = 1 (\bmod\ q)$, by Fermat's Little Theorem, and thus $m^{\phi(n)} = 1 (\bmod\ q)$, since $\phi(n) = (p-1)(q-1)$. Using $ed = 1 + k\phi(n)$, we see that $m^{ed} = m (\bmod\ q)$. By Chinese remainder theorem, it follows that we must have $m^{ed} = m (\bmod\ n)$ and thus the decryption is also successful when m is not co-prime to n. $\square$

A Bit of History

This category of cryptographic protocols, where key for ciphering and deciphering is *shared between the parties* who were unknown to each other a priori, is known as **Public Key Cryptography**. This idea was first proposed *theoretically* in 1976 by two Standard University researchers, W. Diffie and M. Hellman in their landmark paper *"New Directions in Cryptography"*. The basic idea of **digital signature** for authentication among parties who share a secret key is also due to them. But they didn't prescribe any specific method for fully operational public-key ciphers[28]. However, in 1977 it was the trio of **R**ivest, **S**hamir and **A**dleman of MIT who first put this idea into operation using the brilliant application of basic number theory.

---

[28]They did introduce a specific method of key-sharing, based on number theory, known as Diffie-Hellman key agreement. Its security is based on *discrete logarithm* problem.

Appendix G

Dihedral group D_5 and check digit of Aadhaar

Unique Identification (UID) is a numerical identification system where all the residents of a country are allocated with a unique number. The brand name of the Unique Identification number in India is **Aadhaar**. This is a 12 digit identification number, issued by the Unique Identification Authority of India (UIDAI) to all the residents of our country. The first 11 digits (from the left) of this number is machine generated randomly and assigned uniquely to a person. Like all other identification numbers (viz. ISBN for books, UPC for consumer products, Bank Debit or Credit card numbers of an individual etc., each one a string of numbers of different length), one key feature to Aadhaar is the inclusion of an extra digit at the rightmost position, called a **check digit**, designed to detect possible errors in reading/typing the identification number. Our interest in Aadhaar centres on this 12th digit. Amazingly, it involves the group D_5 and a particular permutation of the set $\{0, 1, 2, \ldots 9\}$, as we shall shortly describe.

When we read/type a number, there is always the possibility of the number being read/typed incorrectly. Most common errors[29] committed while reading/typing numbers are

(i) **single digit error** like *transcription error*, which occurs when only a single digit in the whole number is misread/typed wrongly. For example, 8901063026162 is typed as 8201063026162. Here the digit 9 is incorrectly typed as 2.

(ii) **single transposition error**, which occurs when the ith and the $(i + 1)$th digits are replaced by the $(i+1)$th and the ith digits respectively. For example, 8901063026162 typed as 8901036026162. Here the digits 6 and 3 are transposed, leading to a transposition error.

We now discuss a scheme known as **Verhoeff method** based on permutation and the finite group D_5 , which helps us in detecting these common errors in UID. The Verhoeff algorithm for error detection, first published in 1969, was developed by Dutch mathematician Jacobus Verhoeff (born 1927).

Recall that a group G is called nth dihedral group if G is generated by two elements a, b such that (i)$o(a) = n, o(b) = 2$ (ii) $ba = a^{-1}b$. In the light of Example 8.3.8 it can be easily appreciated that the group of all symmetries of a regular pentagon is D_5. More precisely, D_5 is generated by two elements: one is the rotation by angle $\frac{2\pi}{5} = 72°$, denoted by a; the other is the reflection along an axis of symmetry,

---

[29]There are other possible errors also, such as **jump transpositions errors**, e.g., $132 \to 231$, **jump twin errors**, e.g., $131 \to 232$, **phonetic errors**, e.g., $60 \to 16$ ("sixty" to "sixteen") etc.

denoted by b. There are three relations among a and b viz., $a^5 = i = a^0$, $b^2 = i$ and $ba = a^{-1}b$. The group D_5 is a noncommutative group with 10 elements, viz., $\{a^0 = i, a, a^2, a^3, a^4, ba^4, ba^3, ba^2, ba, b\}$.

The Cayley table for the group D_5 is given below.

$\circ$	a^0	a^1	a^2	a^3	a^4	ba^4	ba^3	ba^2	ba^1	b
a^0	a^0	a^1	a^2	a^3	a^4	ba^4	ba^3	ba^2	ba^1	b
a^1	a^1	a^2	a^3	a^4	a^0	ba^3	ba^2	ba^1	b	ba^4
a^2	a^2	a^3	a^4	a^0	a^1	ba^2	ba^1	b	ba^4	ba^3
a^3	a^3	a^4	a^0	a^1	a^2	ba^1	b	ba^4	ba^3	ba^2
a^4	a^4	a^0	a^1	a^2	a^3	b	ba^4	ba^3	ba^2	ba^1
ba^4	ba^4	b	ba^1	ba^2	ba^3	a^0	a^4	a^3	a^2	a^1
ba^3	ba^3	ba^4	b^1	ba^1	ba^2	a^1	a^0	a^4	a^3	a^2
ba^2	ba^2	ba^3	ba^4	b	ba^1	a^2	a^1	a^0	a^4	a^3
ba^1	ba^1	ba^2	ba^3	ba^4	b	a^3	a^2	a^1	a^0	a^4
b	b	ba^1	ba^2	ba^3	ba^4	a^4	a^3	a^2	a^1	a^0

Now replace the elements in the above table with the digits 0 to 9 respectively, keeping the elements in the same order as in the Cayley table of D_5, viz.,

$$a^0 \to 0,\, a^1 \to 1,\, a^2 \to 2,\, a^3 \to 3,\, a^4 \to 4,\, ba^4 \to 5,\, ba^3 \to 6,\, ba^2 \to 7,\, ba^1 \to 8,\, b \to 9.$$

This gives us the following table :

$+$	0	1	2	3	4	5	6	7	8	9
0	0	1	2	3	4	5	6	7	8	9
1	1	2	3	4	0	6	7	8	9	5
2	2	3	4	0	1	7	8	9	5	6
3	3	4	0	1	2	8	9	5	6	7
4	4	0	1	2	3	9	5	6	7	8
5	5	9	8	7	6	0	4	3	2	1
6	6	5	9	8	7	1	0	4	3	2
7	7	6	5	9	8	2	1	0	4	3
8	8	7	6	5	9	3	2	1	0	4
9	9	8	7	6	5	4	3	2	1	0

We now describe Verhoeff method:

Part 1: **Assigning check digit:** Let the number to which the check digit a_0 is to be assigned be $a_{11}a_{10}.....a_2a_1$,where $0 \le a_i \le 9, 1 \le i \le 11$.

Consider the permutation $\sigma = (15894270)(36)$

$$= \begin{pmatrix} 0 & 1 & 2 & 3 & 4 & 5 & 6 & 7 & 8 & 9 \\ 1 & 5 & 7 & 6 & 2 & 8 & 3 & 0 & 9 & 4 \end{pmatrix}$$

used in the Verhoeff scheme. Evaluate $\sigma^1(a_1) + \sigma^2(a_2) + \sigma^3(a_3) + \ldots + \sigma^{11}(a_{11})$ using the binary operation $+$ given in the second group table above and the permutation σ. Let the result obtained be m (it is a single digit number). Then calculate the inverse of m, i.e., the number a_0 for which $a_0 + m = 0$. The inverse of m is the check digit a_0 which is to be appended at the end of the number $a_{11} a_{10} \ldots a_2 a_1$.

Part 2: **Checking whether $a_{11} a_{10} \ldots a_2 a_1 a_0$ is a valid Aadhaar number**. For this, calculate $a_0 + \sigma^1(a_1) + \sigma^2(a_2) + \sigma^3(a_3) + \ldots + \sigma^{11}(a_{11})$. If the result is zero, then the number is correct. If not, there is an error.

Example 1: Let the 11 digit number to which the check digit is to be assigned be **9051 3597 364**. To find the check digit a_0 for this number, we first calculate

$$\sigma^1(4) + \sigma^2(6) + \sigma^3(3) + \sigma^4(7) + \sigma^5(9) + \sigma^6(5) + \sigma^7(3) + \sigma^8(1) + \sigma^9(5) + \sigma^{10}(0) + \sigma^{11}(9).$$

Now, note that order of σ is 8, whence

$$\sigma^8(1) + \sigma^9(5) + \sigma^{10}(0) + \sigma^{11}(9) = \sigma^0(1) + \sigma^1(5) + \sigma^2(0) + \sigma^3(9).$$

So we calculate, $\sigma^1(4) + \sigma^2(6) + \sigma^3(3) + \sigma^4(7) + \sigma^5(9) + \sigma^6(5) + \sigma^7(3) + \sigma^0(1) + \sigma^1(5) + \sigma^2(0) + \sigma^3(9) = 2 + 6 + 6 + 8 + 1 + 0 + 6 + 1 + 8 + 5 + 7 = 9$. Here $+$ is the group operation defined in the second group table above, from which we see that $9 + a_0 = 0$ holds for $a_0 = 9$. Hence the check digit for the given number is 9, whence the correct Aadhaar Number is **9051 3597 3649**.

Example 2: Let the number which is to be checked as a correct Aadhaar number be **5366 0508 7716**. For this, calculate $6 + \sigma^1(1) + \sigma^2(7) + \sigma^3(7) + \sigma^4(8) + \sigma^5(0) + \sigma^6(5) + \sigma^7(0) + \sigma^8(6) + \sigma^9(6) + \sigma^{10}(3) + \sigma^{11}(5)$. The resulting sum is 0. Hence **5366 0508 7716** is a correct Aadhaar number.

The Verhoeff scheme detects all single digit errors. Indeed, we observe that a correct identification number $a_{11} a_{10} \ldots a_i \ldots a_2 a_1 a_0$, where a_0 is the check digit, satisfies $a_0 + \sigma^1(a_1) + \sigma^2(a_2) + \sigma^3(a_3) + \ldots + \sigma^{11}(a_{11}) = 0$. If a_i is replaced by b and the resulting string $a_{11} a_{10} \ldots b \ldots a_2 a_1 a_0$ is still a correct identification number, then we must have $a_0 + \sigma^1(a_1) + \sigma^2(a_2) + \sigma^3(a_3) + \ldots + \sigma^{i-1}(b) + \ldots + \sigma^{11}(a_{11}) = 0$. But this indicates that $\sigma^{i-1}(a_i) = \sigma^{i-1}(b)$. Now, since σ is bijective function, it follows that $a_i = b$. This proves the claim.

Example 3: Consider the Aadhaar number **9051 3597 3445**. Suppose it is typed as **9051 3597 3345**. This is a correct Aadhaar number if $S = 5 + \sigma^1(4) + \sigma^2(4) + \sigma^3(3) + \sigma^4(7) + \sigma^5(9) + \sigma^6(5) + \sigma^7(3) + \sigma^8(1) + \sigma^9(5) + \sigma^{10}(0) + \sigma^{11}(9) = 0$. But we find that $S = 5 + 2 + 7 + 6 + 8 + 1 + 0 + 6 + 1 + 8 + 5 + 7 = 5$. Hence the number **9051 3597 3345** is **not a correct Aadhaar number**. Comparing the numbers we find that the digit 4 of the tenth place from the left is incorrectly typed as 3. This is a single digit transcription error.

The above scheme can also detect all transposition errors among adjacent digits.

Example 4: Consider the Aadhaar number **9051 3597 3445**. Suppose it is typed as **9051 3579 3445**. This is a correct Aadhaar number if $S = 5 + \sigma^1(4) + \sigma^2(4) + \sigma^3(3) + \sigma^4(9) + \sigma^5(7) + \sigma^6(5) + \sigma^7(3) + \sigma^8(1) + \sigma^9(5) + \sigma^{10}(0) + \sigma^{11}(9) = 0$. But we find that $S = 5 + 2 + 7 + 6 + 0 + 9 + 0 + 6 + 1 + 8 + 5 + 7 = 8$. Hence the number **9051 3579 3445** is **not a correct Aadhaar number**. If we compare the numbers we find that the digits 9 and 7 of the seventh and eighth places from the left respectively are interchanged. This is a single transposition error.

Example 5: Consider the Aadhaar number **7494 5469 9021**. Suppose it is typed as **7494 5469 0921**. This is a correct Aadhaar number if $S = 1 + \sigma^1(2) + \sigma^2(9) + \sigma^3(0) + \sigma^4(9) + \sigma^5(6) + \sigma^6(4) + \sigma^7(5) + \sigma^8(4) + \sigma^9(9) + \sigma^{10}(4) + \sigma^{11}(7) = 0$. But we find that $S = 1 + 7 + 2 + 8 + 0 + 3 + 8 + 1 + 4 + 4 + 7 + 5 = 8$. Hence the number **7494 5469 0921** is **not a correct Aadhaar number**. Here we find that this scheme detects error due to transposition of the two-digit sequence 90 to 09 (or vice versa).

We put an end to our present discussion with a remark that while this scheme can always detect the above two types of errors successfully, it cannot detect some other possible errors always. We also point out that the scope of check digit of Aadhaar is restricted only to certify a certain 12 digit integer as a valid Aadhaar number; it cannot tell anything about the identity of the person to whom the number might have been assigned.

Appendix H

Automorphism of Groups

In Section 6.2 we have discussed about isomorphism theorems between two groups and solved some related problems. Interestingly, isomorphism of a group onto itself has some nice algebraic properties that demand special attention. Towards that, we will now discuss isomorphism of a group G onto itself and see some of its salient properties. As an application, we shall come to know about the concepts of some special subclasses of normal subgroups of a group, that play important role in the development of group theory.

Definition 1. An isomorphism $f : G \to G$ from a group G onto itself is called an *automorphism* of the group G.

From the aforesaid definition, we find that for a group G, a mapping $f : G \to G$ is an automorphism if

(i) f is a bijective mapping and

(ii) $f(ab) = f(a)f(b)$ for all $a, b \in G$.

Example 2. Consider the group $(\mathbb{Z}, +)$ of all integers under ordinary addition '+'. Define $f : \mathbb{Z} \to \mathbb{Z}$ by $f(n) = -n$ for all $n \in \mathbb{Z}$. It is easy to see that f is a bijective mapping. Indeed, let $m, n \in \mathbb{Z}$. Then $f(n+m) = -(n+m) = -n-m = -n+(-m) = f(n) + f(m)$. Hence f is a homomorphism. So we find that f is an automorphism.

Example 3. In the group $(\mathbb{Z}, +)$ define $f : \mathbb{Z} \to \mathbb{Z}$ by $f(n) = 2n$ for all $n \in \mathbb{Z}$. Now, $f(n+m) = 2(n+m) = 2n+2m = f(n)+f(m)$ implies that f is a homomorphism. It can be shown easily that f is injective but not surjective, whence f is not an automorphism.

Example 4. In the symmetric group S_3, define $f : S_3 \to S_3$ by $f(\alpha) = \alpha^{-1}$ for all $\alpha \in S_3$. It is routine to show that f is a bijective mapping. Now $(1\ 2), (1\ 3)$ are elements of S_3. Observe that $f\big((1\ 2)(1\ 3)\big) = f\big((1\ 3\ 2)\big) = (1\ 3\ 2)^{-1} = (1\ 2\ 3)$, while $f((1\ 2))f((1\ 3)) = (1\ 2)^{-1}(1\ 3)^{-1} = (1\ 2)(1\ 3) = (1\ 3\ 2)$, whence f is not a homomorphism. This implies that f is not an automorphism.

Theorem 5. *Let G be a group. The mapping $f : G \to G$ defined by $f(a) = a^{-1}$ for all $a \in G$ is an automorphism if and only if G is a commutative group.*

Proof. Suppose G is a commutative group. Then for $a, b \in G$, $f(ab) = (ab)^{-1} = b^{-1}a^{-1} = a^{-1}b^{-1}$ (as G is commutative) $= f(a)f(b)$. Hence f is a homomorphism. Now $f(a) = f(b)$ implies $a^{-1} = b^{-1}$, which implies $a = b$. Hence f is injective. Also for $a \in G$, we have $a^{-1} \in G$ and $f(a^{-1}) = (a^{-1})^{-1} = a$. This implies that f is surjective. Hence f is a bijective homomorphism, i.e., an automorphism.

Conversely, assume that for all $a \in G$, $f(a) = a^{-1}$ is an automorphism. Let $a, b \in G$. Then $f(ab) = f(a)f(b) = a^{-1}b^{-1} = (ba)^{-1} = f(ba)$. Since f is injective, it follows that $ab = ba$ for all $a, b \in G$, whence G is commutative. ☐

For any group G, the identity mapping $I(x) = x$ for all $x \in G$ is an automorphism, called the ***trivial automorphism***. The set of all automorphisms of a group G is denoted by ***Aut(G)***. We now show that $Aut(G)$ is a group with respect to usual composition of mappings.

Theorem 6. *Aut (G) is a group.*

Proof. We first note that the identity mapping I of G belongs to $Aut(G)$. Hence $Aut(G) \neq \emptyset$. Let $f, g \in Aut(G)$. Since f and g are bijective mappings from G onto G, so is fg. We now show that fg is a homomorphism. Let $a, b \in G$. Now, $(fg)(ab) = f(g(ab)) = f(g(a)g(b)) = f(g(a))f(g(b)) = (fg)(a)(fg)(b)$. Hence $fg \in Aut(G)$. Also for $f, g, h \in Aut(G)$, we have $f(gh) = (fg)h$. Now for any $f \in Aut(G)$, $(If)(x) = I(f(x)) = f(x)$ and $(fI)(x) = f(I(x)) = f(x)$ for all $x \in G$. Hence $If = fI = f$ shows that I is the identity element of $Aut(G)$. Towards the existence of inverse of every $f \in Aut(G)$, we see that, since f is a bijective mapping from G onto G, f^{-1} exists and it is also a bijective mapping from G onto G such that, $ff^{-1} = f^{-1}f = I$. We prove that $f^{-1} \in Aut(G)$ by showing that f^{-1} is a homomorphism also. Let $a, b \in G$, whence $f^{-1}(a), f^{-1}(b) \in G$ as well. Note that,

$$f\left(f^{-1}(a)f^{-1}(b)\right) = f\left(f^{-1}(a)\right)f\left(f^{-1}(b)\right) = (ff^{-1})(a)(ff^{-1})(b) = I(a)I(b) = ab.$$

As f is bijective, we see that $f^{-1}(a)f^{-1}(b) = f^{-1}(ab)$. Consequently, $Aut(G)$ is a group. ☐

Consider the group $(\mathbb{Z}, +)$. It can be shown that the identity map I and the map $f_- : \mathbb{Z} \to \mathbb{Z}$ defined by $f_-(n) = -n$ for all $n \in \mathbb{Z}$ are the only two automorphisms of $(\mathbb{Z}, +)$. Hence $Aut(\mathbb{Z}) = \{I, f_-\} \cong \mathbb{Z}_2$.

We now study some special properties of automorphisms. Let G be a group and $a \in G$. Now the mapping $f_a : G \to G$ defined by $f_a(x) = axa^{-1}$ for all $x \in G$. It is a routine exercise to show that f_a is a bijective mapping. Now, $f_a(xy) = axya^{-1} = axa^{-1}aya^{-1} = f_a(x)f_a(y)$. Hence f_a is a homomorphism, whence $f_a \in Aut(G)$ for all $a \in G$.

Definition 7. Let G be a group. An automorphism $f \in Aut(G)$ is called an ***inner automorphism*** if there exists $a \in G$ such that $f = f_a$. We denote the set of all inner automorphisms of a group G by ***Inn(G)***.

Theorem 8. *For a group G, $Inn(G)$ is a normal subgroup of Aut (G).*

Proof. Let $f_a, f_b \in Inn(G)$ for $a, b \in G$. Now,

$$(f_a f_b)(x) = f_a(f_b(x)) = f_a(bxb^{-1}) = a(bxb^{-1})a^{-1} = (ab)x(b^{-1}a^{-1}) = (ab)x(ab)^{-1} = f_{ab}(x).$$

Then $f_a f_b = f_{ab} \in Inn(G)$. Also for the identity element $e \in G$, $f_e(x) = exe^{-1} = exe = x$, whence f_e is the identity automorphism. Further, $f_a f_{a^{-1}} = f_{aa^{-1}} = f_e = f_{a^{-1}a} = f_{a^{-1}} f_a$, shows that $(f_a)^{-1} = f_{a^{-1}} \in Inn(G)$. Hence $Inn(G)$ is a subgroup of G. Let $g \in Aut(G)$ and $f_a \in Inn(G)$. Now, $(g f_a g^{-1})(x) = g f_a(g^{-1}(x)) = g(f_a(g^{-1}(x))) = g(ag^{-1}(x)a^{-1}) = g(a)g(g^{-1}(x))g(a^{-1}) = g(a)xg(a^{-1}) = g(a)x(g(a)^{-1}) = f_{g(a)}(x)$ for all $x \in G$, whence $g f_a g^{-1} = f_{g(a)} \in Inn(G)$. Consequently, $Inn(G)$ is a normal subgroup of $Aut(G)$.   □

Recall that the centre $Z(G)$ of a group is a normal subgroup of G. The next theorem relates it with $Inn(G)$.

Theorem 9. *For a group G, $G/Z(G) \cong Inn(G)$.*

Proof. Define a function $f : G \to Inn(G)$ by $f(a) = f_a$ for all $a \in G$, where f_a is the inner automorphism given by $f_a(x) = axa^{-1}$ for all $x \in G$. Clearly f is a surjective mapping. We now show that f is a homomorphism. Let $a, b \in G$. Now, $f(ab) = f_{ab} = f_a f_b = f(a)f(b)$, whence $f : G \to Inn(G)$ is an epimorphism. Then by first isomorphism theorem $G/ker\, f \cong Inn(G)$. Now

$$
\begin{aligned}
ker\, f &= \{a \in G : f(a) = f_e\} \\
&= \{a \in G : f_a = f_e\} \\
&= \{a \in G : f_a(x) = f_e(x) \text{ for all } x \in G\} \\
&= \{a \in G : axa^{-1} = exe^{-1} \text{ for all } x \in G\} \\
&= \{a \in G : axa^{-1} = x \text{ for all } x \in G\} \\
&= \{a \in G : ax = xa \text{ for all } x \in G\} \\
&= Z(G).
\end{aligned}
$$

Consequently, $G/Z(G) \cong Inn(G)$.   □

Definition 10. A subgroup H of a group G is called a ***characteristic subgroup*** if $f(H) \subseteq H$ for all $f \in Aut(G)$.

It can be shown that $Z(G)$, the centre of the group G is a characteristic subgroup.

Theorem 11. *Every characteristic subgroup of a group G is a normal subgroup of G.*

Proof. Let H be a characteristic subgroup of G. Suppose $g \in G$. The $f_g : G \to G$ defined by $f_g(x) = gxg^{-1}$ is an automorphism of G. As H is characteristic subgroup, we have $f_g(H) \subseteq H$. This implies that $gHg^{-1} \subseteq H$. Consequently H is normal.   □

However, a nontrivial *proper* normal subgroup of a group may not be its characteristic subgroup. Next example justifies our claim.

Example 12. It is known that every subgroup of $(\mathbb{Q}, +)$, the additive group of rational numbers, is a normal subgroup. Suppose, if possible, H is any nontrivial *proper* subgroup of $\mathbb{Q}$, which is also a characteristic subgroup. Note that, for every $r \in \mathbb{Q}$, the mapping $T_r : \mathbb{Q} \to \mathbb{Q}$ defined by $T_r(x) = rx$ for all $x \in \mathbb{Q}$ is an automorphism. Let $0 \neq x \in H$. Suppose $y \in \mathbb{Q}$. Then $r = yx^{-1} \in \mathbb{Q}$ and $y = yx^{-1}x = rx = T_r(x) \in H$, (since H is a characteristic subgroup) whence $H = \mathbb{Q}$ — a contradiction to our choice of H as a nontrivial *proper* subgroup.

Remark 13. We merely point out that $Aut\big((\mathbb{Z}_n, +_n)\big) = (U_n, \cdot_n)$. A general proof to this result is a bit involved and hence not included here. However, some particular cases may be seen in the adjoining Worked-out Exercise and Exercise.

Definition 14. Let a, b be elements of a group G. By the ***commutator*** of a an b we mean the element $[a, b] = a^{-1}b^{-1}ab$. If A and B are subsets of G, then we write

$$[A, B] = \langle \{ [a, b] : a \in A, b \in B \} \rangle.$$

Example 15. Consider $(1\,2), (1\,2\,3) \in S_3$. The commutator $[(1\,2), (1\,2\,3)]$ is

$$(1\,2)^{-1}(1\,2\,3)^{-1}(1\,2)(1\,2\,3) = (1\,2)(1\,3\,2)(1\,2)(1\,2\,3) = (1\,3\,2).$$

Let S be the set of all finite products of commutators that can be made out of the elements of a group G. Following result is interesting.

Theorem 16. *The set S, as defined above, is a normal subgroup of G.*

Proof. Let $x, y \in S$. Then there exist $a_1, a_2, \ldots, a_n$; $b_1, b_2, \ldots, b_n$; $c_1, c_2, \ldots, c_m$; $d_1, d_2, \ldots, d_m$ such that $x = [a_1, b_1][a_2, b_2] \ldots [a_n, b_n]$ and $y = [c_1, d_1][c_2, d_2] \ldots [c_m, d_m]$. Clearly, $xy = [a_1, b_1][a_2, b_2] \ldots [a_n, b_n][c_1, d_1][c_2, d_2] \ldots [c_m, d_m]$ is still a finite product of the commutators, whence $xy \in S$. Note that, for any $a, [a, a] \in S$ and $[a, a] = a^{-1}a^{-1}aa = e$, the identity of the group G. Hence S has the identity element. For $[a, b]$, we find that $[a, b][b, a] = a^{-1}b^{-1}abb^{-1}a^{-1}ba = e = [b, a][a, b]$, whence $[a, b]^{-1}$ exists in S. We can extend this argument to get a similar result for any finite product of commutators. Hence S is a subgroup of G.

Now, for any $[a, b] \in S$, $g[a, b]g^{-1} = ga^{-1}b^{-1}abg^{-1} = ga^{-1}g^{-1}gb^{-1}g^{-1}gag^{-1}gbg^{-1} = [gag^{-1}, gbg^{-1}] \in S$. Extending this result for $x = [a_1, b_1][a_2, b_2] \ldots [a_n, b_n]$, we see that

$$\begin{aligned} gxg^{-1} &= g[a_1, b_1]g^{-1}g[a_2, b_2]g^{-1} \ldots g[a_n, b_n]g^{-1} \\ &= [ga_1g^{-1}, gb_1g^{-1}][ga_2g^{-1}, gb_2g^{-1}] \ldots [ga_ng^{-1}, gb_ng^{-1}], \end{aligned}$$

whence gxg^{-1} is a finite product of commutators. Hence $gxg^{-1} \in S$, so that S is a normal subgroup of G. $\qquad\square$

Definition 17. The normal subgroup S is usually denoted by G' and called the ***commutator subgroup*** or the ***derived subgroup*** of G. Note that it is the smallest subgroup of G containing all its commutators.

Theorem 18. *For a group G, the quotient group G/G' is a commutative group.*

Proof. For $a, b \in G$, $a^{-1}b^{-1}ab \in G'$. Hence $a^{-1}b^{-1}abG' = G'$. Then $abG' = baG'$, which shows that $aG'bG' = bG'aG'$. Consequently, G/G' is a commutative group. □

Remark. It is worth pointing out that the product of any two commutators in an arbitrary group need not be a commutator. This is why the concept of derived subgroup banks on all finite products. However, a counter example to justify the claim is out of the scope of the present text[30].

Worked-out Exercises

Exercise 1. Let $\mathbb{R}^+$ be the set of all positive real numbers. Show that the mapping $f : \mathbb{R}^+ \to \mathbb{R}^+$ defined by $f(r) = \sqrt{r}$ for all $r \in \mathbb{R}^+$ is an automorphism.

Solution. Let $r, t \in \mathbb{R}^+$. Suppose $f(r) = f(t)$. Then $\sqrt{r} = \sqrt{t}$, which implies $r = t$. Hence f is injective. Clearly, $r^2 \in \mathbb{R}^+$ and $f(r^2) = \sqrt{r^2}$ shows that f is surjective as well, whence f is bijective. Now, $f(rt) = \sqrt{rt} = \sqrt{r}\sqrt{t} = f(r)f(t)$ implies that f is a homomorphism. Hence $f \in Aut(\mathbb{R}^+)$.

Exercise 2. Find $Aut(\mathbb{Z}_3)$.

Solution. We know that $\mathbb{Z}_3 = \{[0], [1], [2]\}$ is a cyclic group and $[1], [2]$ are the generators of $\mathbb{Z}_3$. Let $f \in Aut(\mathbb{Z}_3)$. It is well known that if a is a generator of $\mathbb{Z}_3$, then $f(a)$ is also so. Hence $f([1]) = [1]$ or $f([1]) = [2]$. If $f([1]) = [1]$, then $f([n]) = [n]$, while if $f([1]) = [2]$ then $f([n]) = [2n]$. Hence the following mappings, one given by $[0] \to [0], [1] \to [1], [2] \to [2]$ and the other by $[0] \to [0], [1] \to [2], [2] \to [4] = [1]$ are the only two automorphisms of $\mathbb{Z}_3$. As there is only one group of order 2 up to isomorphism, we conclude that $Aut(\mathbb{Z}_3) \cong \mathbb{Z}_2$ or, equivalently, $Aut(\mathbb{Z}_3) \cong U_2$.

Exercise 3. Find $Inn(S_3)$.

Solution. We note that the centre $Z(S_3)$ of S_3 consists of its identity element e only. Now $S_3/\{e\} \cong Inn(S_3)$, whence $S_3 \cong Inn(S_3)$.

Exercise 4. Prove that $Inn(S_3) = Aut(S_3)$.

---

[30]Interested reader may refer to the paper *Commutators and their Products* by I.D. MacDonald published in The Amer. Math. Monthly, Vol. 93, No. 6 (Jun-Juy. 1986), pp.440-444

Solution. Clearly, $Inn(S_3) \subseteq Aut(S_3)$. Also from Exercise 3 above, it follows that $|Inn(S_3)| = |S_3| = 6$. We now show that $|Aut(S_3)| \leq 6$. It is known that S_3 is generated by $\{(1\ 2), (1\ 2\ 3)\}$. Let $f \in Aut(S_3)$. So f is determined by $f((1\ 2))$ and $f((1\ 2\ 3))$. Note that $o((1\ 2)) = 2$ and then $o(f((1\ 2))) = 2$. Again, $o((1\ 2\ 3)) = 3$ and then $o(f((1\ 2\ 3))) = 3$. This shows that, $f((1\ 2)) = (1\ 2)$ or $(1\ 3)$ or $(2\ 3)$ and $f((1\ 2\ 3)) = (1\ 2\ 3)$ or $(1\ 3\ 2)$. Thus there are at most 6 choices of f. Hence the number of elements in $Aut(S_3)$ cannot exceed 6. Thus we see that $|Aut(S_3)| \leq 6 = |Inn(S_3)|$. But $Inn(S_3) \subseteq Aut(S_3)$, whence $Inn(S_3) = Aut(S_3)$.

Exercise 5. Prove that $Z(G)$ is a characteristic subgroup of the group G.

Solution. To prove this we show that $f(Z(G)) \subseteq Z(G)$ for all $f \in Aut(G)$. Let $f \in Aut(G)$ and $a \in Z(G)$. We show that $f(a) \in Z(G)$. Let $b \in G$. Since f is an automorphism there exists $r \in G$ such that $f(r) = b$. Now $f(a)b = f(a)f(r) = f(ar) = f(ra)$ (since $a \in Z(G)$) $= f(r)f(a) = bf(a)$. Hence $f(a) \in Z(G)$ for all $a \in Z(G)$. It then follows that $Z(G)$ is a characteristic subgroup.

Exercise 6. Show that every subgroup of a cyclic group is a characteristic subgroup.

Solution. Let $G = \langle a \rangle$ be a cyclic group and let H be a subgroup of G. If G is infinite, then $G \cong (\mathbb{Z}, +)$, whence $Aut(G) = Aut(\mathbb{Z}) = \mathbb{Z}_2$, from which the result follows trivially. In case when G is a finite cyclic group, $H = \langle a^m \rangle$ for some positive integer m. Let $f \in Aut(G)$. Then $f(a) = a^k$ for some positive integer k. Let $b \in \langle a^m \rangle = H$. There exists a positive integer t such that $b = (a^m)^t = a^{mt}$. Now $f(b) = f(a^{mt}) = (f(a))^{mt} = a^{kmt} = (a^m)^{kt} \in H$ for all $b \in H$. Hence $f(H) \subseteq H$, which shows that H is a characteristic subgroup.

Exercises

1. Show that for $r \in \mathbb{Q}$, the mapping $T_r : \mathbb{Q} \to \mathbb{Q}$ defined by $T_r(x) = rx$ is an automorphism of $(\mathbb{Q}, +)$.

2. Show that for any $n \in \mathbb{Z}$, the mapping $f : \mathbb{Z} \to \mathbb{Z}$ defined by $f(n) = -n$ is an automorphism of $(\mathbb{Z}, +)$.

3. Show that the mapping $f : \mathbb{C} \to \mathbb{C}$ defined by $f(a + ib) = a - ib$ is an automorphism of the additive group of complex numbers.

4. Let $[r]$ be a unit element of $\mathbb{Z}_n$. Show that $f : \mathbb{Z}_n \to \mathbb{Z}_n$, defined by $f([x]) = [r][x]$ is an automorphism.

5. Find $Aut(\mathbb{Z}_4)$ and $Aut(\mathbb{Z}_5)$.

6. If G is a group containing at least 3 elements, then show that $Aut(G)$ contains at least 2 elements.

7. For a group G, if $|Inn(G)| = 1$, then prove that G is a commutative group.

8. Let $C_2 = \{1, -1\}$ be the group of order 2 and $C_2 \times C_2 = \{(1,1), (1,-1), (-1,1), (-1,-1)\}$ is the commutative group of order 4. Prove the following :

    i) $H = \{(1,1), (-1,1)\}$ is a normal subgroup.

    ii) H is not a characteristic subgroup.

9. Let H and K be characteristic subgroups of a group G. Prove that HK and $H \cap K$ are characteristic subgroups of G.

10. For a group G, prove that G' is a characteristic subgroup.

11. Prove that, a group G is commutative if and only if the derived subgroup G' is $\{e\}$.

12. Show that $S_4' = A_4$ and $S_4/S_4' \cong \mathbb{Z}_2$.

13. Find A_4'.

14. Let H, K be subgroups of a group G. Prove that, (i) H is a normal subgroup of G if and only if $[G, H] \subseteq H$ (ii) if H, K are normal subgroups of G, then $[H, K]$ is a normal subgroup of G.

15. Let H be a normal subgroup of G, Prove that G/H is commutative if and only if $G' \subseteq H$.

16. Show that there exist groups G, H such that $Aut(G) \cong Aut(H)$ though $G \not\cong H$.

17. Which of the following are true for a group G?

    (A) If G is infinite so is $Aut(G)$.

    (B) If G is finite so is $Aut(G)$.

    (C) $Aut(G)$ is a subgroup of the group $A(G)$ of all permutations of G.

    (D) If G is cyclic, then $Aut(G)$ is also cyclic.

Hints to some of the Exercises:

7. Now, $|Inn(G)| = 1$ implies $|G/Z(G)| = 1$ and thus $G = Z(G)$ Consequently, G is commutative. **8(ii).** Let $e = (1,1), a = (1,-1), b = (-1,1)$ and $c = (-1,-1)$. Then the mapping $f : C_2 \times C_2 \longrightarrow C_2 \times C_2$, defined by $f(e) = e, f(a) = b, f(b) = c$ and $f(c) = a$ is an automorphism such that $f(H) \not\subseteq H$. **13.** Let $K = \{e, (1\ 2)(3\ 4), (1\ 3)(2\ 4), (1\ 4)(2\ 3)\}$. Now, $(1\ 2)(3\ 4) = (1\ 3\ 4)(3\ 4\ 2)(1\ 4\ 3)(3\ 2\ 4) \in A_4'$. Similarly, $(1\ 3)(2\ 4), (1\ 4)(2\ 3) \in A_4'$ and thus $K \subseteq A_4'$. On the other hand, K is a normal subgroup of A_4' and A_4'/K is commutative implies $A_4' \subseteq K$. Hence $A_4' = K$. **15.** Let H be a normal subgroup of G such that G/H is commutative. Then for any two elements $a, b \in G$, $(aH)(bH) = (bH)(aH)$. This implies $abH = baH$, i.e., $(ba)^{-1}ab \in H$, i.e., $[a, b] = a^{-1}b^{-1}ab \in H$. Hence $G' \subseteq H$. **16.** Consider the groups $(\mathbb{Z}, +)$ and $(\mathbb{Z}_3, +)$. Then $Aut(\mathbb{Z}) = Aut(\mathbb{Z}_3) \cong \mathbb{Z}_2$, but $\mathbb{Z} \not\cong \mathbb{Z}_3$. **17.** (A) *False* : Counter example $(\mathbb{Z}, +)$, (B) True (C) True (D) *False* : Counter example - Consider the group $(\mathbb{Z}_8, +)$. Then $Aut(\mathbb{Z}_8) \cong K_4$, Klein's 4-group, which is non cyclic.

Bibliography

1. **Artin M.** : Algebra, Prentice-Hall India, New Delhi, 1991.
2. **Burton D. M.** : Elementary Number Theory, Allyn & Bacon, Boston, 1980.
3. **Courant R. and Robbins H.** : What is Mathematics? (revised by Ian Stewart), Oxford University Press, New York, 1996.
4. **Dummit D.S. and Foote R.M.** : Abstract Algebra, John Wiley & Sons, New York, 2002
5. **Farmer D.W.** : Groups and Symmetry : A Guide to Discovering Mathematics, Universities Press (India) Ltd. 1998.
6. **Fraleigh J. B.** : A First Course in Abstract Algebra, Narosa Publishing House, New Delhi, 1982.
7. **Goldhaber J. K. and Ehrlich G.** : Algebra, The Macmillan Company, Collier-Macmillan Limited, London, 1970.
8. **Gallian J.A.** : Contemporary Abstract Algebra, Narosa Publishing House, New Delhi, 1999.
9. **Gallian J.A.** : Check Digit Methods, International Jour. of Applied Education,5(40), 1989, pp. 503-505.
10. **Hardy G.H.** : A Mathematician's Apology (Foreword by C.P.Snow) : Cambridge University Press, 1967
11. **Herstein I.N.** : Topics in Algebra, Wiley Eastern Limited, New Delhi, 1991.
12. **Hungerford T. W.** : Algebra, Springer, 1974.
13. **Jacobson N.** : Basic Algebra Vol. I, Hindusthan Publishing Corporation (India), New Delhi, 1994.
14. **Kanankia H., Nathamuni S. and Sarma, S.** : A UID Numbering Scheme, May 2010. (www.uidai.gov.in)
15. **Kirtland J.** : Identification Numbers and Check Digit Schemes, The Mathematical Society of America, 2001.
16. **Luthar I. S. and Passi I. B. S.** : Algebra, Vol. 1 : Groups, Vol. 2 : Rings, Narosa Publishing House, New Delhi, 1996, 1999.
17. **Maclane S. and Birkoff, G.** : Algebra, The Macmillan Company, New York, 1967.
18. **Malik D. S., Mordeson J.M. and Sen M.K.** : Fundamentals of Abstract Algebra, The McGraw-Hill Companies, Inc., 1997.
19. **Martin G.E.** : Transformation Geometry, Springer-Verlag, New York, 1982.
20. **Niven I. and Zuckerman H. S.** : Wiley Eastern Limited, New Delhi, 1989.
21. **Rotman J. J.** : The Theory of Groups: An Introduction, Allyn & Bacon Inc., Boston, 1968.
22. **Russell Bertrand** : The Principles of Mathematics, Routledge, Lond. 1903.
23. **Sepanski M.R.** : Algebra, American Mathematical Society (The Sally Series 11), [Indian Edition by Universities Press], 2013
24. **Smith D. E.** : A Source Book in Mathematics, Dover Publications, Inc. New York, 1959.
25. **Solomon Ronald** : Abstract Algebra, American Mathematical Society (The Sally Series 9), [Indian Edition by Universities Press], 2010
26. **Verhoeff J.** : Error Detecting Decimal Codes, Mathematical Centre Track, Vol.29, The Mathematical Centre, Amsterdam, 1969.

ANSWERS

Chapter 1

Exercises to Section 1.1

1.a)(i) $\{x \in \mathbb{N} \mid 1 \le x \le 10\}$ **(ii)** $\{x \in \mathbb{N} \mid 1 \le x \le 4\}$ **(iii)** $\{1, 2, 9, 10\}$ **(iv)** $\{-2, -1, 5, 6, 7, 8, 9, 10, 11\}$. **2.** $A \cup B = \{x \in \mathbb{R} \mid 1 < x \le 8\}$, $A \cap B = \{x \in \mathbb{R} \mid 3 \le x \le 5\}$, $A \smallsetminus B = \{x \in \mathbb{R} \mid 1 < x < 3\}$, $B \smallsetminus A = \{x \in \mathbb{R} \mid 5 < x \le 8\}$. **3.** Yes, $\emptyset$; any singleton set. **4.** $n(\mathcal{P}(X)) = 2^5 = 32$; $\left\{\emptyset, \{\emptyset\}, \left\{\{\emptyset\}\right\}, \left\{\emptyset, \{\emptyset\}\right\}\right\}$. **5.(i)** $\{m+1, m+2, m+3\ldots\}$ **(ii)** $\emptyset$ **(iii)** $\emptyset$; **9.** 300; **10.(a)** False [Hint : Take $A = \{1, 2, 3, 4, 5\}$, $B = \{4, 5, 6, 7\}$, $C = \{7, 8\}$] **(b)** True **(c)** False [Hint : Take the sets as in part (a).] **(d)** True.

Exercises to Section 1.2

1.(a) Antisymmetric; Transitive **(b)** Symmetric **(c)** Symmetric **(d)** Symmetric; Antisymmetric; Transitive **(e)** Reflexive; Symmetric; Antisymmetric; Transitive **(f)** Antisymmetric **(g)** Reflexive; Symmetric **2.** 1(e); corresponding partition of A is given by $\{1\}, \{2\}, \{3\}, \{4\}$. **3.** 2^6 **4.** 2^6 **5.** $\rho = \{(a, a), (b, b), (c, c), (d, d), (e, e), (b, c), (c, b), (d, e), (e, d)\}$ **7.** (i),(ii),(iv),(vi) are equivalence relations. **8.(a)** yes **(b)** yes. **9.(i)** symmetric **(ii)** reflexive, symmetric, transitive **(iii)** symmetric **(iv)** reflexive, transitive, antisymmetric. **10.** $(2, 1), (3, 2), (1, 1), (2, 2), (3, 3), (3, 1), (1, 3)$ are to be adjoined. **11.** Dom. of $\rho = \{x \in \mathbb{N} \mid 1 \le x \le 20\}$, Range of $\rho = \{y \in \mathbb{N} \mid 1 \le y \le 39$, and y is odd$\}$; **14.** Here $(1, 0), (0, i) \in \mathcal{R}$, but $(1, i) \notin \mathcal{R}$; **16.** [Hint : For symmetry, observe that $(a, b) \in \mathcal{R}$ implies $3a + 4b = 7n$; now $(3a + 4b) + (3b + 4a) = 7(a + b)$ tells that $3b + 4a$ must be $7m$ for some $m \in \mathbb{Z}^+$.] **18.(a)** True **(b)** False [Hint : Let $A = \{1, 2, 3, 4\}$, take $\rho_1 = \{(1, 2), (4, 3)\}$, $\rho_2 = \{(1, 4), (3, 1), (3, 4)\}$; then $\rho_1 \circ \rho_2 = \{(1, 3), (3, 2), (3, 3)\}$ which is not transitive.] **(c)** False [Hint : Let $A = \{1, 2, 3\}$, take $\rho = \{(2, 3), (3, 2), (2, 2)\}$] **(d)** False [Hint : Let $A = \{1, 2, 3\}$, take $\rho = \{(2, 3), (3, 2), (2, 4)\}$] **(e)** True.

Exercises to Section 1.3

1.(i) True **(ii)** False **(iii)** False **(iv)** True **(v)** True. **2.** 1 **3.** 1 **4.** 9 **5.** 7

Exercises to Section 1.4

1.(a) No **(b)** Yes, injective **(c)** Yes, surjevtive **(d)** Yes, bijective **(e)** No; **6.(a)** Bijective **(b)** Bijective **(c)** Neither injective nor surjective **(d)** Injective but not surjective **(e)** Bijective **(f)** Bijective **(g)** Neither injective nor surjective. **8.** No. Take $f(x) = 2x$; $g(x) = \frac{x}{2}$; **12.(a)** Bijective; the inverse is $g : S \to \mathbb{R}$ given by $g(x) = \frac{x}{1 - |x|}$ for all $x \in S$. **(b)** Bijective; the inverse is given by $g(x) = \frac{1}{2(1-x)}$ when $x < 0$, and $g(x) = \frac{1 + 2x}{2(1 + x)}$ when $x \ge 0$; **16.(b)** $\{5, -5\}$, $\{70\}$.

Exercises to Section 1.5

1.(a) Associative and commutative **(b)** Associative and commutative
(c) Associative and commutative **(d)** Associative, not commutative
(e) Associative, not commutative **(f)** Not associative; commutative
(g) Associative and commutative **(h)** Not associative; commutative
(i) Not associative; commutative **(j)** Associative and commutative.
2.(a) 1 **(b)** does not exist **(c)** -2 **(d)** does not exist **(e)** does not exist **(f)** does not exist **(g)** 1 **(h)** does not exist **(i)** does not exist **(j)** does not exist; **3.** 3^9, 3^6
4.   **5.**

$*$	p	q	r	s
p	q	s	q	p
q	s	p	p	r
r	q	p	s	r
s	p	r	r	q

$*$	1	2	3	4
1	1	2	3	4
2	2	1	3	4
3	3	4	3	4
4	4	3	3	4

Chapter 2

Exercises to Section 2.1

11. $\gcd(4235, 315) = 35$; $s = -2, t = 27$. **12.** $\gcd(360, 125) = 5$; $s = 8, t = -23$.

Exercises to Section 2.3

1. (b) **5.** $2, 3, 5, 7, 11, 13, 17, 19, 23, 29$. **9.** $90, 91, \ldots 96$.

Exercises to Section 2.4

1. (a) **2.(a)** $x = -99, y = -333$ **(b)** $x = 228, y = 342$ **(c)** $x = 5, y = -42$ **(d)** $x = 15, y = -5$ **(e)** $x = -9, y = 9$ **(f)** $x = -200, y = -300$ **3.(a)** $x = 5, y = 4$ **(b)** $x = 39, y = 94$ **(c)** $x = 1, y = 16$ **(d)** No positive solution; **(e)** $x = 13, y = 5$ **(f)** Not solvable. **4.** 9 Pens and 6 pencils **5.** 7 baskets of mango and 5 baskets of orange **6.** 25 A-type and 65 B-type.

Exercises to Section 2.5

1.(a) 12; **(b)** 336; **(c)** 6; **(d)** 28 ; **(e)** 16 **2.(a)** 1998; **(b)** 1900; **(c)** 2256; **(d)** 1800;

Exercises to Section 2.6

1.(a) $x \equiv (9 + 5j)(\bmod 15)$, $j = 0, 1, 2$. **(b)** $x \equiv 21(\bmod 26)$; **(c)** $x \equiv (2 + 5j)(\bmod 15)$, $j = 0, 1, 2$; **(d)** $x \equiv 3(\bmod 7)$; **(e)** $x \equiv 23(\bmod 19)$; **(f)** $x \equiv (2 + 3j)(\bmod 9)$, $j = 0, 1, 2$. **(g)** $x \equiv 32(\bmod 36)$; **2.** **(a)** 5; **(b)** does not exist; **(c)** 8; **(d)** 2. **3.(a)** $x \equiv 18(\bmod 35)$ **(b)** $x \equiv 6(\bmod 28)$ **(c)** $x \equiv 427(\bmod 660)$. **(d)** $x \equiv 206(\bmod 210)$ **(e)** $x \equiv 1226(\bmod 2145)$ **(f)** $x \equiv 68(\bmod 165)$; **4.** 838; **5.** 485; **6.** 374; **7.** 117; **8.** 67; **9.** 119; **10.(a)** 1, **(b)** 1, **(c)** 1; **11.** 3; **12.** 6; **13.** 5; **14.(a)** 7; **(b)** 1; **15.** 3; **24.** 4.

Chapter 3

Exercises to Section 3.1

1.(a) Semigroup but not group **(b)** Semigroup but not group **(c)** Semigroup as well as a

group **(d)** Semigroup as well as a group **(e)** not a semigroup **(f)** Semigroup but not group
(g) Semigroup but not group **(h)** Not a semigroup **(i)** Semigroup but not group
(j) Semigroup as well as a group **(k)** Semigroup as well as a group. **2.** Yes; [Hint : Fix some
$c \in \mathbb{R}^-$; define $a \star b = acb$ for all $a, b \in \mathbb{R}^-$.]

8.

$*$	d	a	b	c
d	d	a	b	c
a	a	c	d	b
b	b	d	c	a
c	c	b	a	d

9. **(a)** $n = 3$ **(b)** $n = 4$ **12.** $n = 4$ in U_{10}, $n = 2$ in U_{12}. **13.(a)** $o([6]) = 5$, $o([3]) = 4$. **13.(b)** 2 **18.** [Hint : $aba^{-1} = b^m$ implies $(aba^{-1})^m = b^{m^2}$, so that $ab^m a^{-1} = b^{m^2}$, whence $a^2 b a^{-2} = b^{m^2}$. Now repeat this process to get $a^5 b a^{-5} = b^{m^5}$.] **19.** [Hint : Here $a = a^{-1}$, whence $b^{49} = (b^7)^7 = (ab^4 a^{-1})^7 = ab^{28} a^{-1} = a(ab^4 a^{-1})^4 a^{-1} = a^2 b^{16} a^{-2} = b^{16}$.] **21.** [Hint : Here $(ab)^5 = a^5 b^5$ implies $(ba)^4 = a^4 b^4$ and $(ab)^3 = a^3 b^3$ implies $(ba)^2 = a^2 b^2$, whence $a^4 b^4 = (ba)^4 = (ba)^2 (ba)^2 = a^2 b^2 a^2 b^2$, so that $a^2 b^2 = b^2 a^2$. Now, $baba = (ba)^2 = a^2 b^2 = b^2 a^2 = bbaa$ gives $ab = ba$.] **22.** [Hint : Here, $a = a^{-1}$ for all $a \in G$, whence $ab = (ab)^{-1} = b^{-1} a^{-1} = ba$.] **23.** [Hint : Note that, $a(ba) = (ab)a$, whence by given condition $ba = ab$ for all $a, b \in G$.] **25.** [Hint : From definition of identity, here $x^2 = e$, whence $xx = e$ indicates $x = x^{-1}$.] **26.** 3,15,3. **27.** 6,24,12 **29.** (iii) **30.** (i) **31.** (ii) **32.** (i) **33.** (i) **34.** (ii) **35.** (iv) **36.** (i), (iii) **37.(a)** False [Hint : Take $\mathbb{Z}_n$] **(b)** True **(c)** True **(d)** True **(e)** True.

Chapter 4

Exercises to Section 4.1

1.(i) $\begin{pmatrix} 1 & 2 & 3 & 4 \\ 4 & 2 & 1 & 3 \end{pmatrix}$ **(ii)** $\begin{pmatrix} 1 & 2 & 3 & 4 \\ 2 & 3 & 1 & 4 \end{pmatrix}$ **(iii)** $\begin{pmatrix} 1 & 2 & 3 & 4 \\ 3 & 4 & 1 & 2 \end{pmatrix}$ **(iv)** $\begin{pmatrix} 1 & 2 & 3 & 4 \\ 1 & 3 & 4 & 2 \end{pmatrix}$
(v) $\begin{pmatrix} 1 & 2 & 3 & 4 \\ 2 & 3 & 4 & 1 \end{pmatrix}$ **2.** $k = 4$. **3.** $\begin{pmatrix} 1 & 2 & 3 & 4 & 5 \\ 2 & 5 & 1 & 4 & 3 \end{pmatrix}$
4.(a) $(1\,5\,4\,6)(2\,7)(3\,8)$ **(b)** $(1\,3)(4\,6\,7)(5\,8)$ **5.(a)** $(1\,2\,4)$ **(b)** $(2\,5\,4\,3)$
6.(a) $(1\,4)(1\,3)$ **(b)** $(1\,5)(3\,4)$ **(c)** $(1\,4)(1\,5)(1\,3)$ **7.(a)** odd **(b)** even **(c)** even **(d)** even
(e) odd. **8.** $e, (1\,2\,3), (1\,3\,2)$ where e is the identity permutation of S_3.
9. $e, (1\,2\,3), (1\,3\,2), (1\,2\,4), (1\,4\,2), (1\,3\,4), (1\,4\,3), (2\,3\,4), (2\,4\,3), (1\,2)(3\,4), (1\,4)(2\,3), (1\,3)(2\,4)$
where e is the identity permutation of S_4. **10.** $\beta = (1\,3\,6\,2\,4\,5\,7)$ **11.** $\beta^{99} = (1\,3\,2\,5\,4)$
12. $n = 16$ **13.** $p = (1\,2\,3) = q$. **14.** $(1\,4)(2\,5)(3\,6)$ **15.** (iv) **16.** (iv) **17.** (iv) **18.** (iii) **19.** (iv)
20. (i),(ii),(iii),(iv).

Chapter 5

Exercises to Section 5.1

1.(a) yes **(b)** no **(c)** no **(d)** yes **(e)** no **(f)** yes. **2.(a)** yes **(b)** yes **(c)** no **(d)** yes **3.(a)** yes
(b) yes **(c)** no **(d)** yes **(e)** no **(f)** yes. **18.** $2\mathbb{Z}$ **19.** $\mathbb{Z}$ **20.(c)** Consider $G = (\mathbb{Z}, +)$ and $H = \{n \in \mathbb{Z} \,|\, n \geq 1\}$. **24.** **(a)** False [Hint : Take $H = \{1, -1\}$] **(b)** True **(c)** False [Hint : Consider

$G = S_3$ and $H = \{e, (1\,2), (1\,3)\}](\mathbf{d})$ True. **25.** (ii).

Exercises to Section 5.2

1. All non-identity elements **3.** Yes; $[1], [3], [7], [9]$ are the generators. $\{[0]\}, \{[0], [5]\}$,
$\{[0], [2], [4], [6], [8]\}$ and $\mathbb{Z}_{10}$ are the only subgroups of $\mathbb{Z}_{10}$. **7.(i)** $\{e, a^4, a^8, a^{12}, a^{16}\}$ **(ii)** G.
8. 2 and 6 [Hint: As 6 divides 42, so there is a unique cyclic subgroup, say $H = \langle a \rangle$, of order 6
in G. Hence any element of order 6 belongs to H. As $\gcd(k, 6) = 1$ holds only for $k = 1, 5$, so
$o(a) = 6$ and $o(a^5) = 6$. Hence H has only 2 elements of order 6. This implies that the group
has only two elements of order 6. Other part is similar.]

10.

*	e	a	b	c	d
e	e	a	b	c	d
a	a	d	e	b	c
b	b	e	c	d	a
c	c	b	d	a	e
d	d	c	a	e	b

11. (a) False **(b)** True **(c)** False **(d)** True **12.** (iii) **13.** (ii) **14.** (i) **15.** (ii) **16.** (iv)

Exercises to Section 5.3

1. Let S be the set of all left cosets of H in G. **(a)** $S = \{\{x, -x\} \mid x \in \mathbb{R}^+\}$ **(b)** $S = \{\{7n \mid n \in \mathbb{Z}\}, \{7n+1 \mid n \in \mathbb{Z}\}, \{7n+2 \mid n \in \mathbb{Z}\}, \{7n+3 \mid n \in \mathbb{Z}\}, \{7n+4 \mid n \in \mathbb{Z}\}, \{7n+5 \mid n \in \mathbb{Z}\}, \{7n+6 \mid n \in \mathbb{Z}\}\}$ **(c)** $S = \{H, \{(1\,2), (1\,2\,3)\}, \{(1\,3), (1, 3, 2)\}\}$ **(d)** $S = \{H, \{(1\,2), (2\,3)\}, (1\,3)\}\}$ **2.** $(2 + 3i)H = \{z \in \mathbb{C}^* \mid |z| = \sqrt{13}\}$. **7.(i)** no **(ii)** no. **11.** $G = S_3; H = \{e, (1\,2)\}$;
let $a = (1\,2\,3)$ and $b = (1\,3)$. **13.** Let $K_4 = \{e, a, b, c\}$; then $\{e\}, \{e, a\}, \{e, b\}, \{e, c\}, K_4$ are
the only subgroups of it. **15.** [Hint: Let $a \in G$ such that $a \neq e$. Then $o(a)$ is either 2 or 4.
If $o(a) = 4$ then $G = \langle a \rangle$ and hence G is commutative. Suppose that no element of G is
of order 4. Then every nonidenty element is of order 2. If $o(a) = 2$ then $a = a^{-1} \forall a \in G$,
so G must be commutative.] **20.** $|G| = 315$ **23.** [Hint : For $a \neq e$ in G, $|\langle a \rangle| = 2, 5, 10$.
Here, $|\langle a \rangle| \neq 10$, as otherwise G is cyclic and hence commutative; $o(a) = 2$ for all $a \in G$ is not
possible, as G is non commutative, so there exists some $a \in G$ such that $o(a) = 5$.] **24.** 49 [Hint
: $7 \mid |G|$, so $|G| = 7k$. As G is cyclic, so G must have a subgroup of order k, a contradiction
to the given condition, except when $k = 7$.] **25.(a)** False [Hint : In S_3, take $H = \{e, (2\,3)\}$
and $a = (1\,2)](\mathbf{b})$ False [Hint : 16 does not divide 50] **(c)** False [Hint : Justify that the index
is 7.] **(d)** True [Hint : If H, K are different subgroups of order 7, then as $|H \cap K|$ must divide
$|H| = |K| = 7$, so $|H \cap K| = 1$ whence, $|HK| = 7 \cdot 7$ [by Theorem 5.3.15] $= 49$, which contradicts
$HK \subseteq G$.] **(e)** True **(f)** False [Hint : Take primes $p \neq q$; then $\frac{1}{p} + \mathbb{Z} \neq \frac{1}{q} + \mathbb{Z}$;] **(g)** True **(h)** True.
26. (i) **27.** (iv) **28.** (iii) **29.** (iii)

Exercises to Section 5.4

7. $K = \{e, (1\,2)(3, 4), (1\,3)(2\,4), (1\,4)(2\,3)\}$, $H = \{e, (1\,2)(3\,4)\}$. **14.** $o(a^3 H) = 4$ **15.** yes.
16. 2 **25.(a)** [Hint: Suppose for some $g \in G$, gK is of order n . Then $(gK)^n = K$ i.e.,
$g^n \in K$. Let $o(g) = t$ so that $g^t K = K$ i.e., $(gK)^t = K$. So $n \mid t$, whence $t = nn_1$ (say). Now
$o(g^{n_1}) = \frac{o(g)}{\gcd(t, n_1)} = \frac{t}{n_1} = n$.] **(b)** [Hint: Since $o(x) = 4$, so $\langle x \rangle = \{e, x, x^2, x^3\}$. Index of $\langle x \rangle$

in G is 2 (as $|G| = 8$), whence $\langle x \rangle$ is normal in G. So, for any $g \in G$, $gx^2g^{-1} \in \langle x \rangle$. Clearly, $o(gx^2g^{-1}) = o(x^2) = 2$. Then $gx^2g^{-1} = x^2$, as x^2 is the only element of order 2 in $\langle x \rangle$. Hence $gx^2 = x^2g$ for all $g \in G$.] **30.** (ii). **31.** (iii) **32.** (i) **33.** (ii) **34.** (i). **35.** (i). **36.** (iii). **37.** (ii).

Chapter 6

Exercises to Section 6.1

1.(a) yes, $\ker f = \{1\}$ (b) yes, $\ker f = \{0\}$ (c) yes, $\ker f = \{1, -1\}$ (d) no (e) yes, $\ker f = \{1\}$ (f) no (g) yes, $\ker f = \{a \in \mathbb{R}^* \,|\, a > 0\}$. **4.** The functions f and g given by $f(n) = n$ for all $n \in \mathbb{Z}$ and $g(n) = -n$ for all $n \in \mathbb{Z}$ are the only epimorphisms. **5.** The functions f and g given by $f(n) = [n]$ for all $n \in \mathbb{Z}$ and $g(n) = [5n]$ for all $n \in \mathbb{Z}$ are the only epimorphisms. **6.** The functions f and g given by $f([n]) = [0]$ for all $[n] \in \mathbb{Z}_6$ and $g([n]) = [2n]$ for all $[n] \in \mathbb{Z}_6$ are the only two homomorphisms. **16.** $\ker f = \{e_G\} \times H$ where e_G denote the identity in G. **18** Suppose G has finite number of subgroups. If there is an element $a \in G$ of infinite order, then the cyclic subgroup $\langle a \rangle$ must be infinite and hence isomorphic to $(\mathbb{Z}, +)$, which has infinitely many subgroups $(n\mathbb{Z}, +)$, a contradiction. So all elements of G are of finite order, whence respective cyclic subgroups generated by each of them must be finite and finite union of finite sets must be finite, whence $|G|$ becomes finite. **19** [Hint: $f(\frac{p}{q}) = f(p \cdot \frac{1}{q}) = f(p)f(\frac{1}{q}) = g(p)f(\frac{1}{q}) = g(p)g(\frac{1}{q})g(q)f(\frac{1}{q}) = g(p)g(\frac{1}{q})f(q)f(\frac{1}{q}) = g(\frac{p}{q})$] **20.**(a) False (b) True (c) True (d) True (e) False [Hint : $(\mathbb{Z}, +)$ is cyclic but $(\mathbb{Q}, +)$ is noncyclic] (f) False [Hint : 30 does not divide 100] (g) False [Hint : As $\mathbb{Z}$ is cyclic but $\mathbb{R}$ is not.] (h) True [Hint: Suppose $\exists f$ (epimorphism). Then for $1 \in \mathbb{Z}$, $\exists x(\neq 0) \in \mathbb{Q}$ s.t. $f(x) = 1$, whence $f(\frac{x}{2} + \frac{x}{2}) = 2f(\frac{x}{2}) = 1$ gives a contradiction, as $f(\frac{x}{2}) \in \mathbb{Z}$.] (i) True [Hint : Suppose $\exists f$ (homomorphism) and let $f(1) = m$. Then for any +ve integer n in $\mathbb{Q}$, we have $f(\frac{1}{n} + \frac{1}{n} + \ldots + \frac{1}{n})$ [n-fold sum] $= m$, i.e., $nf(\frac{1}{n}) = m$, whence $n | m \,\forall n$ indicates $m = 0$, so that $f(1) = 0$. Now, for any $q \neq 0$, $f(1) = f(\frac{q}{q}) = qf(\frac{1}{q}) = 0$ shows $f(\frac{1}{q}) = 0$. Hence etc.] (j) False. [Hint : Take $f : (\mathbb{Z}, +) \to (\mathbb{Z}_6, +)$ by $f(n) = [n]$ and $g : (\mathbb{Z}, +) \to (\mathbb{Z}_6, +)$ by $g(n) = [5n]$]. (k) True **21.** (iii) **22.** (iv). [Hint: The number of group homomorphisms $f : \mathbb{Z}_n \to \mathbb{Z}_m$, $f(x) = ax$ is $d = \gcd(m, n)$ where $a = \frac{m}{d}k$, and $k = 0, 1, 2, \ldots d-1$.]

Exercises to Section 6.2

6. Hint : Take the mapping $f : \mathbb{R} \to T$ defined by $f(a) = e^{2a\pi i}$ **8.** Subgroups of $\mathbb{Z}/8\mathbb{Z}$ are $\mathbb{Z}/8\mathbb{Z}$, $2\mathbb{Z}/8\mathbb{Z}$, $4\mathbb{Z}/8\mathbb{Z}$, $8\mathbb{Z}/8\mathbb{Z}$; Subgroups of $\mathbb{Z}/24\mathbb{Z}$ are $\mathbb{Z}/24\mathbb{Z}$, $2\mathbb{Z}/24\mathbb{Z}$, $3\mathbb{Z}/24\mathbb{Z}$, $4\mathbb{Z}/24\mathbb{Z}$, $6\mathbb{Z}/24\mathbb{Z}$, $8\mathbb{Z}/24\mathbb{Z}$ $12\mathbb{Z}/24\mathbb{Z}$, $24\mathbb{Z}/24\mathbb{Z}$, **11.**(a) False [Hint : There are only 4 subgroups of $\mathbb{Z}_6$, to play the role of kernel of epimorphisms from $\mathbb{Z}_6$.](b) True (c) True (d) False (e) True (f) False [Hint : As otherwise, $|\ker f| = \frac{24}{5}$ – impossible.] **12.** (iii) **13.** (ii) **14.** (ii) **15.** (i),(iii).

Chapter 7

Exercises to Section 7.1

11. 24 **12.** $\{[0]_7\} \times \mathbb{Z}_{14}, \mathbb{Z}_7 \times \{[7]_{14}\}$ **13.** $\ker f = \{(n, n) \in \mathbb{Z} \times \mathbb{Z}\}$ **16.**(a) False [Hint : $\mathbb{Z}$ is cyclic, whereas $\mathbb{Z} \times \mathbb{Z}$ is not.] (b) False [Hint : $\{1\}$ and $\{1, -1\}$ are the only finite subgroups of $\mathbb{R}^*$ whereas there are five finite subgroups of $\mathbb{R}^* \times \mathbb{R}^*$](c) True (d) True (e) True (f) False [Hint : $\mathbb{Z}_{24}$ is cyclic, whereas $\mathbb{Z}_6 \times \mathbb{Z}_4$ is not.] (g) True 17. (ii) 18. (i) 19. (i),(iv) 20. (iv). [Hint : Consider $G = S_3 \times S_3$ and $H = \{e, (1\,2)\} \times \{e, (1\,2)\}$. Note that $Z(G) = \{(e, e)\}$.]

Chapter 9

Exercises to Section 9.1

1. G has an element of order 7 and an element b of order 5. Since G is commutative, hence $ab = ba$ and $o(ab) = 35$. 3. G has an element of order 5 and hence $\langle a \rangle$ is a cyclic group of order 5. 5. $G \simeq \mathbb{Z}_5 \times \mathbb{Z}_3 \simeq \mathbb{Z}_{15}$. 7. $G \simeq \mathbb{Z}_p \times \mathbb{Z}_q \simeq \mathbb{Z}_{pq}$, when p, q are distinct. $\mathbb{Z}_2 \times \mathbb{Z}_2$ is not cyclic.

9.

$$
\begin{aligned}
50 &= 2 \cdot 5^2 && \mathbb{Z}_2 \oplus \mathbb{Z}_{5^2},\ \mathbb{Z}_2 \oplus \mathbb{Z}_5 \oplus \mathbb{Z}_5 \\
80 &= 2^4 \cdot 5 && \mathbb{Z}_{2^4} \oplus \mathbb{Z}_5,\ \mathbb{Z}_2 \oplus \mathbb{Z}_{2^3} \oplus \mathbb{Z}_5,\ \mathbb{Z}_2 \oplus \mathbb{Z}_2 \oplus \mathbb{Z}_{2^2} \oplus \mathbb{Z}_5 \\
& && \mathbb{Z}_2 \oplus \mathbb{Z}_2 \oplus \mathbb{Z}_2 \oplus \mathbb{Z}_2 \oplus \mathbb{Z}_5,\ \mathbb{Z}_{2^2} \oplus \mathbb{Z}_{2^2} \oplus \mathbb{Z}_5 \\
100 &= 2^2 \cdot 5^2 && \mathbb{Z}_{2^2} \oplus \mathbb{Z}_{5^2},\ \mathbb{Z}_2 \oplus \mathbb{Z}_2 \oplus \mathbb{Z}_{5^2},\ \mathbb{Z}_{2^2} \oplus \mathbb{Z}_5 \oplus \mathbb{Z}_5 \\
& && \mathbb{Z}_2 \oplus \mathbb{Z}_2 \oplus \mathbb{Z}_5 \oplus \mathbb{Z}_5 \\
200 &= 2^3 \cdot 5^2 && \mathbb{Z}_{2^3} \oplus \mathbb{Z}_{5^2},\ \mathbb{Z}_{2^3} \oplus \mathbb{Z}_5 \oplus \mathbb{Z}_5,\ \mathbb{Z}_2 \oplus \mathbb{Z}_{2^2} \oplus \mathbb{Z}_{5^2} \\
& && \mathbb{Z}_2 \oplus \mathbb{Z}_{2^2} \oplus \mathbb{Z}_5 \oplus \mathbb{Z}_5,\ \mathbb{Z}_2 \oplus \mathbb{Z}_2 \oplus \mathbb{Z}_2 \oplus \mathbb{Z}_{5^2},\ \mathbb{Z}_2 \oplus \mathbb{Z}_2 \oplus \mathbb{Z}_2 \oplus \mathbb{Z}_5 \oplus \mathbb{Z}_5
\end{aligned}
$$

13. $\mathbb{Z}_{p^2} \oplus \mathbb{Z}_{q^3}$, $\mathbb{Z}_p \oplus \mathbb{Z}_p \oplus \mathbb{Z}_{q^3}$, $\mathbb{Z}_{p^2} \oplus \mathbb{Z}_q \oplus \mathbb{Z}_{q^2}$, $\mathbb{Z}_p \oplus \mathbb{Z}_p \oplus \mathbb{Z}_q \oplus \mathbb{Z}_{q^2}$, $\mathbb{Z}_{p^2} \oplus \mathbb{Z}_q \oplus \mathbb{Z}_q \oplus \mathbb{Z}_q$, $\mathbb{Z}_p \oplus \mathbb{Z}_p \oplus \mathbb{Z}_q \oplus \mathbb{Z}_q \oplus \mathbb{Z}_q$.

14. $\mathbb{Z}_{2^2} \oplus \mathbb{Z}_{2^2} \oplus \mathbb{Z}_{3^2}$, $\mathbb{Z}_{2^2} \oplus \mathbb{Z}_{2^2} \oplus \mathbb{Z}_3 \oplus \mathbb{Z}_3$, $\mathbb{Z}_2 \oplus \mathbb{Z}_2 \oplus \mathbb{Z}_{2^2} \oplus \mathbb{Z}_{3^2}$, $\mathbb{Z}_2 \oplus \mathbb{Z}_2 \oplus \mathbb{Z}_{2^2} \oplus \mathbb{Z}_3 \oplus \mathbb{Z}_3$.

15. (ii) and (iii) are correct statements. [Hint: (i) $G = \mathbb{Z}_2 \times \mathbb{Z}_2 \times \mathbb{Z}_2$. Here 4 divides $|G|$, but G has no cyclic subgroup of order 4. (ii) Since G is a finite Abelian group and 6 divides $|G|$, G has a subgroup of order 6. Any group of order 6 must either be S_3 or $\mathbb{Z}_6$. G is Abelian. Hence $\mathbb{Z}_6$ is the subgroup. (iii) Abelian group G of order $77 = 7 \cdot 11$ is cyclic. Hence $G \simeq \mathbb{Z}_{77}$. (iv) Since $12 = 2^2 \cdot 3$, there are 2 Abelian groups, $\mathbb{Z}_{2^2} \oplus \mathbb{Z}_3, \mathbb{Z}_2 \oplus \mathbb{Z}_2 \oplus \mathbb{Z}_3$, of order 12. These groups are nonisomorphic.] 16. (ii) is correct. [Hint: $72 = 2^3 \cdot 3^2$] 17. (ii) 18. (iii) 19. (iv).

Chapter 10

Exercises to Section 10.1

1. $O_1 = O_2 = O_3 = \{1, 2, 3\}$. 2. $O_1 = O_2 = O_3 = \{1, 2, 3\}, O_4 = O_5 = \{4, 5\}$ 11. (i) and (ii) are correct.

Exercises to Section 10.2

6. $cl(a) = \{a, a^3\}$, 7. (i) $8 = 1+1+1+1+1+1+1+1$; (ii) $8 = 2+2+2+2$; (iii) $12 - 1 \mid 3 \mid 4 \mid 4$; (iv) $60 = 1+20+12+12+15$; (v) $120 = 1+10+20+20+30+24+15$. 9. $\{e\}, A_5, S_5$. 14 [Hint: If G is a commutative group, then $G = Z(G)$ and therefore for all $x \in G$ we have $x^p \in G = Z(G)$. If G is a noncommutative group of p^3, where p is prime, then by Exercise 13 [of Section 10.2] we find that $|Z(G)| = p$. Now we consider the quotient group $G/Z(G)$ of order p^2. Since G is noncommutative, it follows that $G/Z(G)$ is noncyclic. So $G/Z(G)$ contains no element of order p^2. Hence every nonidentity element of $G/Z(G)$ is of order p. Therefore, $(xZ(G))^p = Z(G)$ for all $x \in G$. This implies $x^p Z(G) = Z(G)$, i.e., $x^p \in Z(G)$ for all $x \in G$.] 17. (i), (iii), (iv) 18. (iii), (iv).

Exercises to Section 10.3

1. $\langle(1\,2\,3\,4\,5)\rangle, \langle(1\,2\,3\,5\,4)\rangle, \langle(1\,2\,4\,3\,5)\rangle, \langle(1\,2\,4\,5\,3)\rangle, \langle(1\,2\,5\,3\,4)\rangle, \langle(1\,2\,5\,4\,3)\rangle$;

2. $\{e, (1\,2)(3\,4), (1\,3)(2\,4), (1\,4)(2\,3)\}$. **6.** $\mathbb{Z}_{65}$ **8.** 1. **12.** [Hint: $100 = 2^2 \cdot 5^2$. The unique Sylow 2-subgroup A (of order 2^2) must be normal. Number of Sylow 5-subgroups is $n_5 = 5k + 1$, where $n_5 | 100$, whence clearly $n_5 = 1$, so that the unique Sylow 5-subgroup B of order 5^2 is also normal. Here $|AB| = \frac{|A||B|}{|A\cap B|} = 100$, shows that $G = AB$, $A \cap B = \{e\}$, whence $G \simeq A \times B$ (external direct product). $|A| = 2^2$, $|B| = 5^2$, both the orders being square of primes, A, B are commutative, whence their external direct product G is also so.] **13.** $\mathbb{Z}_{26}, D_{13}$. **14.** [Hint: $|G| = 63 = 3^2 \cdot 7$, $\gcd(3,7) = 1$. Here the unique subgroup A of order 9 must be the Sylow 3-subgroup, which is normal in G and commutative, as the order is square of a prime. Number of Sylow 7-subgroups is $n_7 = 7k + 1$, where $n_7 | 63$, whence clearly $n_7 = 1$, so that the unique Sylow 7-subgroup B of order 7 is also normal and commutative. Hence $G \simeq A \times B$. Hence etc.] **20.** (i), (iv) **21.** (iii), (iv) **22.** (i) True. (ii) False [Consider S_3; $|S_3| = 6$, and 2 is a prime divisor of 6 but S_3 has no normal subgroup of order 2.] (iii) False. [In $\mathbb{Z}_{76}$ take [4] and [8].] (iv) True [$\mathbb{Z}_5$ and D_5.] (v) True [$ab = b^{-1}(ba)b$.] (vi) True. [Hint: $99 = 3^2 \cdot 11$; Use Sylow theorems to show that $G = H \times K$, where $|H| = 3^2$ and $|K| = 11$, both being commutative.] **23.** (iii) **24.** (ii) **25.** (i) **26.** (iii) **27.** (i) [Hint : D_{61} and $\mathbb{Z}_{122}$.]

Chapter 11

Exercises to Section 11.1

13.(i) False [Hint: take S_3] **(ii)** False [Hint ; $\mathbb{Z}_{60}$ is not simple] **(iii)** False [Hint : A_4 is not simple]. **(iv)** False **(v)** False **(vi)** False **(vii)** False **(viii)** True **(ix)** True. **14.** (iv) **15.** (ii) **16.** (iii) **17.** (iii) **18.** (iii) **19.** (ii) **20.** (ii), (iii), (iv).

Chapter 12

Exercises to Section 12.1

1. (iii) **3.** yes, 2 is the identity.

4.

$\cdot$	a	b	c	d
a	a	a	a	a
b	a	b	a	b
c	a	a	c	c
d	a	b	c	d

yes, commutative; yes, d is the identity.

5. (i), (ii), (iii), (v). **10.** $M_2(R), +, \cdot)$. Take $A = \begin{bmatrix} 0 & 1 \\ 0 & 0 \end{bmatrix}$ $B = \begin{bmatrix} 1 & 0 \\ 0 & 0 \end{bmatrix}$. **12.** [Hint: Note that, $(c+c)(a+b) = c(a+b) + c(a+b) = ca + cb + ca + cb$; also $(c+c)(a+b) = (c+c)a + (c+c)b = ca + ca + cb + cb$. Clearly, $ca + cb + ca + cb = ca + ca + cb + cb$, i.e., $cb + ca = ca + cb$, i.e., $c(b + a) = c(a + b)$. Now apply left cancellation.] **19.** $[0], [1], [3], [4]$ in $\mathbb{Z}_6$; $[0], [1]$ in $\mathbb{Z}_8$; $[0], [1], [4], [9]$ in $\mathbb{Z}_{12}$; **20.** n is square-free. **21.** $n = p^m$ where p is a prime number and $m \in \mathbb{N}$; **23.(iii)** [Hint: Here $a^2 = a^3b + a^2ba = ab + aaba = ab + a(1_R - ba)a$ so that $a^2 = ab + a^2 - aba^2$, whence $ab(1_R - a^2) = 0$. Again, similarly $a^2 = aba^2 + ba^3$ leads to $(1_R - a^2)ba = 0$. Adding we get $ab(1_R - a^2) + (1_R - a^2)ba = 0$, which on simplification becomes $(ab + ba) - a(ab + ba)a = 0$ i.e., $a^2 = 1_R$.] **24.(a) (i)** $\{[1], [2], \ldots, [6]\}$ **(ii)** $\{[1], [5], [7], [11]\}$ **(iii)** $\{[a] \in \mathbb{Z}_n \,|\, gcd(a, n) = 1\}$. **(b)** [Hint: Let $A = \begin{bmatrix} a & b \\ c & d \end{bmatrix} \in M_2(\mathbb{Z})$ be a unit. Then $|A| \neq 0$ and $A^{-1} = \frac{1}{|A|} \begin{bmatrix} d & -b \\ -c & a \end{bmatrix} \in M_2(\mathbb{Z})$ if and only if $|A| = \pm 1$.] **(c)** [Hint: $f(x)$ is a unit in $\mathbb{Z}[x] \iff \exists g(x)$ in $\mathbb{Z}[x]$, such that $f(x)g(x) = 1 \iff \deg(f(x)g(x)) = \deg 1 = 0 \iff \deg f(x) + \deg g(x) = 0 \iff \deg f(x) = \deg g(x) = 0 \iff f(x)$ and $g(x)$ are constant polynomials, say, $f(x) = a_0$ and $g(x) = b_0$, for some $a_0, b_0 \in \mathbb{Z} \iff a_0 b_0 = 1$ in $\mathbb{Z} \iff a_0$ is a unit in $\mathbb{Z} \iff f(x)$ is a unit in $\mathbb{Z}$.] **26.(a)** [Hint : Let $R = \{a_1, a_2, \ldots, a_n\}$. Let $b \in R$. Then $ba_i \in R$ and $ba_i \neq ba_j$ for $i \neq j$. Indeed, otherwise $a_i = a(ba_i) = a(ba_j) = a_j$ shows a contradiction. Hence there exists $a_t \in R$ such that $ba_t = 1_R \in R$, whence $a(ba_t) = a \implies a_t = a$ so that $ba = ba_t = 1_R$.] **(b)** [Hint: Here, $a(ba - 1_R + b) = aba - a1_R + ab = 1_R a - a1_R + ab = a - a + ab = 1_R$. So by given uniqueness, $ba - 1_R + b = b$, i.e., $ba = 1_R$.] **(c)** [Hint: Here the group $(R, +)$ is of prime order and hence cyclic, say $R = \langle a \rangle$. Then for any $x, y \in R$, $x = na, y = ma$ for some $n, m \in \mathbb{Z}$. So, $xy = na \cdot ma = ma \cdot na$ [both being sum of mn number of a^2] $= yx$.] **30.** No, in $(M_2(R), +, \cdot)$ take $A = \begin{bmatrix} 0 & 1 \\ 1 & 0 \end{bmatrix}$ $B = \begin{bmatrix} 0 & -1 \\ 0 & 0 \end{bmatrix}$. **34.(i)** False [Hint : consider $\mathbb{Z}$] **(ii)** False [Hint: Consider $[1]$ and $[4]$ in the ring $\mathbb{Z}_{12}$]; **(iii)** False [Hint: In $M_2(R), +, \cdot)$ take $A = \begin{bmatrix} 5 & 10 \\ -2 & -4 \end{bmatrix}$ $B = \begin{bmatrix} 7 & -3 \\ 14 & -6 \end{bmatrix}$. **(iv)** False [Hint: In the ring $\mathbb{R} \times \mathbb{R}$ take $a = (1, 0)$, $b - (0, 1)$.] **(v)** False [Hint: Take the subring $\{[0], [2], [4], [6]\}$ in the ring $\mathbb{Z}_8$.] **(vi)** False [Hint: $M_2(F)$ where F is a finite field.] **(vii)** True. **35.** (iv). **36.** (ii) **37.** (iii) **38.** (iii) **39.** (ii) **40.** (iii) **41.** (iii) **42.** (ii).

Exercises to Section 12.2

1. none in $\mathbb{Z}_5$; $[2], [3], [4]$ in $\mathbb{Z}_6$; $[2], [4], [6]$ in $\mathbb{Z}_8$. **2.** $\{[a] \,|\, 1 < a < n, \ gcd(a, n) > 1\}$. **3.** $(\{[0]_5\} \times \mathbb{Z}_{10}) \cup (\mathbb{Z}_5 \times \{[0]_{10}\}) \setminus \{([0]_5, [0]_{10})\}$ in $\mathbb{Z}_5 \times \mathbb{Z}_{10}$ and $(\{[0]_4\} \times \mathbb{Z}_6) \cup (\mathbb{Z}_4 \times \{[0]_6\}) \cup (\{([2]_4, [2]_6), ([2]_4, [3]_6), ([2]_4, [4]_6)\}) \setminus \{([0]_4, [0]_6)\}$ in $\mathbb{Z}_4 \times \mathbb{Z}_6$. **4.** $(\{[0]_m\} \times \mathbb{Z}_n) \cup (\mathbb{Z}_m \times \{[0]_n\}) \cup (\{([a]_m, [b]_n) \,|\, 1 < a < m, 1 < b < n, gcd(a, m) > 1, gcd(b, n) > 1\}) \setminus \{([0]_m, [0]_n)\}$ in $\mathbb{Z}_m \times \mathbb{Z}_n$. **5.** every nonzero nonunit element. **6.** No. **8.(a)** $\mathbb{Z}_3 \times \mathbb{Z}_3$ (char. 3) **(b)** $2\mathbb{Z}$ **(c)** $\mathbb{Z}_p[x]$, where p is prime. **9.** [Hint: Let $a, b \in R$ with $a \neq 0$, $b \neq 0$. We assert that R has no zero divisor, i.e., $ab \neq 0$. Indeed, from given condition, for $a \neq 0, \exists e \in R$, such that $ae = a \ldots (i)$. [Clearly, here $e \neq 0$ as well, as otherwise a becomes 0.] Again, for $b \neq 0$ and $e \in R$, $\exists c \in R$ such that $bc = e \ldots (ii)$. Now, if $ab = 0$, then it implies $abc = 0c = 0 \implies ae = 0$ [by (ii)], i.e., $a = 0$ [by (i)], $-$ a contradiction. So, R has no zero divisor. Now, from (i), $ae = a \implies ae^2 = ae \implies a(e^2 - e) = 0$, whence $e^2 = e$ as $a \neq 0$. So, for any $b \in R$, $be^2 = be$ gives $be = b$, as $e \neq 0$; i.e., e is a right identity, whence (ii) justifies the existence of right inverse.] **10.** [Hint: Here e is also left identity, i.e., $ea - a = 0$. Indeed, otherwise, if $ea - a \neq 0$, then there exists $x \in R$ such that $x(ea - a) = e$, i.e., $xea - xa = e$, i.e., $xa - xa = e$ [since $xe = x$], i.e., $0 = e$, $-$ a contradiction. Now let $a \neq 0$, but $ab = 0$ for some $b \in R$. Then $xab = 0$ implies $eb = 0$ [as $xa = e$], i.e., $b = 0$ [as $eb = b$]. Hence R is free from divisor of zero. Now, for $a \neq 0$, $(e - ax)a = ea - axa = a - ae = a - a = 0$, whence $e - ax = 0$, i.e., $ax = e$, i.e., x is also right inverse of a. Hence R is a division ring.] **11(a)** [Hint: Let $R = \{a_1, a_2, \ldots, a_n\}$. Suppose

$0 \neq a \in R$ and $aR = \{aa_1, aa_2, \ldots, aa_n\}$. As R is free from zero divisor, clearly $aa_i \neq aa_j$ for $a_i \neq a_j$, whence $|aR| = n$ gives that $aR = R$. Hence $a \in R = aR$ gives that $a = aa_{i_0}$, for some $a_{i_0} \in R$. For any $x \in R = aR$, we have $x = aa_k$, for some $a_k \in R$. Now, $xa_{i_0} = (aa_k)a_{i_0} = a(a_k a_{i_0}) = a(a_{i_0} a_k) = (aa_{i_0})a_k = aa_k = x$ shows by commutativity of R that a_{i_0} is the identity of R, say e. Now, $e \in R = aR$ means there exists $a_i \in R$ such that $e = aa_i$, whence every $a \neq 0$ in R is unit.] **11(b)** [Hint: $(ab)^2 = ab^2 + bab - b^2$, i.e., $abab = ab^2 + bab - b^2 = (ab + ba - b)b$, i.e., $aba = (ab + ba - b)$, i.e., $abab^{-1} = a + bab^{-1} - 1$, which simplifies to $(a-1)(bab^{-1} - 1) = 0$. As F does not have divisors of zero, so either $a - 1 = 0$ or $bab^{-1} - 1 = 0$, both of which yield $a = 1$.] **12.** [Hint: If possible, let $f : F \to F^*$ be an isomorphism. Clearly F cannot be finite, as $|F| \neq |F^*|$. Let char$F$=2, so that $2a = 0 \, \forall a \in F$. Since f is isomorphism and $\forall a \neq 0$ in $(F, +)$, $o(a) = 2$, so it must be the same in $(F^*, \cdot)$, whence $a^2 = 1 \forall a \in F^*$. But this gives $a = \pm 1 = 1$, (as $1 = -1$ in F), whence $F^* = \{1\}$, so that $F = \{0, 1\}$, a contradiction. Now suppose, char$F \neq 2$. Clearly $f(0) = 1$ and there must exist some $p \in F$, such that $f(p) = -1$. Hence, $(f(p))^2 = 1 \implies f(p + p) = f(0)$, i.e., $p + p = 0$. As f is bijective, $p \neq 0$, so $p^{-1} \in F$, whence $p^{-1}(p + p) = 0 \implies 1 + 1 = 0$, a contradiction.] **16.** [Hint: Let $ch(R) = n$. If $n = 0$ we are done. Suppose $n \neq 0$. Let $na = 0$ for some $0 \neq a \in R$. If n is not prime, say $n = pq$, $1 < p, q < n$. Now, $(pa)(qa) = pqa^2 = na^2 = (na)a = 0$, whence either $pa = 0$ or $qa = 0$. Let $pa = 0$. Then $pb = 0$ for all $b \in R$. Indeed, $pab = 0b = 0$ for all $b \in R$ implies that the p-fold sum $ab + ab + \ldots + ab = 0$ i.e., $a(b + b + \ldots + b) = 0$ i.e., $a(pb) = 0$. Hence $pb = 0$ for all $b \in R$, a contradiction to the choice of n.] **19.** [Hint: The unity of the ring $\mathcal{P}(S)$ is S and the zero element is ϕ. If $A \in \mathcal{P}(S)$ is a unit, then for some $B \in \mathcal{P}(S)$, $A \cap B = S$ indicates $A = B = S$. Again if $A \in \mathcal{P}(S)$ be a zero divisor, then for some $B \in \mathcal{P}(S)$ we must have $A \cap B = \phi$. Since $A \cap (S \setminus A) = \phi$ for all $A \in \mathcal{P}(S)$ so every element of $\mathcal{P}(S)$ other than ϕ and S are zero divisors. Since a field must be free from zero divisors, so $\mathcal{P}(S)$ is a field only when S does not have a proper subset i.e., S is singleton.] **20.(i)** True **(ii)** False **(iii)** True. **21** (i), (iv). **22** (i), (iii). **23** (iii).

Exercises to Section 12.3

1. (ii) **2.** (i), (ii), (iv) **3.** no **4.** (i), (iii) (iv) (v) **6.** $\mathbb{N}_0$ **8.** $8\mathbb{Z}$ **9.** $n\mathbb{Z}$, $n \geq 0$ **10.** $\{[0]\}$, $\{[0], [5]\}$, $\{[0], [2], [4], [6], [8]\}$ and $\mathbb{Z}_{10}$. **11.** $\{m + n3^{\frac{1}{3}} + k3^{\frac{2}{3}} \mid m, n, k \in \mathbb{Z}\}$ **13.** $\{O_n, \alpha I_n\}$ where $\alpha \in \mathbb{R}$. **14.** [Hint : Let $a^2 = a$; check that $(aba - ba)^2 = 0$ and $(aba - ab)^2 = 0$, whence $aba - ba = 0$ and $aba - ab = 0$ together imply $ba = ab(= aba)$.] **15.** [Hint : Let $a, b \in R$. Then $a^2 - a, b^2 - b$, $(a + b)^2 - (a + b) \in C(R)$, whence $a^2 + ba + ab + b^2 - a - b = (a^2 - a) + (b^2 - b) + ab + ba \in C(R)$ implies $ab + ba \in C(R)$. Now $a(ab + ba) = (ab + ba)a$ shows $a^2b = ba^2$. Again, $(a^2 - a)b = b(a^2 - a)$, whence $a^2b - ab = ba^2 - ba$ yields $ab = ba$.] **17.** (ii) and (iv) **20.** no **21.** $\mathbb{Q}[\sqrt{2}]$ **24.(i)** False [Hint: $\mathbb{Z}_5$ is not a subset of $\mathbb{Z}_{10}$] **(ii)** False [Hint: Consider the subfields $\mathbb{Q}(\sqrt{2})$ and $\mathbb{Q}(\sqrt{3})$ of the field of real numbers] **(iii)** False [Hint: the set is not closed under addition] **(iv)** True. **25** (i). **26.** [Hint: As $m^2p \equiv mp(\mod mp)$, clearly $m\mathbb{Z}_n = \{[0], [m], [2m] \ldots [(p-1)m]\} = \{[am] \mid 0 \leq a \leq p - 1\}$, whence $|m\mathbb{Z}_n| = p$. Showing subring is routine. Let $[am] \in m\mathbb{Z}_n$ be the unity. Then $[am][bm] = [bm]$ for all $[bm] \in m\mathbb{Z}_n$, whence $(am)(bm) - bm$ is a multiple of n, i.e., $bm(am - 1) = kn$ (say) $= kpm$, i.e., $b(am - 1) = kp$, whence $p \mid b(am - 1)$, i.e, $p \mid am - 1$ (as p is prime and $\gcd(p, b) = 1$). Hence $am \equiv 1(\mod p)$.]

Chapter 13

Exercises to Section 13.1

1. (a), (b), (f) **5.** $\{[0]\}, \{[0],[4]\}, \{[0],[2],[4],[6]\}$ and $\mathbb{Z}_8$ itself in $\mathbb{Z}_8$; only trivial ideals in $\mathbb{Z}_5$; $\{[0]\}, \{[0],[3],[6]\}$, and $\mathbb{Z}_9$ itself in $\mathbb{Z}_9$; **10.** $4\mathbb{Z}, 1+4\mathbb{Z}, 2+4\mathbb{Z}, 3+4\mathbb{Z}$; **11.** 16 **13.** $\{12\mathbb{Z}, 3+12\mathbb{Z}, 6+12\mathbb{Z}, 9+12\mathbb{Z}\}$ **15.** $\{[0],[12],[24],[36]\}$ **16.** $\{0\}$ **25.** (b) **26.** (iv) **27.**(a) False **(b)** True **(c)** True.

Exercises to Section 13.2

1. $\{[0],[4],[8]\}$ **2.** $\{0\}$, no **3.** the ideal (x), no **4.** $\{0\}$, yes, no **5.** $\{0\}$ **6.** $\{f(x) \in R \mid f(0) = 0\}$ **8.** identity mapping and zero mapping **9.** $[n] \mapsto [0], [n] \mapsto [n], [n] \mapsto [3n], [n] \mapsto [4n]$ [Hint : $o(f[1])|6$, hence $o(f[1])$ is 1 or 2 or 3 or 6. But $(f[1])$ is idempotent.] **10.(i)** $[n] \mapsto [0], [n] \mapsto [n]$ **(ii)** $[n] \mapsto [0], [n] \mapsto [10n], [n] \mapsto [15n], [n] \mapsto [25n]$ **11.** identity mapping and zero mapping **12.** identity mapping and zero mapping **22.(i)** [Hint: Let $T = \{n1_R \mid n \in \mathbb{Z}\}$. Since $0 = 01_R \in T$ so $T \neq \phi$. Clearly T is a subring of R. Suppose m and n are two integers such that $n1_R = m1_R$. If $n > m$, then $(n-m)1_R = 0$, which contradicts that char$(R) = 0$. Similar is the case for $m > n$. Hence $m = n$. Thus, for each $a \in T$, there is a unique $n \in \mathbb{Z}$ such that $a = n1_R$, whence the mapping $f : \mathbb{Z} \to T$ given by $f(n) = n1_R$ is an isomorphism.] **23.(i)** True **(ii)** False **(iii)** False **(iv)** False **(v)** False.

Exercises to Section 13.3

1. All of the following ideals are prime as well as maximal. **(i)** $\{[0],[3]\}, \{[0],[2],[4]\}$ **(ii)** $\{[0],[3],[6]\}$ **(iii)** $\{[0]\}$. **(iv)** $\{[0],[5]\}, \{[0],[2],[4],[6],[8]\}$ **(v)** $\{[0],[3],[6],[9]\}$, $\{[0],[2],[4],[6],[8],[10]\}$ **(vi)** $\{0\}$ **(vii)** $\mathbb{R}\times\{0\}$ and $\{0\}\times\mathbb{R}$. **2.** Yes. **8.(b)** [Hint: Let $0 \neq a \in R$. If $a^2R = R$, then $1 = a^2b$. Hence a is a unit. Suppose $a^2R \neq R$. Then a^2R is a proper ideal of R and hence a prime ideal. Now $a^2 \in a^2R$ (as $1 \in R$), and as it is prime ideal, so $a \in a^2R$ (since $ab \in I \implies$ either $a \in I$ or $b \in I$). Then $a = a^2b$ for some $b \in R$; i.e., $a(1 - ab) = 0$. Since R is an ID and $a \neq 0$, so $1 - ab = 0$ i.e., $ab = 1$, whence a is a unit in R. Hence R is a division ring.] **10.** no, 25 **11.** yes, 49 **12.** 25 **13.** 2 **15.(a)** False **(b)** True **(c)** True **(d)** True **16.** (d). **17.** (a), (c).

Exercises to Section 13.4

1. (a) not regular (b) not regular (c) not regular (d) not regular (e) regular (f) regular (g) regular (h) not regular (i) regular (j) regular **5.** [Hint: Here $xyxy = xy$ shows that xy is an idempotent. Now, $(xy)(xy)(xy) = (xy)^3 = xy$ and $(xy)1_R(xy) = (xy)^2 = xy$, together imply $xy = 1_R$ from the given condition of uniqueness. Similarly the other.] **6.** (ii) and (iii).

Exercises to Section 13.5

1. $\mathbb{Q}[\sqrt{5}]$ **2.** $\mathbb{Q}$ **3.** $\mathbb{Q}(x)$ **4.** $\left\{\frac{f(x)}{g(x)} \mid f(x), g(x) \in D[x], g(x) \neq 0\right\}$; both are $E(x)$.

Chapter 14

Exercises to Section 14.1

1. $[2], [4], [6], [8]$ **3.** $\pm 1, \pm i$ **4.** $8+3i, -8-3i, -3+8i, 3-8i$ **5.** ± 1 **6.** units are $[1], [2], \ldots, [6]$;

associates are $x^2 + [2], [2]x^2 + [4], [3]x^2 + [6], [4]x^2 + [1], [5]x^2 + [3], [6]x^2 + [5]$ **7.** $1 + i, -1 - i, -1 + i, 1 - i$ **8.(i)** prime : $[2], [3], [9], [10]$; irreducible : $[2], [10]$; **(ii)** all are irreducible but not prime; **(iii)** $3, 11, 2 + i, 2 - i, 1 - i$ are both prime and irreducible; 5 and $3 + i$ are neither. **(iv)** all are irreducible but none is prime. [Hint: $23 \mid (1 + i3\sqrt{5})(1 - i3\sqrt{5})$ but $23 \nmid (1 + i3\sqrt{5})$ and $23 \nmid (1 - i3\sqrt{5})$; $(1 + i3\sqrt{5}) \mid 23 \cdot 2$ but $(1 + i3\sqrt{5}) \nmid 23$ and $(1 + i3\sqrt{5}) \nmid 2$; $(3 + i\sqrt{5}) \mid 2 \cdot 7$ but $(3 + i\sqrt{5}) \nmid 2$ and $(3 + i\sqrt{5}) \nmid 7$; $(2 + i\sqrt{5}) \mid 3 \cdot 3$ but $(2 + i\sqrt{5}) \nmid 3$; $(7 + i3\sqrt{5}) \mid 2 \cdot 47$ but $(7 + i3\sqrt{5}) \nmid 2$ and $(7 + i3\sqrt{5}) \nmid 47$.] **19.(i)** True **(ii)** False [Hint : $5 = (2 + i)(2 - i)$] **(iii)** False [Hint: $13 = (3 + 2i)(3 - 2i)$] **(iv)** True **(v)** False [Hint: consider 5] **(vi)** True **(vii)** False [Hint: 3 is unit in $\mathbb{Q}$] **(viii)** False [Hint: $\sqrt{3}$ is unit in $\mathbb{R}$] **(ix)** True. **20.** (i).

Exercises to Section 14.2

6. $q = 2 - 5\sqrt{3}, r = 1 + \sqrt{3}$ **13.** $-2 + i$ **14.** $x = -3i$ and $y = 1$;

Chapter 15

Exercises to Section 15.1

1. $[3] + [3]x + [3]x^2 + [5]x^3 + [3]x^4 + [2]x^5$, $[2] + [3]x + [5]x^2 + [4]x^3 + [5]x^4 + [4]x^5 + [3]x^6 + [4]x^7 + [4]x^8$, 5 4 5 8; **2.** $[3] + [3]x + [3]x^2 + [5]x^3 + [3]x^4 + [2]x^5$, $[2] + [3]x + [5]x^2 + [2]x^3 + [2]x^4 + [2]x^5 + [3]x^6 + [4]x^7 + [3]x^8 + [6]x^9$, 5 4 5 9 ; **4.** $(x + [1])(x + [2])(x + [3])(x + [4])$ **5.** $(x + [1])(x + [2])(x + [4])$ **6.** $[2], [3], [6]$ **7.** $(2, 3), (2, 11), (3, 3), (3, 11); \{(-4, n) \mid n \in \mathbb{Z}\}$ **8.** quotient:$[3]x^2 + [3]x + [3]$; remainder: x **9.** $q(x) = 6x^3 + 5x^2 - 2x - 3; r(x) = 4x^2 - 11x - 15$ **10.** $q(x) = x^2 - [4]x + [3]; r(x) = [2]x^2 - [4]x + [1]$ **11.(i)** $x^2 + 2x + 5$ **(ii)** $x^2 + x + [2]$ **(iii)** $x^2 + [7]x + [4]$ **12.** $x^2, x^2 + [1], x^2 + x, x^2 + x + [1]$; **22.** $(x - 1)(x^2 + x + 1)$ in $\mathbb{Z}[x], \mathbb{Q}[x], \mathbb{R}[x]$ and $\mathbb{Z}_5[x]$; $(r - 1)(r - \frac{-1 + i\sqrt{3}}{2})(x \quad \frac{-1 - i\sqrt{3}}{2})$ in $\mathbb{C}[x]$; $(x - 1)(x - 1)(x - 1)$ in $\mathbb{Z}_3[x]$. **23.** Take any field F and its maximal ideal $\{0\}$. **25.** no [Hint: Note that $\mathbb{Z}$ is a PID but $\mathbb{Z}[x]$ is not] ; no **26.(a)** (iii) **(b)** (i)**(c)** (ii)**(d)** (iii)**(e)** (i) **27.(a)** True **(b)** False **(c)** False [Hint: In $\mathbb{Z}_2[x]$, the polynomial x has no inverse] **(d)** True **(e)** True **(f)** True **(g)** True **(h)** True **(i)** True **(j)** True **(k)** False [Hint: Here $2x + 4 = 2(x + 2)$ is not irreducible in $\mathbb{Z}[x]$ but irreducible in $\mathbb{Q}[x]$]. **28.** $f(x) = 2$ and $g(x) = x$. **29.** (iii). **30.** (i),(ii),(iii),(iv). **31.** (iii).

Exercises to Section 15.2

4. In $\mathbb{Z}_3[x]$: $x, x + [1], x + [2], x^2 + [1], x^2 + x + [2], x^2 + [2]x + [2]$ and their associates. In $\mathbb{Z}_5[x]$: $x, x + [1], x + [2], x + [3], x + [4], x^2 + [2], x^2 + [3], x^2 + x + [1], x^2 + x + [2], x^2 + [2]x + [3], x^2 + [2]x + [4], x^2 + [3]x + [3], x^2 + [3]x + [4], x^2 + [4]x + [1], x^2 + [4]x + [2]$ and their associates; **6.** $(x + [3])(x + [5])(x + [6])$ **7.** $(x + [1])(x + [1])(x + [1])$ **10.** $x^2 + 1$ **14.(a)** True **(b)** False [Hint: $x^2 + x + [1]$ is not irreducible in $\mathbb{Z}_3[x]$] **(c)** False [Hint : $(x + [1])^2 = x^2 + [2]x + [1] = x^2 + [1] \in (x^2 + [1])$ but $x + [1] \notin (x^2 + [1])$] **(d)** True. [Hint : $(x^2 + 1)$ is a maximal ideal in $\mathbb{Q}[x]$ as $x^2 + 1$ is irreducible in $\mathbb{Q}[x]$.] **15.** (iii). **16.** (ii), (iii). **17.** (i), (iv). **18.** (iv) **19.** (ii) **20.** (i), (iii).

Index